Quantitative Business Applications

Hudson Valley Community College

Taken from:

Mathematics of Interest Rates and Finance
by Gary L. Guthrie, and Larry D. Lemon

Understanding Finance: Money, Capital, and Investments
by Karen D. Halpern

Cover Art: *Excavation Series*, by Brian Stevens.

Taken from:

Mathematics of Interest Rates and Finance
by Gary L. Guthrie and Larry D. Lemon

Published by Prentice-Hall
Upper Saddle River, New Jersey 07458

Understanding Finance: Money, Capital, and Investments
by Karen D. Halpern

Published by Prentice-Hall

This special edition published in cooperation with Pearson Custom Publishing.

Printed in the United States of America

10 9 8 7 6 5 4 3 2 1

ISBN 0-536-94292-7

2005160089

BK

Please visit our web site at *www.pearsoncustom.com*

PEARSON CUSTOM PUBLISHING
75 Arlington Street, Suite 300, Boston, MA 02116
A Pearson Education Company

CONTENTS

PART 1: Taken from: *Mathematics of Interest Rates and Finance* by Gary L. Guthrie and Larry D. Lemon

PART 2: Taken from: *Understanding Finance: Money, Capital, and Investments* by Karen D. Halpern

PART I

Taken from:

Mathematics of Interest Rates and Finance

by Gary L. Guthrie, and Larry D. Lemon

Preface

This is a math text with the primary goal of teaching students the mathematical concepts necessary for other courses dealing with finance, insurance, and investments. It presents the basic core of mathematics needed to understand the impact of interest on the world of investments, real estate, corporate planning, insurance, and securities transactions. The value of a good foundation in the mathematical principles of finance and interest becomes apparent if you peruse the mathematics found in an investment or financial management text. Basic ideas like the present value of an annuity, the net present value, the internal rate of return, and discounted cash flows are often burdened with cumbersome notation and messy formulas. The novice learner with no previous experience often finds these to be difficult and perplexing.

This text has avoided the tedious arithmetic and transcription of data from finance tables by requiring the use of financial calculators. We emphasize the use of technology with preprogrammed features, but in the advanced sections we also encourage students to program their calculators. We feel this exercise will give them an understanding of the formulas and how their financial calculators perform the various computations. Because this is a problem-solving course, students will have to demonstrate an understanding that goes beyond the numbers spit out by a calculator. This understanding comes from recognizing and diagramming the structure of the problem so that the application of a formula is natural and not just an educated guess. Our goal is for students to understand well those few underlying principles that play out in nearly every finance and interest problem.

After years of experience teaching this subject, we have developed certain simplifying techniques that have helped many students to have a successful experience in their studies of finance and interest. One of the most interesting principles involving the numbering of payments we have named the *Fence Post Principle*. This tricky little idea shows up in all walks of life, but especially in business matters. We have also found that the use of the effective interest rate makes calculations involving general case annuities just another annuity calculation without the frustrations inherent in the equivalent payment method. Students are often frustrated trying to decide whether an exercise requires present value or future value, so we teach them how to recognize certain scenarios and clue words that simplify the decision process. Most of our students reach the point at which they always get the present value/future value issue correct.

This text is intended to open the door of financial understanding to many other academic majors besides business, accounting, and the actuarial sciences. Over the years we have received considerable feedback from former students who have expressed appreciation for how this course prepared them for dealing with personal financial matters and investments. Although there are many exercises dealing with business and finance, there are many others that deal with practical issues and the profound effect of interest on the value of money. In fact, the time value of money is the basic principle underlying everything we do in finance. Those who grasp the significance of this principle are not surprised when confronted with a situation where $100 cash can actually be a larger piece of money than, say, $108 located a year from now. To emphasize this principle, we have coined a phrase called the *Golden Rule of Finance*: Monies cannot be added or reconciled unless they are valued at the same point in time. This concept drives the development of formulas and equations of value so pieces of money can be moved both forward and backward on the time line. Once the student understands where on the time line he or she wants the money, it is an easy matter to pick the right mathematical tool to get it there.

We have tried to personalize the exercises by using first names of individuals as the players in the finance problems to be solved. Most of the names of companies used are fictitious, with a few exceptions. Using the names of real companies can lead to misunderstandings if the data are not factually representative of the financial status of those companies. All problems (even a few with names of real companies) have been made up to serve the same function as any other laboratory learning situation. They are as realistic as possible, but your day-to-day financial dealings will of course be somewhat different. Interest rates are always in a state of flux, so rates in problems and examples that seem a little high for today's market may be too low in a year or two. In the summer of 2003 the prime rate had dropped to 4.00%, an impossibly low figure from the perspective of the mid-1990s, when it hovered around 8% to 9%. Backing up another decade to the 1980s, you find that the prime rate was generally above 9%.

Adaptability of the Text

We envision that this text can be adapted for use at three different levels. They could be identified as sophomore, junior, and senior; but basic, intermediate, and advanced give a better picture. The basic level would serve as a first course aimed at an audience that certainly includes, besides others, finance, management, and accounting majors. The intermediate level would provide a good background and introduction for those headed toward the actuary and insurance professions as well as financial management. The advanced level provides the additional opportunity to apply stochastic processes to finance and interest theory.

Basic Level

For those who wish to cover this material at a sophomore level in a business or accounting program, the theory sections can be omitted without loss. For this use the authors presuppose a working knowledge of only basic algebra, arithmetic, and percents, but nothing more than what would be covered in a couple of years of high school math.

Content: Cover Chapters 1 through 8, but omit the theory sections 1.10, 2.6, 3.3, 3.8, 3.9, and 5.7. This level should concentrate on the Concept and Calculation sections of the exercise sets.

Intermediate Level

Those using this text at the intermediate level would need at least an introductory-level calculus background that covered differentiation and integration along with limits and summation notation.

Content: Cover the basic material in Chapters 1 and 2 in about three class periods, cover all of Chapters 3 through 8, and four sections of Chapter 9. Give special attention to the theory sections 1.10, 2.6, 3.3, 3.8, 3.9, 5.7, 9.1–9.4. These theory of interest sections are very important to those headed toward the actuary field. Programmable calculators should be used for the Chapter 9 material. This level should plan to do a representative amount of the Concept and Calculation exercises but should do all of the Theory and Extension exercises.

Advanced Level

Those at the advanced level should not only have a Calculus prerequisite but a mathematics statistics class with adequate experience with the normal distribution from an applied as well as a theoretical standpoint. This material will assume the student can handle expected value, variance, covariance, and the lognormal distribution.

Content: Cover the same material as the intermediate level with only 1 or 2 class periods on the basic material of Chapters 1 and 2, plus all of Sections 9.5–9.9. This level should plan to do a limited amount of the Concept and Calculation exercises, all of the Theory and Extension exercises, and all of the exercises in Chapter 9.

Notation

There is a fair amount of diversity of notation among finance, investment, and actuary work. Our goal in choosing notation was two fold: (1) Keep it as simple as possible for the student learning this material, and (2) use dual notation where possible to make future transitions to other texts as smooth as possible. We have used all the basic interest theory notation that is familiar to those in the actuarial field but have tried to use more user-friendly notation in areas where the very compact methods of notation are easily forgotten with disuse. As an example of this, in Chapter 9 we use the following notation for present value of a variable payment annuity with arithmetic difference: A_n(Arith, Var. Pmt). The Society of Actuary (SOA) notation would be $(Ia)_{\overline{n}|i}$ for an increasing variable payment annuity and $(Da)_{\overline{n}|i}$ for a decreasing variable payment annuity. The nice feature of the user-friendly notation is that those teaching actuarial science students can use the SOA notation with our text with little or no difficulty.

To the Student

The style, presentation, and features of this text are presented with the student in mind. You should have a sense that you are sitting in our class as we make every effort to help you grasp the concepts. After we introduce and explain new concepts and principles, we try to have several relevant examples to reinforce and clarify those principles. Your goal in the study of the mathematics of finance and interest should be to gain a solid understanding of the few, but important, concepts presented in this text. When you understand what a formula does, it will be easy to remember. It will be a tool in your hand, not a burden on your back. In fact, there are not very many formulas, and what there are have been presented so they are not a mystery. Even within the theory sections every effort has been made to simplify and focus on the key elements. You will be using a financial calculator to perform all the tedious tasks like multiplying two ten-digit numbers, but punching buttons to get the correct answer is far less important than the underlying concepts. Plan to make extensive use of time lines to organize and visualize the exercises. A good time line often makes the needed steps and choice of a formula jump right out of the given information. You should carefully study the examples in the text and even work them out on your own. But if you merely use the examples as templates for working the exercises, you may find yourself deficient in the ability to reason out test questions that are slightly different. Strive for understanding.

Some words of caution and direction are in order about exercise sets. The exercises are divided into three types: *concept and short answer exercises*; *calculation exercises*; and *theory and extension*. As a further student help, Appendix D contains a complete worked-out key for all of the concept and short answer exercises, for the odd-numbered calculation exercises, and for theory and extension exercises. Such a key is a valuable aid to learning, but it can also be the road to ruin if you believe that copying the key is doing the homework. Each section's homework remains incomplete until you understand and are comfortable with the concepts in that section.

Acknowledgments

We wish to thank our students and colleagues who for three years have contributed so much with their helpful suggestions and editorial comments for the prepublication text. We are especially grateful for suggestions, comments, and sources of information from Alan Carper and Kris Martin in the School of Business. A special word of thanks is due to two former students, Josh Jensen for text editing and Ge, Su for courageously undertaking the task of working all the exercises in the basic version of the text. We also wish to gratefully acknowledge the helpful comments and constructive suggestions of reviewers H. Pat Goeters, Lajos Horvath, Curtis E. Huntington, Janusz Kawczak, Michael Mays, Maria Rizzo, and Bostwick F. Wyman.

The Society of Actuaries has graciously given permission for us to reprint some of their test questions from the May and November Course 2 exams, Copyrighted 2001 by the Society of Actuaries. These questions can be identified by the ♦ mark. Some questions may have variations in quantities and interest rates from the 2001 exams.

Gary L. Guthrie Gguthrie@bju.edu

Larry D. Lemon Llemon@bju.edu

Chapter 1

Simple Interest

1.1 Money, Interest, and the Federal Reserve System

Money is often defined as the medium of exchange for buying and selling goods and services. Historically people used a barter or trade system to exchange goods or services of equal value. This created many complications for the two parties. A craftsman building and selling shovels can use only so many potatoes when he needs raw materials to build more shovels. Eventually people began using money made out of metals like copper, silver, and gold. This type of money has intrinsic value just like shovels or potatoes. Because of the limited supply of gold and silver, nations were eventually forced to use paper currency. The value of money can fluctuate, however, because its purchasing power depends on the price of the goods and services for which it is exchanged. Those prices in turn are dependent on the supply of and demand for goods and services. The second factor determining the value of money is its availability. When the money supply is small, each unit of money has greater purchasing power; but when there is too much money available it can purchase less, so the prices of goods and services increase. We refer to this condition as inflation. The most notable cause of inflation is the excess printing of paper money by a government in order to meet its financial obligations. This subtle tax quickly results in such rapid devaluation of the currency that sometimes people quit accepting it as a medium of exchange. By the end of the Revolutionary War the excessive printing of currency by the Continental Congress resulted in such rampant inflation that in 1790 the United States government paid one U.S. penny for every Continental dollar. Such devaluation has historically forced people to return to gold and silver—even to the currency of another nation with more stable money.

Many of the world's industrialized nations have tried to regulate the value of their paper currency by tying it to a gold or silver standard. During the early part of the nineteenth century, the United States used a gold standard; later it adopted a bimetallic standard based on both gold and silver. Defining a paper currency under a metallic standard means that its value is defined by a fixed amount of that metal rather than by its purchasing power. You could actually exchange your paper currency for an equivalent amount of gold or silver. It is easy to see how a shortage of gold or silver could lead to a decline in prices and wages and ultimately to economic hard times. Under the bimetallic standard, as gold became more valuable and less available, it was hoarded, until it finally disappeared from the marketplace.

Between 1914 and 1968 the United States slowly eliminated the gold standard for U.S. currency (Federal Reserve Notes). Now the assets of the Federal Reserve banks provide the only backing for the well over $600 billion in U.S. currency. Between 1968 and 1972 the United States led an effort to stop the industrialized nations' use of gold as a basis for determining the value of their currency. The goal was to free the foreign exchange rate from the gold market's influence. Gold standard nations agreed on a government-to-government exchange rate of $42.22 per troy ounce of gold. These nations also consented not to buy and sell gold in the private sector. The price of gold in the private markets fluctuates much like stocks or bonds and is typically eight to tens times higher than the national gold price. The value of each nation's currency relative to the other nations is now closely related to the strength of its economy or means of production. The U.S. dollar has become a standard of comparison among the industrialized nations. The currencies of the various nations are themselves commodities, much like wheat, steel and electronics. When you exchange money in a foreign country you are buying a commodity that serves as a convenient medium of exchange for other commodities like food and shelter. Just like other goods in the marketplace, one currency may appear more valuable to the buyers than another. The U.S. dollar may buy lots of rubles in Moscow, but buying dollars with rubles may result in a disappointing "exchange."

In the modern economic climate the acceptable mediums of exchange (money) have become more diversified. Coin and paper currency are still called legal tender, but checkable deposits make up about two-thirds of the nation's money supply. Monies in a bank that are the basis for writing checks and making electronic transfers are called **demand deposits**. Most individuals use either paper checks or check cards to access their funds when making purchases or paying accounts. Banks and business are using computer-driven electronic transfers far more than individuals, but this method is growing rapidly in the private sector, as well. Stored value cards, like phone cards and transportation fare cards, are a new and innovative prepaid medium of exchange that provides convenience, eliminates making change, and speeds up transactions. Some people mistakenly think credit cards are a medium of exchange, but a credit card is really just a delayed payment device that acts like a prearranged loan. Users who think credit cards are money often find themselves in debt far beyond their means to repay. Credit card loan rates are typically 9% to 12% higher than the prime rate. The **prime rate** is the interest rate that banks charge their best, most financially capable corporate customers. This puts credit card rates in the 15% to 21% range. For example, repaying $35 per month (about the minimum allowed) on a $2000 balance at 18% will take approximately ten years to pay off, even if no additional charges are made.

Classifying what constitutes the money supply can be difficult. The money supply includes more than coin, currency and checkable demand deposits. Most of the nation's money resides in what might be called **near monies**: instruments that may be quickly transferred into liquid assets. *Near money* includes such assets as U.S. government and corporate bonds, pension funds, cash value life insurance, money market holdings and various other interest-earning deposits and securities.

The Federal Reserve System's responsibility is to regulate the money supply to keep it from getting too large or too small. Late in the nineteenth century and early in the twentieth, money and banking crises were occurring frequently, and it became apparent that the whole system needed overhauling. Though it may sound ludicrous, an elastic money supply was the critical need. When inflation starts to take over, the money supply needs to be shrunk, and when the economy starts to lag, the money supply needs to be expanded. The bank panic of 1907 painfully pointed out the need for a major change in the nation's money and banking system. Considerable study and evaluation over a period of three years by the Aldrich Commission resulted in recommendations that gained little support. Finally, in 1912, the House Committee on Banking and Finance formulated a plan in response to the concerns of various factions. This plan addressed the need for a central bank with the authority to set monetary policies. In 1913, during the presidency of Woodrow Wilson, Congress passed the Federal Reserve Act. Due to the need for significant political compromise, the Federal Reserve System became a quasi-government agency. The Federal Reserve consists of twelve regional Federal Reserve Banks that are private corporations serving together as the central bank. But the seven-member Board of Governors is an agency of the United States federal government. The members of this board are appointed by the president to fourteen-year nonrenewable terms, and each must be confirmed by the Senate. Another component of the Fed is a twelve-member Federal Open Market Committee, which sets the monetary policies of the United States. This committee consists of the seven members of the Board of Governors and five of the Federal Reserve Bank presidents, one of whom is the president of the Federal Reserve Bank of New York. The Fed also includes twenty-five Federal Reserve branch banks and about nine hundred sixty commercial banks as members. [See Appendix A Endnote 1.]

It may be hard to see how twelve regional Federal Reserve Banks scattered throughout the country can be a central bank; however, they form a powerful banking structure for controlling the money supply, bank interest rates, and the amount of reserves in the banking system. They also serve as the lender of last resort to guarantee liquidity for the nation's banks. These banks are profit-making institutions with the ability to finance their own operations. Their earnings of $15 to $20 billion per year are sufficient to pay dividends on stock owned by the member banks, pay operating expenses and return all but 5% to the United States Treasury. There are a number of other functions performed by the Federal Reserve Banks that improve the efficiency of the national payments mechanism: They expedite check collection and transfer of funds, make loans to banks, provide safekeeping of securities, act as an agent for the U.S. Treasury, introduce new currency and coins into circulation, and serve as the bank of the U.S. government.

The Federal Reserve sets the per cent of reserves its member banks must have in order to back up their designated liabilities. It also defines those reserves to be vault cash and deposits at the Federal Reserve banks. The Fed can regulate the amount of banking reserves by buying and selling government securities on the open market. When the Fed buys securities, reserves and the money supply increase, and when the Fed sells securities, the reserves and money supply decrease. The Federal Reserve Bank of New York acts on behalf of the Fed in the open-market operations of buying government securities, dealing in foreign currencies, and interacting with the central banks of other nations.

The Fed also uses the discount rate charged to depositories who borrow from the Fed either to encourage or discourage banks from borrowing reserves. A higher discount rate discourages borrowing, and a lower rate encourages borrowing. These monetary policies relating to the cost of borrowing (interest) trickle down through the entire economic structure of the United States. We often refer to it as tight money or easy money, depending on whether interest rates are high or low. Most of us see these rate-setting policies reflected in home mortgage rates, automobile loan rates, and equity loan or line-of-credit rates. Personal loan rates and credit card rates are much higher than commercial loans to business and industry because commercial loans are often made at the bank's prime rate. Figure 1.1 shows a recent history of the yearly highs and lows of the prime rate from 1973 until 2001. [Fed of NY]

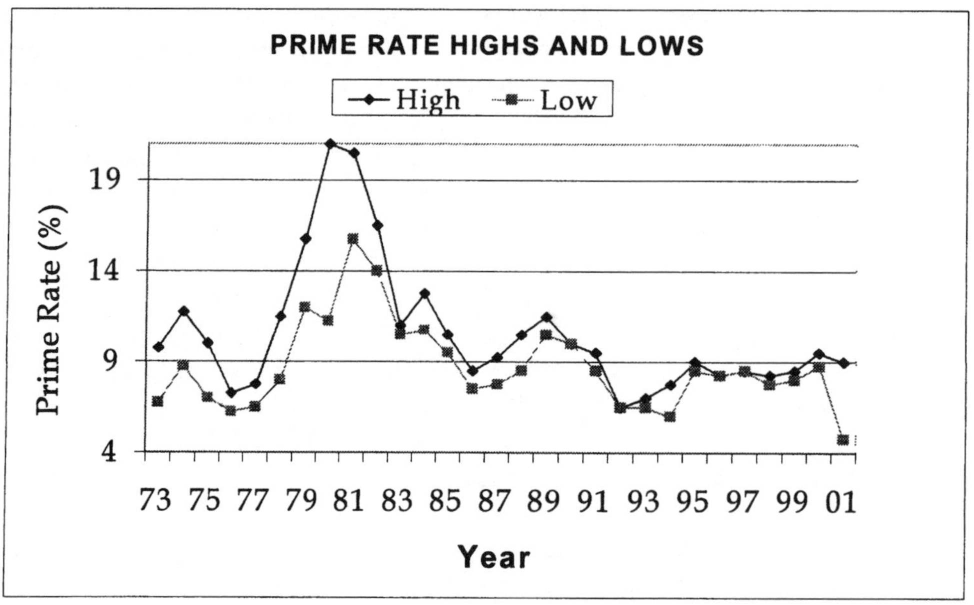

FIGURE 1.1

1.2 The Importance of Interest and the Basic Formula

In ancient times people called the cost of borrowed money *usury*. Today we call it **interest**. Interest increases the value of our money over time. Because of inflation money stored in a jar or under the mattress actually loses value in a year. On the other hand, money that is invested at a rate exceeding inflation will be worth more in a year. Because of interest earned, money has time value. Every transaction involving money and time must consider the **time value of money**. In order to compare or add different pieces of money we must place the monies at the same point in time, called the **focal date**. This will require us to move money on the time line, either forward into the future or backward into the past. Important formulas have been developed to move money so it can be compared or added. In this chapter we will give particular attention to those formulas that relate to simple interest.

Many of our applications will pertain to borrowing money by means of loans, but the calculations are the same whether the money is borrowed or invested.

Practical applications like borrowing for a home or automobile, making investment analyses, and using savings accounts and bonds will receive considerable attention in this text. A person who understands the principles of finance will be able to make reasonable financial decisions throughout life.

There are several terms that you will need in order to navigate this chapter successfully. Money that is borrowed or invested is called the **principal.** The cost or charge for the use of borrowed money is called **interest**. For investments, it is often called *interest earned*, but it goes by other names, such as *return on investment*, *dividend*, and *coupon*. The amount of interest charged for a loan is usually expressed as a percent of the original principal for a given time period. This percent is referred to as the **interest rate**. The measurement period for the interest rate on simple interest loans is almost always yearly. Thus the rate is given per annum (year). A 5% per annum rate would cost the borrower 5% of the principal for every year of the loan. This does not mean all simple interest loans are for one year, but that the time must be expressed in years if the rate is per annum. The actual length of the loan is called the **term** of the loan. If the interest charged is based merely on the original principal but paid at the end of the term, we call it a **simple interest** loan.

Summary of Basic Definitions

Principal	amount of money invested or borrowed (*present value*)
Interest	cost or charge for the use of borrowed money
Interest Rate	percent of the principal that is the basis for the interest
Term	length of the loan in time units corresponding to the rate

These definitions lead us to a basic mathematical calculation of the interest and hence a formula. The letters used for this literal equation follow naturally from the four terms.

The Basic Simple Interest Formula: $I = Pit$ **(1.1)**

I = interest P = principal i = rate per year t = time in years

In this text uppercase letters will represent money and lowercase letters will represent nonmonetary values like rates or time.

Simple interest loans and investments may not have the prominence in the finance world that they once had, but they are still in significant use with home equity loans, promissory notes, stocks, bonds, and credit card debt. The average daily balance used to figure credit card interest charges requires the issuer to employ a sort of modified simple interest calculation. On the other hand, mortgages, most savings accounts, and certificates of deposit involve interest computed with compound interest, which we define in Chapter 3. Some lending institutions lend money using a simple interest calculation but require the borrower to pay the loan back in payments. This is called an **add-on loan.** It is not a true simple interest loan.

Example 1.2.1

A simple interest loan for $800 at 7% per annum is paid off after 6 months. What are the interest charges?

■ Since the interest is needed, use the formula $I = Pit$ and substitute the values. Note that 6 months will be 6/12 of a year or .5. Remember to change the rate to a decimal, so 7% = .07.

$$I = (\$800)(.07)(.5) = \$28$$

Example 1.2.2

If the interest charges on a $950 loan for 9 months amount to $42.75, what is the interest rate for the loan?

■ Since the rate is needed, solve the formula for i either before or after substituting the known information. Nine months will be written as 3/4 of a year or .75.

$$i = \frac{I}{Pt} = \frac{42.75}{(950)(.75)} = .06 = 6\%$$

Example 1.2.3

How long will it take $4000 invested at 7% per annum to earn $350?

■ The time is needed, so solve the formula for t either before or after substituting the known information.

$$t = \frac{I}{Pi} = \frac{350}{(4000)(.07)} = 1.25 \text{ years or 15 months}$$

A **promissory note** is a document on which one party (the maker) writes his or her promise to pay another party (the payee) the principal and interest for a loan due at some date in the future. It often looks like a fancy check, but it can be as simple as a handwritten piece of paper. Certain information must appear on the note: the principal borrowed, the interest rate, the length of the term or **maturity date**, the signing date, and the borrower's signature. Sometimes a note will have an additional signature of a witness to the borrower's signature. Often this witness is a notary public. The amount of money the borrower will pay back is the sum of the principal and interest, and it is called the **maturity value**, the **future value**, or the **amount**. The letter S represents the maturity value, so that $S = P + I$.

Example 1.2.4

A promissory note for \$5000 at 8% per annum is due in 18 months. What is the maturity value of the note?

■ The interest charges are calculated first and then added to the principal. This total is the maturity value (or future value) of the note. Remember that 18 months is 18/12 of a year or 1.5.

$$I = Pit = 5000(.08)(1.5) = \$600$$

$$\text{Maturity value: } S = P + I = \$5000 + \$600 = \$5600$$

◀ EXERCISES 1.2 ▶

Concept and Short Answer Exercises

1. As the principal increases, what happens to the interest?
2. As the interest rate increases, what happens to the interest?
3. As the term increases, what happens to the interest?
4. Why is the basic formula for interest, $I = Pit$, reasonable?
5. What is the formula for computing i? For computing t?
6. In paying off a loan, each payment must cover at least the ____ (*principal* or *interest*), or else the loan will balloon larger and larger.

Calculation Exercises

In Exercises 7–16, compute the simple interest for the given amounts of money.

	Principal	Interest Rate	Time
7.	\$425	6.5%	8 months
8.	\$1000	8.2%	1.5 years
9.	\$1580	8%	14 months
10.	\$300.20	18%	7 months
11.	\$2950.50	7.75%	20 months
12.	\$150,000	4.3%	14 weeks
13.	\$255.35	12%	3 months
14.	\$600	9%	23 months
15.	\$640.45	6.5%	7 months
16.	\$9000	2 ¾ %	40 weeks

17. On 11/2/02 Mark invests \$1000 at 5%. Find the interest and the future value of the investment on 4/2/04.
18. On 11/2/02 Kristie invests \$5000 at 4.5%. Find the interest and the future value of the investment 9 months later.

19. On 9/5/03 Penny takes out a loan for $5000 from her parents, who are charging 8%. When Penny graduates on 5/5/07, how much interest does she owe, and what is the amount she will repay her parents?

20. On 10/5/03 Edwin purchases a used car by taking out a loan for $10,000 from his parents, who are charging 3%. When Edwin repays the loan on 10/5/04, how much interest does he owe, and what is the amount he will repay his parents?

21. Ethan requires a loan of $100,000 to start an Internet business. He found a loan agent that charges 12%. He is not willing to pay more than $1000 per month. Why is this an impossible situation?

22. Heather requires a quick loan of $4000 and uses a credit card that charges 12%. She can pay at most $40 per month. Why is this an impossible situation?

23. A loan shark lets you borrow $100 and pay back $105 in 1 week. Find the annual interest rate.

24. A quick check-cashing agent is willing to hold your check of $500 for 2 weeks for only $30. Find the annual interest rate.

25. On 1/2/03 Joe lends his brother Wes $1000. Wes pays off the loan on 7/2/03 with $1050. Find the annual percentage rate.

26. On February 3 Vicky lends her brother James $10,000. James pays off the loan on October 3 with $11,000. Find the annual percentage rate.

27. To the nearest month how long does it take to increase your investment by 50% if you can get 8% on your investment?

28. To the nearest month how long does it take to increase your investment by 80% if you can get 9% on your investment?

29. If you hope to double your money and you have $1000 to invest at 6%, how long will it take you? (Note that the $1000 is unnecessary information. Explain why.)

30. If you desire to triple your money at 10%, how long will it take you?

1.3 Types of Time and Interest

Most loans do not have terms measured in months. Typically a loan has an initial signing date and a due date that may or may not fall on the same day in some future month. With these two dates given, we would expect to use the number of days between the dates for the term. Note that every day has a **serial number** between 1 and 366 that we can find in a **serial table**. (A serial table is printed inside the back cover of the text.) Two methods of computing the number of days have become common practice. The first method, called **exact time**, uses every day of the term but the first day. This interest-free day is not there because lenders are generous; rather, it is due to the math: The serial number of the starting date is subtracted from serial number of the maturity date. As a simple example, if the starting date were January 1 and the maturity date were January 10, we would compute $10-1=9$. Since

9 days of interest are charged, we say that every day but the first day is used in computing the interest.

Example 1.3.1

Find the *exact time* for a loan taken out on April 14 and due on October 20.

■ The serial number for April 14 is 104 and for October 20 is 293. $293 - 104 = 189$ days.

The second method of finding time is called **approximate time**. With this method we assume that every month has 30 days. The number of months is measured from the starting day of the loan in a given month to the same day in the month containing the maturity date. The number of months that results is multiplied by 30 days. If there are additional days in the term of the loan beyond these 30-day blocks, exact time is used for the remainder of the term.

Example 1.3.2

Find the *approximate time* for the loan in Example 1.3.1.

■ April is the 4th month and October is the 10th month, so there are 6 months of 30 days each from April 14 to October 14. The exact time from October 14 to October 20 is 6 days. The math gives us

$$6 \times 30 + 6 = 180 + 6 = 186 \text{ days.}$$

In practice, those who are lending money will strongly favor exact time because it will earn more money. In the previous examples exact time gave three more days of interest. The calculation of exact time has a couple of pitfalls to avoid. If a given year is a leap year (29 days in February), and the two dates fall with one before and one after February 29, the serial table calculation will be short by one day. The best approach is to add a day to all serial numbers after February 29. Another difficulty occurs when the two dates for the loan span two or more years. To avoid getting the days of the wrong part of the year, find the exact days for the portion of the term in the first year and add them to the number of days of the term that are in the second year. The next two examples will illustrate these two situations.

Example 1.3.3

Find the exact time for a promissory note signed on February 11, 2004, with a maturity date of July 31, 2004.

■ The serial number for 2/11/04 is 42 and the serial number for 7/31/04 is $212 + 1$ (leap year). The number of days is $213 - 42 = 171$.

Example 1.3.4

Find the exact time for a note signed on December 1, 2005, with a maturity date of March 15, 2006.

■ There are 30 exact days in December ($365-335=30$) and the serial number of March 15 is 74. The exact number of days is $30+74=104$.

An interest calculation that uses days in the numerator of the time fraction must likewise have the number of days in a year for the denominator. In the last section when time was given in months, the denominator was 12 months. The resulting units were years, because months divided by months/year leaves years. When time is given in days, the denominator will need to be days, because days divided by days/year will leave years. Two methods of computing interest have become common practice. **Ordinary interest** uses a 360-day year in the denominator of the time fraction. This is like 12 months of 30 days each. **Exact interest** uses a 365-day year (366 for leap year) in the denominator of the time fraction. The next two examples will illustrate the use of these two types of interest and show that *ordinary interest* generates slightly more interest income for the lender. Those who lend money will obviously favor ordinary interest.

Example 1.3.5

Calculate the simple interest on a $12,000 loan for 65 days at 7% per annum by using **a**. ordinary interest, and **b**. exact interest.

■ **a.** Substitute the given parameters into the formula using ordinary interest. Use the original form since we are looking for interest.

$$I=Pit=12{,}000(.07)(^{65}/_{360})=\$151.67$$

■ **b.** Using exact interest, we get

$$I=Pit=12{,}000(.07)(^{65}/_{365})=\$149.59.$$

Example 1.3.6

Calculate the simple interest on a $2500 loan signed June 30, 2005, with a maturity date of November 2, 2005, and bearing interest at 9.5% per annum. Use exact time and ordinary interest.

■ The serial date of November 2 is 306, and the serial date of June 30 is 181. The exact time is $306-181=125$. Now calculate the simple interest.

$$I=Pit=2500(.095)(\tfrac{125}{360})=\$82.47$$

Example 1.3.7

Anthony has $5680 in a Money Market account paying 4.25%; interest is paid every quarter. Any money withdrawn between interest dates will earn no interest for the entire quarter. If Anthony has a pressing $4550 financial need 45 days before interest accrues, should he withdraw the money or take a credit card loan that will cost him 18%?

■ If he withdraws $4550 he will lose the following interest:

$$I=Pit=4550(.0425)(.25)=\$48.34.$$

- The credit card loan will cost the following:

$$I = Pit = 4550(.18)(45/360) = \$102.38.$$

- In fact, the amount of money he withdraws from the account is immaterial since

$.0425(.25) < .18(45/360)$. He should take the money from savings.

Because bankers lend money on a regular basis, the use of *exact time* and *ordinary interest* has been called **Banker's Rule**. *In this text Banker's Rule will be used unless the exercise says otherwise.* The time in all of the previous problems was given in months and years, so exercises given that way are actually using approximate time and ordinary interest. Thus 90 days divided by 360 gives the same result as 3 months divided by 12 months.

When a loan or obligation does not have a maturity date given but rather a length of time, it may be necessary to find the due date. There are two situations to consider:

▶ First, if the time is given in days, the maturity date is the exact number of days after the term of the loan starts. Serial numbers are used for this calculation.

▶ Second, if the time is given in months, the maturity date is the same day in the due month as the day on which the term of the loan starts. There are a few exceptions. With a loan that began on the 30th of November and ran to February we would use the last day of the month (28th or 29th) since February does not have 30 days.

Summary of Time and Interest

Exact Time	every day of the term except the first day
Approximate Time	each month is assumed to be 30 days with exact time used for any portion of a month
Ordinary Interest	the length of a year is assumed to be 360 days
Exact Interest	the length of a year is taken as 365 days (366 for leap year)

The two types of time and two types of interest generate the following four ways to calculate interest:

1. Exact time and Ordinary Interest	Banker's Rule
2. Exact time and Exact Interest	used by credit card companies
3. Approximate Time and Ordinary Interest	time is given in months or years
4. Approximate Time and Exact Interest	rarely used

◀ EXERCISES 1.3 ▶

Concept and Short Answer Exercises

1. Is 2044 a leap year? How do you know?

2. Is 2133 a leap year? How do you know?

3. How is exact time calculated?

4. How is approximate time calculated?
5. How is exact interest calculated?
6. How is ordinary interest calculated?
7. How is Banker's Rule calculated?
8. The Banker's Rule is so named because ______.

Calculation Exercises

Calculate the exact time and approximate time for Exercises 9–14.

9. June 1, 2004, to October 15, 2004
10. January 31, 2004, to September 30, 2004. Note the leap year.
11. November 12, 2003, to April 15, 2004
12. September 7, 2004, to December 20, 2004
13. September 7 to November 22
14. November 22, 2003, to September 7, 2004
15. Complete Table 1.3.1 by finding all four types of interest on $2000 at 8% between March 5, 2005 and June 9, 2005.

TABLE 1.3.1

Type of time	Exact Interest: Divide by 365	Ordinary Interest: Divide by 360
Exact Time = 96 days		
Approx. Time = 94 days		

16. Find all four types of interest on $2000 at 8% between March 5, 2005 and June 5, 2005.

Use Banker's Rule for Exercises 17–28.

17. On June 6 you borrow $15,000 for business equipment at 10%. How much is the interest and what is the payoff on August 15?
18. On April 12 Phoebe buys a $20,000 car. With $5000 paid down on the loan, Phoebe must borrow $15,000 until June 12 when she can repay the loan. At 10%, how much is the interest owed, and what is the payoff on June 12?
19. A 182-day $1,000,000 Treasury bill (T-bill) is bought with a bid of 96.2%. Find the rate of return (ROR), which is the interest rate the investor earns. Please note that for a T-bill the face value (in this case the $1,000,000) is the future value while the bid price (here 96.2% of $1,000,000 = $962,000) is the present value. Explain in your own words how to solve this exercise.
20. A 182-day $2,000,000 T-bill is bought with a bid of 98.32%. Find the ROR.
21. A 91-day $500,000 Treasury bill is bought with a bid of 98.33% of face value. Find the ROR.
22. A 273-day T-bill is bought with a bid of 92.3%. Find the ROR.

23. You borrow $500 at 4% on February 3, 2008. Find the amount you repay on May 5, 2008.

24. You borrow $1500 at 5% on December 3, 2007. Find the amount you repay on May 3, 2008.

25. On 1/1/03 you deposit $7000 at 8% into a money market account that pays interest on 1/1/04. On 8/1/03 you need $5000 to pay off a school bill and you find a broker on e-commerce.com that will lend you money at 12%. Should you get the loan or should you withdraw the money from your money market account? How much do you save using the better method? Explain your solution.

Rules for your decision:

a. If you withdraw any part of the money in your account early, you will lose all of the interest on the part withdrawn.

b. You can repay the loan after the money market account pays its interest since you can withdraw the required money without penalty.

Hence, compute all interests with maturity date 1/1/04.

26. On 2/5/08 Pierce has $10,000 in a savings account that is earning 5%. The next date that interest is posted (added) to his account is 6/1/08. If Pierce withdraws his money early, he will lose all of the interest on the amount withdrawn. On 4/8/08 Pierce needs $8000 for medical bills. If he can get a loan at 10%, should Pierce withdraw the money from his savings account or should he get the loan?

27. On 5/1/04 James has $3000 in his savings account, which earns only 2.75%. The next interest date is 11/1/04. If James withdraws his money early, he will lose all of the interest on the part withdrawn. On 8/5/04 he needs $2000 to pay for a diamond ring for his fiancé, so he finds a broker on e-commerce.com that will lend him money at 12%. Should he get the loan or should he withdraw the money from his savings account? How much does he save using the better method?

28. On 5/1/04 Rebecca has $5000 in her savings account. Her savings account earns only 1.75%, and it pays interest on 7/1/04. If Rebecca withdraws her money early she will lose half of the interest on the part withdrawn. On 6/1/04 she needs $2000. She can get a loan from her mother at 2%. Should she get the loan or should she withdraw the money from her savings account? How much does she save using the better method?

1.4 Future Value at Simple Interest

In Example 1.2.4 the maturity value of a promissory note was calculated. The simple interest of $600 was computed and then added to the principal $5000 to give a maturity value of $5600. The net effect of this calculation was the movement of the $5000 18 months into the future at 8% simple interest. The general terms **future value** or **amount** refer to the value of money at some future date due to the accrual of interest. However, using the term **maturity value** fits better with notes, other debt instruments, and even bonds. Since the calculation of the future value is just principal plus interest, a useful formula can be developed.

Derivation of the Formula

The future value = principal + interest

$S = P + I$

$S = P + Pit$ replace I with the simple interest formula

$S = P(1+it)$ factor out the common term P

Future Value Formula: $S = P(1+it)$ **(1.2)**

The factor $(1+it)$, or **simple interest factor**, becomes a tool to move money on the time line at simple interest. In Chapter 2 we identify this as an accumulation function. Whenever money is to be moved forward on the time line, the formula $S = P(1+it)$ should be used. On the other hand, if the interest, principal, interest rate, or time is needed, the basic formula $I = Pit$ should be used.

Example 1.4.1

Find the maturity value of a \$1680 note dated 4/20/04 with interest at 7.5% and a due date of 10/30/04. Use Banker's Rule.

■ Even though 2004 is a leap year, both dates are on the same side of February 28, so just use the printed serial numbers. 10/30/04 → 303 and 4/20/04 → 110.
The exact time = 303 − 110 = 193.

$$S = P(1+it) \rightarrow \quad S = 1680(1 + (.075)(\tfrac{193}{360})) \rightarrow$$

$$S = 1680(1.040208333) = \$1747.55$$

Example 1.4.2

A credit union pays 9.2% on savings accounts. An account has a balance of \$3582.38 on January 1. A \$250 deposit is made on March 4, and a \$375 deposit is made on April 28. How much will be in the account on June 30 if no other deposits are made? Use Banker's Rule.

■ The future value of three pieces of money is needed. Using $S = P(1+it)$, set up the three amounts. The exact time can best be found using serial numbers.

$t_1 = 181 - 1 = 180, \qquad S_1 = 3582.38(1 + (.092)(\tfrac{180}{360})) = \$3747.17$

$t_2 = 181 - 63 = 118, \qquad S_2 = 250(1 + (.092)(\tfrac{118}{360})) = \$257.54$

$t_3 = 181 - 118 = 63, \qquad S_3 = 375(1 + (.092)(\tfrac{63}{360})) = \$381.04$

$$\text{Account total} = S_1 + S_2 + S_3 = \$4385.75$$

Example 1.4.3

The average daily balance on a Visa card is \$648.20. The card carries an 18.5% interest charge for balances not paid within 25 days. If the payment of the balance were one day late, how much would the cardholder owe in interest, and what would the new balance be? Use exact time and exact interest.

■ For the interest owed use $I = Pit$ and for the balance use $S = P + I$.

$$I = 648.20(.185)\left(\tfrac{26}{365}\right) = \$8.54$$

Balance at the time of the payment = \$648.20 + \$8.54 = \$656.74

An interesting application of simple interest involves invoices that have *prompt payment discounts* incorporated into their payment structure. One good example relates to the billing of contractors by building supply companies. Many of these invoices are very large amounts for which the supplier would like to receive payment as quickly as possible. To encourage prompt payment, the suppliers offer a discount of 1–3% if the invoice is paid within 10 days. They also impose a 1–3% surcharge if the invoice is not paid within 30–60 days. An invoice may have terms which say, for example, that a 2% discount is offered if paid within 10 days. Otherwise the net is due in 45 days. Before the computer age, the shorthand notation for such an invoice was 2/10, n/45. Most modern invoices are computer-generated and have a brief paragraph at the bottom that spells out the terms of the discount and indicates the surcharges that will result if the payment is late. If the money used to pay the invoice and receive the discount is not already in an interest-bearing account, the purchaser should always take advantage of the discount offer. Therefore, the question to be answered about these invoices is whether the discount (as interest earned) gives a better return than leaving the money in a bank. The next two examples will illustrate how to make this judgment.

Example 1.4.4

Find the simple interest rate for a \$135,550 invoice with terms 2/10, n/45 if the payment is made on the 10th day. Use exact time and ordinary interest.

■ The discount is simply the rate times the money owed. It represents the amount earned if the balance of the invoice is paid 35 days before it is due. The payer is actually making an investment that will give a return.

Discount = (135,550)(.02) = \$2711. This leaves \$132,839 to pay. Now solve the basic formula for i and substitute.

$$i = \frac{I}{Pt} = \frac{2711}{(132{,}839)\left(\tfrac{35}{360}\right)} = .2099 \approx 21\%$$

This is a better rate than banks can pay.

Example 1.4.5

Suppose the invoice in Example 1.4.4 were paid at 60 days instead of at the due date of 45 days. What interest charges will the late invoice cost the payer if the company uses a 1.5% surcharge rate? What rate of interest will this be?

■ The surcharge = (135,550)(.015) = \$2033.25 and the payment is 15 days late.

$$i = \frac{I}{Pt} = \frac{2033.25}{(135{,}550)(\frac{15}{360})} = .36 = 36\%$$

This is not good business and results in a loss of \$2711 + \$2033.25 = \$4744.25. If the \$135,550 is left to earn interest at a typical 6% bank rate from the 10th to the 60th day, it earns the following:

$$I = (135{,}550)(.06)(\tfrac{50}{360}) = \$1129.58.$$

The net loss for this situation is \$4744.25 – \$1129.58 = \$3614.67.

◀ EXERCISES 1.4 ▶

Concept and Short Answer Exercises

1. What are the differences among the formulas $I = Pit$, $S = P + I$, and $S = P(1 + it)$? When should you use each?
2. How do we know that money is being moved forward? What words are used to represent a value of money in the future?
3. When does one use the Banker's Rule for time and when not?
4. On an invoice, what does 3/10, n/45 mean?

Calculation Exercises

5. What is the amount of \$1000, 6 months from now at 8%?
6. What is the amount of \$1000, 8 months from now at 10%?
7. Find the future value of \$800 that is due in 2 years at 6%.
8. Find the future value of \$800 that is due in 10 years at 3.5%.
9. Miranda owes \$1000 on 12/5/03 and \$4000 on 3/8/04. Find the single value on 7/1/04 that she must pay to discharge both amounts if money is worth 7% simple interest.
10. Jeremy owes \$1500 on 12/10/03 and \$6000 on 3/15/04. Find the single value on 7/21/04 that he must pay to settle both amounts if money is worth 10% simple interest.
11. Sasha owes \$1000 on 12/5/03 and \$4000 on 3/5/04. Find the single value on 7/5/04 that he must pay to repay both amounts if money is worth 7% simple interest.

12. Brittany owes $50,000 on 12/31/03 and $40,000 on 3/31/04. Find the single value on 2/28/05 that she must pay to repay both amounts if money is worth 7% simple interest. (Note: We can use months since all the dates are the last day.)

13. On June 3, 2005, you will be required to pay $5000. On August 3, 2005, you paid $4000. How much do you still owe on August 3, 2005? Money is worth 8.2%.

14. On October 3 you owe $5000 to the Sidell State Bank. On December 3 you pay $5000 and are given a receipt. What does the receipt say you still owe? Money is worth 12%.

15. If Randolf buys a new $5520 furnace/air conditioner for his home and receives an invoice with terms 2/10, n/45, what rate of interest will he earn if he makes his payment on the 10th day? Explain your solution.

16. If Aaron buys $5520 worth of building materials for his basement renovation and receives an invoice with terms 3/10, n/60, what rate of interest can he make if he pays on the 10th day? Explain your solution.

17. Mark's Studio buys a new $10,000 Yamaha piano and receives an invoice from Case Brothers with the terms 3/5, n/60. If Mark pays on the 5th day, what rate of interest will he earn?

18. Parker Hardware orders plastic piping worth $20,000 and receives an invoice from Charlotte Plastics with the terms 3/5, n/30. If Parker Hardware pays on the 5th day, what rate of interest will they earn?

19. The Classic Construction Company receives an invoice from Upstate Builder's Supply for $59,865 with terms 2/10, n/45. If CCC pays this invoice on the 8th day, what rate of return will they make?

20. In exercise 19 the Upstate Builder's invoice also states that late payments will be charged 1.5% per month simple interest. Suppose the foreman of CCC lost the invoice on the dash of his pickup and did not find it until 62 days after the invoice date. If it is paid that day, what rate of simple interest did CCC pay for this oversight?

21. A note for $2500 is due on March 1, 2005, and another for $3850 on June 1, 2005. If money is worth 8%, what single payment on August 1, 2005, will discharge these obligations?

22. The Piedmont Interstate Trust Company pays 6.75% on Money Market savings accounts, and deposits by the 10th earn interest from the 1st of the month. Interest is credited on June 30 and December 31 each year. Aunt Martha's account had a balance of $2569.35 on December 31, 2003. She deposited $348.55 on February 8, 2004, and $185.30 on April 4, 2004. If no other deposits were made, what is her balance on June 30, 2004? Use Banker's Rule.

1.5 Present Value at Simple Interest

To prepare for an obligation due in the future, we could invest money in an interest-bearing account so that the principal and interest together would pay the obligation when it comes due. It is always better to save money and earn interest than to borrow it and pay interest. How much you should invest for a future obligation is determined by the amount of the future obligation as well as the due date and interest rate. It is cumbersome to solve for P after substituting the other values, so the future value formula is here solved algebraically for the present value. The resulting formula will provide a method of moving money backward on the time line. Moving money on the time line is essential for getting all of the various payments and debts to the same focal point in time.

TIME LINE DIAGRAM 1.5.1

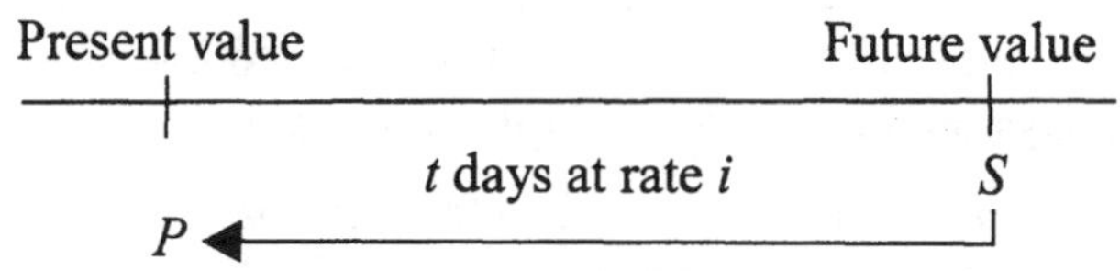

$S = P(1+it)$	the future value formula
$\dfrac{S}{1+it} = \dfrac{P(1+it)}{1+it}$	Divide each side by the factor $1+it$.
$\dfrac{S}{1+it} = P$	Cancel the common factor.

Present Value Formula: $$P = \frac{S}{1+it} \qquad (1.3)$$

Notice that this formula makes sense for what it accomplishes. S is the larger piece of money, and it is being divided by a factor greater than 1, resulting in a smaller value for P. The calculation demonstrates the time value of money principle: *Money gets smaller as it is moved back in time.* Sometimes students choose to multiply the rate times the future value times the time fraction and then subtract from the future value. What they have really figured is discount interest. This idea is the topic of Chapter 2.

WARNING: *Do not use the simple interest formula ($I = Pit$) when moving money on the time line. Always use the future value or present value formulas.*

Example 1.5.1

If money can be invested at 7% per annum, find the present value of a \$1600 obligation due in 15 months.

■ Substitute into the present value formula.

$$P = \frac{S}{1+it} = \frac{1600}{1+(.07)(\frac{15}{12})} = \frac{1600}{1.0875} = \$1471.26$$

Example 1.5.2

If money is worth 6.5% per annum, what would it cost to buy an item today that will cost \$950 in 10 months?

■ Substitute into the present value formula.

$$P = \frac{S}{1+it} = \frac{950}{1+(.065)(\frac{10}{12})} = \frac{950}{1.0541666} = \$901.19$$

Note that \$901.19 today is equivalent to \$950 in 10 months if money earns 6.5%.

Example 1.5.3

If money is worth 7.25%, is it better to pay \$580 cash for a desk or \$600 in 9 months? Give the cash equivalent of the savings resulting from the better buy.

■ Since we need the cash equivalent of the savings, find the present value of the \$600 and compare to the cash price of \$580.

$$P = \frac{S}{1+it} = \frac{600}{1+(.0725)(\frac{9}{12})} = \frac{600}{1.054375} = \$569.06$$

It is better to buy in 9 months to save a cash equivalent of: $\$580 - \$569.06 = \$10.94$.

◀ EXERCISES 1.5 ▶

Concept and Short Answer Exercises

1. How do you identify a present value problem? What words are used to identify a present value problem?
2. Identify the differences and the use for each of the three formulas: $I = Pit$, $S = P(1+it)$, and $P = \dfrac{S}{1+it}$.
3. Why the warning? *Do not use the simple interest formula (I = Pit) when moving money on the time line. Always use the future value or present value formulas.*
4. How do you handle the "is it better" problems?

Calculation Exercises

5. The Fairmount State Bank is charging 7% on a debenture (unsecured loan). Meredith owes \$12,000 on December 1, 2004, but decides to pay off the loan early on January 1, 2004. Find the payoff.
6. The Shelbyville Bank and Trust is charging 12.6% for an unsecured loan. Brad owes \$21,000 on December 1, 2004, but decides to pay off the loan early on February 1, 2004. Find the payoff.
7. Bryan is leasing land for his hunting club and has incurred debts of \$3000 due on 8/1/03 and \$2000 due on 10/2/03. On 6/15/03 Bryan has enough cash from club dues to pay off both debts. Find the payoff at 6.5%.

8. Lawrence is leasing land for his soccer club and has incurred debts of $6000 due on 8/1/03 and $4000 due on 10/2/03. On 6/15/03 Lawrence has enough cash to pay off both debts. Find the payoff at 6.5%.

9. Suppose that in Exercise 7 Bryan is late on the first debt, but on 8/15/03 he has enough cash to pay off both debts. Find the payoff at 6.5%.

10. Suppose that in Exercise 8 Lawrence is late on the first debt, but on 8/15/03 he has enough cash to pay off both debts. Find the payoff at 6.5%.

11. Find the cash equivalent at 10% on 1/1/03 of $1000 due on 7/1/03 and $2500 due on 3/1/04.

12. Find the payoff on 1/1/03 of $1000 due on 7/1/03 and $2500 due on 3/1/05 at 6%.

13. If money costs 8%, is it better to pay $3000 in cash or to wait 6 months and pay $3200? What is the cash equivalent of the savings from the better buy? Explain your solution.

14. Is it better to pay $3000 in cash for a dining room set or to wait 6 months and pay $3200 if money can earn 18%? What is the cash equivalent of the savings resulting from the better buy? Explain your solution.

15. Nadya needs parts to repair her boat. If she is earning 18% on her money, should she pay $2000 in cash or wait a year and pay $2400?

16. Eric needs to pay for the parts to repair his tractor. Assuming he can earn 18% on his money, should he pay $2000 in cash or wait a year and pay $2200?

17. What should you pay to buy a security that matures at $25,000 in 5 months if you wish to earn 11% on the investment?

18. If a capital expenditure costs $29,850 on September 6, 2004, and $30,000 on January 3, 2005, which is the better date to make the purchase if money is worth 7.25%? Give the cash equivalent of the savings realized.

19. What investment now will provide the resources in 15 months to pay an $8525 obligation, if money is worth 6.5%?

20. MIT Developers has obligations of $32,000 due on 8/14/04 and $59,500 due on 10/3/04. How much should MIT invest at 6.5% on 2/6/04 to provide the resources to pay these future obligations when they come due?

21. Providence Bank and Trust paid off a reserve requirement loan on 8/21/04 with an electronic transfer of $7,849,987.43. How much did they borrow on 8/16/04 at 2.5% and what were the interest charges? Use exact time and exact interest.

22. The sale of some property allowed Randy to pay off two notes early. What did he pay on 3/15/05 to discharge a $4500 note due on 7/10/05 and a $6000 note due on 9/25/05 if the interest rate is 7.25%?

23. RanPro Corporation intends to make two equal deposits on 5/1/05 and 7/15/05 to provide for a capital expenditure of $568,950 on 10/18/05. Find the value of those deposits if money is worth 5.25%.

1.6 Simple Interest Debt Instruments

Simple interest loans, when properly prepared and signed, are sometimes sold to a third party. The investor who buys the note will pay the seller less than the maturity value. This is called discounting the note, and it can be done using simple interest or discount interest. In effect, discounting means to find the current value (present value) of some future obligation using the rate of interest the buyer wants to make. The new owner of the note will receive the maturity value of the loan on the due date. It is very common for home mortgages to be sold several times during their term. The discounting process requires two steps. The first is to calculate the maturity value (unless it is already written on the note). The second is to find the current value, using the maturity value as the future value. It is not necessary that the two interest rates be the same. Typically, they will be different.

Example 1.6.1

A merchant holds a promissory note signed by one of his customers on 5/18/04. The note is for $32,500 at 8.5% per annum and has a maturity date of 12/1/04. On 7/5/04 he sells the note to a banker who charges 12% simple interest to discount the note. Using Banker's Rule, what will the merchant receive for the note the day he sells it?

■ The first step is to get the maturity value of the note.

$$\text{Exact time} = 335 - 138 = 197$$

$$\text{Maturity value: } S = P(1+it) = 32{,}500(1 + (.085)(\tfrac{197}{360})) = \$34{,}011.70$$

$$\text{The second exact time} = 335 - 186 = 149$$

$$\text{Discounted value: } P = \frac{S}{1+it} = \frac{34{,}011.70}{1+(.12)(\frac{149}{360})} = \$32{,}402.38$$

Example 1.6.2

Find the value of a note for $8000 with interest at 9.25% due in 18 months if it is discounted at 8% simple interest 5 months before maturity.

■ Compute the maturity value of the note:

$$S = P(1+it) = 8000(1 + (.0925)(1.5)) = \$9110.$$

■ Discount the maturity value 5 months at 8%:

$$P = \frac{S}{1+it} = \frac{9110}{1+(.08)(\frac{5}{12})} = \$8816.13.$$

◀ EXERCISES 1.6 ▶

Concept and Short Answer Exercises

1. Give the general method of selling financial instruments like bonds, notes, and CDs.

2. What is the difference between a non-interest-bearing note and an interest-bearing note? How can you tell if a note is interest-bearing or not? How do you mature a non-interest-bearing note? How about an interest-bearing note?

3. Why are there two different rates for some of these problems?

4. Why would the seller dispose of a bond after he has invested in it? Why would someone else buy his bond?

Calculation Exercises

5. On March 1, 2004, Jim bought a $1000, 90-day note. On April 20, 2004, Jim needed cash and sold his note to Pete, who requires 10% on his investments. How much did Pete pay Jim for his note? Explain your solution.

6. On March 1, 2005, Shawnte bought a $10,000, 180-day note. On April 20, 2005, she needed cash and sold her note to Anthony, who requires 15% on his investments. How much did Anthony pay Shawnte for her note? Explain your solution.

7. Suppose Jim's note in Exercise 5 pays interest at 7%. If on April 20, 2004, Jim needed cash and sold his note to Charise, who requires 10% on her investments, how much did Charise pay Jim for his note? Explain your solution.

8. Suppose Shawnte's note in Exercise 6 pays interest at 7%. If on April 20, 2005, she needed cash and sold her note to Dennis, who requires 15% on his investments, how much did Dennis pay Shawnte for her note? Explain your solution.

9. A $4000 corporate note paying 5% interest is bought on 3/5/04 and matures on 9/5/04. On 7/5/04 this note is sold to a third party requiring 7%. Find the amount the third person paid for the corporate bond. Find the actual interest the original holder made on his investment. Why would the original holder ever sell?

10. A $4000 corporate note paying 4.5% interest is bought on 3/5/04 and matures on 9/5/04. On 7/5/04 this note is sold to a third party requiring 4%. Find the amount the third person paid for the corporate note. Find the actual interest the original holder made on her investment. Why would the original holder ever sell?

11. A corporate note is bought on 3/5/05 and matures to $4000 on 9/5/05. On 7/5/05 this note is sold to a third party requiring 7%. Find the amount the third person paid for the corporate note. Find the actual interest the original holder lost on his investment. Why would the original holder ever sell?

12. A tax-free municipal security is bought on 3/5/05 and matures to $40,000 on 9/5/05. On 7/5/05 this security is sold to a third party requiring 10%. Find the amount the third person paid for the municipal security. Find the actual interest the original holder lost on his investment. Why would the original holder ever sell?

13. On 1/1/04 the city of Greenville issues a tax-free $2000 municipal security that matures on 4/10/04 with interest at 8%. If the owner of a security sold it on 2/1/04 for $1920.60, what rate of return did the buyer get?

14. On 1/1/04 the city of Simpsonville issues a tax-free $2000 municipal security that matures on 4/10/04 with interest at 8%. If the owner of a bond sold it on 2/1/04 for $2020, what rate of return did the buyer get?

15. A $5000 note costing 10% and dated March 15, 2001, matures in 120 days. If this note is discounted on June 10, 2001, at a bank charging 12%, what will the seller receive?

16. The following interest bearing notes are sold on October 1, 2004, at a bank charging 11%. Find what the seller received for the two notes.

Note A:	$4500	6/30/04	180 days	8%
Note B:	$8750	9/4/04	90 days	9%

1.7 Equations of Value

An **equation of value** is a mathematical expression that equates several pieces of money at some chosen date, called the **focal date**. Some of the money may originally be at the focal date while other monies are either present values or future values relative to that date. We can use the formulas already developed to move the money. An equation is written to equate obligations to payments. Hence, what you owe equals what you pay. Usually one of the values is the unknown and a variable is used to represent it. The variable is isolated and the result gives the solution for the equation of value.

A time line diagram makes a great tool for solving an equation of value. This is simply a line with the appropriate dates and pieces of money located. A focal date is selected and arrows drawn to indicate which pieces of money are being moved to the focal date. The arrows also suggest whether the movement of a given piece of money is a present value calculation or a future value calculation. It even helps to put the amount of time on the arrow so it is readily available in the formula. *Equation of value* problems are an appropriate place to emphasize the following principle.

The Golden Rule of Finance: *Monies cannot be added or reconciled unless they are valued at the same point in time.*

Example 1.7.1

A purchase agreement calls for $200 down and two payments of $300 in 6 months and $400 in 9 months. If the interest rate is 12%, what is the cash price for the item purchased.

■ Make a time line diagram and place the three bundles of money at their appropriate dates. Because the cash price is present value, choose the present as the focal date and move the later payments.

TIME LINE DIAGRAM 1.7.1

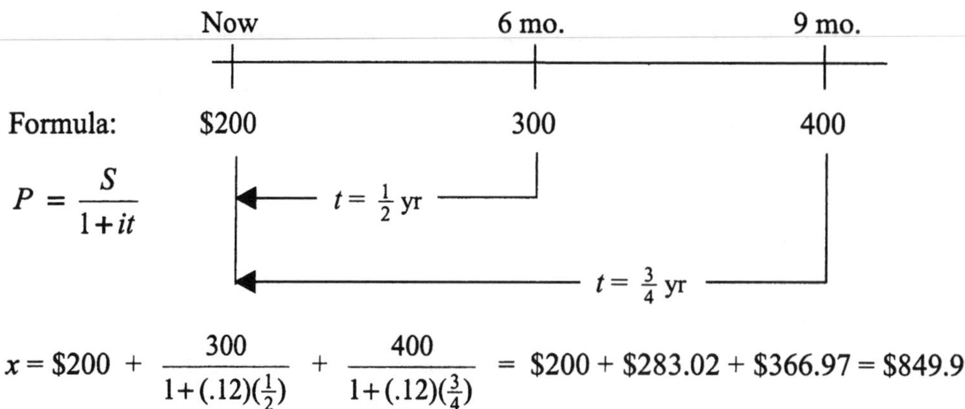

$$x = \$200 + \frac{300}{1+(.12)(\frac{1}{2})} + \frac{400}{1+(.12)(\frac{3}{4})} = \$200 + \$283.02 + \$366.97 = \$849.99$$

Example 1.7.2

A debt of \$4500 incurred on October 2, 2004, must be paid back with two equal payments, one on January 15, 2005, and the other on April 15, 2005. If the interest rate is 7.5%, find the size of the payments. Use Banker's Rule.

■ Make a time line diagram with x as the unknown payment at both payment dates. Choose October 2 as the focal date, though any one of these dates would be acceptable. This solution will require a little algebra to isolate the unknown. We will use the present value formula to move the two payments to the date of the \$4500 debt. The dates span two years, so first find the time from October 2 to December 31 (90 days), then add this 90 to each of the other serial numbers 15 and 105.

TIME LINE DIAGRAM 1.7.2

10/2/04 (90)	1/15/05 (15)	4/15/05 (105)
\$4500	x	x

$t = 105$ days

$t = 195$ days

Formula:

$$P = \frac{S}{1+it}$$

$$4500 = \frac{x}{1+(.075)(\frac{105}{360})} + \frac{x}{1+(.075)(\frac{195}{360})} = \frac{x}{1.021875} + \frac{x}{1.040625}$$

$$4500 = x\left(\frac{1}{1.021875} + \frac{1}{1.040625}\right)$$

$$4500 = x(1.93955\ldots) \quad \text{Therefore, } x = \$2320.12$$

Example 1.7.3

A man owes two obligations, one for \$825 due in 3 months and one for \$1248 due in 15 months. If the interest rate is 5.5%, what payment in 9 months will settle the obligations?

■ Use the payment date as the focal date and move one piece of money forward and the other backward.

TIME LINE DIAGRAM 1.7.3

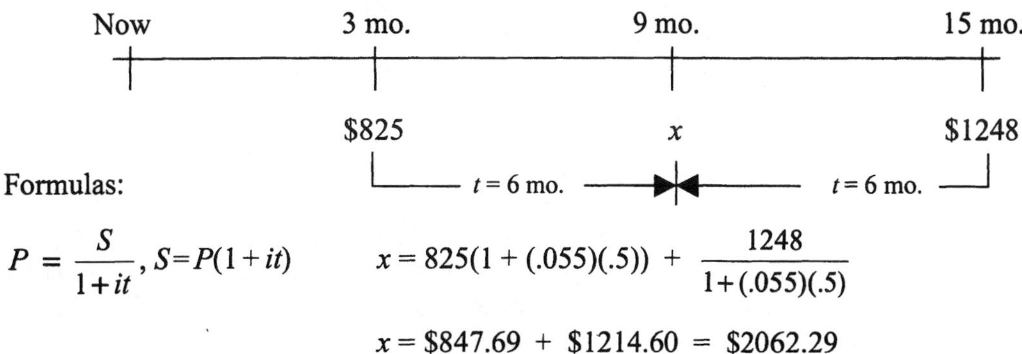

$$P = \frac{S}{1+it},\ S=P(1+it) \qquad x = 825(1+(.055)(.5)) + \frac{1248}{1+(.055)(.5)}$$

$$x = \$847.69 + \$1214.60 = \$2062.29$$

◀ EXERCISES 1.7 ▶

Concept and Short Answer Exercises

1. "What I owe equals what I pay" is an example of_____.
2. "My savings account equals what I originally deposited less what I have withdrawn" is an example of______.
3. The payoff on a loan equals what is originally owed less the payments already made if all monies are moved to the same _____ .
4. In simple interest equations of value, does the focal date make a difference in calculating the answer?
5. If no focal date is set by the problem, what is the default focal date on cash equivalent problems?
6. If no focal date is set by the problem, what is the default focal date on final payment (payoff) problems?

Calculation Exercises

7. At 10%, what one amount of money in 1 year is equivalent to $500 now and $1000 in 6 months if we
   a. Use today as the focal date?
   b. Use 6 months as the focal date?
   c. Use 1 year as the focal date?
8. At 8%, what one amount of money in 2 years is equivalent to $500 in 3 months and $1000 in 6 months if we
   a. Use today as the focal date?
   b. Use 6 months as the focal date?
   c. Use 1 year as the focal date?
9. A woman owes $900 due in 1 year and $9000 due in 3 years. What is the cash equivalent of these two amounts at 8%?

10. Nozomi owes $1000 due in 1 year and $3000 due in 5 years. What is her cash equivalent (payoff now, outstanding balance now) of these two amounts at 3.5%?

11. Mike buys a $3000 car on 1/1/04 and agrees to make payments. If he pays $1000 down, pays another $1000 on 12/1/04 and another $1000 on 5/1/05, find his payoff on 12/1/05 if the auto loan is costing him 8%.

12. Raphael buys inventory worth $30,000 on 1/1/04 and agrees to three future payments. If he pays $1000 down, another $10,000 on 12/1/04, and another $10,000 on 5/1/05, find his payoff on 12/1/05 if the loan is costing him 8%.

13. Suppose that on 6/1/04 Mr. Harmon buys a $500 yellow lab puppy from a championship line and agrees with the breeder to make two equal payments on 12/1/04 and 6/1/05. If the breeder charges 10% for credit, find the amount of the two payments. Use the default focal date of 6/1/05.

14. Randall buys a $500 chocolate lab puppy from a championship line on 6/1/04 and agrees with the breeder to make three equal payments on 12/1/04 and 6/1/05 and 12/1/05. If the breeder charges 10% for credit, find the amount of the three payments. Put the focal date at the default date of 12/1/05.

15. Repeat Exercise 13, but with the focal date at 12/1/04.

16. Repeat Exercise 14, but with the focal date at 6/1/05.

17. A woman has figured that her tax obligation for self-employment on March 15, 2005, will be about $6500. If she makes a $1400 payment on September 1, 2004, and another $2550 payment on December 15, 2004, what will she still owe on March 15, 2005, if money is worth 7%?

18. The owner of The Craftshoppe has figured that her tax obligation for self-employment on March 15, 2005, will be about $8500. If she makes a $2400 payment on September 15, 2004, and another $2550 payment on December 15, 2004, what will she still owe on March 15, 2005, if money is worth 4.2%?

19. An obligation for $6800 is due November 13, 2004, and a second one for $5500 is due January 8, 2005. What single payment on September 6, 2005, will discharge these two obligations if money is worth 7.5%?

20. A debt of $8500 incurred on 5/10/05 must be paid back with two installments. The first is on 8/10/05 and the second one, 50% larger, on 11/10/05. If the interest rate is 7%, find the two payments using time in months.

21. A corporation has two loans that come due in the current fiscal year. The first loan for $1.75 million was due April 15 and the second for $2.5 million is due October 1. If the corporation missed the payment of the first loan and sold assets sufficient to pay both loans on June 20, what is the payoff if figured at 5.25%? Use Banker's Rule.

1.8 Investments — Net Present Value and Internal Rate of Return

When a corporation makes an investment in goods or assets, it wants to predict whether the expenditure will give a good rate of return. One method of comparing costs with expected returns is the use of an equation of value to find the **net present value (NPV)**. As the name suggests, it is the "net," or difference, between income and expenses, all of which are moved to the present. The rate of return used in this calculation is called the *cost of capital* and generally corresponds with the company's goals and requirements for investments. The cost of capital varies from industry to industry. The **internal rate of return (IRR)** is the rate at which the returns and investments make the NPV zero. The ability to predict accurate returns on investment and the associated risks may also have a significant impact on the resulting internal rate of return. Some returns on investment generate a continuous stream of income while others produce inflows of cash at regular or irregular intervals. An investment analysis that accurately describes these situations may require the use of compound interest or the methods of calculus or statistics. In this chapter we will simplify the investment income by assuming it all occurred at the end of the income period. This still gives satisfactory results from the analysis.

This chapter's simplified investment analysis plan requires all returns to be moved to the present at some chosen rate of return (cost of capital). The present value of these returns is then compared to the present value of the investment by using an equation of value. We will let the returns be positive numbers and the investments negative numbers. If the resulting net present value is positive, then the investment will meet the company's goals. The actual IRR for simple interest can be found using an interpolation method, algebra, or the TI 83 SOLVER. (See Appendix B.1.) If you are using a scientific calculator, the BA II Plus, or the El 733A, you should use interpolation.

Example 1.8.1

Find the net present value at 14% of an investment of $25,000, which is expected to bring returns of $14,000 in 9 months and $15,000 in 14 months.

■ Draw a time line diagram and write an equation of value for the net present value.

TIME LINE DIAGRAM 1.8.1

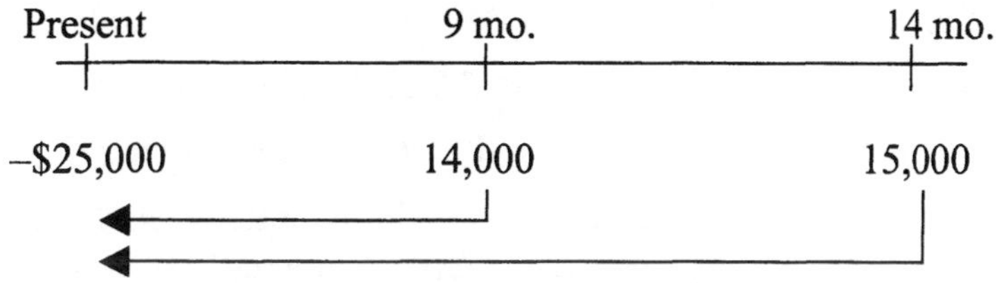

Present	9 mo.	14 mo.
–$25,000	14,000	15,000

$$NPV_{@14\%} = -\$25{,}000 + \frac{14{,}000}{1+(.14)(\frac{9}{12})} + \frac{15{,}000}{1+(.14)(\frac{14}{12})}$$

$$NPV_{@14\%} = -\$25{,}000 + \$12{,}669.68 + \$12{,}893.98$$

$$NPV_{@14\%} = -\$25{,}000 + \$25{,}563.66 = \$563.66$$

Example 1.8.2

Find the internal rate of return for the investment in Example 1.8.1.

■ The method of interpolation requires that we find another net present value. In this case it will require a higher rate and result in a negative NPV. The actual IRR will generate a NPV = 0. The method of interpolation assumes that the rates will be in the same ratio as the net present values. Note that if the first rate used had given a negative NPV, we would chose a smaller rate for the second. Now pick a larger rate and recompute the NPV.

$$\text{NPV}_{@18\%} = -\$25{,}000 + \frac{14{,}000}{1+(.18)(\frac{9}{12})} + \frac{15{,}000}{1+(.18)(\frac{14}{12})}$$

$$\text{NPV}_{@18\%} = -\$25{,}000 + \$12{,}334.80 + \$12{,}396.69$$

$$\text{NPV}_{@18\%} = -\$25{,}000 + \$24{,}731.49 = -\$268.51$$

$$4\% \left[d \begin{bmatrix} 14\% & 563.66 \\ i\% & 000.00 \end{bmatrix} d_1 \atop 18\% \quad -268.51 \right] d_2 \qquad \frac{d}{4} = \frac{d_1}{d_2} \rightarrow \frac{d}{4} = \frac{563.66}{832.17} \rightarrow d = 2.71\%$$

$$i = \text{IRR} = 14\% + 2.71\% = 16.71\%$$

When we write the equation of value to solve directly for the IRR we use a variable x for the unknown rate. The resulting quadratic equation can be solved quickly with the TI 83 SOLVER routine.

$$0 = -25{,}000 + \frac{14{,}000}{1+(x)(\frac{9}{12})} + \frac{15{,}000}{1+(x)(\frac{14}{12})} \rightarrow x = 16.679\%$$

◀ EXERCISES 1.8 ▶

Concept and Short Answer Exercises

1. Suppose the NPV is \$402 at 8%. What does that mean?
2. Suppose the NPV is –\$402 at 8%. What does that mean?
3. Suppose the NPV is \$402 at 8%. Is the IRR more or less than 8%?
4. Suppose the NPV is –\$402 at 8%. Is the IRR more or less than 8%?
5. The focal date for all NPV and IRR problems is where?
6. Why is an IRR problem that uses simple interest very hard to solve if it contains more than two inflows and/or outflow monies? How then are they solved?
7. Suppose that the NPV is \$402 at 8% and the NPV is –\$75 at 9%. What is your interpolated value for the IRR?
8. Suppose that the NPV is \$40.50 at 8% and the NPV is –\$75.33 at 10%. What is your interpolated value for the IRR?

Calculation Exercises

9. Janel invests $2000 now and gets back $3000 in 2 years. Find the NPV at 20% and at 30%, and find the IRR.

10. Brandon invests $20,000 now and gets back $30,000 in 2 years. Find the NPV at 20% and at 30%, and find the IRR.

11. Marlon agrees to pay $500 now to get a return of $700 in a year. Find his NPV at 30% and his IRR.

12. A&R Plumbing contracts for a new home plumbing job. The contract stipulates that the homeowner will pay A&R $15,400 in 6 months if the job is complete. Supplies are estimated to cost A&R $11,200 now. Assuming the job is done on time, find the NPV at 70% and the IRR.

13. Jon is starting a business that requires $8000 startup money but will return $4000 in 1 year and $6000 in 2 years. Find the NPV at 10% and 20%, and find the IRR to one decimal place.

14. In Exercise 12, the A&R estimator realizes he has forgotten to include several other expenses. He calculates these expenses to total another $2000 at 3 months. Keeping the rest of Exercise 12 unchanged, find the NPV at 40% and the IRR.

15. Jan's Boutique needs some new equipment. The cost of the equipment is $500 now. The returns on that investment are $300 in a year and $800 in 2 years. Assuming all returns are figured at the end of the calendar year, find the NPV at 70% and at 80%, and find the IRR to two decimal places.

16. A $25,000 investment will bring returns of $10,000 in 9 months, $10,000 in 15 months and $10,000 in 18 months. Find the NPV at 20% and the IRR.

17. An investment requires a cash outlay of $4500 and is expected to bring returns of $2500 in 9 months and $3200 in 18 months. What is the net present value at 15% and what is the internal rate of return?

18. Peery Construction is renovating a home and has expenses of $20,000 now and $5000 in 6 months. The project will bring three returns of $10,000 in 9 months, 15 months and 18 months. What is the internal rate of return on this project?

1.9 Partial Payments

Money borrowed at simple interest has a maturity date when the principal and interest come due. The borrower is under no obligation to pay on the loan until that date; however, he may choose to pay some of the principal earlier to help reduce interest charges. The borrower and the lender should have a mutual understanding about the method used to allow credit on these early payments. Historically the two methods have been called the **Merchant's Rule** and the **United States Rule.**

1. The **Merchant's Rule** uses an equation of value technique, which sets the focal date at the final settlement date. Usually this date is the maturity date or due date of the loan. The balance due is the algebraic sum of the maturity value (negative) and

the various partial payments (positive) on the focal date. This assures the borrower that his or her early partial payments received interest at the same rate as the loan principal accrued it. The Merchant's Rule is rarely used today but it is of pedagogical value because it gives us a good application for focal dates and equations of value. It was used almost exclusively until the early 1800s.

2. The **United States Rule** computes the interest due on any day that a partial payment is made. The payment is subtracted as cash on that day from the sum of the principal and interest. This leaves a new balance (principal) that accrues interest until the next time a partial payment is made or until the due date arrives. Payments that are not large enough to cover the interest due are not credited. Credit card interest on an account with no new purchases would operate under the United States Rule.

Example 1.9.1

A simple interest loan of \$5000 is due in 15 months with interest at 9% per annum. If the borrower made a \$1200 payment at 4 months and a \$950 payment at 9 months, find the balance on this loan by the Merchant's Rule and by the United States Rule.

■ Draw a time line diagram and then compute the future value of each piece of money using 15 months as the focal date.

TIME LINE DIAGRAM 1.9.1

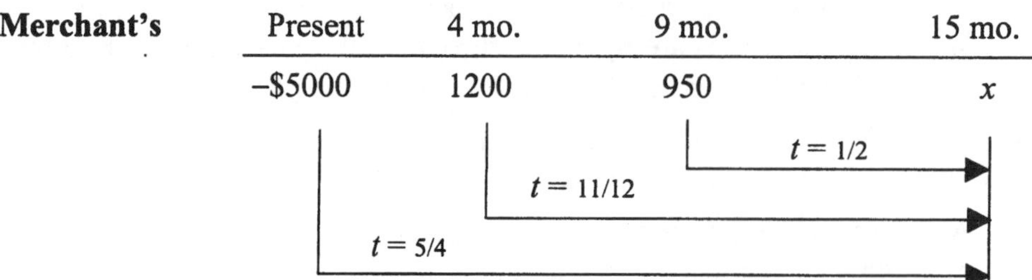

Formula: $S = P(1 + it)$

$$x = -\$5000(1 + (.09)(5/4)) + 1200(1 + (.09)(11/12)) + 950(1 + (.09)(1/2))$$

$$x = -\$5562.50 + \$1299 + \$992.75$$

$$x = -\$5562.50 + \$2291.75$$

$$x = -\$3270.75$$ ◀ Balance Due

TIME LINE DIAGRAM 1.9.2

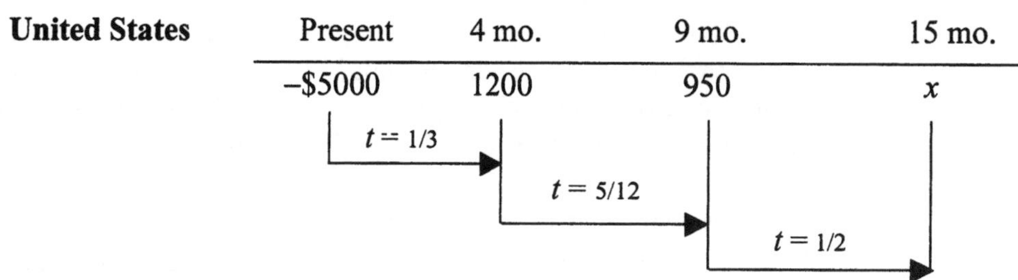

\$5000 @ 9% for 4 months	$S_1 = 5000(1 + (.09)(\frac{1}{3})) =$	\$5150.00
\$1200 payment at 4 months		−1200.00
New Balance		\$3950.00
\$3950 @ 9% for 5 months	$S_2 = 3950(1+(.09)(5/12)) =$	\$4098.13
\$950 payment at 9 months		−950.00
New Balance		\$3148.13
\$3148.13 @ 9% for 6 months	Balance due ▶	\$3289.80

Example 1.9.2

A homeowner has a 9.5% simple interest line of credit on his home equity. On January 28 he takes a \$6500 advance for some improvements. He made payments of \$600 on March 3, \$850 on April 7, and \$780 on May 19. He plans to pay off the loan on June 21 with an anticipated insurance settlement. Using the United States Rule, find the payoff on June 21. Credits cards and equity lines of credit typically use exact time and exact interest.

■ Draw a time line diagram and add the serial numbers with the dates. Complete the calculations like part 2 of Example 1.9.1.

TIME LINE DIAGRAM 1.9.3

Jan. 28	Mar. 3	April 7	May 19	June 21
(28)	(62)	(97)	(139)	(172)
−\$6,500	600	850	780	x

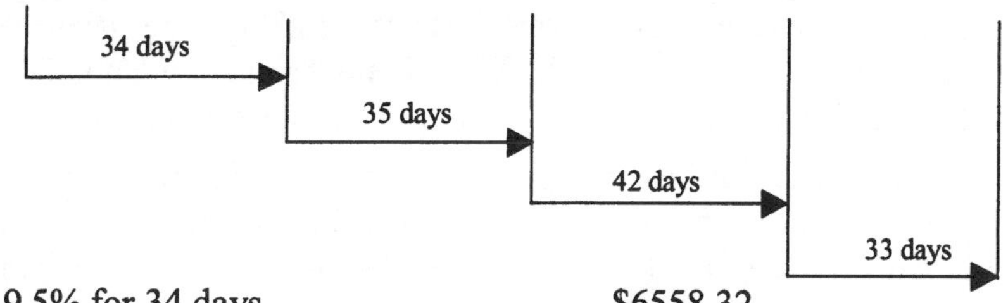

34 days

35 days

42 days

33 days

\$6500 @ 9.5% for 34 days	\$6558.32
\$600 payment	−600.00
New balance	\$5958.32
\$5958.32 @ 9.5% for 35 days	\$6013.35
\$850.00 payment	−850.00
New balance	\$5163.35
\$5163.35 @ 9.5% for 42 days	\$5220.58
\$780 payment	−780.00
New balance	\$4440.58
\$4440.58 @ 9.5% for 33 days	\$4479.25 ◀ Payoff amount

◀ EXERCISES 1.9 ▶

Concept and Short Answer Exercises

1. Explain the procedure for finding the final payment using the U.S. Rule.
2. Explain the procedure for finding the final payment using the Merchant's Rule.
3. Where is the focal date for the U.S. Rule?
4. What is the final payment commonly called?

Calculation Exercises

5. Adrienne borrows $1000 and makes two monthly payments of $200. On the third month she decides to pay off the loan. If Adrienne is being charged 20% on her credit card loan, find the payoff. Use both the Merchant's and the U.S. Rules.
6. David borrows $1000 by taking a cash advance on his credit card. He makes the first three monthly payments of $200, but he misses the 4th and 5th month payments. On the,6th month he decides to pay off the loan. If David is being charged 12% on his credit card loan, find the payoff. Use both the Merchant's and the U.S. Rules.
7. Rebecca borrows $5000 on 3/10/05 and pays back $2000 on 6/17/05. What is the outstanding balance on the loan on 8/10/05 at 5%? Use both techniques.
8. Maribeth borrows $5000 on 3/15/05 and pays back $1000 on 6/17/05 and $2000 on 7/1/05. What is the outstanding balance on the loan on 8/10/05 at 5%? Use the Merchant's Rule.
9. On January 1, 2003, Gregory has a balance of $850 on his charge card at a rate of 18%. Suppose he pays the 15% minimum on the last day of each month. Track his balances and payments to the end of June using exact interest and exact time and the U.S. Rule. What is his balance on June 30 after making his payment? Assume that no further purchases were made with his credit card.
10. During her senior year in college, on January 20, 2005, Faith borrowed $3500 from her uncle at 5%. She made the following payments: $400 on May 30, $1580 on August 10, and $950 on October 5. Find the amount needed to discharge her debt on December 1 using the Merchant's Rule.
11. Katrina purchased a used car on July 1 for $8500 and paid $1500 down. The dealer agreed to a 7% interest rate and two partial payments of $2000 on September 15 and $2000 on December 5 with the stipulation that the balance be due on February 12. Use the U.S. Rule to find Katrina's final payment.
12. Reliance Hardware owes their paint supplier $12,800 on April 1. The supplier will agree to three payments of $4000 on June 1, $3500 on August 1, and $2500 on October 1, provided that the balance is paid on December 1 and Reliance Hardware pays 8% interest. Find the final payment using the Merchant's Rule.

13. Blake owes $1860 on 2/1/05 to a lender charging 6.75%. If he makes a payment of $800 on 3/15/05 and one of $500 on 7/20/05, what payment on 9/10/05 will settle the loan obligation using the Merchant's Rule?

14. An $80,000 home loan financed for 30 years at 7% has a monthly payment of $532.24. Use the U.S. Rule to find how much of the first two payments goes to interest and how much goes to principal.

15. A $15,000 car loan financed for 5 years at 9% has a monthly payment of $311.38. Use the U.S. Rule to find how much of the first two payments goes to interest and how much goes to principal.

16. If Carlos makes quarterly tax installments of $860 on June 15, 2004; $1250 on September 15, 2004; and $625 on January 15, 2005, what will he still owe on March 15, 2005, to meet his $3580 tax obligation from March 15, 2004? Assume money is worth 6%.

1.10 Equivalent Time

In our study of equations of value and partial payments we have solved for unknown debts and payments equivalent to other obligations at some selected point in time called the *focal date*. This allowed us to make, for example, a single payment that was equivalent to several other obligations that were positioned at several points in time. With the Merchant's Rule method we found the payoff or settlement for a debt after first making a number of partial payments. A very practical use for equations of value is to find several equal size future payouts from an estate or inheritance.

This section addresses the problem of discharging several known obligations or debts with a single equivalent payment at some unknown point in time. This does not mean that we will violate the golden rule of finance; rather, we will pay the same amount of money at one point in time that would have been paid using several payments at several points in time. Because of the time value of money we could also pay more or less than the sum of the original debts and still find the date where a single equivalent payment will discharge several obligations. But when the single payment equals the sum of the original debts, the unknown date of that payment will be called the **average due date**. The reason for this name will be apparent after we make a few generalizations.

In the following examples our unknown quantity will be the date $\bar{t}$ that is usually measured in days from the present. To simplify the present calculations we will be using future debts whose values are known, rather than current values of debts whose maturity values must first be calculated. The exercises will include some problems in which the amounts and dates of future obligations will have to be found before finding the date of the single equivalent payment.

Example 1.10.1

Two payments of $1800 are due in 45 days and 90 days. Using an interest rate of 7%, find the date when a single payment of $3590 will discharge these debts.

■ Make a time line and find the value of the two $1800 debts at 90 days. This will tell us where $\bar{t}$ is located relative to 90 days. We can then write an equation of value with $\bar{t}$ as the unknown.

TIME LINE DIAGRAM 1.10.1

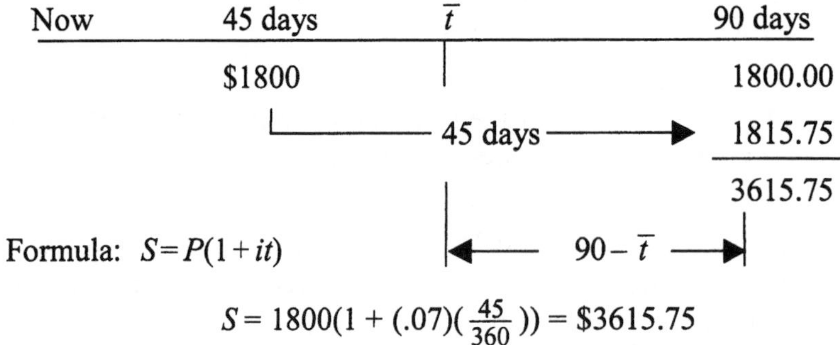

Formula: $S = P(1 + it)$

$$S = 1800(1 + (.07)(\tfrac{45}{360})) = \$3615.75$$

Since the future value of the two debts, $3615.75, is larger than the single payment ($3590), $\bar{t}$ must fall between now and 90 days from now. Let the $3590 payment be the present value of the $3615.75 and solve for $\bar{t}$ in the equation of value.

$$3615.75 = 3590(1 + (.07)(\tfrac{90-\bar{t}}{360}))$$

$$\frac{3615.75}{3590} - 1 = (.07)(\tfrac{90-\bar{t}}{360})$$

$$\frac{.0071727}{.07} = \frac{90-\bar{t}}{360}$$

$$36.89 = 90 - \bar{t} \qquad \text{Therefore, } \bar{t} = 53 \text{ days}$$

For a more general treatment of Example 1.10.1, see Exercises 15–19.

Example 1.10.2

A developer has obligations for contract work of $15,000 due in 35 days, $21,000 due in 45 days, and $30,000 due in 75 days. Find the average due date if money is worth 5.5%.

■ Make a time line with the three obligations at their respective dates. Then find the value of the three obligations at 75 days. This will give the location of $\bar{t}$ relative to 75 days so we can write an equation of value with $\bar{t}$ as the unknown.

TIME LINE DIAGRAM 1.10.2

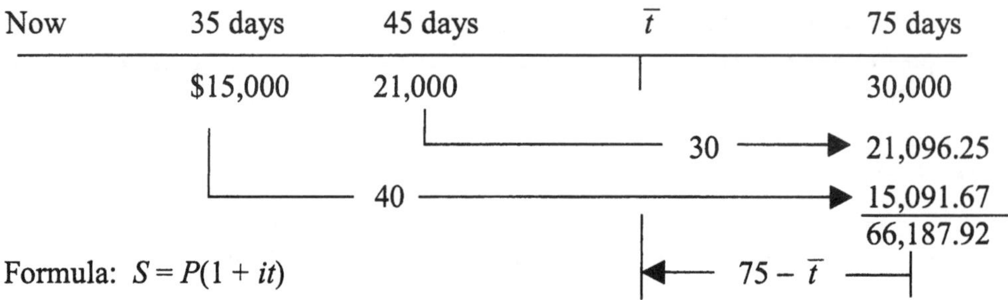

Formula: $S = P(1 + it)$

$$S = 15{,}000(1 + (.055)(\tfrac{40}{360})) + 21{,}000(1 + (.055)(\tfrac{30}{360}) + 30{,}000$$
$$S = 15{,}091.67 + 21{,}096.25 + 30{,}000 = 66{,}187.92$$

The total of the three obligations is 15,000 + 21,000 + 30,000 = \$66,000, which is less than the 75-day total debt. Therefore, the *average due date* is earlier than 75 days, and we can let the single payment of \$66,000 be the present value of \$66,187.92 and solve for $\overline{t}$ in the equation of value.

$$66{,}187.92 = 66{,}000(1 + (.055)(\tfrac{75-\overline{t}}{360}))$$
$$1.0028473 = 1 + (.055)(\tfrac{75-\overline{t}}{360})$$
$$0.0028473 = (.055)(\tfrac{75-\overline{t}}{360})$$
$$18.64 = 75 - \overline{t} \qquad \text{Therefore, } \overline{t} \approx 56 \text{ days}$$

The developer will make a single payment of \$66,000 at 56 days to discharge these obligations.

In mathematics we find that generalizing a computation or pattern often leads to a rather simple and elegant formula or relationship. Such a relationship often makes it apparent which of the parameters are pertinent and which have no effect on the final outcome. In order to generalize the average due date computation, we will assume that the single payment is the sum of the given obligations. This is necessary in order to simplify the algebraic expression and will also assure us that the average due date $\overline{t}$ falls before the last of the obligations. This is true since moving the other obligations forward to the date of the last one will always give a value that exceeds the sum of the obligations. Consider the following variables for the payments and their due dates.

P_1 = the first payment due in t_1 days
P_2 = the second payment due in t_2 days
P_3 = the third payment due in t_3 days
⋮
P_n = the nth payment due in t_n days
P = the single equivalent payment due in $\overline{t}$ days

$$P = P_1 + P_2 + P_3 + \cdots + P_n \qquad \textbf{(1.4)}$$

Let the average due date $\overline{t}$ be the focal date and i the rate per unit time. This avoids the 360 in the denominator of the time fraction. Now write an equation of value with all of the payments at the focal date $\overline{t}$.

$$P[1+i(\overline{t}-\overline{t})] = P_1[1+i(\overline{t}-t_1)] + P_2[1+i(\overline{t}-t_2)] + \cdots + P_n[1+i(\overline{t}-t_n)]$$

Distribute all of the payments.

$$P + Pi(0) = P_1 + P_1i(\overline{t}-t_1) + P_2 + P_2i(\overline{t}-t_2) + \cdots + P_n + P_ni(\overline{t}-t_n)$$

By equation (1.4) the single payment P equals the sum of the original payments at the average due date. Use this to subtract P from both sides of the equation.

$$0 = P_1 i(\bar{t} - t_1) + P_2 i(\bar{t} - t_2) + \cdots + P_n i(\bar{t} - t_n)$$

The rate i can be factored out and cancelled from every term. After canceling, distribute the payments and transpose the negative terms. This step in the derivation shows that the average due date is not a function of the interest rate unless it is zero. It also does not matter whether we use exact or ordinary interest.

$$P_1\bar{t} + P_2\bar{t} + P_3\bar{t} + \cdots + P_n\bar{t} = P_1t_1 + P_2t_2 + \cdots + P_nt_n$$

$$(P_1 + P_2 + \cdots + P_n)\bar{t} = P_1t_1 + P_2t_2 + \cdots + P_nt_n$$

$$P\bar{t} = P_1t_1 + P_2t_2 + \cdots + P_nt_n$$

Average Due Date: $$\bar{t} = \frac{P_1t_1 + P_2t_2 + \cdots + P_nt_n}{P} \quad \textbf{(1.5)}$$

It is now apparent that the average due date is just a weighted average of the times when the obligations occur and that their weights are the payments due at those dates. We can use this concept to advantage in Example 1.10.3.

If we let each of the n obligations be equal to R, then the single payment is $P = nR$. Applying the distributive property and reducing the expression will show that the average due date for n equal obligations is the mathematical average of the given due dates of the known obligations.

$$\bar{t} = \frac{R(t_1 + t_2 + \cdots + t_{n-1} + t_n)}{n \cdot R} = \frac{t_1 + t_2 + \cdots + t_{n-1} + t_n}{n} \quad \textbf{(1.6)}$$

Example 1.10.3

The Brunswick Tool and Die Corporation has five obligations: \$3200 due in 30 days, \$2400 due in 48 days, \$5000 due in 60 days, \$4500 due in 90 days, and \$7000 due in 118 days. At what date can they make a single \$22,100 payment to discharge these debts?

■ Substitute into the average due date formula. A time line is not needed.

$$\bar{t} = \frac{3200(30) + 2400(48) + 5000(60) + 4500(90) + 7000(118)}{22{,}100}$$

$$\bar{t} = 78.8 \text{ or approximately 79 days}$$

On a statistical calculator let the due dates be the sample points and the respective payments their weights. Enter the preceding data as 30×3200 DATA, 48×2400 DATA, ... 118×7000 DATA, and compute $\bar{X}$. All of the average due date exercises can be done with a statistical calculator or an equivalent.

◀ EXERCISES 1.10 ▶

Concept and Short Answer Exercises

1. If a borrower owes $300 due on a particular date, $400 due on another date, and $1000 due on a third date, how much will she repay on the average due date?
2. What is the definition of the average due date?
3. Why is it reasonable that the value of the rate is immaterial in finding the average due date as long as the rate is not zero?
4. The weighted average of the dates gives the ____.

Calculation Exercises

In each of the following exercises, assume that the rate is not zero.

5. Find the average due date for the following obligations: $325 due in 24 days, $680 due in 40 days, $450 due in 60 days.
6. Find the average due date for debts of $400 due in 20 days, $500 due in 45 days, $600 due in 65 days, and $700 due in 80 days.
7. When will a single payment of $4.65 million pay obligations of $1.2 million due in 5 months, $1.6 million due in 8 months, and $1.85 million due in a year?
8. What is the average due date for four debts of $500 each due in 35 days, 48 days, 60 days, and 81 days?
9. Starting in one month, Johannes needs to pay $100 per month for 12 months for his business license. When will a single payment of $1200 satisfy these obligations?
10. During the next fiscal year Lloyd Kryston must pay four quarterly payments of $750, $920, $635, and $1250. When will a single payment of $3555 satisfy these debts? Use approximate time.
11. Standard Vending, Inc. received the following invoices from suppliers: $5200 due in 3 weeks, $8900 due in 5 weeks, and $6150 due in 9 weeks. Find the average due date of these invoices.
12. Bright and Beautiful Decorators has a service fee due every two weeks over the course of 10 weeks. The first is for $300 in 2 weeks and each one thereafter is 10% larger than the previous one. If money is worth 6%, when will $1820 pay these obligations? What single payment at 13 weeks would be required? Use Banker's Rule.
13. Newport Contractors received the following invoices: February 10, $18,000 due in 45 days; March 25, $23,580, due in 35 days; April 6, $14,860 due in 30 days. Find the date when $56,440 will satisfy these obligations. If money is worth 7%, what will the single payment be on June 1? Use Banker's Rule.
14. Given the following promissory notes in Table 1.10.1 with their respective rates and terms, find the date when $12,463.38 will satisfy these notes. Assume money is worth 7% and use Banker's Rule.

TABLE 1.10.1

Interest Bearing Promissory Notes			
Face Value	**Signing Date**	**Length of Term**	**Interest Rate**
\$4000	March 15	120 days	5%
\$2500	April 10	150 days	6.5%
\$5800	June 30	30 days	6%

15. The problem in Example 1.10.1 can also be reduced to a more general form just like we were able to do with the average due date problem in Example 1.10.3. As the basic assumption, let us pay back K dollars more (or less if K is negative) than the total of what was borrowed. Hence our payback, $P = P_1 + P_2 + \cdots + P_n + K$, where $K \neq 0$. Prove that the single payment P has due date $\bar{t}$ given by the following expression.

$$\bar{t} = \left[\frac{P_1t_1 + P_2t_2 + \cdots + P_nt_n}{P_1 + P_2 + \cdots + P_n}\right] + \frac{K}{(P_1 + P_2 + \cdots + P_n)i}$$

We will call this the *adjusted average due date* formula. Remember that i is the rate per unit time. For example, using Banker's Rule and due dates as time in days, $i = \frac{\text{per annum rate}}{360}$.

16. Use the adjusted average due date formula given in Exercise 15 to solve Example 1.10.1.

17. If money is worth 8%, find the date for a single payment of \$1450 to satisfy the debts in exercise 5.

18. Millennium Brokers has the following debts: \$0.78 million due in 55 days, \$0.52 million due in 75 days, \$1.12 million due in 90 days, and \$0.70 million due in 110 days. If money earns 6.5%, when will \$3 million satisfy these debts?

19. Peter McAllister owes four more payments on his studio. If the first is \$500 due in 2 months and each month thereafter another payment is due that is 20% less than the previous one, when will \$1500 satisfy these obligations at 9%?

Chapter 1 Summary of Concepts

Simple Interest: $I = Pit$

Exact Time and Approximate Time

Exact Interest and Ordinary Interest

Banker's Rule

Future Value at Simple Interest: $S = P(1 + it)$

Equations of Value

Present Value at Simple Interest: $P = \dfrac{S}{1+it}$

Golden Rule of Finance

Net Present Value

Internal Rate of Return

Merchant's Rule

United States Rule

Equivalent Time

Average Due Date

Chapter 1 Vocabulary Check

Amount	*Maturity Date*	*Principal*
Demand Deposits	*Maturity Value*	*Promissory Note*
Focal Date	*Near Monies*	*Serial Number*
Future Value	*Partial Payment*	*Simple Interest*
Interest Rate	*Payee*	*Term*
Maker	*Prime Rate*	*Time Value of Money*

Chapter 1 Skills Check

1. Given any three of the parameters, compute the fourth with the basic formula.

   Section 1.2 Examples 1–4; Exercises 17, 23, 25, 27

2. Find exact time and approximate time and exact interest and ordinary interest.

   Section 1.3 Examples 1, 2, 5; Exercises 9, 11, 15

3. Find the future value of a sum of money using simple interest.

   Section 1.4 Example 2; Exercises 5, 7, 9, 11

4. Find the interest rate earned by taking advantage of early payment discounts.

   Section 1.4 Example 4; Exercises 15, 17, 19

5. Find the present value of a future sum using simple interest.

   Section 1.5 Examples 1, 2, 3; Exercises 5, 7, 15

6. Find the purchase price of a note due in the future to realize a given rate.

   Section 1.6 Examples 1, 2; Exercises 5, 7, 11

7. Find a single payment to settle several obligations due in the future.

   Section 1.7 Examples 1, 2, 3; Exercises 11, 19

8. Find the net present value and the internal rate of return for an investment that is expected to bring several returns at future dates.

   Section 1.8 Examples 1, 2; Exercises 9, 17

9. Find the settlement for an obligation paid off via several partial payments using the United States Rule and Merchant's Rule.

   Section 1.9 Examples 1, 2; Exercises 5, 11

10. Find the average due date for several obligations paid off with a single payment that equals the total of the several smaller payments.

    Section 1.10 Examples 1, 2; Exercises 7, 11, 19

Review Test for Simple Interest

Multiple Choice

1. What is the exact time from January 25, 2004, to July 1, 2004?

   a. 156 b. 157 c. 158 d. 159

2. What is the approximate time from November 29, 2005, to March 15, 2006?

   a. 105 b. 104 c. 103 d. 106

3. What is the simple interest for a 13-week $1500 loan at 7%?

   a. $26.18 b. $26.25 c. $26.54 d. $25.27

4. If money earns 6.25% simple interest, is it better to buy computer updates for $23,000 cash or for $25,000 in 15 months?

   a. $23,000 cash b. $25,000 in 15 months

5. If a general contractor receives a building materials invoice for $94,580 with terms 4/10, n/60, what rate of interest would he earn by paying by the 10th?

   a. 24% b. 25% c. 28.8% d. 30%

Calculation Exercises

6. A 182-day T-bill is bought with a bid of 90.9%. Find the ROR.

7. On July 1, 2004, Jim bought a $4000, 90-day note. On August 20, 2004, Jim needed cash and sold his note to Pete who requires 10% on his investments. How much did Pete pay Jim for his note?

8. Suppose that on 6/1/04 Mrs. Harmon contracts to pay a renovator $5000 for her new kitchen and agrees with the renovator to make two equal payments on 12/1/04 and 6/1/05. If the renovator charges 10% for credit, find the amount of the two payments. Put the focal date at the default date of 6/1/05.

9. Juan is eyeing an investment that requires $80,000 up front but will return $40,000 in 1 year and $60,000 in 2 years. Find the NPV at 10% and 20% and find the IRR to one decimal place. Argue that Juan should invest here if he believes the investment is fairly safe and if he needs to get at least a _____% return.

10. Rebecca Jean borrows $5000 on 3/10/05 and pays back $4000 on 6/10/05. What is the outstanding balance on the loan on 8/10/05 at 5%? Use the United States Rule.

11. Laura Kay borrows $5000 on 3/10/05 and pays back $4000 on 6/10/05. What is the outstanding balance on the loan on 8/10/05 at 5%? Use the Merchant's Rule.

12. Find the average due date for the following obligations: $300 due in 40 days, $600 due in 80 days, $1000 due in 100 days.

Chapter 2

Discount Interest

2.1 Discount Interest Basic Formulas and Applications

People like to get a discount when they go shopping. If there were a 10% discount you would expect to pay 90% of the cost. If you go to a bank for a loan and the bank uses discount interest for short-term loans, you might be surprised by what happens. If you borrow $500 for a year at a 10% discount rate, the banker would give you a check for $450 and expect you to pay back $500 at the end of a year. The lending institution is collecting its interest "up front." If it were a simple interest loan, you would get the entire $500 but pay back $550 at the end of a year. With *simple* interest the $500 is the *present* value, but with *discount* interest the $500 is the *future* value. **Bank discount** or **simple discount** interest is based on future value with the interest paid at the beginning of the term. The money that is borrowed is called the **amount** (future value). The percent used to figure the interest charges is called the **discount rate**. As with simple interest, the measurement period for the discount rate is almost always yearly. The actual length of the loan is called the **term** of the loan. The interest charged for the use of borrowed money is called the **discount**. The money received when the loan is initiated is called the **proceeds** (present value).

Summary of Basic Definitions

Amount	amount of money borrowed (future value)
Discount	cost or charge for the use of borrowed money
Proceeds	money received from the loan (present value)
Discount Rate	percent of the amount that is the basis for the discount
Term	length of the loan in units corresponding to the rate

Remembering that the proceeds is the amount minus the discount and that the discount is the amount times the rate times the time, we can understand the mathematical calculation that gives the basic formulas for discount and proceeds. These formulas are quite similar to those for simple interest.

The Basic Discount Interest Formula: $D = Sdt$ (2.1)

D = discount S = amount d = rate per year t = time in years

Discount interest loans are not as common as simple interest loans, but it is a widely used method for computing interest. Negotiable securities like promissory notes, certain types of bonds, treasury bills and commercial paper are all sold at discount. As long as they have a known maturity value at a known future date, buyers will purchase these financial instruments at a price (proceeds) that assures them of a desired rate of return.

Example 2.2.1

If a security that matures in 6 months at a value of $6000 can be purchased today for $5745, what discount rate will the buyer make?

■ Since you want the rate, use the basic formula and solve for the discount rate d. The discount D is the difference between the maturity value and the purchase price (proceeds).

$$D = Sdt \rightarrow d = \frac{D}{St} = \frac{6000-5745}{6000(\frac{1}{2})} = \frac{255}{3000} = .085 = 8.5\%$$

Example 2.1.2

A promissory note with a maturity value of $3500 is due November 28. If it can be sold at a discount rate of 7.5% on June 30, what will the discount be? What will the proceeds be? Use Banker's Rule.

■ First find the exact time using the serial numbers. November 28 (332) – June 30 (181) = 151. Then substitute the known information into the basic formula (2.1).

$$D = Sdt = 3500(.075)(\tfrac{151}{360}) = \$110.10$$

The discount of $110.10 will be subtracted from the maturity value (amount) to give the proceeds.

$$P = S - D = \$3500 - \$110.10 = \$3389.90$$

This last example was actually a case of moving money on the time line. The future value $3500 was moved to the present at 7.5% discount interest to give a present value of $3389.90. With discount interest the terms *amount* and *proceeds* are typically used instead of future value and present value. A formula can now be developed for proceeds.

Proceeds = Amount – Discount

$P = S - D$

$P = S - Sdt$ Replace D by the discount formula.

$P = S(1 - dt)$ Factor out the common term S.

Discount Proceeds Formula: $P = S(1 - dt)$ (2.2)

The factor $1-dt$ becomes a tool to move money on the time line at discount interest. The **discount interest factor** moves money backward, as in the proceeds formula above. It can also move money forward if we solve algebraically for the amount. This is important if the proceeds are known, as in a loan where a certain amount of money is needed. The following algebra gives us the amount formula for discount interest. In Section 2.6 we will discuss the related accumulation function.

$P = S(1-dt)$	the proceeds formula
$\dfrac{P}{1-dt} = \dfrac{S(1-dt)}{1-dt}$	Divide each side by the factor $1-dt$.
$\dfrac{P}{1-dt} = S$	Cancel the common factor on the right.

Discount Amount Formula: $\boldsymbol{S = \dfrac{P}{1-dt} = P(1-dt)^{-1}}$ **(2.3)**

Example 2.1.3

A bank charges 7% for short-term discount loans. What are the proceeds for an 8-month loan for $6850?

■ Substitute the known information into the proceeds formula. Calculate the factor first by figuring the product and subtracting it from 1. The ± button is handy for this computation.

$$P = S(1-dt) = 6850(1-(.07)(\tfrac{8}{12})) = \$6530.33$$

Example 2.1.4

A used car dealer charges his customers 12% discount for financing the balance on purchases. If a customer has a balance of $5600 after trade allowances and taxes, what is the amount of the loan she will need for 15-month financing?

■ The $5600 balance is actually the proceeds because the customer needs this amount now to complete the purchase. Since the amount is needed, substitute the known information into the amount formula. After computing the discount interest factor $1-dt$, use the $1/x$ button and multiply the result by 5600.

$$S = \frac{P}{1-dt} = \frac{5600}{1-(.12)(\frac{15}{12})} = \$6588.24$$

Example 2.1.5

An heir received three $15,000 savings bonds from an estate on December 4, 2003. Two of the bonds have a maturity date of January 1, 2005, and one has a maturity date of June 30, 2005. The bonds were immediately sold to a bank charging 8% discount. What were the heir's proceeds on December 4, 2003? Use exact time and exact interest.

■ A time line diagram will be very helpful to get the money and time correctly positioned. Note that there is a whole year (2004) to be accounted for. Use the proceeds formula (2.2).

TIME LINE DIAGRAM 2.1.1

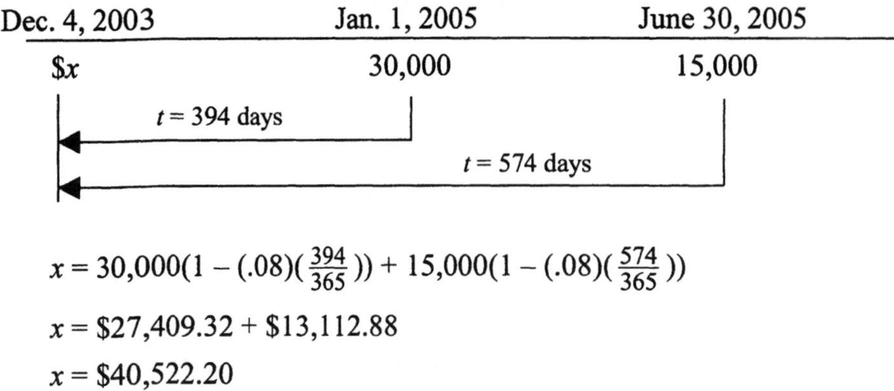

$$x = 30{,}000(1 - (.08)(\tfrac{394}{365})) + 15{,}000(1 - (.08)(\tfrac{574}{365}))$$

$$x = \$27{,}409.32 + \$13{,}112.88$$

$$x = \$40{,}522.20$$

◀ EXERCISES 2.1 ▶

Concepts and Short Answer Exercises

1. Complete using *present value* or *future value*: Simple interest is calculated on the _____ while bank discount is calculated on the _____.
2. Given the present value, you would never use $S = P + D$ to compute the future value. Why?
3. For a bank discount problem, the loan value is _____. (Pick from P or S.)
4. What is the difference in the terms *discount* and *bank discount*?
5. Which is worth more: a discount at a bank discount rate of 5% or interest at an interest rate of 5%? Why?
6. When using bank discount, why not find I (the interest) and subtract it from S to find P?

Calculation Exercises

7. Find the bank discount and the present value of $1000 in 2 years at a bank discount rate of 8%.
8. Find the bank discount and the present value of $5000 in 4 years at a bank discount rate of 6%.
9. $2000 is due on 5/3/06. Find the bank discount and the value on 2/10/06 at a bank discount rate of 7.8%.
10. $20,000 is due on 5/3/06. Find the bank discount and the value on 4/10/06 at a bank discount rate of 5.4%.
11. Find the proceeds of a 9-month loan of $8000 at a bank discount rate of 10%.
12. Find the proceeds of a 2-year loan of $8000 at a bank discount rate of 10%.

13. A $10,000 loan at 5% discount matures on 12/1/04. Find the proceeds on 2/5/04.

14. A $1000 loan at 5.8% discount matures on 12/2/04. Find the proceeds on 5/5/04.

15. Suppose you buy a $15,000 piece of art with nothing down using a bank discount loan at 8% for a term of 3 years. Find the amount of the loan needed.

16. Suppose a $28,000 property is sold on a bank discount basis of 8% for a term of 3 years. If the buyer pays $3000 down, find the amount financed.

17. Virginia is renovating her kitchen. The cost of the $5000 renovation will be financed on a bank discount basis at a rate of 9% for 1 year. What will be the amount financed?

18. Junior is planning to build a workshop. The $15,000 cost of the building will be financed with a bank discount loan at a rate of 8.2% for 2 years. What will be the amount financed?

19. The Smith family gets a home improvement loan from Great South Bank & Trust, which charges 9% discount for such loans. If they need $6500 for 15 months, what amount will they need to borrow?

20. The Lopez family gets a home improvement loan from the Tidewater Bank & Trust, which charges 3.8% discount for such loans. If they need $65,000 for 15 months, what amount will they need to borrow?

2.2 Comparing Simple and Discount Interest

Because simple interest is based on present value and discount interest is based on future value, discount interest costs the borrower slightly more for a stated rate. For example, a one-year loan with a present value of $450 at a rate of 10% will cost $45 if it is simple interest loan; however, it will cost $50 if it is a discount interest loan. If the interest charges were the same, then the stated interest rates would have to be different, and the simple rate would be the larger. It is often important to know the simple interest rate that is equivalent to a given discount rate. This simple interest rate is called the **coupon equivalent**. Note that the term *equivalent* implies that they produce the same interest charges. If both a discount and a simple interest loan have identical future and present values, we know that the interest charges (but not the rates) will be the same. A little algebra will allow us to reduce the equated formulas to an expression where we can solve for each rate in terms of the other rate.

Discount interest loan **Simple interest loan**

$P = S(1-dt)$ $P = \dfrac{S}{1+it}$

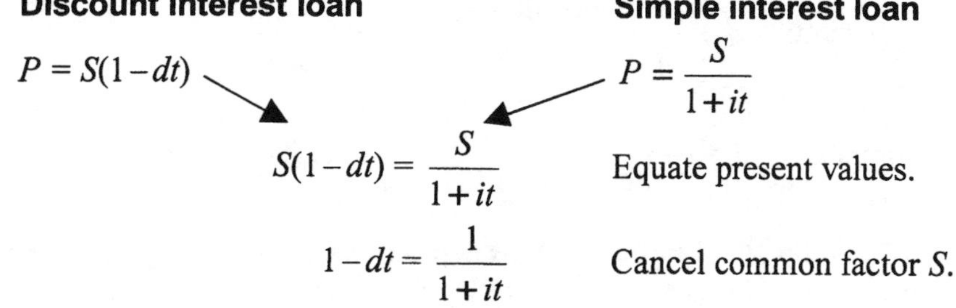

$$S(1-dt) = \frac{S}{1+it}$$ Equate present values.

$$1-dt = \frac{1}{1+it}$$ Cancel common factor S.

$$1+it = \frac{1}{1-dt}$$ Reciprocate fractions.

$$it = \frac{1}{1-dt} - 1$$ Transpose the 1.

$$it = \frac{1-(1-dt)}{1-dt}$$ Combine terms.

$$it = \frac{dt}{1-dt}$$ Simplify the numerator.

Coupon Equivalent: $$i = \frac{d}{1-dt}$$ Cancel the common factor t. **(2.4)**

Solving for d gives $$d = \frac{i}{1+it}.$$ **(2.5)**

These formulas are easy to remember and have a certain elegance because you find the equivalent rates by dividing each of the rates by its own interest factor.

Example 2.2.1

What simple interest rate is equivalent to a discount rate of 12% for 15 months?

■ Substitute the known information into the coupon equivalent formula (2.4).

$$i = \frac{d}{1-dt} = \frac{.12}{1-(.12)(\frac{15}{12})} = .141 = 14.1\%$$

Example 2.2.2

What discount rate is equivalent to a simple interest rate of 9.5% for 9 months?

■ Substitute the known information into the formula for discount interest (2.5).

$$d = \frac{i}{1+it} = \frac{.095}{1+(.095)(\frac{9}{12})} = .0887 \approx 8.9\%$$

Example 2.2.3

If a negotiable security can be purchased for $65,000 and 56 days later it is worth $66,500, what is the rate of return expressed as a discount rate and as a simple interest rate? Use exact interest.

■ Either basic formula can be used to find the rate. Here we will solve the discount formula (2.1) for the discount rate and then convert it to the coupon equivalent.

Discount: $$d = \frac{D}{St} = \frac{66{,}500-65{,}000}{66{,}500(\frac{56}{365})} = \frac{1500}{66{,}500(\frac{56}{365})} = .147 = 14.7\%$$

Simple: $$i = \frac{d}{1-dt} = \frac{.147}{1-(.147)(\frac{56}{365})} = .1504 \approx 15\%$$

Note carefully that the only difference between computing the interest rate and the discount rate in the first step is placing the present value $65,000 in the denominator instead of the future value $66,500. Try this to confirm the answer in the second part.

◀ EXERCISES 2.2 ▶

Concept and Short Answer Exercises

1. If the rate of return as a bank discount rate is 10%, then the equivalent rate of return on a simple interest rate is _____. (Pick *higher* or *lower*.)
2. What is meant by *coupon equivalent*?
3. If you are calculating the coupon equivalent i, given that $d = 8\%$ and $t = 2$ years, what formula will you use?
4. Explain why the formula $S = P/(1 - dt)$ gives a value for S that exceeds P and tell why this is necessary for most financial problems.
5. If you are given $P = \$1000$ and $S = \$1200$, what formula do you use to find D? To find I? To find d? To find t? To find i?
6. If you are given $i = 8\%$ over 3 years, what formula do you use to find d?

Calculation Exercises

7. Find the bank discount rate equivalent to a 92-day simple interest rate of 8%.
8. Find the bank discount rate equivalent to a 5-month simple interest rate of 8%.
9. Find the coupon equivalence of a 92-day bank discount rate of 8%.
10. Find the coupon equivalence of a 12-week bank discount rate of 8%.
11. Find the bank discount rate equivalent to a 2-year simple interest loan at 10%.
12. Find the bank discount rate equivalent to a 2.5-year simple interest loan at 8%.
13. Find the coupon equivalence of a 2-year bank discount rate of 10%.
14. Find the coupon equivalence of a 5-year bank discount rate of 10%.
15. A \$5000 financial instrument is worth \$5400 in 8 months. Find the rate of return at a simple interest rate and at a bank discount rate.
16. A \$50,000 financial instrument is worth \$50,400 in 3 months. Find the rate of return at a simple interest rate and at a bank discount rate.
17. A man invests \$14,000 on 8/2/03 and gets a return of \$20,000 on 6/1/04. Find the rate of return on a simple interest and bank discount basis.
18. A woman invests \$104,000 on 8/2/03 and gets a return of \$130,000 on 6/20/04. Find the rate of return on a simple interest and bank discount basis.
19. A security purchased for \$125,000 on June 23, 2000, will be worth \$127,200 on September 11, 2000. Find the rate of return (ROR) using simple interest and discount interest. Use exact interest and exact time.
20. A \$25,000 promissory note signed on June 23, 2004, will be paid off by a \$27,200 check on September 21, 2004. Find the rate charged for the loan using simple interest and discount interest. Use exact interest and exact time.
21. If a 90-day discount loan for \$6000 on February 28, 2004, netted the borrower \$5886.75, what is the discount rate and when is the loan due?

22. If a 180-day discount loan for \$6000 on February 28, 2005 netted the borrower \$5886.75, what is the discount rate and when is the loan due?

2.3 Discounting Negotiable Instruments—Notes

Negotiable financial instruments like notes, certificates of deposit, and time deposits are all called **promises to pay**. Promissory notes are sold on the basis of discount interest, even though they usually accrue interest on the basis of simple interest. The selling and interest-accrual are separate transactions that usually take place at considerably different points in time. You can think of the note holder going to a bank with the signed paper and selling it at discount to the banker. Since discount interest is based on future value, it will always be necessary to compute the maturity value of the note before discounting it. Sometimes a note is said to be non-interest-bearing. This simply means that the maturity value is stated on the note rather than the present value and the interest rate. Obviously, companies and investors do not lend money interest-free. But why would someone want to sell a promissory note? The answer lies in the note holder's need for cash and the buyer's need to put extra cash to work earning interest. This explains what drives the whole securities market. To find the selling price of a discounted promissory note requires the following two steps.

▸1. Find the maturity value of the promissory note, unless it is non-interest-bearing.
▸2. Find the proceeds when the note is discounted to the date of the sale.

Example 2.3.1

A \$12,000 promissory note dated June 12, 2004 and bearing interest at 6.5% has a 270-day term. The note is sold on October 20, 2004 at a bank charging 8% discount. What are the proceeds from the note? Use Banker's Rule.

▪ This problem needs a good time line diagram on which to place the dates, their serial numbers, and the money. Careful attention must be paid to the time, because the term of the note spans dates in two years. Leap year can be ignored because the dates fall beyond February 29 in the year 2004.

TIME LINE DIAGRAM 2.3.1

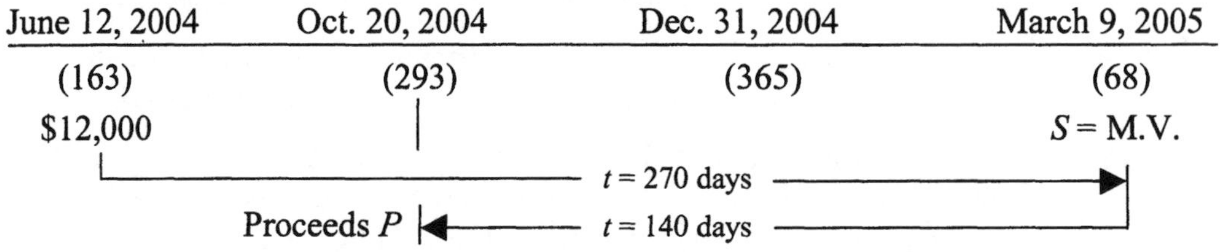

June 12, 2004	Oct. 20, 2004	Dec. 31, 2004	March 9, 2005
(163)	(293)	(365)	(68)
\$12,000			S = M.V.
		t = 270 days →	
	Proceeds P ←	t = 140 days	

Maturity Value: $S = P(1+it) = 12,000(1 + (.065)(\frac{270}{360})) = \$12,585$

Proceeds: $P = S(1-dt) = 12,585(1 - (.08)(\frac{140}{360})) = \$12,193.47$

Example 2.3.2

In Example 2.3.1 the original holder of the note still earned some interest before selling it on October 20. What was the rate of return the original holder made on a simple interest basis?

■ Solve the simple interest formula for the rate i and substitute the information from the problem. Remember that the time is from June 12 to October 20 and simple interest is based on present value.

$$i = \frac{I}{Pt} = \frac{193.47}{12{,}000(\frac{130}{360})} = .0446 \approx 4.5\%$$

Example 2.3.3

The following interest-bearing notes were discounted on July 10, 2004 at an institution using a 10.5% discount rate. Find the proceeds from the sale.

TABLE 2.3.1

Face Value	Date of the Note	Term of the Note	Interest Rate
\$8000	Feb. 3, 2004	270 days	7%
\$5000	April 5, 2004	120 days	8%

■ Draw a time line diagram and place the money and dates appropriately. The dates span February 28, so take leap year into account in figuring serial numbers. These are interest-bearing notes, so their face value is at the date of the note. The maturity date and the maturity value will have to be found for each note.

TIME LINE DIAGRAM 2.3.2

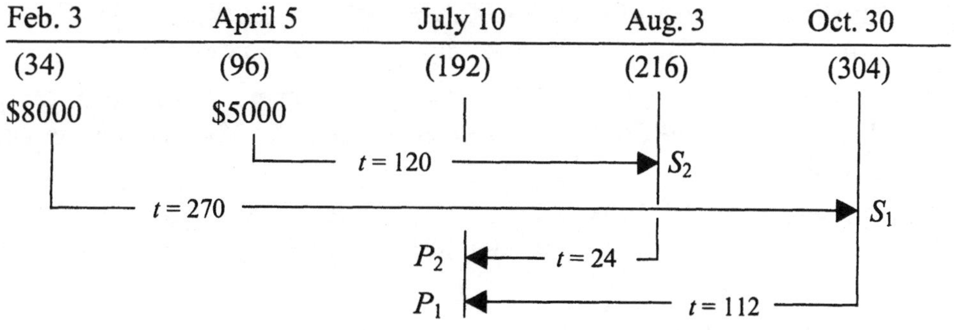

$$S_1 = P(1+it) = 8000(1+(.07)(\tfrac{270}{360})) = \$8420.00$$

$$S_2 = 5000(1+(.08)(\tfrac{120}{360})) = \$5133.33$$

$$P_1 = S(1-dt) = 8420(1-(.105)(\tfrac{112}{360})) = \$8144.95$$

$$P_2 = 5133.33(1-(.105)(\tfrac{24}{360})) = \$5097.40$$

Total proceeds = \$8144.95 + \$5097.40 = \$13,242.35

◀ EXERCISES 2.3 ▶

Concept and Short Answer Exercises

1. There are two steps in buying and selling financial instruments or in calculating the value of financial instruments at a point in time. List them.
2. Where is the focal date on any cash value or cash equivalent problem?
3. What are proceeds in a financial problem? What are synonyms for the word *proceeds*?
4. If a problem has a 5% rate and does not indicate whether it is a simple interest rate or a bank discount rate, then you would surmise it is a _____ rate.
5. Outline the steps for finding the simple interest rate in a problem.
6. Outline the steps for finding the bank discount rate in a problem.

Calculation Exercises

7. Darlene has one savings bond for $1000 that matures with interest at 6% in 2 years and another non-interest bond for $2000 that matures in 3 years. Find the cash value of the two at a bank discount rate of 8%.
8. Ivan has a $100 CD that matures with interest at 6% in 2 years and another non-interest bond for $2000 that matures in 3 years. Find the cash value of both at a bank discount rate of 10%.
9. On March 3, 2003, Maleta bought a 90-day, $5000 CD earning 8%. Later, on April 5, 2003, she bought a 180-day, $4000 note earning 6%. Find Maleta's proceeds for both of the securities on May 15, 2003 at a discount rate of 8%.
10. On March 3, 2003, Garcia invested in a 180-day, $5000 CD earning 8%. Garcia also invested in a 90-day, $4000, 8% note on April 5, 2003. Find Garcia's proceeds for both of the above on May 10, 2003, at a discount rate of 7%.
11. Caroline buys a 1-year, $1000, 10% CD on September 25, 2005. On July 25, 2006, the CD is sold to Grace on a discount basis of 9%. Find the amount Grace pays for the CD.
12. On September 25, 2005, Mike buys a $10,000, 8% 2-year note. On July 25, 2007, Gary buys Mike's note on a discount basis of 8%. Find the amount Gary pays for the note.
13. Jorja has 3 municipal bonds:

    1st is a 1-year, $1000, 8% bond bought on 4/1/05.

    2nd is an 18-month, $3000, 7% bond bought on 6/1/05.

    3rd is a 6-month, $2000, non-interest-bearing bond bought on 7/1/06.

    Find the proceeds on 3/1/06 for all three bonds, at a discount rate of 10%.

14. Akhil has made the following investments:

1st is a 2-year, $10,000, 9% CD bought on 4/1/05.
2nd is an 18-month, $3000, 7% CD bought on 6/1/05.
3rd is a 6-month, $20,000, non-interest-bearing bond bought on 7/1/06.

Find Akhil's proceeds on 3/1/06 for all three at a bank discount rate of 12%.

15. An $8400 note dated March 15, 2005, bearing interest at 9% matures in 93 days. The note is sold on May 10, 2005, at a bank charging 10.5% discount. Find the proceeds using Banker's Rule.

16. A 9-month, $1000, 9% note is bought on March 15, 2004. The note is sold on May 15, 2004, at a bank charging 10.5% discount. Find the proceeds using Banker's Rule.

17. The following interest-bearing notes were discounted on October 2, 2004 at a banking institution charging 9.5% discount. Find the proceeds from the sale of the notes.

Face Value	Date of the Note	Term of the Note	Interest Rate
$23,600	August 1, 2004	140 days	7%
$14,500	July 24, 2004	181 days	8%

18. The following interest-bearing notes were discounted on June 30, 2004, with a broker charging 8% discount. Find the proceeds from the sale of both notes.

Face Value	Date of the Note	Term of the Note	Interest Rate
$1200	April 14, 2004	120 days	6.5%
$850	June 1, 2004	60 days	5%

19. Kirk signed the following three notes when borrowing money for a new home he built. Find the equivalent value (payoff) on January 10, 2005 at a bank willing to buy his notes at a discount rate of 5%.

Face Value	Date of the Note	Term of the Note	Interest Rate
$20,000	January 10, 2004	2 years	7%
$54,500	July 10, 2004	18 months	8%
$40,000	October 10, 2004	13 months	Non-interest-bearing

20. As a speculative builder, David often finds it necessary to borrow money when building a new home. When he sells the home, he pays off the loans. Often the maturity dates do not correspond to the closing date for the sale of the house, so he finds a money broker to buy his notes so that he can get out from under the debt. Find the payoff to the broker on November 10, 2005 (the closing date) if the broker is willing to buy David's notes at a discount rate of 6% for the following loan notes:

Face Value	Date of the Note	Term of the Note	Interest Rate
\$200,000	January 10, 2004	2 years	7%
\$60,000	July 10, 2004	1.5 years	6%
\$40,000	October 10, 2004	2 years	10%

2.4 Discount Applications—Treasury Bills

Have you ever wondered how the United States government borrows money? With a national debt of around \$6 trillion, the government has obviously borrowed a lot. Treasury bills are short-term securities issued by the U.S. Treasury department in denominations of \$1000, \$10,000, \$15,000, \$50,000, \$100,000, \$500,000, and \$1 million. They mature in about 4, 13, 26, or 52 weeks, although the times are in exact days: 28, 91, 182, and 364. A T-bill is a non-interest-bearing, negotiable security that is sold at competitive public auctions via bank discount. The difference between the proceeds and the maturity value represents the buyer's return on the investment. The bids are given as a percent with no more than three decimal places. A successful bid of 96.250 on a \$10,000 bill would mean the buyer pays \$9625 and will receive the face amount of \$10,000 at maturity. The return on investment would be \$375. In this section we will calculate the rate of return on T-bills as a discount rate using the Banker's Rule.

Treasury bills are an attractive form of investment because they are risk free, have short terms and can be bought and sold easily on the *secondary market* (Section 2.5). Treasury bills provide institutions and companies investment opportunities for large amounts of cash that will be needed in the near future to meet obligations. These short-term securities keep money at work, while providing reasonably quick access and low risk.

Example 2.4.1

Find the rate of return (ROR) on investment for a \$10,000, 91-day Treasury bill that was purchased with a bid of 96.250.

■ To find the purchase price, multiply the bid in decimal form times the face value. Note also that the discount is the difference between the face value and the purchase price. The basic discount formula (2.1) should be solved for the discount rate *d*.

$$D = S - P. \text{ So } D = \$10{,}000 - (.9625)(10{,}000) = \$10{,}000 - \$9625 = \$375$$

$$d = \frac{D}{St} = \frac{375}{10{,}000\left(\frac{91}{360}\right)} = .1484 \approx 14.8\%$$

Since the bid for a Treasury bill is actually a percent, a formula can be derived that uses the bid directly instead of first finding the purchase price and the discount. Assume that the purchase price is the bid, like the 96.250 in the last example. This means that the maturity value is 100%, or 100. If the time is entered as the number of days over 360, the t in the formula will be in days (i.e., the term of the bill). Put these assumptions into the proceeds formula and do some algebra.

$P = S(1 - d(\frac{t}{360}))$ proceeds formula

$B(\text{Bid}) = 100(1 - d(\frac{t}{360}))$ Substitute for proceeds and amount.

$\frac{B}{100} = 1 - d(\frac{t}{360})$ Divide both sides by 100.

$d(\frac{t}{360}) = 1 - \frac{B}{100}$ Transpose terms.

$d(\frac{t}{360}) = \frac{100 - B}{100}$ Add terms on the right.

Bid Form of Rate: $d = \frac{360}{t}\left(\frac{100 - B}{100}\right)$ Divide both sides by $\frac{t}{360}$. **(2.6)**

Example 2.4.2

The successful bid for a $500,000, 182-day Treasury bill was 96.625. Find the rate of return (ROR) on a discount and a simple interest basis.

■ The discount rate can be found quickly using the bid formula (2.6), and then the coupon equivalent formula (2.4) can be used to find the simple interest rate.

$$d = \frac{360}{t}\left(\frac{100 - B}{100}\right) = \frac{360}{182}\left(\frac{100 - 96.625}{100}\right) = .0668 \approx 6.7\%$$

$$i = \frac{d}{1 - dt} = \frac{.0668}{1 - (.0668)(\frac{182}{360})} = .0691 \approx 6.9\%$$

◀ EXERCISES 2.4 ▶

Concepts and Short Answer Exercises

1. What are Treasury bills (T-bills) used to finance?
2. How do you make money on a T-bill?
3. A bid of 96.3 on a $1,000,000 T-bill means the *present value* is _____.
4. A bid of 96.3 on a $1,000,000 T-bill means the *discount* is _____.

Calculation Exercises

5. On May 3, 2004, Valjean bids 96.2 on a 182-day $500,000 T-bill. Find the present value, future value, and the ROR both as a discount rate and as an interest rate.
6. On May 3, 2004, Cosette bids 96.4 on a 271-day $500,000 T-bill. Find the present value, future value, and the ROR both as a discount rate and as an interest rate.
7. On August 5, 2004, Valjean (in Exercise 5) sells the T-bill to a woman desiring a 6% simple interest return on her investment. Find the amount the woman paid for the T-bill and the ROR Valjean got on his investment on a simple interest basis.

8. On August 15, 2004, Cosette (in Exercise 6) sells the T-bill to a man desiring a 6% simple interest return on his investment. Find the amount the man paid for the T-bill and the ROR Cosette got on her investment on a simple interest basis.

9. On December 10 Javiar buys a 1 million dollar 91-day CD with a bid of 93.34. Find his ROR as an interest rate and as a discount rate.

10. On December 25 Birmania buys a 1 million dollar 182-day CD with a bid of 91.11. Find her ROR as an interest rate and as a discount rate.

11. On February 10 of the next year Sven buys Javiar's CD (see Exercise 9) at a discount rate of 12%. Find the amount Sven pays for Javiar's CD. Also find the ROR Javiar got on his investment on a bank discount basis.

12. On February 20 of the next year Hilde buys Birmania's CD (see Exercise 10) at a discount rate of 10%. Find the amount Hilde pays for Birmania's CD. Also find the ROR Birmania got on her investment on a bank discount basis.

13. On September 15, 2004, a 91-day $500,000 Treasury bill is purchased with a bid of 98.2. Find the ROR on this investment using discount interest. Also find the coupon equivalent.

14. On September 25, 2004, a 180-day $100,000 Treasury bill is purchased with a bid of 98.5. Find the ROR on this investment using discount interest. Also find the coupon equivalent.

15. If the T-bill in Exercise 13 was sold in the secondary market on November 6, 2004, for $496,500, what was the original buyer's ROR on a simple interest basis?

16. If the T-bill in Exercise 14 was sold in the secondary market on November 1, 2004, for $99,200, what was the original buyer's ROR on a simple interest basis?

17. In Exercise 15 find the ROR (simple and discount) the new buyer made on the T-bill if he held it to maturity.

18. In Exercise 16 find the ROR (simple and discount) the new buyer made on the T-bill if she held it to maturity.

19. If a buyer at a Treasury bill auction wants to make a 7.8% ROR on a $1,000,000 181-day T-bill, what is the highest he can bid and still make what he wants?

20. If a buyer at a Treasury bill auction wants to make a 5.4% ROR on a $1,000,000 half-year T-bill, what is the highest she can bid and still make what she wants?

2.5 Various Discounted Securities

The term **money market** refers to an informal telephone network for buying and selling short-term credit instruments with maturities under one year. Governments and corporations issue these short-term securities to raise cash. Besides Treasury bills, there are corporate IOUs called commercial paper, negotiable certificates of deposit, banker's acceptances, short-term Treasury securities, term Eurodollars, and repurchase agreements. The money market provides short terms to maturity, low risk (due to the financial standing of the borrowing institutions), and rates below what banks would charge. The money market also provides lenders who have capital surpluses an opportunity to lend to those with capital needs so they can invest in inventory or means of production. Because the credit instruments involve large sums of money, even fractions of a percent can result in large differences in earnings.

The term **secondary market** refers to organized exchanges located in specific places. At the New York or American stock exchanges ownership of immense quantities of financial assets is regularly transferred between buyers and sellers. This market includes the government securities dealer market as well as the Federal Reserve's open market activities.

Commercial paper is a type of promissory note that may have a term anywhere from five days to nine months. The notes range in denominations from \$100,000 up to several million dollars. They are typically unsecured, and their risk to a lender depends on the financial stability of the issuing firm. Historically, very few companies have ever defaulted on the repayment of commercial paper that they have issued. Large credit corporations like General Electric Credit Corporation, General Motors Acceptance Corporation, Ford Motor Credit Corporation, and Chrysler Credit Corporation borrow huge sums in the commercial paper market.

Federal funds are loans between commercial banks for terms as short as one day. Large banks are typically the borrowers and small banks the lenders. Banks use these funds to maintain their minimum legal reserve funds. The transactions are typically electronic and the transfer system is called the **Fed wire** since it is under the direction of the Federal Reserve System. Interest is charged on a simple interest basis using exact time and interest.

Banker's acceptances are money market securities in which one bank promises to pay a specific sum to another bank on some maturity date within a year. These loan instruments are used to expedite trade transactions between importers and exporters. The importer's bank assumes the legal obligation to make payment on the date stipulated for the goods received. Whoever owns a banker's acceptance on the maturity date will collect its face value from the bank that accepted or guaranteed it. These acceptances are sold at discount with typical maturities of 30, 90, or 180 days.

Example 2.5.1

A 120-day, \$2,000,000 General Motors Acceptance Corporation note issued on June 21, 2004 was discounted on September 1, 2004 at a discount rate of 5.8%. What were the proceeds from this note?

■ The maturity date October 19 (292) minus the selling date September 1 (244) gives the time to maturity as 48 days. Substitute into the proceeds formula (2.2).

$$P = S(1-dt) = 2{,}000{,}000(1-(.058)(\tfrac{48}{360})) = \$1{,}984{,}533.33$$

Example 2.5.2

A 91-day, \$1,000,000 issue of commercial paper was issued on January 4, 2005 at a discount rate of 7.3%. If the buyer discounted the security in the secondary market on February 24, 2005, at a discount rate of 8%, what was his return on investment on a simple interest basis? Use exact time and exact interest.

■ The problem requires us to find the proceeds from the original purchase of the security on 1/4/05 (4) and from the sale on 2/24/05 (55). The first proceeds will give the amount of money invested and the second proceeds will provide a way to find the dollar value of the return. The maturity date's serial number is 4 + 91 = 95, which is April 5, 2005.

$P_1 = 1{,}000{,}000(1-(.073)(\frac{91}{365})) = \$981{,}800$ the original investment

$P_2 = 1{,}000{,}000(1-(.08)(\frac{40}{365})) = \$991{,}232.88$ the selling price

The original owner earned $991.232.88 – $981,800.00 = $9,432.88 for 51 days.

The ROR on a simple interest basis: $i = \frac{I}{Pt} = \frac{9432.88}{981{,}800(\frac{51}{365})} = .06876 \approx 6.9\%$

◀ EXERCISES 2.5 ▶

Concept and Short Answer Exercises

1. Can municipalities ever default (fail to pay back) on their municipal bonds?
2. What is the advantage of some government bonds over corporate bonds?
3. What is meant by the phrase, "These bonds are sold on a discount basis"?
4. If you were going to buy widgets (*widget* is an accounting education term for nearly any product or service you wish to buy or sell) from a foreign country, why would you likely use a banker's acceptance?

Calculation Exercises

5. On August 1, 2005, Ransom purchases a 200-day municipal bond on a 6% bank discount basis that matures to $250,000. What does he pay for the bond? Later Ransom needs cash, so he discounts the bond on January 1, 2006, at a bank charging a 7% discount rate. Find his proceeds and ROR on a discount basis.
6. On August 1, 2004, Coart purchases a 6-month municipal bond on a 5% bank discount basis that matures to $25,000. What does he pay for the bond? Later Coart needs cash, so he discounts the bond on January 1, 2005, at a bank charging a 7% discount rate. Find his proceeds and ROR on a discount basis.
7. A 60-day corporate note was purchased on July 14, 2004, at a discount rate of 6.5%; the note matures to $2,000,000. If the buyer discounted the note in the secondary market on August 28, 2004, at a discount rate of 7.75%, what was his return on investment on a simple interest basis? What was the new owner's ROR if she holds the note to maturity? Use exact time and exact interest.
8. A 90-day corporate note was purchased on July 14, 2004, at a discount rate of 5.4% and matures to $2,000,000. If the buyer discounted the note in the secondary market on September 28, 2004, at a discount rate of 7.5%, what was her return on investment on a simple interest basis? What was the new owner's ROR if he holds the note to maturity? Use exact time and exact interest.

9. Taylor buys a \$10,000, 8% simple interest corporate bond from the Universal Widgit Corporation on 6/1/03 that matures on 6/1/04. On 4/1/04 David buys this corporate bond from Taylor on an 8% discount basis. Find the proceeds Taylor gets from the sale and her ROR on a discount basis. Use approximate time and ordinary interest.

10. Bryce buys a \$10,000, 9% simple interest corporate bond from Universal Ratchet Inc. on 6/1/03 that matures on 6/1/05. On 4/1/04 Whitney buys this corporate bond from Bryce on an 8% discount basis. Find the proceeds Bryce gets from the sale and his ROR on a discount basis.

11. On May 22 Patricia invests \$50,000 in General Phone corporate bonds. General Phone is paying a 6% simple interest rate, and the bonds mature in 182 days. On August 12 Patricia sells the corporate bonds to Wesley, who requires 8% discount interest on his money. Find the proceeds Patricia gets from the sale and her ROR on a simple interest basis. Use Banker's Rule.

12. On May 22 Nelson Securities invests \$100,000 in Pacific Phone corporate bonds. Pacific Phone is paying a 5.4% simple interest rate, and the bonds mature in 273 days. On December 12 Nelson Securities sells the corporate bonds to Bondmart Inc., who require 8% discount interest on their money. Find the proceeds Nelson Securities gets from the sale and their ROR on a simple interest basis. Use Banker's Rule.

2.6 Theory of Interest—Simple Interest and Simple Discount

The first two chapters have presented an overview of the formulas and computations for simple interest and bank discount as they have been used in business for over two hundred years. Now we can consider these ideas from a theoretical viewpoint with a fairly good idea of where we are going. The flow from application to the general concepts should be fairly easy. First we will set down a few basic assumptions and the related notation.

1. The measurement period for time t will continue to be annual.
2. The amount (future value) of a given principal at time t will be designated by $A(t)$.
3. The effective rate of *simple interest* (as defined below) for the nth measurement period will be i_n.
4. The effective rate of *simple discount* (as defined below) for the nth measurement period will be d_n.
5. The amount of interest earned during the nth measurement period will be I_n.

Simple Interest

We have already developed formulas for the amount function $A(t)$ for simple interest and simple discount. The amount of money accumulated after t measurement periods was the product of the principal and the interest factors. By letting the principal be \$1, we get a meaningful representation for an accumulation function, which corresponds to the interest factor of the previous sections. In the context of simple interest we begin with the basic premise that the interest earned in each measurement interval is constant. This tacitly implies that we do not reinvest the interest; that is, interest does not accrue interest. The following definition introduces the familiar calculus idea of the area under a curve to express the accumulation function for simple interest.

Definition 2.6.1 *An accumulation function expresses the accumulated change in a quantity as the area of the region between the rate of change function and the horizontal axis.*

This is just the definite integral on the interval $[0, t]$ for t measurement periods, and it is a function of t. This accumulation function, $a(t)$, will be based on \$1 principal at $t = 0$, so $a(0) = 1$. First, we obtain the result using a graphing approach; then we evaluate the integral.

The area under the constant rate of change function $1 \cdot i$ is the area of a rectangle with width t and height i, giving the accumulated change as it. Looking at successive measurement periods, we notice the following accumulated growth.

$$f(0) = 0$$
$$f(1) = i \cdot 1$$
$$f(2) = i \cdot 2$$
$$f(3) = i \cdot 3$$
$$\vdots$$
$$f(t) = it$$

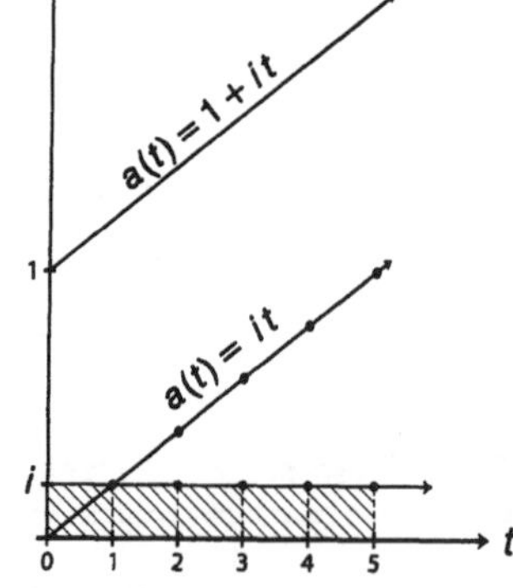

FIGURE 2.1

We need to translate this result one unit in the vertical direction in order to meet the requirement that $a(0) = 1$. Now we see that $a(t) = 1 + it$. This graphing approach is easily adapted to an initial principal of $A(0) = P$ by noting that the constant rate of change function is now Pi. This leaves us with the familiar form of the simple interest amount formula: $A(t) = P + Pit = P(1 + it)$. Any theoretical considerations about the measure of interest based on simple interest can be addressed by using $a(t)$. The following approach using the definite integral assures us that the accumulation function is applicable to all values where $t \geq 0$, and not to just integer values. Our only assumption is that the rate of change function is constant and hence integrable. Let s be a dummy variable.

$$a(t) = 1 + \int_0^t i\,ds = 1 + is\Big|_0^t = 1 + [i(t) - i(0)] = 1 + it$$

We conclude that our accumulation function for simple interest is a linear function with slope i and y-intercept 1. The amount function $A(t)$ is a linear function with slope Pi and y-intercept P. In summary we have established the following functions.

Accumulation function: $\mathbf{a(t) = 1 + it}$ where $t \geq 0$ and $a(0) = 1$ **(2.7)**

Amount function: $\mathbf{A(t) = P(1 + it)}$ where $t \geq 0$ and $A(0) = P$

Definition 2.6.2 *The effective rate of interest i is the ratio of the interest earned in a given measurement period to the principal at the beginning of that interval.*

You may recognize this definition as the decimal form of the percentage change in a quantity. We can also think of it as the rate of growth. Recall that simple interest is based on the present value with interest being paid at the end of the measurement period. Apply this definition to our amount function $A(t) = P(1+it)$ for the first interval $t = 0$ to $t = 1$. The result is what we expect for the first period.

$$\frac{A(1)-A(0)}{A(0)} = \frac{P(1+i(1))-P(1+i(0))}{P(1)} = \frac{P[(1+i)-1]}{P} = i$$

Theorem 2.6.1 The effective rate of interest i_n for simple interest during the nth measurement period as given, is a decreasing function of the measurement period.

$$i_n = \frac{i}{1+i(n-1)}$$

Proof

For the nth measurement period call the effective rate i_n and apply our definition using the accumulation function $a(t)$.

$$i_n = \frac{a(n)-a(n-1)}{a(n-1)} = \frac{1+in-(1+i(n-1))}{1+i(n-1)} = \frac{i}{1+i(n-1)} \quad \blacksquare$$

Since only the denominator is increasing as n increases, the effective rate fraction is decreasing. The next example will illustrate this result; but in practice this is not very significant since very few simple interest loans have terms beyond a couple of years. From the perspective of the lender his rate of return is diminishing. From the perspective of the borrower, he does better than he would with compound interest.

Example 2.6.1

Find the effective rates for 5% simple interest for 1, 2, 3, and 4 years.

■ By the above results, $i_1 = i = .05 = 5\%$.

$$i_2 = \frac{.05}{1+.05(2-1)} = .04762 \approx 4.76\%$$

$$i_3 = \frac{.05}{1+.05(3-1)} = .04545 \approx 4.55\%$$

$$i_4 = \frac{.05}{1+.05(4-1)} = .04348 \approx 4.35\%$$

We can make several observations about simple interest and its measurement that will reinforce our previous work and broaden our understanding. Most of these are based on the amount function, but the results are applicable to the accumulation function. Most of these could be thought of as properties of the amount or accumulation function.

1. The interest paid for any measurement period is the same.

$$I_1 = Pi \text{ and } I_k = A(k) - A(k-1)$$
$$\begin{aligned} I_k &= P(1+ik) - P(1+i(k-1)) \\ &= P - Pik - P - Pik + Pi \\ &= Pi \end{aligned}$$

2. The accumulated interest is $A(k) - A(0)$ since

$$I_1 = A(1) - A(0);$$
$$I_2 = A(2) - A(1);$$
$$\ldots$$
$$I_k = A(k) - A(k-1).$$

Adding gives $I_1 + I_2 + \ldots + I_k = A(k) - A(0)$.

3. The amount at any period k is just $1 + i_k$ times the amount at the previous period.

$$A(k) = (1+i_k)A(k-1)$$

4. Using the definition, we can find the effective rate for any measurement period, as illustrated in Example 2.6.2.

5. Using the accumulation function $a(t)$, the present value of 1 is

$$a^{-1}(t) = (1 + it)^{-1}.$$

6. Based on the amount function $A(t)$, the present value is

$$P = A(t)(1 + it)^{-1}.$$

7. If i_k is the effective rate for the kth measurement period, then the discount factor, $(1 + i_k)^{-1}$, for the kth period can be expressed in terms of the amount function as

$$(1+i_k)^{-1} = \frac{A(k-1)}{A(k)}.$$

Example 2.6.2

If a security can be purchased for \$58,500 and is worth \$60,000 in 90 days, find the 90-day effective rate and the simple interest rate.

■ The 90-day effective rate is $\dfrac{60{,}000 - 58{,}500}{58{,}500} = \dfrac{1500}{58{,}500} = .02564 \approx 2.56\%$.

■ Using Banker's Rule, the simple interest rate is just 4 times the 90-day effective rate or 10.26%.

Example 2.6.3

Find the measurement period when the effective rate for 5% simple interest is 4%.

■ Since the effective rate is $i_n = \dfrac{i}{1+i(n-1)}$, substitute and solve for n:

$.04 = \dfrac{.05}{1+.05(n-1)}$. After a little algebra we find that $n = 6$.

Example 2.6.4

A \$900 investment will accumulate to \$990 at time t. Find the accumulated value of an investment of \$2000 at a simple interest rate 2% higher and a term 1.5 times longer.

■ The original investment is used to find it.

$$990 = 900(1 + it) \rightarrow 1.10 = 1 + it, \text{ so } it = .10$$

The unknown accumulated value $x = 2000(1 + (1.02i)(1.5t)) = 2000(1 + 1.53it)$

$$= 2000(1 + 1.53(.10))$$

$$= 2000(1.153) = \$2306$$

Simple Discount

We will now consider some similar theory for simple discount. Developing an accumulation function for simple discount like we did for simple interest requires us to know the rate of change function for discount. This is not as obvious as it was for simple interest where the rate of change was constant. Earlier in the chapter we developed the amount function for discount interest as $A(t) = A(0)(1 - dt)^{-1}$. Letting $A(0) = 1$ makes the accumulation function be $a(t) = (1 - dt)^{-1}$. The derivative $a'(t) = d(1 - dt)^{-2}$ gives us the rate of change function, and it is an increasing function rather than constant. To find the accumulation function from this would mean returning to where we started. Our main interest for now is to address the effective rate of discount and establish relationships between simple interest and simple discount. In chapter 3 we will give more attention to the general concepts involving rates of change.

Definition 2.6.3 *The effective rate of discount d is the ratio of the interest earned in a given measurement period to the value of the investment at the end of that period.*

Recall that discount interest was based on the future value with the interest (discount) being paid at the beginning of the measurement period. With discount loans the interest was paid up front, so the borrower received only the proceeds but payed the full amount of the loan at the end of the term. We would expect the effective rate of discount to be d for the first measurement period and can confirm this by using the amount function $A(t) = A(0)(1 - dt)^{-1}$ for the interval $t = 0$ to $t = 1$.

$$\frac{A(1) - A(0)}{A(1)} = \frac{A(0)(1 - d(1))^{-1} - A(0)(1 - d(0))^{-1}}{A(0)(1 - d(1))^{-1}} = \frac{(1-d)^{-1} - 1}{(1-d)^{-1}} = 1 - (1 - d) = d$$

Theorem 2.6.2 The effective rate of interest d_n for simple discount during the nth measurement period as given is an increasing function of the measurement period.

$$d_n = \frac{d}{1 - d(n-1)}$$

Proof

For the nth measurement period, call the effective rate of discount d_n and apply our effective rate definition using the accumulation function $a(t)$.

$$d_n = \frac{a(n) - a(n-1)}{a(n)} = \frac{(1-dn)^{-1} - (1-d(n-1))^{-1}}{(1-dn)^{-1}} = 1 - \frac{(1-d(n-1))^{-1}}{(1-dn)^{-1}} = \frac{d}{1-d(n-1)}$$ ∎

Example 2.6.5

Using the formula, find the effective rate of discount for 6% per annum for 1, 2, and 3 years.

■ $d_1 = \frac{.06}{1-.06(0)} = .06 = 6\%$ $d_2 = \frac{.06}{1-.06(1)} = .06383 \approx 6.38\%$

$d_3 = \frac{.06}{1-.06(2)} = .06818 \approx 6.82\%$

This example illustrates the increasing value of the effective rate of discount for each measurement period.

Equivalent Interest Rates

In Section 2.2 we established the equivalence between a simple interest rate and a simple discount rate. We referred to this as the *coupon equivalent.* We want to return to this concept of equivalence by first defining equivalent rates and then by establishing the relationships between them.

Definition 2.6.4 *Equivalent interest rates produce the same return for a given investment and term (measurement period).*

Looking at this definition from another perspective, we expect the given principal to have the same accumulated value for a given amount of time. Assume a starting principal of 1 and use the accumulation functions for t measurement periods.

At simple interest: return $I = a(t) - a(0) = 1 + it - 1 = it$.

At discount interest: return $I = a(t) - a(0) = \frac{1}{1-dt} - 1 = \frac{1-(1-dt)}{1-dt} = \frac{dt}{1-dt}$.

Equate and divide out the common t. $it = \frac{dt}{1-dt} \rightarrow i = \frac{d}{1-dt}$ or $d = \frac{i}{1+it}$

By considering the first measurement interval, we see other interesting relationships emerge. In chapter 3 the use of compound interest and compound discount will allow these relationships to be applied to any measurement period.

$i = \frac{d}{1-d}$ and $d = \frac{i}{1+i} = i\left(\frac{1}{1+i}\right) = iv$ (where $v = \frac{1}{1+i}$ is the discount factor)

$d = iv$ needs some interpretation and an example. Since we are considering a starting principal of 1, then d is the return paid at the beginning of the period, while i is the return paid at the end of the period. Our equation says their present values are equal; that is, discounting i to the beginning of the measurement period gives d.

Example 2.6.6

Find the discount rate equivalent to a simple interest rate of 7% for 1 year and for 2 years.

- Since $d = iv$, we know $d = .07\left(\frac{1}{1.07}\right) = .06542 \approx 6.54\%$, and
- $d_2 = \frac{i}{1+it} = \frac{.07}{1+.07(2)} = .0614 \approx 6.14\%$.

What if we consider our investment to be 1 at the end of the period and find the value at the beginning of the period under equivalent rates of simple interest and simple discount?

At simple interest, 1 at the end of the period has a beginning value of

$$v = (1+i)^{-1}.$$

At simple discount, 1 at the end of the period has a beginning value of

$$1 - d.$$

We conclude that $v = 1 - d$.

This is easily verified by a little algebra:

$$d = 1 - v = 1 - \frac{1}{1+i} = \frac{1+i-1}{1+i} = \frac{i}{1+i}.$$

This was our basic equivalent rate formula relating d and i.

The two relationships $d = iv$ and $v = 1 - d$ can be combined to demonstrate another interesting idea about the difference in borrowing via simple interest or simple discount.

$$d = iv = i(1-d) = i - id$$

Transposing the terms yields $i - d = id$.

If you borrow 1 at simple discount, you receive $1-d$ now and pay back 1 in a year. If you borrow 1 at simple interest, you receive 1 now and pay back $1+i$ in a year. If these are equivalent interest and discount rates, then $i-d$ represents the difference in interest charges—in particular, how much more it cost at simple interest. Of course, this resulted from receiving the smaller principal $1-d$ to use during the year under the discount interest scheme. Since you had d dollars less to use, simple interest id on that money represents the difference in interest charges. Thus we have $i - d = id$. Consider the following example.

Example 2.6.7

Compare borrowing \$1000 for 1 year at 6% simple interest to borrowing \$1000 at an equivalent simple discount rate.

- Find the equivalent discount rate. $d = \frac{i}{1+i} = \frac{.06}{1.06} = .0566037736 \approx 5.66\%$

Discount: the proceeds $= 1000(1 - .0566) = 943.40$

the interest charges $= 1000 - 943.4 = 56.60$

Simple: the principal received $= 1000$

the interest charges $= 1000(.06) = 60$

difference $= 3.40$

the interest on 56.60 at 6% simple interest $= 56.60(.06) = 3.40$

◂ EXERCISES 2.6 ▸

Concept and Short Answer Exercises

1. Explain the differences between simple interest and simple discount.
2. If a process has a growth rate of $3t + 4$, what is the accumulation function?
3. If a process has an amount function defined by $A(t) = .5t^3 + 2t + 2$, find the associated accumulation function.
4. Find the effective rate of 8% simple interest and 8% discount interest during the 5th measurement period.
5. Find the equivalent rate of simple discount for an 18-month simple interest loan at 6.5%.
6. Find the equivalent rate of simple interest for a 27-month simple discount loan at 7.25%.

Calculation Exercises

7. a. Find d_4 if the simple interest rate is 8%.
   b. Find d_4 if the simple discount rate is 8%.
8. a. Find i_6 if the simple interest rate is 9%.
   b. Find i_6 if the simple discount rate is 9%.
9. If an account earns 6% simple interest, in what measurement period does the effective rate first fall below 5%?
10. If an account earns 6% simple discount, in what measurement period does the effective rate of simple discount first exceed 7%?
11. If \$580 accumulates to \$720 in t measurement periods, find the accumulated amount of \$5500 at a rate 1.5% higher and a term twice as long.

Theory and Extension Exercises

12. Prove that the relationship $i - d = id$ for equivalent simple and discount rates also holds for t measurement periods; that is, $i - d = idt$.
13. Develop a formula to find the simple interest rate from the bid as a percent and term in days for a T-bill.
14. If i_t is the rate of simple interest for period t, then show that

$$a(k) - a(0) = i_1 + i_2 + i_3 + \ldots + i_k.$$

Chapter 2 Summary of Concepts

Discount Interest: $P = Sdt$

Present Value at Discount Interest (Proceeds): $P = S(1-dt) = A(t)(1-dt)$

Effective Rate of Simple interest: $i_n = \dfrac{i}{1+i(n-1)}$

Effective Rate of Simple Discount: $d_n = \dfrac{d}{1-d(n-1)}$

Future Value at Discount Interest (Amount): $S = \dfrac{P}{1-dt}$ or $A(t) = A(0)(1-dt)^{-1}$

Coupon Equivalent: $i = \dfrac{d}{1-dt}$

Discount Equivalent: $d = \dfrac{i}{1+it}$

Chapter 2 Vocabulary Check

Accumulation Function
Banker's Acceptance
Certificate of Deposit
Commercial Paper
Discount Interest
Discount Rate
Effective Rate of Interest
Equivalent Rates
Federal Funds
Fed Wire
Holder
Money Market
Negotiable Instrument
Proceeds
Promise to Pay
Rate of Return (ROR)
Secondary Market
Treasury Bill

Chapter 2 Skills Check

1. Find the bank discount, proceeds, and future value using discount interest.
   Section 2.1 Examples 1, 3, 4; Exercises 7, 9, 17
2. Change between simple interest rates and discount rates.
   Section 2.1 Examples 1, 2, 3; Exercises 9, 11, 13, 15
3. Find maturity values and discounted prices for various marketed securities.
   Section 2.3 Examples 1, 2, 3; Exercises 11, 13, 19
   Section 2.5 Examples 1, 2; Exercises 5, 7
4. Find the selling price and discount rate for T-bills sold at auction. Find the rate of return for T-bills sold before maturity.
   Section 2.4 Examples 1, 2; Exercises 5, 7, 9, 11
5. Find the effective rate of interest or discount for various measurement periods. Find equivalent rates of interest or discount. Given a rate of growth function find the related accumulated function.
   Section 2.6 Examples 3, 4, 6; Exercises 2, 5, 7, 8

Review Test for Discount Interest

1. Find the value on 5/4/03 of \$1000 due on 8/6/03 using
   a. 8% simple interest rate
   b. 8% bank discount rate
2. Mr. Seratov borrows \$2000 and pays back \$400 in 3 months. Find Mr. Seratov's payoff in 1 year at 8% if he
   a. Uses the United States Rule
   b. Uses the Merchant's Rule

3. If money is worth a bank discount rate of 10%, is it better to pay $2500 cash for a Yamaha or to wait 2 years and pay $3000?

4. On 4/1/03 Mr. Barton bids 94.2 on a million-dollar 91-day T-bill. Find the ROR on a simple interest basis that Mr. Barton gets on his T-bill.

5. On 6/2/03 Mr. Barton sells the above T-Bill to an SCN bank that requires 8% on their moneys.
   a. Find the proceeds Mr. Barton gets.
   b. Find the ROR for Mr. Barton on a bank discount basis.

6. Ms. Naler in purchasing gets a bill for $3000 on a 5/10, *n*/60 basis. Find the ROR Ms. Naler gets for her money if she pays on the 10th day.

7. Mr. Jones has a $5000 6-month CD that pays 8% simple interest. Four months into the CD Mr. Jones needs $2000 for an auto repair. If early withdrawal from the CD results in loss of all interest on the part withdrawn, should Mr. Jones withdraw the money from his CD or should he charge the auto repair on his 12% VISA charge card? Tell which is better and by how much.

8. How long does it take to increase your worth by 60% at
   a. An 8% interest rate?
   b. An 8% discount rate?

9. A man invests $5000 and gets a return of $2000 in 6 months and another return of $4000 in 12 months. Find
   a. NPV at 30%
   b. NPV at 20%
   c. IRR

Chapter 3

Compound Interest

3.1 Compound Interest—Future Value Formula

Money invested at compound interest grows faster than money left to grow at simple interest even if it is invested at the same rate. The accrual of simple interest is always based on the original principal, but compound interest is added to the principal in such a way that each time interest is computed, it is based on a larger principal than the previous time. For example, $100 invested at 5% annually will amount to $125 in five years at simple interest, but in five years at compound interest it will amount to $127.63. This may not seem like much difference, but if the time is extended to one hundred years, the simple interest account grows to just $600, whereas the compound account grows to $13,150.13. On the graph in Figure 3.1, the simple interest account is a straight line (a linear function) while the compound interest account is an exponential curve (an exponential function).

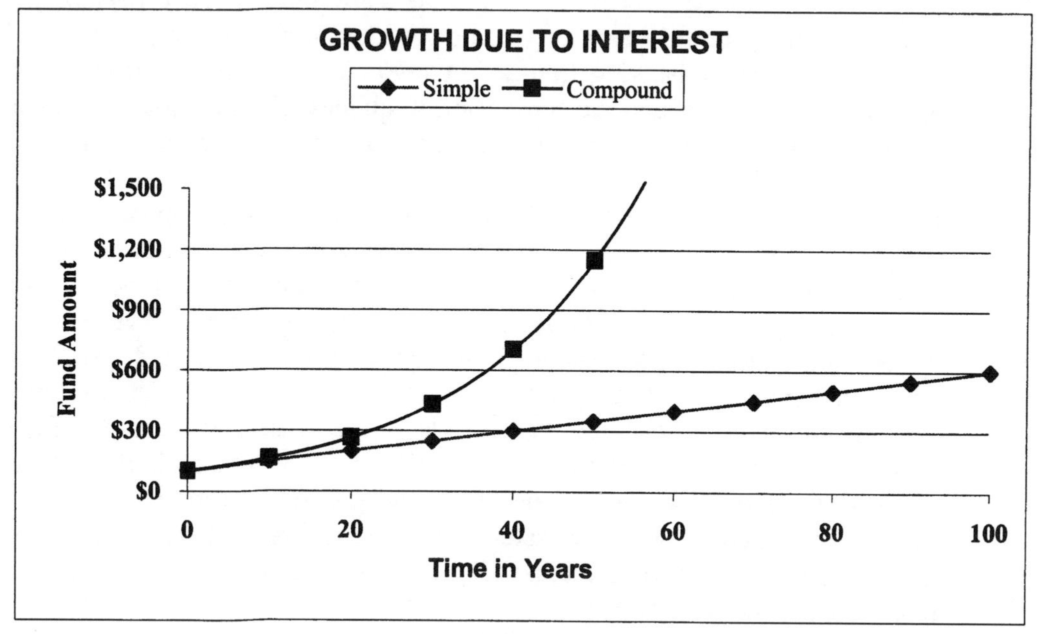

FIGURE 3.1

To better understand the power of compound interest, let us consider the philanthropy of Andrew Carnegie who lived from 1835 to 1919. As a Scottish immigrant to the United States in 1848, he worked his way from messenger boy and telegraph operator to owner and operator of the Pittsburgh Carnegie Steel Company. He began donating modest amounts of money to various public causes in 1870; but in 1900, when he retired from business at age 65, he began in earnest to distribute his considerable wealth of more than $300,000,000. During his lifetime he donated in excess of $333,300,000 through gifts and bequests to various foundations, churches, cities, colleges and universities. His special interest in quality organs and public literacy prompted him to give more than $60,000,000 in Carnegie grants for the construction of at least 2500 libraries and for the purchase and installation of over 7600 organs. The Carnegie Corporation of New York, established in 1911 for the advancement and diffusion of knowledge, gave in excess of $182,000,000 during its first 29 years. Even though the average rate of interest was only about 4.5%, the endowment of $135,336,800 generated this huge sum for many projects in higher education. Besides the Carnegie Corporation of New York, Mr. Carnegie founded and separately endowed five other agencies in the United States, plus other trusts and foundations benefiting his native Scotland [Lester]. As a tool for growth and development, compound interest is amazing, but it can also become a crushing burden for those in debt. It is certainly a topic worth our consideration.

Whenever compound interest is used, the interest conversion period must be given. The **conversion period** (or **interest period**) tells the length of time between successive computations of interest. These periods of time are either a year or parts of a year, such as semiannual, quarterly, monthly, or daily. Continuous compounding will be treated separately in Section 3.8 because it requires a mathematical limit to deal with an infinite process. To find the **rate per interest period,** divide the **nominal rate** (**annual percentage rate**) by the number of conversion periods per year. A business or banking transaction involving compound interest will always provide the yearly rate and the conversion frequency. For example, 8% compounded quarterly has a 2% rate per period. If the transaction involved simple interest for one quarter, the interest computation (.08)(¼) would also give 2%. This means that simple and compound interest are exactly the same for one conversion period. If an exercise is obviously compound interest but no conversion period is given, we may assume it is compounded annually. To calculate the total number of conversion periods, multiply the number of periods per year by the number of years.

Previously we learned how to move money with simple and discount interest. Compound interest provides yet a third way to move money on the time line. A formula will be developed shortly that relates the present value to the future value (*amount*). There is not a simple formula, like in the last two chapters, that directly computes the interest using the rate, time, and present or future value. To calculate the interest earned or paid, we instead find the difference between the present and future values. The interest, therefore, is the amount of an investment's growth or, for a loan, the cost of borrowing.

Summary of Basic Definitions with Notation

$i(m)$ Nominal Rate	shorthand for nominal rate converted m times/year
Conversion Period	time between interest computations
m	number of conversion periods per year
i **Interest Rate per Period**	nominal rate divided by periods per year, $\frac{i(m)}{m}$
n **Total Interest Periods**	conversion periods per year times years, mt
P **Present Value**	principal borrowed or invested at compound interest
S **Amount**	future value of the principal at compound interest

The symbol $\frac{i(m)}{m}$ is also denoted in some theory of interest texts as $\frac{i^{(m)}}{m}$. In order to let the symbol i consistently be the interest rate per conversion period, we will let $i(m)$ be the nominal rate so that $i = \frac{i(m)}{m}$. The other approach is to let i always be the rate per measurement period taken as a year. This introduces the convention that compounding periods of less than a year are fractions of a measurement period, which leads to confusion about interest computed for a fraction of a conversion period.

The following inductive process applies the principle of compound interest to a given principal P several times to provide a derivation of the compound amount formula. In each interest conversion period the principal for that period is multiplied by the rate i. The steps in this derivation are repeated applications of the distributive property and the laws of exponents.

Conversion Period	Computation of interest	New Principal (amount)
1	$S = P + iP$	$S = P(1 + i)$
2	$S = P(1 + i) + iP(1 + i) = P(1 + i)(1 + i)$	$S = P(1 + i)^2$
3	$S = P(1 + i)^2 + iP(1 + i)^2 = P(1 + i)^2(1 + i)$	$S = P(1 + i)^3$
	$\vdots$	$\vdots$
n	$S = P(1 + i)^{n-1} + iP(1 + i)^{n-1} = P(1 + i)^{n-1}(1 + i)$	$S = P(1 + i)^n$

Compound Amount Formula: $S = P(1 + i)^n$ **(3.1)**

The compound interest factor $(1+i)^n$, called the **accumulation factor** (or function), is the basic tool to move money on the time line using compound interest. In Section 3.2 the amount formula will be solved for P to derive the present value formula.

The accrual of compound interest could also have been viewed as a geometric sequence with the first term as the starting principal and the common ratio as $(1+i)$. Note that the first term $a = P$, so n compounding periods will actually give a geometric sequence with $n+1$ terms.

Geometric sequence: $a, \quad ar, \quad ar^2, \quad ar^3, \ldots, ar^{n-1}$
Compound interest: $P, P(1+i), P(1+i)^2, P(1+i)^3, \ldots, P(1+i)^{(n+1)-1} = P(1+i)^n$

Example 3.1.1

Find the rate per period i for each of the following nominal compounded rates:

a. 12%(2); **b.** 8%(12); **c.** 6%(4); **d.** 7%(12).

▪ Use the formula $i = \frac{i(m)}{m}$, where m is number of the conversion periods per year.

a. $i = \frac{12}{2} = 6\% = .06$

c. $i = \frac{6}{4} = 1.5\% = .015$

b. $i = \frac{8}{12} = \frac{2}{3}\% = .00\overline{6}$

d. $i = \frac{7}{12} = .58\overline{3}\,\% = .0058\overline{3}$

Example 3.1.2

Find the number of compounding periods for each of the following rates and years: **a.** 12%(2) for 4 years and 6 months; **b.** 8%(12) for 5 years and 6 months; **c.** 7%(12) for 15 years.

▪ Express each time period in decimal parts of a year and multiply by the periods per year.

a. $n = 2 \times 4.5 = 9$ periods

b. $n = 5.5 \times 12 = 66$ periods

c. $n = 15 \times 12 = 180$ periods

Example 3.1.3

Find the compound amount of \$4500 invested for 8 years and 6 months at

a. 12%(2); **b.** 8%(12); **c.** 6%(4); **d.** 7%(12).

▪ Use the values of i from Example 3.1.1 and substitute the given information into the future value formula, $S = P(1+i)^n$. Instead of rounding the rate, use all the available digits.

a. $n = 8.5 \times 2 = 17$, $\quad S = 4500(1.06)^{17} = \$12{,}117.48$

b. $n = 8.5 \times 12 = 102$, $\quad S = 4500(1.006666666)^{102} = \$8862.43$

c. $n = 8.5 \times 4 = 34$, $\quad S = 4500(1.015)^{34} = \$7465.48$

d. $n = 8.5 \times 12 = 102$, $\quad S = 4500(1.005833333)^{102} = \$8144.55$

In the next example it will be necessary to find the time in interest periods between two different dates. Dates given as year-month-day (or possibly year-month if the days are equal) are called denominate numbers. Examples 3.1.4 and 3.1.6 demonstrate the conversion of dates into interest periods using denominate numbers.

Example 3.1.4

On July 10, 2003, \$7500 was invested in a fund paying 8%(4). How much is in this fund on October 10, 2006?

■ The rate per period is 2%, but the number of interest periods takes a little more thought. By July 10, 2006, 3 years have passed, and from July to October another 3 months have passed (one quarter): $n = 3 \times 4 + 1 = 13$. A method of denominate numbers can also be used: (2006 – 10) minus (2003 – 7) = 3 years and 3 months.

$$S = 7500(1.02)^{13} = \$9702.05$$

Remember that each year consists of 12 months, and certain denominate numbers will require that you rename in order to subtract.

$$\begin{array}{lcl} 2005-3-1 & \rightarrow & 2004-15-1 \\ \underline{2003-9-1} & & \underline{2003-\ \ 9-1} \\ & & 1 \text{ yr.} - 6 \text{ mo.} \end{array}$$

Example 3.1.5

An education fund worth \$6580 was invested at 6%(12) on a child's 12th birthday, 2/22/94. How much is in the fund when the 18-year-old youth goes off to college in August? How much interest did the fund earn?

■ From February to August is 6 months and from 1994 to 2000 is 6 years (age 12 + 6 = age 18). The number of conversion periods $n = 12 \times 6 + 6 = 78$. The rate $i = \frac{1}{2}\% = .005$. Use the amount formula for the future value and take the difference between the present value and the amount to get the interest earned.

$$S = P(1 + i)^n = 6580(1.005)^{78} = \$9709.09$$

$$\text{Interest} = \$9709.09 - \$6580 = \$3129.09$$

Example 3.1.6

A realtor invests \$9500 at 7.5%(4) on September 1, 2000. What is the value of the fund on July 15, 2004? Use simple interest and Banker's Rule for part of a period.

■ Find the interest date using quarterly compounding that is as close to July 15, 2004 as possible. Note that the integral interest dates fall on 9/1, 12/1, 3/1, and 6/1. Simple interest will be required from June 1, 2004 until July 15, 2004. Therefore, $t = 196 - 152 = 44$ days. Ignore leap year because both dates are on the same side of February 29. Using denominate numbers, (2004 – 6) minus (2000 – 9) = 3 years and 9 months. Therefore, $n = 3.75 \times 4 = 15$ periods. We will use a time line and the compound amount formula (3.1) and the simple interest future value formula (1.2).

TIME LINE DIAGRAM 3.1.1

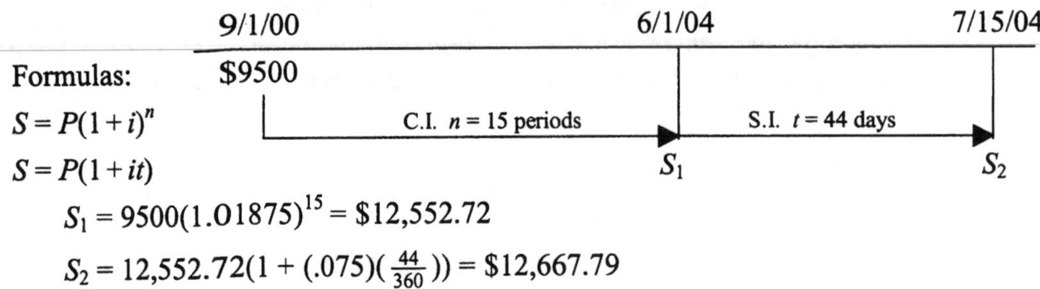

◀ EXERCISES 3.1 ▶

Concept and Short Answer Exercises

1. Accruing the interest to the account means _____.
2. In simple interest problems, when is the one time that interest is accrued?
3. Name all of the times that the interest is accrued in compound interest problems.
4. Compound interest is sometimes described as a sequence of several simple interest problems each having the same term. Explain why.
5. Using the formula for the future value at simple interest, explain why simple interest is called *linear growth.*
6. Using the formula for the future value at compound interest, explain why compound interest is called an *exponential growth.*

Find n, the number of compounding periods, for the following:

	Present Value Date	Future Value Date	Compounded
7.	July 1, 2005	July 1, 2010	Yearly
8.	April 1, 2005	July 1, 2010	Quarterly
9.	July 1, 2005	January 1, 2010	Monthly
10.	8/2/06	2/2/12	Semiannually
11.	0	5.5 years later	Monthly
12.	8/2/06	2/2/08	Quarterly

13. 8%(2) may be worded in a problem as 8% compounded _____ or 8% converted _____.
14. In this and all subsequent chapters 5% means 5% compounded _____ or 5%(__).
15. If money is worth 8%(4) and the term is 3 years and 5 months, then use compound interest for _____ quarters and simple interest for _____ months.
16. If money is worth 8%(2) and the term is 3 years and 5 months, then use compound interest for _____ half years and simple interest for _____ months.

Calculation Exercises

17. Compute the future value of $1000 for 3 years at 8%(1):
    a. Using simple interest 3 times
    b. Using the compound interest formula
18. Compute the future value of $100 for 4 years at 10%(1):
    a. Using simple interest 4 times
    b. Using the compound interest formula
19. Tim invests $2000 for 2 years at 8%. Find the amount if
    a. Money is compounded quarterly.
    b. Money is compounded monthly.
    c. Money is compounded daily (use 360 days/year).
20. Toni invests $20,000 for 3 years at 10%. Find the amount if
    a. Money is compounded quarterly.
    b. Money is compounded monthly.
    c. Money is compounded daily (use 360 days/year).
21. Juanita owes $6000 to a firm charging 8% compounded semiannually. Find the amount Juanita owes in 2.5 years and find the compound interest she paid.
22. Larry owes $1000 to a bank charging 6% compounded semiannually. Find the amount Larry owes in 2.5 years and find the compound interest he paid.
23. On February 2, 2005, Robert buys a $10,000 CD that matures on August 2, 2010, at 9%(2). Find the worth of the CD when it matures.
24. On February 2, 2005, Mindi buys a $10,000 CD that matures on August 2, 2010, at 9%(4). At maturity Mindi withdraws the money for a down payment on a car. How much does Mindi have toward the car?
25. When Jonathon was born, his grandfather bought him a $250 savings bond that paid 5%. When Jonathon started college at age 18, he cashed in the savings bond. How much did Jonathon get?
26. Repeat Exercise 25, but change the interest rate to 5%(4).
27. If home values are growing at 4% per year, how much will a $100,000 home be worth in 14 years?
28. If home values are growing at 3.5% per year, how much will a $100,000 home be worth in 20 years?
29. A $5000 savings bond paying 8%(4) is bought on September 30, 2004 and matures on December 31, 2010. Find its value at maturity.
30. Repeat Exercise 29, but change the interest rate to 8%(12).
31. Suppose your savings account is paying 4%(12). On February 1, 2002 you have $382.50 in your account. How much remains in your savings account on November 1, 2008 when you withdraw $500?
32. Repeat Exercise 31, but let the ending date be February 1, 2010 and the rate be 4%(1).

33. On 9/1/03 you borrow \$5000 at 6%(2), and on 3/1/05 you pay \$3000. At that point what is your outstanding balance?

34. Repeat Exercise 33 except at an interest rate of 6%(12).

35. Suppose your savings account is paying 4%(12). On February 1, 2002, you have \$382.50 in your account. How much remains in your savings account on November 12, 2008, if you withdraw \$500? (Use simple interest for part of a period.)

36. Suppose your savings account is paying 1.75%(12). On February 10, 2002, you have \$382.50 in your account. How much remains in your savings account on December 1, 2008 when you withdraw \$500? (Use simple interest for part of a period.)

37. On 9/1/03 you borrow \$5000 at 6%(2) and on 2/1/05 you pay \$3000. At that time what is your outstanding balance?

38. If the Carnegie Corporation of New York invested the endowment of \$135 million in 1911 at 4.5%(1), how much would have been in the fund in 1940, assuming none of the interest was used during that time?

3.2 The Present Value Formula and Discounting

Institutions and investors frequently set financial goals or have debt obligations that require current investments in order to provide the capital to meet those goals at some future date. Since the time and value of the future monies are typically known, the current investments will be the present value computed at the best available compound rate. Moving money to an earlier date on the time line requires that we solve the compound amount (future value) formula for the present value.

One interesting and useful type of computation lets us find the value of several future income streams that may not be equal but are related, are located at different points in time, and together are equivalent to a known present value. In Section 3.7 we will address these calculations under the topic of equations of value.

The **present value** is the sum of money that will increase at compound interest to some known future amount at a given date in the future. The present value can also be called the **cash value** of a future amount of money. The amount of interest earned during the term of the investment is called the **compound interest**. Taken in the reverse perspective the difference between the present value and the future amount is the **discount**. The discount is the shrinkage that occurs when a piece of money is moved back in time at compound interest. The following algebra shows how to solve the compound amount formula for the present value.

$$S = P(1+i)^n$$ the *amount formula*

$$\frac{S}{(1+i)^n} = \frac{P(1+i)^n}{(1+i)^n}$$ Divide both sides by $(1+i)^n$.

$$\frac{S}{(1+i)^n} = P$$ Cancel the common factor on the right.

$$P = \frac{S}{(1+i)^n} \qquad \text{Transpose so } P \text{ is on the left side.}$$

Present Value Formula: $P = S(1+i)^{-n} = Sv^n$ **(3.2)**

We typically use the negative exponent form, since it is easier for an algebraic calculator. The factor $(1+i)^{-n}$ is called the **discount factor** or the **present worth of 1** factor. We should note that it is simply the reciprocal of the *accumulation factor* (Section 3.1). In the context of interest theory in Section 3.3, the *discount factor* is denoted as $v^n = (1+i)^{-n}$.

Example 3.2.1

How much should be invested today at 7%(4) in order to meet a $22,650 obligation due in 42 months?

■ Note carefully that a year contains 4 quarters and that each quarter is 3 months. Quarterly interest requires that we divide 42 months by 3 months to arrive at $n = 14$ interest periods. The rate per quarter is $7 \div 4 = 1.75\%$. We are finding the present value, so we substitute the known information into the present value formula. (Use the ± button to make 14 a negative.)

$$P = S(1+i)^{-n} = 22{,}650(1.0175)^{-14} = \$17{,}765.86$$

Example 3.2.2

A note for $24,890 that matures on March 1, 2009 is sold on October 6, 2003 to yield 8%(12). Find the selling price on October 6 and the discount.

■ Since we are not given the rate for the note, we assume that the $24,890 is the future value. The closest we can get to October 6 when finding the present value at 8%(12) is November 1. We will need to use simple interest for the remaining time. Make a time line diagram. To find *n*, use (2009 – 3) minus (2003 – 11) = 5 years, 4 months. Therefore, $n = 64$.

TIME LINE DIAGRAM 3.2.1

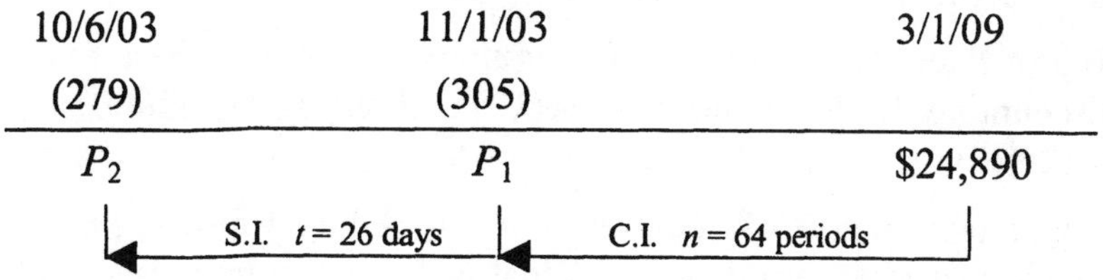

10/6/03	11/1/03	3/1/09
(279)	(305)	
P_2	P_1	$24,890
S.I. $t = 26$ days	C.I. $n = 64$ periods	

$$P_1 = S(1+i)^{-n} = 24{,}890(1.006666666)^{-64} = \$16{,}268.25$$

$$P_2 = \frac{S}{1+it} = \frac{16{,}268.25}{1+(.08)(\frac{26}{360})} = \$16{,}174.80$$

$$\text{Discount} = \$24{,}890 - \$16{,}174.80 = \$8715.20$$

◀ EXERCISES 3.2 ▶

Concept and Short Answer Exercises

1. Solve $S = P(1 + i)^n$ for P and thus derive the formula for the present value under compound interest.
2. In $P = S(1 + i)^{-n}$ the $-n$ indicates that money is moving which way in time?
3. On most financial calculators, and in Excel, $n = 20$ must be entered as ___ when solving for FV (future value) and as ___ when solving for PV. Why?
4. In Excel, PV (rate = .08, nper = 20, pmt = 0, fv = \$5000) = –\$1072.74 is correct, while PV (rate = .08, nper = –20, pmt = 0, fv = \$5000) = –\$23,304.79 is absurd.
   a. Explain the first equation.
   b. Explain why the second is absurd.
   c. Explain what the second actually finds.
5. Suppose a rate of 8%(2) and suppose a time of 4 years and 8 months. The FV is found by staging the problem as compound interest for the maximum number of full compounding periods, which is ____ periods, and simple interest is accrued on that resulting future value for the rest of the time, which is ____ days.
6. Repeat Exercise 5 but let the interest rate be 9%(4).

Calculation Exercises

7. Find the present value of \$2000 due in 2 years at 9% converted semiannually.
8. Find the present value of \$20,000 due in 4 years at 9% converted quarterly.
9. Find the value on June 30, 2004 of a note whose maturity value is \$4068.65 and whose maturity date is September 30, 2006 at 7% converted quarterly.
10. Repeat Exercise 9 except at 7% converted monthly.
11. Gerald has two notes coming due. The first is a \$5000 note due on 1/1/02. The second is a \$2000 note due on 5/1/04. Find the equivalent worth of these two debts on 7/1/02, discounting the \$2000 note at 8%(12) and letting the \$5000 note accrue interest at 7%(2).
12. Repeat Exercise 11, but find the equivalent worth of these two debts on 1/1/03, discounting the \$2000 note at 9%(12) and letting the \$5000 note accrue interest at 12%(2).
13. A man owes a note of \$6000 in 3 years. A buyer desiring 8%(2) on her money should pay what for this note? What is the compound discount?
14. Repeat Exercise 13 except at 9%(4).
15. Natasha sees an investment that she thinks will be worth \$25,000 in 10 years. What should she pay for this investment if she desires 9%(4) on her money? What is the compound discount?
16. Holly sees an investment that she thinks will be worth \$5000 in 2 years. What should Holly pay for this investment if she desires 9%(2) on her money? What is the compound discount?

17. A businessman holds a note worth \$6000 in 3 years and 2 months. A buyer desiring 8%(2) on his money should pay what for this note? What is the discount?

18. Repeat Exercise 17 except at 8%(4).

Theory and Extension Exercises

Exercises 19–22 generalize Chapter 3 concepts and anticipate Chapter 5 by using compound interest for part of a period.

19. Repeat Exercise 17, but use compound interest for part of a period.

20. Repeat Exercise 18, but use compound interest for part of a period.

21. 8%(2) ≈ ___%(12). Use this result and redo Exercise 17 as a monthly problem. Compare the answer to Exercise 19.

22. 8%(4) ≈ ___%(12). Use this result and redo Exercise 18 as a monthly problem. Compare the answer to Exercise 20.

3.3 Theory of Interest—Compound Interest and Compound Discount

Compound Interest

In Section 3.1 we used an inductive argument to establish the amount formula for compound interest. In keeping with our notation of Section 2.6, we will establish the amount function as $A(t) = A(0)(1+i)^t$, where i is the compound rate per interest period and t is the number of interest periods. Letting $A(0) = 1$ gives us the accumulation function $a(t) = (1+i)^t$ for compound interest, and at this point $t \geq 0$ is an integer. Recall the definition of effective interest and then apply it to our compound interest accumulation function.

Definition 3.3.1 *The effective rate of interest i is the ratio of the interest earned in a given measurement period to the principal at the beginning of that period.*

$$i_n = \frac{a(n)-a(n-1)}{a(n-1)} = \frac{(1+i)^n-(1+i)^{n-1}}{(1+i)^{n-1}} = \frac{(1+i)-1}{1} = i$$

This offers several insights. First, a fixed compound rate implies a fixed effective rate that is equal. Second, since $a(0) = 1$ and the effective rate is constant, we can start with these two basic assumptions and establish our accumulation function.

Theorem 3.3.1 If $a(t)$ is an accumulation function with $a(0) = 1$ and the effective rate is constant, then $a(t) = (1+i)^t$.

Proof

Use the effective rate definition in the form $a(n) - a(n-1) = a(n-1)k$, k being a constant. Then apply the inductive method of Section 3.1 to establish the result.

$a(1) - a(0) = a(0)k \rightarrow a(1) - 1 = 1k \rightarrow a(1) = 1 + k$

$a(2) - a(1) = a(1)k \rightarrow a(2) = a(1) + a(1)k \rightarrow a(2) = a(1)(1+k) = (1+k)^2$

$a(3) - a(2) = a(2)k \rightarrow a(3) = a(2) + a(2)k \rightarrow a(3) = a(2)(1 + k) = (1 + k)^3$

$\vdots$

$a(t) - a(t-1) = a(t-1)k \rightarrow a(t) = a(t-1) + a(t-1)k \rightarrow a(t) = (1 + k)^t.$ ∎

Our previous notation and effective rate calculation suggests that $k = i$.

Besides the constant effective rate, the compound interest accumulation function (as an exponential) has the property that $a(n + m) = (1 + i)^{n+m} = (1 + i)^n(1 + i)^m = a(n)a(m)$. This property of exponential functions holds for any finite sum of interest periods. We can now establish the validity of the accumulation function for any real value of t. This property is necessary so that we can perform bond calculations between interest dates, especially finding the yield rate from a given quote. It is not always realistic to expect compound interest payments to be made between interest periods, unless the interest is compounded continuously. Simple interest is often the preferred means of computing interest for fractions of an interest period.

Theorem 3.3.2 If $a(t)$ is differentiable for $t \geq 0$ and $a(t+r) = a(t)a(r)$, then $a(t) = (1 + i)^t$ for all real $t \geq 0$.

Proof

Use the definition of the derivative of $a(t)$ and the property $a(t+r) = a(t)a(r)$.

$$a'(t) = \lim_{h \to 0} \frac{a(t+h) - a(t)}{h}$$

$$= \lim_{h \to 0} \frac{a(t) \cdot a(h) - a(t)}{h}$$

$$= a(t) \lim_{h \to 0} \frac{a(h) - 1}{h}$$

$$= a(t) \lim_{h \to 0} \frac{(1+i)^h - 1}{h} \qquad \text{by L'Hôpital's Rule } \lim_{h \to 0} \rightarrow \ln(1+i)$$

$$= a(t)\ln(1+i)$$

$$\frac{a'(t)}{a(t)} = \ln(1+i)$$

$$\frac{d}{dt}[\ln a(t)] = \ln(1+i) \qquad \text{Now integrate both sides on } [0,t].$$

$$\int_0^t \frac{d}{ds}[\ln a(t)] = \int_0^t \ln(1+i)\, ds \qquad \text{Use dummy variable } s.$$

$$\ln a(t) - 0 = t\ln(1+i) - 0 = \ln(1+i)^t$$

$$a(t) = (1+i)^t \text{ for all real } t \geq 0$$ ∎

Shortly we will be able to extend this definition to all real t.

If we are given the accumulation function, $a(t)$, which represents the value of 1 after t measurement periods, what function will discount it to time $t=0$? We are looking for a *discount function*. In simple algebraic terms, $a^{-1}(t)\times a(t) = 1$. Now we apply this to the compound interest accumulation function $a(t) = (1+i)^t$ under the properties of exponents and we see that

$$a^{-1}(t) = (1+i)^{-t} = \frac{1}{(1+i)^t} = v^t.$$

Since $1+i$ is never zero and since we have previously established the validity of $(1+i)^t$ for all real $t \geq 0$, then it is clear that the function $a(t) = (1+i)^t$ holds for all real t. We have established the following theorem:

Theorem 3.3.3 The *present value* of 1 paid at the end of t interest periods invested at a compound rate i per period is $a^{-1}(t) = (1+i)^{-t} = v^t$.

Note: The use of v^n in the context of theory problems has a notational advantage over writing out $(1+i)^{-n}$ each time, but it also can be easily mistaken for $(1+i)^n$.

Example 3.3.1

What current deposit invested at 10% compounded yearly would provide an investor \$1,000,000 for a retirement fund in 40 years?

■ The present value of \$1,000,000 is found as $\$1{,}000{,}000v^{40} = \$1{,}000{,}000(1.10)^{-40} =$ \$22,094.93.

Compound Discount

Since compound interest is merely simple interest computed each period on the previous amount, we can think of compound discount as the repeated discounted value of the previous proceeds. From Chapter 2 we understand that the discounted value of 1 for one measurement period is just $1-d$. In the diagram below this process is illustrated for n measurement periods at a compound discount rate d per period.

TIME LINE DIAGRAM 3.3.1

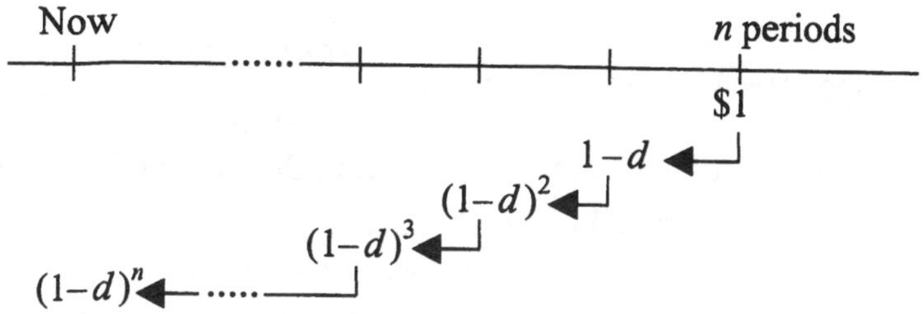

Now ...... n periods

\$1

$1-d$

$(1-d)^2$

$(1-d)^3$

$(1-d)^n$ .....

This shows the present value or discounted value of \$1 for n periods at a compound discount rate of d. In the notation of Sections 3.1 and 3.2 we can write the following:

Present Value: $P = S(1-d)^n$ $\quad [A(0) = A(t)(1-d)^t]$ **(3.3)**

From this formula we can solve for the future value to give the following amount function for a principal P accumulated at a compound discount rate d per period.

Future Value: $S = P(1-d)^{-n}$ $\qquad [A(t) = A(0)(1-d)^{-t}]$ **(3.4)**

There is a theoretical interest in establishing compound discount, and it certainly completes the comparison between simple interest versus compound interest and simple discount versus compound discount. But it is of little practical value in the world of finance. Compound interest is the dominant tool in modern financial transactions, although simple discount is used frequently in establishing yield rates for the sale of short-term financial instruments like treasury bills. Simple interest is still in limited use for short-term notes, and it is used in conjunction with compound interest for fractions of an interest period.

We now address the question of whether the effective rate of compound discount is a constant like we have determined for the effective rate of compound interest. Recall the definition of effective rate given as Definition 2.6.3 in Section 2.6.

Definition 3.3.2 *The effective rate of discount d is the ratio of the interest earned in a given measurement period to the value of the investment at the end of that period.*

For the nth measurement period, let d_n be the effective rate of discount and apply the definition.

$$d_n = \frac{a(n)-a(n-1)}{a(n)} = \frac{(1-d)^{-n}-(1-d)^{-(n-1)}}{(1-d)^{-n}}$$

$$= \frac{(1-d)^{-n}}{(1-d)^{-n}} - \frac{(1-d)^{-n+1}}{(1-d)^{-n}} = 1-(1-d)^1 = d$$

Again, this demonstrates that a fixed compound discount rate implies a fixed effective rate of discount that is the same. Starting with the two assumptions that $a(0) = 1$ and the effective rate of discount is constant, we can also establish the compound discount accumulation function.

Theorem 3.3.4 If $a(t)$ is an accumulation function with $a(0) = 1$ and a constant effective rate of discount, then $a(t) = (1-d)^{-t}$.

Proof

Express the effective rate as a constant: $\dfrac{a(n)-a(n-1)}{a(n)} = k$.

Now use an inductive approach as we did in the proof of Theorem 3.3.1.

$$a(1) - a(0) = a(1)k \rightarrow a(1) - a(1)k = a(0)$$
$$\rightarrow a(1)(1-k) = 1$$
$$\rightarrow a(1) = (1-k)^{-1}$$

$$a(2) - a(1) = a(2)k \rightarrow a(2) - a(2) = a(1)$$
$$\rightarrow a(2)(1-k) = (1-k)^{-1}$$
$$\rightarrow a(2) = (1-k)^{-2}$$

$$\vdots$$

$$a(t) - a(t-1) = a(t)k \rightarrow a(t) - a(t)k = a(t-1)$$
$$\rightarrow a(t)(1-k) = (1-k)^{-(t-1)}$$
$$\rightarrow a(t) = (1-k)^{-t}$$

From our previous discussion we know $k = d$ and $a(t) = (1-d)^{-t}$. ∎

Example 3.3.2

Find the accumulated value of \$2500 after 2 years under the four types of interest if they all are accruing interest at 9%.

■ Simple interest: $A(t) = A(0)(1+rt) = 2500(1+.09(2)) = \$2950$
Compound interest: $A(t) = A(0)(1+i)^t = 2500(1.09)^2 = \$2970.25$
Simple discount: $A(t) = A(0)(1-dt)^{-1} = 2500(1-.09(2))^{-1} = \$3040.78$
Compound discount: $A(t) = A(0)(1-d)^{-t} = 2500(1-.09)^{-2} = \$3018.96$

These obviously are not equivalent rates, and it is apparent that a simple interest loan at a stated rate of 9% is the best situation for the borrower. In order for a simple discount loan to be equivalent to the simple interest loan it would need a discount rate of 8.25%. As a savings or investment program, simple discount shows the best return; however, these discount rate investment options are not available in the real world of finance.

We can now address some relationships using compound interest that we established for simple interest and simple discount in Section 2.6. These relationships are based on equivalent rates (i.e., rates that produce the same return for a given investment and term). For a principal of \$1 and t measurement periods, we can state the equivalence of compound interest and compound discount as

$$a(t) = (1+i)^t = (1-d)^{-t}$$

$$(1+i)^t = \left(\frac{1}{1-d}\right)^t. \qquad \text{Write in fraction form.}$$

$$\left[(1+i)^t\right]^{\frac{1}{t}} = \left[\left(\frac{1}{1-d}\right)^t\right]^{\frac{1}{t}} \qquad \text{Take the } 1/t \text{ power of each side.}$$

$$1+i = \frac{1}{1-d} \rightarrow i = \frac{1}{1-d} - 1 = \frac{1-(1-d)}{1-d} = \frac{d}{1-d}$$

$$1-d = \frac{1}{1+i} \rightarrow d = 1 - \frac{1}{1+i} = \frac{1+i-1}{1+i} = \frac{i}{1+i}$$

Summary for equivalent rates: $i = \dfrac{d}{1-d}$ and $d = \dfrac{i}{1+i}$

These are the same results we got with simple interest and simple discount for the first measurement period. However, with compound interest these relationships between equivalent rates are independent of the number of measurement periods. We previously used the formulas above to establish the following additional properties:

(1) $d = iv$ (2) $v = 1-d$ (3) $i - d = id$ where $v = \dfrac{1}{1+i}$.

It is easy to verify these results by using a specific compound rate like 7% and its equivalent compound discount rate of 6.542056%. To interpret these results in the context of actual financial calculations over several interest periods, we need to broaden our analysis and compare interest I and discount interest D instead of the equivalent rates. The next example will illustrate this for Property 3.

Example 3.3.3

Compare borrowing \$5000 for 4 years at a compound interest rate of 7%(1) to borrowing the same amount for 4 years at an equivalent compound discount rate.

■ Using the formula $d = \dfrac{i}{1+i}$, find d.

$$d = \frac{.07}{1.07} = .06542056$$

■ Compound interest: $A(t) = A(0)(1 + i)^t = 5000(1.07)^4 = \$6553.98$

The loan amount received was \$5000 with $A(t) = \$6553.98$ due in 4 years.

The interest $I = \$1553.98$, due in 4 years.

■ Compound discount: $A(0) = A(t)(1 - d)^t = 5000(.934579439)^4 = \$3814.48$

The loan amount received was \$3814.48, with $D = \$1185.52$ paid immediately and \$5000 due in 4 years.

In illustrating Property 3 we note that $I - D = \$368.46$ and that the compound interest earned on \$1185.98 over 4 years is also \$368.46. That is, $1185.52(1.07)^4 = \$1553.98$.

Example 3.3.4

The interest earned on X for 3 years at compound interest is \$765, and the equivalent compound discount on X for 3 years is \$645. What is the value of investment X?

■ First find the accumulation factor $(1 + i)^3$ by applying Property 3 and the principle from Example 3.3.3—that the accumulated value of the discount is the same as the compound interest.

$$645(1 + i)^3 = 765 \quad \rightarrow \quad (1 + i)^3 = 765/645 = 1.186046512$$

$$X(1 + i)^3 - X = 765 \quad \rightarrow \quad X[(1 + i)^3 - 1] = 765$$

$$\rightarrow \quad X = \frac{765}{1.186046512 - 1} = \frac{765}{.186046512} \approx \$4111.88$$

Example 3.3.5

Suppose that the annual compound rates for 5 consecutive years were 5%, 7%, 7.5%, 8%, and 9.5%. What is the annual effective rate of compound interest that would give the same return during those 5 years?

■ An earlier property of compound interest stated that $a(t+r) = a(t)a(r)$. Apply this to the given 5 years to obtain the expression below.

$$(1 + i)^5 = (1.05)^1(1.07)^1(1.075)^1(1.08)^1(1.095)^1 = 1.421778015$$

$$1 + i = (1.421778015)^{1/5} = 1.072917574 \quad \rightarrow \quad \text{effective rate} \approx 7.3\%(1)$$

We mentioned previously that simple interest is used to compute interest for a fraction of a compound interest period, so simple discount would naturally parallel this scheme when using compound discount. Since the compound interest accumulation function has been established for all real t, it would also be reasonable to use compound interest for a fraction of an interest period. The preferred method would certainly be at the discretion of the institution paying the interest. The following example will confirm that compound discount for part of a period produces slightly less interest than simple discount.

Example 3.3.6

Find the proceeds for a \$2000 loan for 17 months from a bank charging 6%(4) compound discount under the following schemes: **a.** simple discount for a fraction of a period; **b.** compound discount for a fraction of a period.

TIME LINE DIAGRAM 3.3.1

Now	2 months	17 months
		\$2000
P_1 ← $t=2$ m	P_2 ← $t=5$ q	

m = months, q = quarters

■ **a.** $P_2 = S(1-d)^t = 2000(1-.015)^5 = \$1854.43$

$P_1 = S(1-dt) = 1854.43(1-(.06)(2/12)) = \$1835.89$ ⇐ costs \$.05 more

■ **b.** $P_1 = S(1-d)^t = 2000(1-.015)^{5.666666} = \$1835.84$

◀ EXERCISES 3.3 ▶

Concept and Short Answer Exercises

1. Explain the difference between compound interest and compound discount.
2. In the notation of effective interest, what is d_5 in terms of i?
3. In the notation of effective interest, what is i_7 in terms of d?
4. What is the equivalent compound discount rate for a given compound rate of 6.5%?
5. What is the equivalent compound rate for a given compound discount rate of 8.75%?
6. Assuming equivalent rates for compound interest and compound discount, derive each of the following relationships between i and d.

   a. $\frac{1}{d}-\frac{1}{i}=1$ **b.** $i(2-d)=d(2+i)$ **c.** $di^2=\frac{d^3}{(1-d)^2}$
7. Under the assumption of equivalent rates, interpret $(1+i)^n(1-d)^n=1$.

Calculation Exercises

8. If \$1000 invested in the Litchfield Fund was worth \$9000 in 20 years, how much must be invested now to provide X in 30 years, $3X$ in 40 years, and $9X$ in 50 years? Assume that the fund continues to perform as it has in the past.

9. Show that the current values of \$1000 k periods from now and \$1000 k periods in the past are together worth more than \$2000. Assume compound interest.

10. If a \$2500 loan costs 8.5%(1) compound discount, how much interest accrues in the 7th year of the loan?

11. ♦If an investment accrues at compound discount and if the interest earned on X in the 11th interest period is the same as the interest earned on $2X$ in the 4th interest period, what is the compound discount rate?

12. The interest earned on X for 5 years at quarterly compound interest is \$1200, while the equivalent compound discount on X for 5 years quarterly is \$800. Find the amount of the investment X.

13. If I_k is the interest earned in the kth interest period for some amount function $A(t)$, then show that $A(k) - A(0) = I_1 + I_2 + I_3 + \cdots + I_k$.

14. A \$5000 note earning 8%(2) for 5 years is sold 2.5 years before maturity to an investor desiring 9%(2) compound discount. What is the nominal yield rate the original owner made on the note?

15. Find the proceeds for a \$10,000 loan due in 37 months at a compound discount rate of 7%(4). Use simple discount for a fraction of an interest period.

16. Find the proceeds for Exercise 15 if compound discount is paid for a fraction of an interest period.

17. ♦Early withdrawal of a 30-month \$1000 CD earning 6%(2) has two penalty options: first, the rate drops to 4%(2); or second, forfeit 6 months of interest. Which choice is more favorable to the depositor if he cashes in the CD at **a.** 18 months or at **b.** 2 years?

18. An investor has two accounts—the one at Bank X earns 5%(1), and the one at Bank W earns 7%(1). The accumulated value of the two accounts at 16 years is \$3024.09. At 8 years the accumulated value of the account in Bank W is 60% of the value of the account in Bank X. What is the total of both accounts after 10 years?

3.4 Nominal Rates and Effective Interest

Frequently in investment decisions a comparison must be made between two different rates at different conversion frequencies. For example, is 8% compounded monthly greater than or less than 8.25% compounded annually? Expressing both rates on a nominal basis (converted annually) will allow us to compare rates even though they were originally at different conversion frequencies. Based on Definition 2.6.4 of equivalent rates we need an annually converted rate $i(1)$ that gives the same interest earnings as the rate $i(m)$ converted m times per year, where $m \neq 1$. (This definition of an **annual effective rate** sometimes goes by the term *annual percentage yield*, APY. It also is a variation of the definition of the effective rate of interest.) In Chapter 5 we make further use of effective rate calculations to change any compounded rate to an equivalent one with a different frequency of conversion.

In order to derive the annual effective rate formula, we assume that the nominal compounded rate $i(m)$ yields the same future value for $1 invested for one year as the annually compound rate $i(1)$. Equating these eliminates the money and leaves a relation between the nominal and annual rates. Note that the simple interest formula, $S = P(1+it)$, for $t=1$ year gives $S = P(1+i(1)) = P(1+i)$, which is the same as compounding once a year.

Derivation of the Formula

$S = (1+i)^1$ for \$1 invested	compound interest at rate $i(1)$ for one year
$S = [1+\frac{i(m)}{m}]^m$ for \$1 invested	nominal compound rate $\frac{i(m)}{m}$ for one year
$(1+i) = [1+\frac{i(m)}{m}]^m$	Set them equal to each other.
$i = [1+\frac{i(m)}{m}]^m - 1$	Transpose the 1 to the right side.

The Annual Effective Rate Formula (APY): $i = [1+\frac{i(m)}{m}]^m - 1$ **(3.5)**

When using this formula, remember that the value of the *rate per period* comes from dividing the nominal rate $i(m)$ by m, where m is the number of conversion periods per year. Occasionally we know the annual rate and would like to know an equivalent nominal rate. This will require solving the above formula for the nominal rate $i(m)$.

$(1+i) = [1+\frac{i(m)}{m}]^m$	Start at line 3 in the derivation above.
$(1+i)^{1/m} = [1+\frac{i(m)}{m}]^{m\frac{1}{m}}$	Take the $1/m$ power of each side.
$(1+i)^{1/m} = 1+\frac{i(m)}{m}$	Eliminate the power on the right.
$\frac{i(m)}{m} = (1+i)^{\frac{1}{m}} - 1$	Transpose terms to solve.
$i(m) = m[(1+i)^{\frac{1}{m}} - 1]$	Solve for the nominal rate

Example 3.4.1

Find the annual effective rates for **a.** 8%(4); **b.** 8%(12); **c.** 8%(365).

■ On the calculator compute part **a** as .08 ÷ 4 = .02, add 1, use y^x and 4 =, then subtract 1.

a. $i = (1.02)^4 - 1 = .0824 = 8.24\%$

b. $i = (1.006666666)^{12} - 1 = .082999507 = 8.3\%$

c. $i = (1.000219178)^{365} - 1 = .08327757 = 8.33\%$

Example 3.4.2

What nominal rate converted quarterly is equivalent to an annual effective rate of 10%?

■ Use the formula $i(m) = m[(1+i)^{\frac{1}{m}} - 1] \rightarrow i(4) = 4[1-(1.10)^{\frac{1}{4}}] \approx 9.65\%(4)$.

Example 3.4.3

Find the effective rate for 8% compounded daily using Banker's Rule.

■ Banker's Rule says to use exact time and ordinary interest, so we have to use the formula with a slight modification. There is not universal agreement about this modification, because we are applying a simple interest principle to compound interest. Note in the calculation that we use two different values of m. Much of the disagreement comes from the fact that the computation yields a slightly larger value than continuous compounding.

$$i = (1 + \tfrac{.08}{360})^{365} - 1 = (1.000222222)^{365} - 1 = .0844816 \approx 8.45\%$$

We may also calculate the annual effective rate of compound discount. A nominal rate of compound discount $d(m)$ payable m times per year would mean the rate is $d(m)/m$ for each conversion period. Recall that discount interest is payable at the beginning of each conversion period, so we assume equivalence of the present values of \$1 payable in a year using the nominal rate and \$1 payable in a year using the annual effective rate.

Derivation of the Formula

$P = (1-d)$ for \$1 in a year	compound discount $d(1)$ for one year
$P = [1 - \frac{d(m)}{m}]^m$ for \$1 in a year	nominal rate of discount $\frac{d(m)}{m}$
$(1-d) = [1 - \frac{d(m)}{m}]^m$	Set them equal to each other.
$d = 1 - [1 - \frac{d(m)}{m}]^m$	Transpose the 1 to the right side.

Annual Effective Rate of Compound Discount: $d = 1 - [1 - \frac{d(m)}{m}]^m$ **(3.6)**

Sometimes we know the annual effective compound discount rate, but we need to find the nominal rate of discount. Solving the above formula for the nominal rate gives the following:

$$d(m) = m[1 - (1-d)^{\frac{1}{m}}] = m[1 - v^{\frac{1}{m}}] \quad (3.7)$$

It is interesting to note the relationship between nominal rates of interest and nominal rates of discount. In Section 3.3 we established for any measurement period that $v = 1-d$, so $v^{-1} = (1-d)^{-1}$. This allows us to establish the relationship between these two nominal rates.

$$(1-d) = [1-\tfrac{d(k)}{k}]^k \rightarrow (1-d)^{-1} = [1-\tfrac{d(k)}{k}]^{-k} \rightarrow 1+i = [1-\tfrac{d(k)}{k}]^{-k}$$

Also, $1+i = [1+\frac{i(m)}{m}]^m \rightarrow [1-\frac{d(k)}{k}]^{-k} = [1+\frac{i(m)}{m}]^m$ **(3.8)**

Since the relationship between d and i is not dependent on the measurement period, the above conclusion also holds for nominal rates of interest and discount for different numbers of conversion periods per year. If $m = k$ we have the following:

$$[1-\tfrac{d(k)}{k}]^{-1} = [1+\tfrac{i(m)}{m}] \qquad \textbf{(3.9)}$$

Example 3.4.4

Find the nominal rate of discount compounded quarterly that is equivalent to an 8% nominal rate of interest compounded monthly.

■ Use the relationship $[1-\frac{d(k)}{k}]^{-k} = [1+\frac{i(m)}{m}]^m \rightarrow [1-\frac{d(4)}{4}]^{-4} = [1+\frac{.08}{12}]^{12}$

$\rightarrow [1-\frac{d(4)}{4}] = [1.0066666]^{-3}$

$\rightarrow \frac{d(4)}{4} = 1-.98026375 = .01973626$

$\rightarrow d(m) = 4(.01973626) \approx 7.89\%.$

In Section 3.3 we established the property for equivalent rates of compound interest and compound discount that $i-d = id$. In the context of nominal rates of interest and discount, this property would be stated in the following form. (The proof is left as an exercise.)

$$\frac{i(m)}{m} - \frac{d(m)}{m} = \frac{i(m)}{m} \times \frac{d(m)}{m} \qquad \textbf{(3.10)}$$

◀ EXERCISES 3.4 ▶

Concept and Short Answer Exercises

1. An effective rate problem is finding _____.
2. If \$1 is worth \$1.085 in 1 year, use the simple interest formula for i to argue that the effective rate = 8.5%.
3. If \$1 is worth \$1.07632 in 1 year, use the simple interest formula for i to argue that the effective rate = 7.632%.
4. Explain this formula: the effective rate $= (1+\frac{i(m)}{m})^m - 1$.
5. 8%(4) ≈ 8.2432%. Argue that $\$1000(1+\frac{8\%}{4})^{20} = \$1000(1+8.2432\%)^5$.
6. 9%(2) ≈ 9.2025%. If $\$200(1+\frac{9\%}{2})^{20} = \$200(1+9.2025\%)^n$, then $n =$ _____.

Calculation Exercises

7. Find the effective rate to two decimal places of 8% if money is compounded
   a. Semiannually
   b. Quarterly
   c. Monthly
   d. Daily

8. Find the effective rate to two decimal places of 12.4% if money is compounded
   a. Semiannually
   b. Quarterly
   c. Monthly
   d. Daily

9. Find the effective rate for a nominal rate of 12% if money is compounded
   a. Semiannually
   b. Quarterly
   c. Monthly
   d. Daily

10. Find the effective rate for a nominal rate of 5% if money is compounded
   a. Semiannually
   b. Quarterly
   c. Monthly
   d. Daily

11. Which is higher: 7.2%(1) or 7%(4)?

12. Which is higher: 7.2%(2) or 7%(12)?

13. Which is higher: 12%(12) or 12.3%(4)?

14. Which is higher: 12%(12) or 12.3%(2)?

15. How much additional interest would you get on $10,000 for 3 years if money is worth 8%(4) instead of 8%(2)?

16. How much additional interest is earned on $100,000 for 3 years if money is worth 6%(12) instead of 6%(1)?

17. Jamil can get a $5000 loan from two banks. The first charges 9%(4) and the second charges 9.1%(2). If he wants to pay off his loan in 2 years, which bank is better and by how much?

18. Janet can get a $50,000 home improvement loan from two banks. The first charges 7%(12) and the second charges 7.05%(2). If she wants to pay off her loan in 5 years, which bank is better and by how much?

Theory and Extension Exercises

Exercises like 19–23 will not be used further in Chapter 3 but will be used in Chapter 5.They are extensions of the equivalent interest problem and are meant to reinforce that concept.

19. If $1 is worth $1.042 in 6 months, argue that the equivalent nominal rate compounded semiannually is 8.4%(2).

20. Use the logic of Exercise 19 to solve 8%(4) ≈ ___%(2).

21. Use the logic of Exercise 19 to solve 8%(12) ≈ ___%(2).

22. Use the logic of Exercise 19 to solve 8%(1) ≈ ___%(2) if compound interest is used for a part of a period.

23. Use the logic of Exercise 19 to solve 9%(2) ≈ ___%(12) if compound interest is used for a part of a period.

24. Prove property (3.10): $\frac{i(m)}{m} - \frac{d(m)}{m} = \frac{i(m)}{m} \times \frac{d(m)}{m}$, assuming equivalent rates.

25. Use the results of Exercise 24 to prove that $i(m) = d(m)(1+i)^{\frac{1}{m}}$ and explain what this relationship means where i is the effective rate of $\frac{i(m)}{m}$.

26. Express a nominal rate of interest compounded quarterly in terms of a nominal rate of discount compounded monthly.

27. If \$1000 grows to \$1055 in 1 quarter, find the quarterly effective rate, the nominal interest rate compounded quarterly, and the nominal discount rate compounded monthly.

3.5 Finding the Compound Rate

What if we know the present value, the future value, and the number of compounding periods? Can we find the compound rate that connects these values? The compound rate is a growth rate that gives valuable information to those who manage financial and economic matters. The compound rate gives a more realistic view of what happens when assets increase. If a fund doubles in five years, we are tempted to say there was a 100% growth; however, the rate is actually 14.9% compounded yearly. The fund increased 100%, but the growth rate was only 14.9%. Knowing rates of growth becomes important for investments, industrial output, population changes, inflation, wages, and many other financial matters. In other contexts even compounded rates of decrease might be important.

There are two approaches to finding the compounded rate. The algebraic approach gives a formula to use. The second method makes use of the programmed capacity of business calculators. These time value of money (TVM) functions make it possible to compute the rate by simply entering the present value, future value, number of conversion periods, and then pressing the interest rate button. In this section the formula is developed first, and then the TVM method is illustrated.

$S = P(1+i)^n$	compound amount formula
$\frac{S}{P} = (1+i)^n$	Divide both sides by P.
$\left(\frac{S}{P}\right)^{\frac{1}{n}} = [(1+i)^n]^{\frac{1}{n}}$	Raise each side to the $\frac{1}{n}$ power.
$\left(\frac{S}{P}\right)^{\frac{1}{n}} = (1+i)^{\frac{n}{n}}$	Multiply exponents of right term.
$\left(\frac{S}{P}\right)^{\frac{1}{n}} = (1+i)$	The exponent on the right term equals 1.
$i = \left(\frac{S}{P}\right)^{\frac{1}{n}} - 1$	Transpose the 1 and write in formula order.

Compound Rate Formula: $i = \left(\dfrac{S}{P}\right)^{\frac{1}{n}} - 1$ **(3.11)**

The expression on the right can be evaluated using the y^x button on the calculator. Compute $\left(S/P\right)$, enter into y^x, select n, compute $1/n$, evaluate with the = button, then subtract 1.

Example 3.5.1

For a sum of money to double in 8 years, at what rate must it compound quarterly?

■ We do not need to know the sum of money, just that $S = 2P$. Quarterly interest means that the number of conversions periods $n = 8 \times 4 = 32$. Use (3.11).

$$i = \left(\frac{S}{P}\right)^{\frac{1}{n}} - 1 = (2)^{\frac{1}{32}} - 1 = .0219 = 2.19\% \text{ per quarter} = 8.76\%(4) \text{ nominal}$$

Example 3.5.2

If the population of a city increased from 23,480 in 1980 to 42,650 in 1998, what was the annual rate of increase?

■ Eighteen years pass from 1980 to 1998. Since the compounding is annual, $n = 18$.

$$i = \left(\frac{S}{P}\right)^{\frac{1}{n}} - 1 = \left(\frac{42{,}650}{23{,}480}\right)^{\frac{1}{18}} - 1 = .0337 = 3.37\%(1)$$

The preprogrammed functions on a financial calculator will actually compute the rate using the formula we developed. Since we are just putting information into the calculator registers, it is wise to know what the calculator is doing to compute the various time value of money computations. The manual for your calculator explains the functions that it performs and gives examples to study. If your calculator has multiple modes, be sure to put it in the financial mode (FIN). If you have been using the financial registers, then clear them with a 2nd C·CE or C/CE before starting a new problem. This button clears the financial registers and the current entry. See Appendix B for further help with calculators.

Example 3.5.3

If an investment increased from $18,000 to $21,410 in 2 years and 6 months, find the rate of increase compounded quarterly.

■ The number of interest periods $n = 2.5 \times 4 = 10$. If you are computing n or i, most financial calculators want the present value and future value to be opposite signs. Enter the information as follows: $n = 10$, PV = –18,000, FV = 21,410. Compute i. Answer = 1.749999. This is the quarterly rate, so multiply by 4 to get 6.99999 or 7%(4).

Example 3.5.4

A fund increased 85% during the last 5 years. Find the annual compounded rate of increase.

■ If the original principal was P, then the balance in the fund after 5 years is expressed by $S = P + .85P$. By factoring, we find that $S = P(1+.85) = P(1.85)$. Using the calculator, we can let PV = –1 and FV = 1.85, while $n = 5$. The computed annual rate is 13.09%(1).

Example 3.5.5

A fund increased 175% during a 10-year period. Find the semiannual compounded rate of increase.

■ Apply the same method as in Example 3.5.4: $S = P + 1.75P = P(2.75)$. Using the FIN mode, let PV = –1 and FV = 2.75, while $n = 20$. Compute i to get 10.38%(2).

◀ EXERCISES 3.5 ▶

Concept and Short Answer Exercises

1. Compare the rate necessary to mature \$1 to \$3 in 5 years with the rate necessary to mature \$1000 to \$3000 in 5 years.
2. If 8%(2) matures \$1000 to \$1368.57 in 4 years, then 8%(2) will take \$1 to \$_____ in 4 years.
3. On many financial calculators and in Excel, to compute either the number of periods or the rate, how must one enter the PV and the FV?
4. In calculating the rate necessary to mature \$100 to \$200 in 3 years, if the PV is entered as 1, then the FV must be entered as _____ on most financial calculators and in Excel.
5. Give the steps to predict the population of a city in the future, given that you know the population of a city in 1980 was 1000 people and in 2000 was 3320 people. No calculations are necessary.
6. If we use values from 1980 and from 2000 to calculate the rate of growth, why might it be unwise to use that rate to predict a value for the year 2050? What additional assumptions and factors might make the prediction a good one?

Calculation Exercises

7. At what rate converted monthly is \$200 worth \$500 in 4 years? Express the answer as a rate per month and as a nominal rate.
8. At what rate converted semiannually is \$200 worth \$500 in 5 years? Express the answer as a rate per half year and as a nominal rate.
9. At what rate converted semiannually could Debbie double her investment in just 5 years? Express the answer as a rate per half year and as a nominal rate.
10. At what rate converted quarterly could Michael double the value of his college fund in just 3 years? Express the answer as a rate per quarter and as a nominal rate.
11. At what rate converted quarterly could Bertram's bank account increase by 60% in just 2 years? Express the answer as a rate per quarter and as a nominal rate.

12. At what rate converted yearly would a money market account increase by 60% in just 2 years? Express the answer as a rate per year and as a nominal rate.

Use the compound interest model for the predictions in the following exercises.

13. A city grew from 100 people in 1900 to 3400 in 2000. Find the rate of growth. Predict the city population in 2010 assuming the same rate of growth.
14. A city grew from 150 people in 1950 to 1080 in 2000. Find the rate of growth. Predict the city population in 2050 assuming the same rate of growth.
15. Suppose a church budget has grown from $20,000 in 1990 to $35,000 in 2000. Find the percent growth and predict the budget in 2010.
16. The budget of your marketing firm grew from $20 million in 1990 to $55 million in 2000. Find the percent growth and predict the budget in 2040.
17. On the average gas cost $1.85 per gallon in 1995 and $1.35 per gallon in 1997. Predict the cost in 2010. What is wrong with this prediction?
18. On the average gas cost $0.18 per gallon in 1945 and $1.35 per gallon in 1997. Predict the cost in 2010. What is wrong with this prediction?
19. Simplex Algorithms Inc. had sales of $12 million in 1988 and doubled that to $24 million in 2002. When would you predict the sales to be $30 million?
20. A baby weighs 10 lb at 1 month and 20 lb at 4 months. Predict when she will weigh 50 lb.

Theory and Extension Exercises

21. Develop a formula for the rate of compound discount and use it to find the discount rate that will double your money in 7 years.
22. Starting with the answer to Exercise 21 and using the interest discount equivalency relations, develop the formula for the compound interest rate.
23. Find the nominal discount rate compounded semiannually that will accumulate the following invested sums to $2000 in 4 years: $500 current value, $400 in 2 years and $800 in 4 years.

3.6 Finding the Time for an Investment to Grow

Investors, accountants, and financial managers occasionally need to know how long it will take a sum of money to increase a certain percent, maybe even double. If a fund, growing at a certain rate, will take too long to reach the desired future value, the manager may have to look for higher risk with a larger rate of increase. Finding the time for an investment to reach a known future value is only slightly more complicated than simply finding the rate.

The fourth parameter in the compound interest relationship is time, expressed in conversion periods. The fact that n is in the exponent makes the mathematics of solving for n more complicated. To bring the exponent down to the same level as the base requires taking the log of each side of the equation.

We now develop a formula for n, the number of conversion periods.

$S = P(1 + i)^n$	the compound amount formula
$\frac{S}{P} = (1 + i)^n$	Divide both sides by P.
$\ln\left(\frac{S}{P}\right) = \ln(1 + i)^n$	Take the natural log of each side.
$\ln\left(\frac{S}{P}\right) = n[\ln(1 + i)]$	Use the property $\log M^N = N \log M$.
$\frac{\ln\left(\frac{S}{P}\right)}{\ln(1+i)} = n$	Divide both sides by $\ln(1 + i)$.

Formula for the Number of Conversion Periods: $n = \frac{\ln\left(\frac{S}{P}\right)}{\ln(1+i)}$ **(3.12)**

There are three cases to consider when finding the time. These will determine how we give our answer. When we compute the value of n (conversion periods), it will almost always be a decimal fraction requiring the following interpretation.

1. *To the nearest number* of periods will require rounding to a whole number by standard rounding techniques. If the decimal is .5 or larger we round up; otherwise, drop the fraction.
2. *At least* enough periods to reach the amount of the desired future value will require that we always round up. When the decimal fraction is very small, like .01, we can round down.
3. *To the day* will require that simple interest be given for part of a conversion period. We compute the future value based on the whole number part of the computed n, but we use simple interest to take this future value to the desired goal.

Example 3.6.1

To the nearest period, how long will it take \$5500 to grow to \$8000 at 7%(12)?

■ We will compute the value of n with the formula. Substitute the parameters into the formula and do the math. It helps to compute the denominator first and store it. After computing the numerator, divide by the stored denominator. Note that $S \div P =$ 1.454545.

$$n = \frac{\ln\left(\frac{S}{P}\right)}{\ln(1+i)} = \frac{\ln(1.454545)}{\ln(1.0058333)} = 64.42\text{; therefore, use } n = 64. \ (n = 64 \text{ gives } \$7980.46)$$

Example 3.6.2

How long will it take \$2600 to grow to *at least* \$5000 at 6.5%(4)?

■ We will use the TVM registers on the financial calculator. Let i = 1.625%, PV = –2600, and FV = 5000. The rate must be entered as a percent. The answer is 40.5677.

Because the problem said at least \$5000, we round this up to 41 interest periods. If you replace the computed value of n by 41 and compute the FV, it will be \$5034.96. Rounding up gave us \$34.96 more than the desired goal.

Example 3.6.3

Find the time and the date when \$16,000 will amount to \$24,000 if it is invested on June 5, 2004 in an institution that pays 7.25%(4) and allows *simple interest for part of a period.*

■ Make a time line diagram and use it to place the money and dates. Use the TVM registers to get the whole number value of n and use it to move the money forward as far as possible at compound interest. Use the simple interest formula to get the remaining time needed.

TIME LINE DIAGRAM 3.6.1

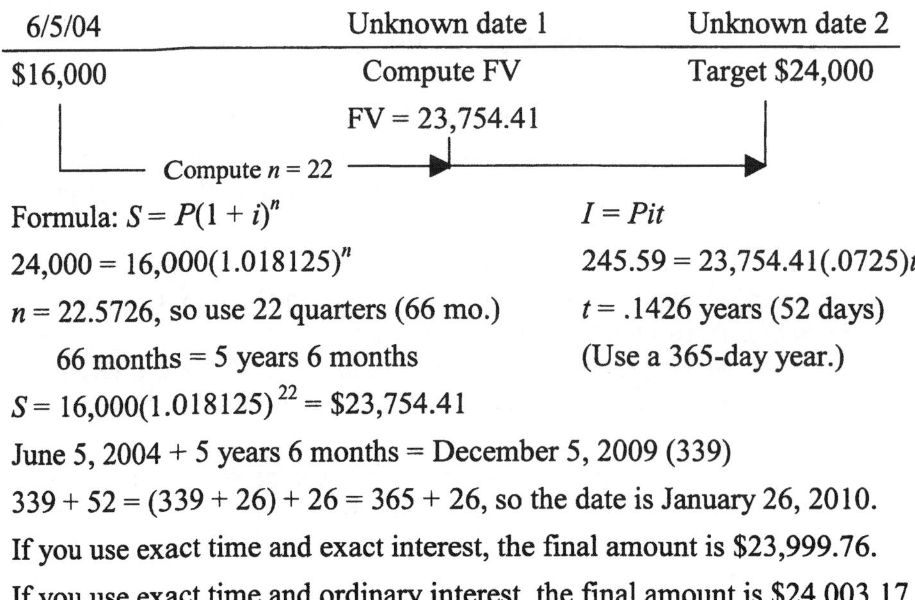

Formula: $S = P(1 + i)^n$

$24{,}000 = 16{,}000(1.018125)^n$

$n = 22.5726$, so use 22 quarters (66 mo.)

66 months = 5 years 6 months

$I = Pit$

$245.59 = 23{,}754.41(.0725)t$

$t = .1426$ years (52 days)

(Use a 365-day year.)

$S = 16{,}000(1.018125)^{22} = \$23{,}754.41$

June 5, 2004 + 5 years 6 months = December 5, 2009 (339)

339 + 52 = (339 + 26) + 26 = 365 + 26, so the date is January 26, 2010.

If you use exact time and exact interest, the final amount is \$23,999.76.

If you use exact time and ordinary interest, the final amount is \$24,003.17.

◀ EXERCISES 3.6 ▶

Concept and Short Answer Exercises

In Exercises 1–4, suppose that the computed value of n equals 19.48 half years for \$1000 to mature to \$3000 at 11.6%(2).

1. $n =$ _____ half years if the problem says to round n to the nearest half year.
2. If no interest is paid for a portion of a period or, equivalently, if you are asked "How long until there is at least \$3000?", then n equals at least _____ half years.
3. If we are using simple interest for part of a period, outline the procedure to find the length in days of the partial period.
4. If we are using compound interest for a part of a period, find the length in days of the partial period.

In Exercises 5 – 8, suppose that the computed value of n equals 39.78 quarters for $300 to mature to $900 at 11.2%(4).

5. $n =$ _____ quarters if the problem says round n to the nearest quarter.

6. If no interest is paid for a part of a period or, equivalently, if you are asked "How long until there is at least $900?", then n equals at least _____ quarters.

7. If we are using simple interest for part of a period, outline the procedure to find the length in days of the partial period.

8. If we are using compound interest for a part of a period, find the length in days of the partial period.

9. If 8.2 months are needed for $1 to be worth $1.40, then how long, at the same rate, will it take $1000 to be worth $1400?

10. If it takes 4.6 years for $2000 to mature to $3500, then, at the same rate, it will take 4.6 years for $1 to mature to _______.

Calculation Exercises

11. How long will it take $1000 to be worth $1388 at 8%(12) if
    a. You answer to the nearest (rounded) n?
    b. No interest is given for a part of a period and the worth is at least $1388?
    c. You use simple interest (Banker's Rule) for part of a period?

12. How long will it take $1000 to be worth $2388 at 8%(4) if
    a. We answer to the nearest (rounded) n?
    b. No interest is given for a part of a period and the worth is at least $2388?
    c. We use simple interest (Banker's Rule) for part of a period?

13. How long will it take to triple our worth at 12%(2) if
    a. We answer to the nearest (rounded) n?
    b. No interest is given for a part of a period and worth is at least triple?
    c. We use simple interest (Banker's Rule) for part of a period?

14. How long will it take to increase our worth by 80% at 12%(1) if
    a. We answer to the nearest (rounded) n?
    b. No interest is given for a part of a period and worth is at least 80%?
    c. We use simple interest (Banker's Rule) for part of a period?

15. Ian and Gretchen will need $20,000 for a down payment on a home. They have $12,000 in their savings account. At 7%(4), how long will it be before they have their down payment? Answer all three ways.

16. Brad and Kathi will need a 10% down payment on a home costing $300,000. They have $20,000 in their savings account. At 7%(12), how long will it be before they have their down payment? Answer all three ways.

17. On June 1, 2002, a college has $100,000 in a scholarship fund. When the fund reaches $250,000, the school plans to start distributing the scholarships. If monies are getting 8% converted semiannually, give the dates that the school can start distributing the scholarships. Answer all three ways.

18. On June 1, 2002, The Heritage Foundation has $100,000 in an endowment fund. When the fund reaches $250,000, the foundation plans to start distributing grants to promising writers of children's literature. If monies are getting 8% converted quarterly, give the dates that the foundation can start distributing the grants. Answer all three ways.

Theory and Extension Exercises

19. Develop a formula like (3.12) for the time in interest periods, but base it on compound discount. Use it to determine how long it takes to at least double your money at 8%(4) compound discount.

3.7 Equations of Value to Find the Unknown

In many financial transactions the obligations and payments must be reconciled to find a settlement payment at some other date. As in Chapter 1, we use an **equation of value**, a mathematical expression that equates the value of several pieces of money at some chosen date called the **focal date**. Finding the internal rate of return was one very significant application. In this chapter the money will be moved to the focal date using compound interest. A well-planned time line diagram will help us write the equation of value. The choice of the focal date determines whether certain pieces of money are moved forward to a future value or moved backward to a present value. However, with compound interest the answers for a problem are the same regardless of the choice of focal dates.

Example 3.7.1

A businessman signs a note for $8500 due in 18 months at 7.5%(4). With some extra income, he makes a $4200 payment after 1 year. How much will he owe on the original due date?

■ Chose the original due date as the focal date and move the payment and amount to that day. The difference between the payment and the amount will be the settlement cost.

TIME LINE DIAGRAM 3.7.1

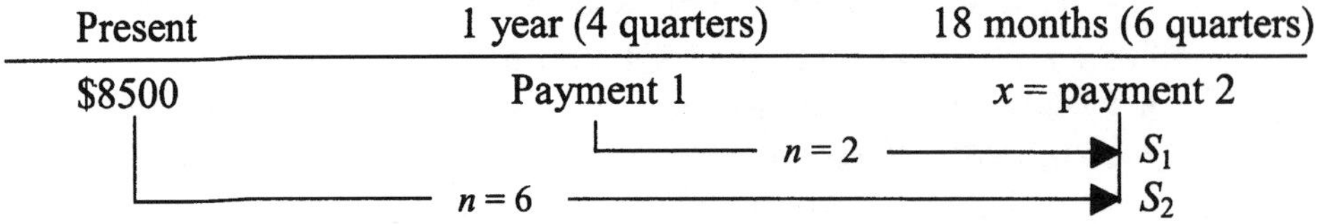

Present	1 year (4 quarters)	18 months (6 quarters)
$8500	Payment 1	x = payment 2
	└── $n = 2$ ──▶	S_1
└── $n = 6$ ──▶		S_2

$$x = S_2 - S_1 = 8500(1.01875)^6 - 4200(1.01875)^2$$
$$= \$9502.21 - \$4358.98 = \$5143.23$$

Example 3.7.2

An estate worth $458,000 is left to two children ages 12 and 16. If the money is invested in a fund paying 5.5%(2), and the two heirs are to receive equal amounts at age 21, how much will each receive?

■ Let an x represent the two unknown payments at their respective dates and let the present be the focal date. There are three possible focal dates, but the present is the most convenient. The number of conversion periods are $n_1 = 2\times(21 - 16) = 10$, and $n_2 = 2\times(21 - 12) = 18$.

TIME LINE DIAGRAM 3.7.2

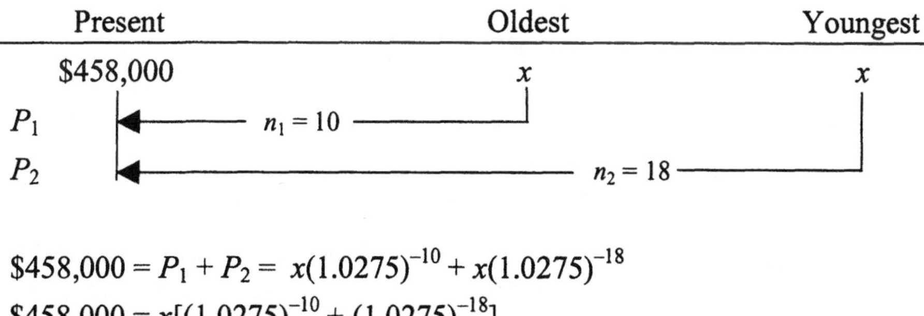

$$\$458{,}000 = P_1 + P_2 = x(1.0275)^{-10} + x(1.0275)^{-18}$$
$$\$458{,}000 = x[(1.0275)^{-10} + (1.0275)^{-18}]$$
$$\$458{,}000 = x(.7623979 + .6136589)$$
$$\$458{,}000 = x(1.3760568)$$
$$x = \$332{,}835.09$$

Example 3.7.3

A business wants to invest in some new equipment that will require an outlay of \$47,500. The chief financial officer (CFO) expects this to bring additional revenues of \$30,000 in 7 months and \$25,000 in 15 months. Find the net present value at 16%(12) and the internal rate of return.

■ Draw a time line diagram with the investment as a negative at the present, then put the two inflows at their respective places on the time line and find their present values at 16%(12).

TIME LINE DIAGRAM 3.7.3

Present	7 months	15 months
–\$47,500	30,000	25,000

$n_1 = 7$

$n_2 = 15$

$$\text{NPV @ } 16\%(12) = -47{,}500 + 30{,}000(1.01333333)^{-7} + 25{,}000(1.01333333)^{-15}$$
$$= -47{,}500 + 27{,}343.55 + 29{,}495.34$$
$$= -47{,}500 + 47{,}838.89$$
$$= 338.89$$

$$\text{NPV @ } 18\%(12) = -47{,}500 + 27.030.80 + 19{,}996.29 = -472.91$$

The interpolation proportion for the IRR is $\frac{d}{2\%} = \frac{338.89}{811.80}$; therefore, $d = .83$ and

IRR $\approx 16\% + .83\% = 16.83\%$.

See Appendix B for finding the NPV and IRR using the TI 83, BA II Plus, and Sharp El 733A.

◀ EXERCISES 3.7 ▶

Concept and Short Answer Exercises

1. Unlike simple interest equations of value the focal date is _____ in compound interest equations of value. (*relevant* or *not relevant*)
2. In equations of value it is helpful to think of money coming to me (inflow) as a positive number and money leaving me (outflow) as negative. Hence one might enter all payments as _____ numbers and all loans as _____ numbers (although the reverse will also work).
3. To analyze before investing, all pertinent information must be valued at _____. Hence NPV and IRR have a focal date at _____.
4. Find the NPV at 15% and the IRR of –\$1000, \$500, \$600, \$400 all one year apart starting at time 0 using either
   a. Your financial calculator, or
   b. An Excel spreadsheet

Calculation Exercises

5. Bruce owes \$10,000 due in 3 years and \$20,000 due in 5 years. At 8%(4) find the single payment that will cover both obligations if that payment is located
   a. Now
   b. In 4 years
   c. In 8 years
6. Repeat Exercise 5 except at 9%(12).
7. Louis owes \$500 on 7/1/02. On 10/1/02 he makes a \$200 payment and on 4/1/03 he makes another \$300 payment. Find his payoff on 7/1/03 at 7% compounded quarterly.
8. Find Megan's payoff on 7/1/04 at 7% compounded semiannually if she owes \$500 on 7/1/02 and on 1/1/03 she makes a \$200 payment and on 7/1/2003 she makes another \$300 payment.
9. Stewart charges \$12,000 on his VISA and makes three monthly payments of \$2000. Steward desires to pay the loan off on the 4th month. Find the payoff if VISA charges 16.9% compounded monthly.
10. Find the payoff if MasterCard charges 12.8% compounded monthly for Marvin, who charges \$2000 on his MasterCard and makes three consecutive monthly payments of \$100. He desires to pay off the loan on the 4th month.

11. A father deposits $7000 on his son's 10th birthday into an education money market fund that has a yield rate of 7%(2). The fund is to be distributed in two equal amounts on the son's 20th and 21st birthdays. Find the two equal amounts.

12. Repeat Exercise 11 except with the fund distributed in 4 equal amounts on the son's 20th through 23rd birthdays. Find the four equal amounts.

13. A mother leaves the $150,000 proceeds from her life insurance to her three children ages 10, 11, and 14. Her will stipulates that each will get an equal amount in the year of their 21st birthday. Find that amount if money is earning 6%(12).

14. A grandmother's trust fund of $250,000 is to be distributed to her grandchildren, children ages 5, 10, and 12. Her trust stipulates that each will get an equal amount in the year they reach 18. Find that amount if money is earning 6%(4).

15. A $2000, 8%(2) note matures in 3 years. In 2 years it is sold to a third party who requires 6%(4) on his money. Find the purchase price and find the ROR for the original holder.

16. A $5000, 8%(4) note matures in 5 years. In 3 years it is sold to a third party who requires 6%(2) on his money. Find the purchase price and find the ROR for the original holder.

17. A $4000, 2-year note is sold in 1 year to a person requiring 7% on his money. Find the proceeds.

18. A $10,000, 5-year note is sold in 1 year to a person requiring 7(4)% on her money. Find the proceeds.

19. Find the NPV at 20%(2) and 25%(2) and the IRR for an investment that requires a $10,000 outlay of cash now to receive an $8000 return in 1 year and a $5000 return in 2.

20. Find the NPV at 20%(1) and 25%(1) and the IRR for an investment that requires a $5000 outlay of cash now to receive a $4000 return in 1 year and a $2500 return in 2.

21. Find the NPV at 20%(1) and 30%(1) and the IRR of an investment costing $500 now and returning $400 in 1 year and $300 in 2.

22. Find the NPV at 20%(4) and 30%(4) and the IRR of an investment costing $500 now and returning $400 in 1 year and $300 in 2.

Theory and extension Exercises

23. An investment of $20,000 now will realize returns of $12,000 in 6 months and $15,000 in 15 months. Write an equation of value in v for the nominal yield rate compounded semiannually.

24. Solve the equation in Exercise 23 to find the actual rate of return.

3.8 Continuous Compounding

When we computed effective interest rates (APY) in Section 3.4, we found that increasing the number of compounding periods per year also increased the effective rate. For example, 5%(4) was equivalent to 5.09%(1), and 5%(12) was equivalent to 5.12%(1). This increase in the effective rate prompts us to ask whether or not the increase in the effective rate will continue. We know that the increase slows down because 5%(daily) is only 5.13%(1). This represents very little change from monthly compounding. So what if we let the value of m in the formula, $i = (1 + \frac{i(m)}{m})^m - 1$, become infinitely large? This limit for m means that interest compounds more often than every second; in fact, we say it is **compounded continuously**. To generate a formula for a continuously compounded effective interest rate, we must somehow evaluate the limit in the following expression for the effective rate. We can then revise our future value and present value formulas.

$$i = \lim_{m \to \infty} \left(1 + \tfrac{i(m)}{m}\right)^m - 1 \qquad \textbf{(3.13)}$$

In trigonometry and calculus the natural log base e is an important irrational number that shows up in many applications of physics and mechanics. Someone familiar with the definition of the natural log base e would recognize our effective rate expression as just a value derived from the definition of e, which is

$$\lim_{m \to \infty} \left(1 + \tfrac{1}{m}\right)^m. \qquad m \text{ is a positive real number.}$$

The following substitutions will give us an expression for the effective rate compounded continuously. A theorem of limits from calculus helps complete the evaluation of the limit: $\lim_{x \to \infty} (g(x))^j = (\lim_{x \to \infty} g(x))^j$.

In formula (3.11), let $k = \dfrac{m}{i(m)} = \dfrac{m}{\delta}$, so that $m = k\delta$. As $m \to \infty$ we see $k \to \infty$.

Substituting gives $\lim_{k \to \infty} \left(1 + \tfrac{1}{k}\right)^{k\delta} = \left[\lim_{k \to \infty} \left(1 + \tfrac{1}{k}\right)^k\right]^\delta = e^\delta$ (limit goes to e).

This leaves us with the *annual effective rate* equivalent to a nominal rate δ compounded continuously.

Continuous Compounding Annual Effective Rate: $i = e^\delta - 1$ **(3.14)**

Example 3.8.1

Find the effective rate for 8% compounded continuously.

■ Express 8% as the decimal .08 and substitute into formula (8.12):

$i = e^{.08} - 1 = 1.083287 - 1$. As a percent, $i = 8.3287\%(1)$.

We easily developed a formula for the annual effective rate at a nominal rate compounded continuously, but suppose we look at this from the opposite perspective. Suppose we desire a particular effective rate for an investment, but we want to know the nominal rate compounded continuously that must be earned. We may also wish to find nominal rates at various compounding intervals that will produce a desired effective rate. Remember, at this point we have used the effective rate as the annual rate that is equivalent to a rate compounded more often than annually. Relating this to Definition 3.3.1, i is the ratio of the interest earned in one year to a beginning principal of \$1.

Begin with the effective rate formula (3.14) for continuous compounding and use the following properties of logs:

$$\ln(M^N) = N\ln(M) \text{ and } \ln(e) = 1 \quad (\log_e e = 1).$$

Solve for δ algebraically:

$1 + i = e^{\delta}$	Transpose the 1.
$\ln(1 + i) = \ln(e^{\delta})$	Take the ln of each side.
$\ln(1 + i) = \delta \ln e$	Use property of logs.
$\ln(1 + i) = \delta$	$\ln(e) = 1$

The formula for the nominal rate compounded continuously that will produce an annual effective rate i:

$$\boldsymbol{\delta = \ln(1 + i)} \qquad \textbf{(3.15)}$$

We will return to this function through a different approach in the next section where the application of calculus in the context of rates of change will broaden the meaning of this concept. In the context of the theory of interest we call this the *force of interest* function for continuously compounded interest, where i is the annual effective rate.

Example 3.8.2

Find the nominal rate $i(m)$ compounded continuously that will produce an effective rate of 8%.

▪ Substitute the effective rate $i = .08$ into formula (3.15).

$$\delta = \ln(1.08) = .07696, \text{ therefore, } \quad \delta = 7.696\%$$

Example 3.8.3

Find the nominal rate i compounded quarterly that will produce an effective rate of 8%.

▪ Substitute into the original effective rate formula and solve for i.

$$i = \left(1 + \frac{i(m)}{m}\right)^m - 1$$

$$.08 = \left(1+\frac{i(4)}{4}\right)^4 - 1$$

$$1.08 = \left(1+\frac{i(4)}{4}\right)$$

$$(1.08)^{\frac{1}{4}} = 1+\frac{i(4)}{4}$$

Therefore, $i(4) = 4\left[(1.08)^{\frac{1}{4}} - 1\right] = .0777 = 7.77\%(4)$.

Note that monthly compounding would yield $i(12) = 7.72\%(12)$.

These results were predictable, since quarterly and monthly compounding do not give as rapid growth as continuous compounding.

Future and Present Value Formulas for Continuous Compounding

We can now revise our future value (compound amount) and present value formulas to reflect the use of continuous compounding.

$S = P(1 + i)^n$ is the amount (or future value) formula in which i equals the rate per period and n represents the total interest periods. Recall that n equals the periods per year times the number of years. For our continuous compounding case, we will always be expressing the time in years (t), since the rate is an effective annual rate. Now we will substitute and simplify.

$S = P(1 + i)^n$	future value formula
$S = P(1 + e^{\delta} - 1)^t$	Replace i by the effective rate and n by the number of years.
$S = P(e^{\delta})^t$	Simplify inside the parentheses.
$S = Pe^{\delta t}$	Eliminate the parentheses for the final form of the formula.

Future Value Formula: $S = Pe^{\delta t}$ **(3.16)**

Example 3.8.4

Find the future value of $4000 invested for 42 months at 8% compounded continuously.

■ Note that the number of years does not have to be integral, because we can express the decimal part of any year and use it in formula (3.16). 42 months = 3.5 years.

$$S = Pe^{\delta t} \rightarrow S = 4000e^{(.08)(3.5)} = 4000(1.323129812) = \$5292.52$$

Example 3.8.5

On June 1 a savings account paying 7%(∞) has a balance of \$3568.25. What is the balance on October 8?

■ To find the part of the year for our calculation we need the number of days between dates. 6/1 is day 152 and 10/8 is day 281: (281 − 152) = 129 days. Therefore, $t = {}^{129}/_{365} = .353424657$.

$$S = Pe^{\delta t} \rightarrow S = 3568.25e^{(.07)(.353424657)} = \$3657.63$$

Our present value formula will follow readily from the future value formula by simply solving for the variable P. Algebraically, we multiply each side by $e^{-\delta t}$.

$$S = Pe^{\delta t} \rightarrow Se^{-\delta t} = Pe^{\delta t}e^{-\delta t} \rightarrow \textbf{Present Value Formula: } P = Se^{-\delta t} \qquad (3.17)$$

Example 3.8.6

How much must be invested now at 9%(∞) in order to have \$8500 in 5 years and 9 months?

■ The time in years will be 5.75 and we want the present value.

Using (3.17), $P = Se^{-\delta t} \rightarrow P = 8500e^{-(.09)(5.75)} = \$5066.07$

Example 3.8.7

What is the continuous compounded rate of return on an investment that triples in 5 years?

■ This calculation requires the use of logarithms, since we are solving for the rate δ, which is in the exponent of the formula. We will take the natural log of each side and then use algebra to solve for δ.

$S = Pe^{\delta t} \rightarrow 300 = 100e^{\delta(5)} \rightarrow 3 = e^{\delta(5)} \rightarrow \ln(3) = \ln[e^{\delta(5)}]$

We use two properties of logs: $\ln(M^N) = N\ln(M)$ and $\ln e = 1$

The last equality becomes $\ln(3) = (\delta)(5)\ln e, \rightarrow \ln(3) = (\delta)(5)$.

Thus, $\delta = \dfrac{\ln(3)}{5} = 21.97\%(\infty)$.

◀ EXERCISES 3.8 ▶

Concept and Short Answer Exercises

1. What does 8%(∞) mean?
2. Which earns more: 8%(12) or 8%(∞)?
3. Calculate:

   a. FV of \$1000 at 8%(∞) for 4 years

b. FV of $1000 at 8%(1000) for 4000 periods
c. FV of $1000 at 8%(10,000) for 40,000 periods
d. Why are they close?
e. Hence you can approximate continuous compounding by doing what?

4. Fill in the blanks to make all of these calculations approximately the same:
a. FV of $100 at 5%(∞) for 10 years
b. FV of $100 at 5%(1000) for _____ periods
c. FV of $100 at 5%(10,000) for _____ periods

Calculation Exercises

Where applicable, use exact time and exact interest.

5. The PC Corporation purchased a $200,000 piece of commercial paper paying 6.5% compounded continuously and maturing in 182 days. What is the value of this investment if held to maturity?

6. Mr. Chapman invests in a $250,000 municipal bond that pays 8% compounded continuously and that matures in 26 weeks. What is the value of his investment if held to maturity?

7. If the PC Corporation in exercise 5 held the commercial paper for 70 days and then sold it in the secondary market to a buyer wanting 7% compounded continuously, what did the seller get for it?

8. In Exercise 6, Mr. Chapman held the municipal bond for 10 weeks and then sold it to Ms. Whittington who wants a return of 10% compounded continuously. How much did Mr. Chapman get for the bond?

9. What ROR on a simple interest basis did the PC Corporation of Exercise 5 make during the 70 days it held the commercial paper?

10. What ROR on a simple interest basis did Mr. Chapman of Exercise 6 make during the 70 days he held the commercial paper?

11. The Bank of Traveler's Rest advertises certificates of deposit with 15 months maturity and paying 6.75% compounded continuously. What is the maturity value of a $5000 CD?

12. The Greer Bank and Trust advertises certificates of deposit with 30-year maturity and paying 7.5% compounded continuously. What is the maturity value of a $5000 CD?

13. Three children ages 8, 12, and 15 are to receive equal shares of their grandfather's estate of $65,000 when they reach age 21. If the money is invested at 7.5%(∞), what amount will they each receive at age 21?

14. Three children ages 6, 8, and 10 are to receive equal shares of their grandfather's estate of $165,000 when they reach age 18. If the money is invested at 7.5%(∞), what amount will they each receive at age 18?

15. An investor put $26,500 into a project that returned $67,850 in 75 months. What was her ROR if it is figured via
a. Quarterly compounding?

b. Continuous compounding?

16. An investor put \$2000 into a project that returned \$3600 in 66 months. What was his ROR if it is figured via
    a. Quarterly compounding?
    b. Continuous compounding?

17. What is the equivalent annual interest rate of 9%(∞)?

18. What is the equivalent annual interest rate of 6%(∞)?

19. What is the equivalent semiannual interest rate of 9%(∞)? [*Hint*: Find the amount of \$1 for 6 months at 9%(∞).]

20. What is the equivalent monthly interest rate of 6%(∞)?

3.9 Theory of Interest—Rates of Change and the Force of Interest

A study of functions involving rates of change naturally leads to calculus, because calculus is the mathematics of change. Calculus studies have traditionally begun with elementary ideas that underlie the derivative, which is an extremely useful concept allowing us to find instantaneous rates of change associated with smooth continuous functions. With the derivative we can maximize and minimize, find rates of change, determine changes in concavity and inflection points, and determine asymptotic behavior. When only the rate of change is known, the associated accumulation function (integral) can be recaptured. This means that the function is actually the definite integral over an interval $[0, t]$. Recall our definition of accumulation function in Section 2.6.

Definition 2.6.1 *An accumulation function expresses the accumulated change in a quantity as the area of the region between the rate of change function and the horizontal axis.*

For example, when a quantity of substance varies directly with the amount of that substance present (like bacteria or compound interest) that quantity can easily be modeled with a rate of change function using the derivative. This function is then integrated to produce an accumulation function, which yields the quantity as a function of time.

Rate of change function: $\dfrac{dA}{dt} = kA$, where A is the quantity of substance

The equation should be read as follows: *The rate of change of A with respect to time t is proportional to the amount of substance A which is present.*

In order to integrate to find the accumulation function, we will separate the variables so that the left side is a familiar integral form:

$$\int \frac{A'(t)}{A(t)} = k\int dt \rightarrow \ln(A(t)) = kt + C$$

Change to exponential form and apply initial conditions.

Exponential form: $A(t) = C_1 e^{kt}$

Initial conditions: If $A(0) = P$ (the principal or initial amount of bacteria), then $C_1 = P$. If the rate k is compounded continuously and t is in years, the result is just like the formula we derived in Section 3.8 for the future value. Other accumulation functions for simple and discount interest were not exponential since their rates of change were not proportional to the amount present.

Our recaptured accumulation function: **amount function:** $A(t) = Pe^{kt}$

Example 3.9.1

If a fund is growing at 9% at time t in years, how long will it take the fund to double?

■ Since we have already solved for the amount at time t, we can write $2 = e^{.09t}$. Now to solve for t, take the ln of each side:

$$\ln(2) = .09t(\ln e) \rightarrow t = \frac{\ln(2)}{.09} = 7.7 \text{ years.}$$

Rates of Change—An Overview

Since accumulation functions arise from the definite integral of *rate of change functions*, it is important to consider several rate of change concepts. The **average rate of change** for a function (or quantity) is the change in the value of that function over an interval. It expresses how rapidly the quantity is changing during that interval. For example, the speed of a vehicle expressed in kilometers per hour gives the change in distance traveled over the interval of an hour. If the function is plotted on a graph, the average rate of change is the slope of a secant line through two points on that curve. If the function is defined as $A(t) = Pa(t)$, then the average rate of change as t goes from a to b becomes

$$\text{Average ROC} = \frac{A(b) - A(a)}{b - a}. \tag{3.18}$$

When we apply the average rate of change to a single unit of time from $t-1$ to t, the denominator reduces to 1, giving

$$\frac{A(t) - A(t-1)}{t-(t-1)} = A(t) - A(t-1).$$

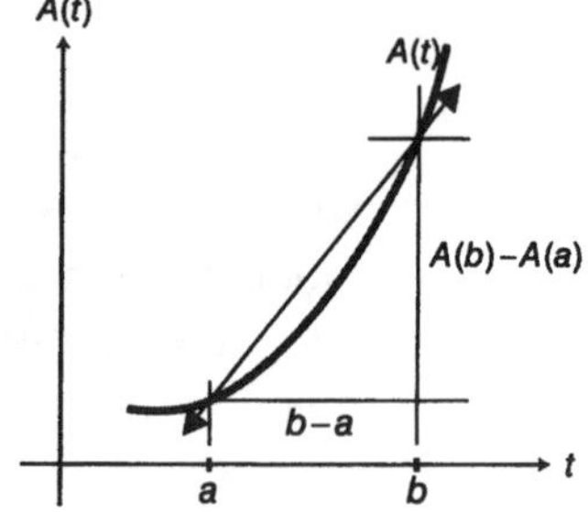

FIGURE 3.2

The change in a function or quantity over an interval divided by the value of the function at the beginning of that interval yields the decimal form of the **percentage change**. The percentage change expresses the amount of the change compared to the base or initial value. In Sections 2.6 and 3.3 this was called the *effective rate* for that interval of time. If an investment of \$100 grew by \$6 during a year, we say it increased $\frac{6}{100} = .06$ or 6%. If the value of the investment at any time t is expressed as $A(t)$, we can write the *effective rate* (i_t) or *percentage change* over one unit of time as

$$i_t = \frac{A(t)-A(t-1)}{A(t-1)} = \frac{Pa(t)-Pa(t-1)}{Pa(t-1)} = \frac{a(t)-a(t-1)}{a(t-1)} \text{ for } t \geq 1. \tag{3.19}$$

The rate of change in calculus typically means the slope of a curve at a point, or the slope of the tangent line to the curve at that point. It is characterized by the derivative. We call the derivative at a point the **instantaneous rate of change** because it expresses the rate of change at a point rather than over an interval. The term *instantaneous* might be construed to mean that the independent variable is always time; however, the variables for a function in an economics problem might be Revenue $R(n)$ and number of items sold n. The speedometer on an automobile gives the instantaneous rate of change as the speed in miles per hour. A one-hour trip of 60 miles would be an average rate of change of 60 miles per hour, but during that trip the instantaneous rate of change may have varied anywhere from 0 to 70 miles per hour.

The usual definition of the derivative of a function $y = f(x)$ at $P(c, f(c))$ is

$$f'(c) = \lim_{h \to 0} \frac{f(c+h) - f(c)}{h}. \tag{3.20}$$

This is the limit of the slope of the secant line through two points on a curve. The result of letting the point $Q(c+h, f(c+h))$ approach the point $P(c, f(c))$ is the slope of the tangent line at the point $(c, f(c))$.

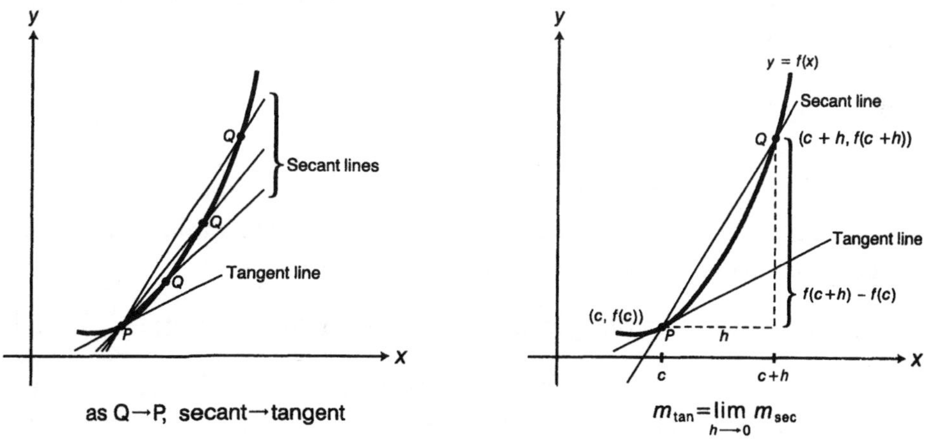

FIGURE 3.3

For our general amount formula $A(t)$, we write the derivative as $A'(t) = Pa'(t)$. The instantaneous rate of change of a function at a point divided by the value of the function at that point gives the **percentage rate of change**. If $A(t)$ is the value of an investment at time t, then we can express the *force of interest* or percentage rate of change in the following way.

Definition 3.9.1 *The force of interest for an accumulation function a(t) is the instantaneous rate of change per unit and expresses the percentage rate of change at any time t.*

$$\delta_t = \frac{A'(t)}{A(t)} = \frac{Pa'(t)}{Pa(t)} = \frac{a'(t)}{a(t)} = \frac{d}{dt}[\ln(a(t))] \qquad \textbf{(3.22)}$$

The beauty of this measure is that it gives the change per unit and makes comparisons more realistic since it does not depend on the amount in an investment. It simply expresses a measure of the intensity of interest at time t. We also saw in the last section on compound interest that the expression $\delta = \ln(1 + i)$ gives the nominal rate of interest compounded continuously.

Example 3.9.2

Find the percentage rate of change for two funds that are both growing at an instantaneous rate of change of \$5000 per month when one fund contains \$50,000 and the other contains \$250,000.

■ The fund containing \$50,000 that is growing at a rate of \$5000 per month has a percentage rate of change of 10% per dollar invested. The fund containing \$250,000 that is growing at a rate of \$5000 per month has a percentage rate of change of only 2% per dollar invested. Using the force of interest gave a much more perceptive view of the change in each fund.

Simple Interest Rates of Change

We can now apply each of the first three rate of change concepts (3.16) to (3.19) to simple interest.

▶ The *average rate of change* for simple interest:

Start with $\dfrac{a(t)-a(t-1)}{t-(t-1)}$. Substitute to give $\dfrac{(1+it)-(1+i(t-1))}{t-(t-1)} = i.$

The numerator is simply the interest earned by \$1 at simple interest for 1 year, while the denominator represents an interval of 1 year and $t \geq 1$.

▶ The *instantaneous rate of change* for simple interest: $a'(t) = \dfrac{d}{dt}\left[1+it\right] = i$

The average rate of change and the instantaneous rate of change (slope) are the same because the simple interest accumulation function is a straight line with slope i.

▶ The *percentage change* for simple interest expressed as a decimal:

$$i_t = \frac{a(t)-a(t-1)}{a(t-1)} = \frac{(1+it)-(1+i(t-1))}{1+i(t-1)} = \frac{i}{1+i(t-1)} \quad \text{(This gives } i \text{ for } t = 1.)$$

Remember that this percentage change expressed as a decimal is also the **effective rate** since it expresses the ratio of the interest earned during a unit interval to the principal at the beginning of that interval. Note that as t increases the effective rate is decreasing asymptotically to zero. In a practical sense, this is not a serious concern since simple interest is seldom used for times beyond two or three years.

Example 3.9.3

Find the effective rates of 6% per annum simple interest for 1, 2, and 3 years.

■ $$i_1 = \frac{.06}{1+(.06)(0)} = .06 = 6\%$$

$$i_2 = \frac{.06}{1+(.06)(1)} = .0566 = 5.66\%$$

$$i_3 = \frac{.06}{1+(.06)(2)} = .05357 = 5.357\%$$

We might conclude that it is not wise to invest money at simple interest.

Simple Discount Rates of Change

We next apply the first three rate of change concepts (3.16) to (3.19) to simple discount interest.

▶ The *average rate of change* for discount: $\dfrac{a(t)-a(t-1)}{t-(t-1)} = \dfrac{d(1-dt)^{-1}}{1-d(t-1)} = \dfrac{i}{1-d(t-1)}$

▶ The *instantaneous rate of change*: $a'(t) = \dfrac{d}{dt}(1-dt)^{-1} = \dfrac{d}{(1-dt)^2} = \dfrac{i}{(1-dt)}$

These first two rates of change do not have significant practical value, but the results do illustrate that rates of change for discount interest depend on the interest interval t. We also see that these rates of change are increasing functions.

▶ The *percentage change* for discount interest expressed as a decimal:

$$\frac{a(t)-a(t-1)}{a(t)} = \frac{(1-dt)^{-1}-(1-d(t-1))^{-1}}{(1-dt)^{-1}} = 1 - \frac{(1-dt)^{-1}}{(1-d(t-1))^{-1}} = \frac{d}{1-d(t-1)}$$

The percentage change is based on the later value since discount is based on future value. We saw this in Chapter 2 when we introduced the basic interest formula: $D = Sdt$. The percentage change is called the **effective rate of simple discount** since it expresses the discount earned (or paid) compared to the amount at the end of the given unit of time. We could also interpret it as the interest earned compared to the returned investment. Note that it is an increasing function.

Example 3.9.4

Find the effective rates for 6% per annum discount interest for 1, 2, and 3 years.

■ $d_1 = \dfrac{.06}{1-.06(0)} = .06 = 6\%$

$d_2 = \dfrac{.06}{1-.06(1)} = .0638 = 6.38\%$

$d_3 = \dfrac{.06}{1-.06(2)} = .0732 = 7.32\%$

Compound Interest Rates of Change

We next apply the first three rate of change concepts (3.18) to (3.20) to compound interest.

▶ *Average rate of change* for compound interest: $\dfrac{a(t)-a(t-1)}{t-(t-1)} = \dfrac{(1+i)^t-(1+i)^{t-1}}{t-(t-1)}$

This simplifies to $i(1+i)^{t-1}$ or $\left(\dfrac{i}{1+i}\right)(1+i)^t = d(1+i)^t$, where $t \geq 1$.

This can be interpreted either as the compound interest rate per period times the beginning value of the accumulation function, or as the compound discount rate times the ending value of the accumulation function. The average rate of change is an increasing function of t. For example, an investment with an average rate of change of 2% for the first compounding period will be 2.69% for the 16th compounding period.

▶ The *percentage change* or *effective rate* for compound interest will be the change per period over the initial value:

$$i_t = \frac{a(t)-a(t-1)}{a(t-1)} = \frac{(1+i)^t-(1+i)^{t-1}}{(1+i)^{t-1}} = (1+i)-1 = i$$

Again, this is the *effective rate* per interest period and shows both that compound interest has a constant percentage change and that the rate per period and the effective rate per period are the same. We should emphasize that for simple interest the *average rate of change* was constant (i), while for compound interest the *percentage change* is constant (i). This is equivalent to saying that *growth* in functional values is constant for simple interest while *relative growth* in functional values is constant for compound interest.

▶ The *instantaneous rate of change* for compound interest: $a'(t) = \dfrac{d}{dt}(1+i)^t$

This derivative has the form $\dfrac{d}{dt}(b^t) = b^t \ln b$, so $a'(t) = (1+i)^t \ln(1+i)$.

Compound Discount Rates of Change

We next apply the first three rate of change concepts (3.18) to (3.20) to compound discount interest.

▶ The *average rate of change*: $\dfrac{a(t)-a(t-1)}{t-(t-1)} = \dfrac{(1-d)^{-t}-(1-d)^{-(t-1)}}{1} = d(1-d)^{-t}$

▶ The *percentage change* for compound discount will be based on the later value $a(t)$ since discount is based on future value.

$$\frac{a(t)-a(t-1)}{a(t)} = \frac{(1-d)^{-t}-(1-d)^{-(t-1)}}{(1-d)^{-t}} = 1-\frac{(1-d)^{-(t-1)}}{(1-d)^{-t}} = 1-(1-d) = d$$

We should recognize this as the result we saw in Section 3.3 under the definition of the *effective rate of discount*. It expresses the ratio of the interest earned in a given measurement period to the value of the investment at the end of the period. We can interpret this as follows: A fixed rate of compound discount implies a fixed effective rate of discount that is the same.

▶ The *instantaneous rate of change* for compound discount: $a'(t) = \dfrac{d}{dt}(1-d)^{-t}$

This derivative is of the form $\dfrac{d}{dt}(b^t) = b^t \ln b$, where $b = (1-d)^{-1} = v^{-1} = 1+i$.

$$a'(t) = (1-d)^{-t}\ln(1+i)$$

Force of Interest for Simple and Compound Interest

We now consider the *percentage rate of change* or **force of interest** for the general accumulation function and for each of the four types of interest. Using the results we have established for the instantaneous rate of change for each of these types of interest, we divide by the value of the accumulation function at time t to get the force of interest at time t.

▶ General accumulation function $a(t)$: $\delta_t = \dfrac{a'(t)}{a(t)} = \dfrac{d}{dt}\ln a(t)$

▶ Simple interest: $\delta_t = \dfrac{a'(t)}{a(t)} = \dfrac{i}{1+it} = d$ for $0 \le t$

▶ Simple discount: $\delta_t = \dfrac{a'(t)}{a(t)} = \dfrac{-(1-dt)^{-2}(-d)}{(1-dt)^{-1}} = \dfrac{d}{1-dt} = i$ for $0 \le t < 1/d$

▶ Compound interest: $\delta_t = \dfrac{a'(t)}{a(t)} = \dfrac{(1+i)^t\ln(1+i)}{(1+i)^t} = \ln(1+i)$

▶ Compound discount: $\delta_t = \dfrac{a'(t)}{a(t)} = \dfrac{(1-d)^{-t}\ln(1-d)^{-1}}{(1-d)^{-t}} = \ln v^{-1} = \ln(1+i)$

We note that the forces of interest for simple interest and simple discount are functions of the time t, so we do not consider them constant, even though they reduce to an equivalent rate (d or i). These equivalent rates for simple interest and simple discount are also functions of the measurement interval. However, the force of interest for compound interest and compound discount are constant and equal. We expect this equality since the effective rates of compound interest and compound discount are constant. We could have constant effective rates with nonconstant forces of interest, but those situations are not particularly applicable to the topics of this text.

We can draw a few other interesting conclusions from the above relationships. In Section 3.4 the following effective rate formula was established for a nominal compound interest rate $i(m)$.

$$1+i=[1+\tfrac{i(m)}{m}]^m$$

Since $\delta=\ln(1+i)$ gives $1+i=e^\delta$, we substitute to give $e^\delta=[1+\frac{i(m)}{m}]^m$.

We conclude that δ is also the nominal effective rate compounded continuously. Likewise for a nominal compound discount rate $d(k)$, we get the equivalent relationship.

$$1+i=v^{-1}=(1-d)^{-1}=[1-\tfrac{d(k)}{k}]^{-k}=e^\delta$$

Example 3.9.5

Find the annual effective rate of interest and the value after 26 weeks for a \$10,000 investment at $\delta=7\%$.

■ $i=e^\delta-1=e^{.07}-1=7.25\%$; $S=Pe^{\delta t}=10{,}000e^{(.07)(.5)}=\$10{,}356.20$

Example 3.9.6

An investment X at 5% simple discount has the same force of interest at time t as an investment Y at 9% simple interest. Find the time t.

■ From the force of interest results we know $\dfrac{i}{1+it}=\dfrac{d}{1-dt}$.

Substitute the rates to get $\dfrac{.09}{1+.09t}=\dfrac{.05}{1-.05t}$. Solving for t gives $t=40/9$.

Example 3.9.7

Show that doubling the force of interest more than doubles the effective annual compound rate.

■ $i=e^\delta-1$, so consider a rate $i^*=e^{2\delta}-1=(e^\delta)^2-1=(1+i)^2-1=i^2+2i+1-1$

So the new rate $i^*=i^2+2i$, which is greater than $2i$ by the positive number i^2.

◀ EXERCISES 3.9 ▶

Concept and Short Answer Exercises

1. Explain the phrase *force of interest.*
2. Using force of interest results, explain why compound interest is more financially reasonable than simple interest.

3. Calculate the force of interest at 3 years and at 10 years for the following rates:
   - **a.** $8\%(\infty)$
   - **b.** 8% simple interest
   - **c.** 8% bank discount
4. **a.** Show the force of interest for $8\%(1) = 7.696\%$.
   - **b.** Hence, show that $7.696\%(\infty) \approx$ ______$\%(1)$.
   - **c.** Use **a** and **b** to give another description of the force of interest.
5. Find an equivalent value of δ for the given rates:
   - **a.** $i = .09$
   - **b.** $d = .09$
   - **c.** $i(2) = .09$
   - **d.** $d(12) = .09$

Calculation Exercises

Using the following two models for amount at time t in years, let $A(0) = \$1000$ and $A(1) = \$1050$. For each model solve for the needed parameters and evaluate for the information at the appropriate times.

6. Model 1: $A(t) = P^{(1+kt)}$
7. Model 2: $A(t) = P^{\left(\frac{1}{1-kt}\right)}$
   - **a.** Give $A(t)$ for the initial investment of \$1000.
   - **b.** Find the value of k based on the first year's growth.
   - **c.** Evaluate $A(3)$ and $A(4)$ and interpret your answers.
   - **d.** Find the growth of the investment in year 4 as an average rate of change and as a percentage change.
   - **e.** Find the instantaneous rate of change at $t = 4$.
   - **f.** Find δ_4 and give its interpretation.
   - **g.** Predict whether i_t and δ_t are growing or declining. Justify your answer.
   - **h.** Prove that model 1 is just another form of continuous compounding.
   - **i.** Use your answers from parts **a** and **b** to do the rest of the questions on a spread sheet (like Excel) for all $t = 1, 2, \ldots, 20$.

Theory and Extension Exercises

8. Develop a formula for $i(m)$ as a function of the force of interest δ.
9. Use your result from number 8 and L'Hôpital's Rule to show that

   $\lim_{m \to \infty} i(m) = \delta$.
10. Develop a formula for $d(m)$ as a function of the force of interest δ.
11. Use your result from number 10 and L'Hôpital's Rule to show that

    $\lim_{m \to \infty} d(m) = \delta$.
12. An investment earning 8% simple discount has the same force of interest at $t = 3$ as an investment earning $i\%$ simple interest. Find the simple interest rate.

13. Which gives the greater force of interest at 270 days: a \$10,000 fund earning 6% simple interest or a \$7000 fund earning 5.5% simple discount?

14. Prove that the amount of money in each fund has no bearing on the answer in Exercise 13.

15. If $m > 1$, place the three measures i, $i(m)$, and δ in order smallest to largest and justify your answer.

16. If $m > 1$, place the three measures d, $d(m)$, and δ in order smallest to largest and justify your answer.

17. Given that $\delta_t = \dfrac{.08}{(1-2t)}$, find an appropriate expression for $a(t)$.

18. Show that doubling the force of interest gives an effective annual rate of compound discount that is less than double.

19. ♦Grace opens a bank account accruing interest at a nominal rate of 8%(2), and at the same time Roger opens an account with a \$2500 deposit at a bank paying simple interest. At the end of 4 years, the forces of interest for these two accounts are equal. Find the accumulated value of Roger's account at that time.

20. ♦At time $t = 0$, \$1 is deposited into each of two investment funds A and B. Fund A accumulates at a force of interest $\delta_t = 3t^2/k$, while fund B accumulates at a nominal rate of discount 8%(2). Find the value of k if the accumulated values of the funds are equal at $t = 4$.

21. One account is accumulating at simple interest and another at simple discount. If their forces of interest are equal at $t = 3$, which account is larger at $t = 3$ if they both started at \$100?

Chapter 3 Summary of Concepts

Compound Interest Future Value: $S = P(1+i)^n$

Compound Interest Present Value: $P = S(1+i)^{-n}$

Compound Discount: $D = S - P$

Compound Discount Future Value: $S = P(1-d)^{-n}$

Compound Discount Present Value: $P = S(1-d)^n$

Compound Rate: $i = \left(\dfrac{S}{P}\right)^{\frac{1}{n}} - 1$

Number of Conversion Periods: $n = \dfrac{\ln\left(\frac{S}{P}\right)}{\ln(1+i)}$

Effective Rate at Compound Interest: $i = (1 + \frac{i(m)}{m})^m - 1$

Effective Rate at Compound Discount: $d = 1 - (1 - \frac{d(m)}{m})^m$

Effective Rate at Continuous Compounding: $i = e^{\delta} - 1$

Force of Interest at Compound Interest: $\delta = \ln(1+i)$

Future Value at Continuous Compounding: $S = Pe^{\delta t}$

Present Value at Continuous Compounding: $P = Se^{-\delta t}$

Chapter 3 Vocabulary Check

Accumulation Factor	*Force of Interest*
Accumulation Function	*Instantaneous Rate of Change*
Average Rate of Change	*Internal Rate of Return*
Continuous Compounding	*Net Present Value*
Conversion Period	*Nominal Interest Rate*
Effective Rate	*Percentage Change*
Equation of Value	*Percentage Rate of Change*
Focal Date	*Rate per Period*

Chapter 3 Skills Check

1. Find the future and present values of given sums using compound interest.
   Section 3.1 Examples 4, 5, 6; Exercises 23, 31
   Section 3.3 Examples 1, 2; Exercises 11, 15
2. Find the effective interest rate for rates compounded several times per year.
   Section 3.2 Examples 1, 2; Exercises 7, 9, 17
3. Find the rate at various compounding intervals to produce the given growth in a fund.
   Section 3.4 Examples 1-5; Exercises 7, 9, 13
4. Find the time for an investment to grow at a given compound rate.
   Section 3.5 Examples 1, 2, 3; Exercises 11, 15
5. Solve equations of value for a given focal date and interest rate.
   Section 3.6 Examples 1, 2; Exercises 7, 11, 13
6. Find effective rates for continuous compounding and the present value or future value of given sums using a continuous compounded rate.
   Section 3.7 Examples 1, 4, 6, 7; Exercises 3, 5, 7, 13
7. Find the effective rates for simple and discount interest for 1 or 2 years and the force of interest at a given continuous rate for a given time period.
   Section 3.8 Examples 3, 4, 5; Exercises 3, 5

Review Test for Compound Interest

1. On 3/1/04 Beth owes \$5000. If money is worth 8% compounded quarterly, find the payoff on her loan if
   a. Beth discharges the loan early on 5/1/03.
   b. Beth discharges the loan late on 12/1/04.
2. What is the equivalent annual interest rate of
   a. 9.2% compounded monthly?
   b. 9.2% compounded continuously?
3. At age 8, Jonathon's dad buys him a \$500, 8% bond.
   a. Find the worth of the bond when Jonathon turns 21 and cashes it in.
   b. How much compound interest did Jonathon's money earn?
4. Find the rate of return compounded semiannually that will make \$2000 worth \$3000 in 3 years.
5. If your firm's outstanding debt grew from \$40,000 in 2000 to \$60,000 in 2005, predict its outstanding debt in 2013.
6. You need \$10,000 for a down payment on your home. You have \$6000 in your savings account on 5/1/04. On what date would this account accrue enough interest to give you the \$10,000 you need if your savings account is earning 4.2%(4) and if
   a. We round n?
   b. We give no interest for a portion of a period?
   c. We pay simple interest for a portion of a period?
7. Marie owes \$2000 on 4/1/05 and another \$5000 on 1/1/06. She made a payment of \$6000 on 10/1/06. Find Marie's payoff on 4/1/07 at 10%(12).
8. Conrad leaves \$200,000 in a trust paying 8%(2) for his two children, ages 6 and 8, with the stipulation that each will receive the same amount at age 18. Find the amount each child receives at age 18.
9. Find the NPV at 15%(2) and the IRR converted semiannually of an investment of \$10,000 that returns \$7000 in 1 year and another \$6000 in 2 years.
10. Find the NPV at 15%(12) and 18%(12) as well as the IRR for an investment of \$2.5 million that brings returns of \$1.1 million in 8 months and \$1.9 million in 15 months.

Chapter 4

Ordinary Annuities

4.1 Future Value of an Ordinary Annuity

Most people borrow a large amount of money to buy a home, and it takes many years to pay back the principal and interest. Because of the size of the loan and the length of the term, lenders require the purchased property to serve as security. A legal document called a **mortgage** is written up and recorded at the county seat in the county where the property is located. Among other things, the mortgage requires the borrower to make a specific payment every month. This payment consists of two amounts: a portion of the principal to be repaid and the compound interest that has accrued during that month. The purchase of an automobile or other real property often requires a contract similar to a mortgage.

People who regularly make payments into a retirement fund or bank savings account have the accrued compound interest added regularly to the deposited principal. (Remember that a retirement fund tied to the stock market may fluctuate with the rise and fall of the market.) Mortgages, savings accounts, life insurance premiums, and credit card debt are all annuities. Other annuities include regular payments of bond interest, income-producing investments like rental property, and preferred stock dividends. An **annuity** is simply a sequence of payments (usually equal), dispersed or received, at equal intervals of time. These intervals of time, or **payment intervals**, are tied to a compound interest rate, and generally the payment and interest intervals match. For example, a home mortgage is paid monthly using a rate that is compounded monthly. The periodic payment for an annuity often goes by the term **periodic rent**. Using the word *rent* indicates that the rent we pay for a house or apartment is also an annuity. Like our previous loans, the life of an annuity is called the term. The **term** of an annuity runs from the beginning of the first rent period to the end of the last rent period.

Annuities can be classified in several ways:

▶1. The first classification deals with the term of the annuity.

Annuities certain begin and end at a set point in time. A mortgage is the best example of an annuity certain. **Contingent annuities** have a beginning or ending date that depends on some event. The payment structure of retirement funds, life annuities [Endnote 2], and life insurance is typically a contingent annuity, because the end of the payments depends on an event. A **perpetuity** is an annuity with a specific starting time but an infinite number of payments. Perpetuities provide periodic income from a sum of money without using any of the principal.

▶2. The second classification deals with the placement of the periodic rent.

An **ordinary annuity** (*annuity immediate*) places the payments at the end of each rent period, and an **annuity due** places the payments at the beginning of each rent period. From a different perspective these annuities are the same sequence of payments but are just valued at different points in time. The annuities to be studied in this chapter will all be ordinary annuities certain. (The actuarial sciences and insurance industry favor the term *annuity immediate* whereas the business and banking industry favor the term *ordinary annuity*. Neither of these terms is especially descriptive of the actual situation.)

▶3. The third classification depends on the alignment of the compound interest conversion periods and payment intervals.

With a **simple annuity** the interest is compounded at the same frequency as the payments are made. With a **general annuity** the payments and conversion periods do not align. The interest conversions may occur more or less often than the payments.

Besides the periodic rent, every annuity also has a present value or a future value, or both. The **present value** is located at the beginning of the term for loans or mortgages. This location makes sense because the borrower receives this "bundle" of money at the start of the loan and the payments occur in the months that follow. The **future value** is located at the end of an annuity's term. This value is important for savings or retirement accounts. Here the saver makes periodic payments that accumulate and earn interest until some future date where the "bundle" is located. The future value of an annuity also goes by the term **amount** (or *accumulated value*) just as it did for the promissory notes, investments, and savings accounts in the previous chapters.

With the preceding basic ideas in mind, we can develop a formula for the future value of an ordinary annuity. We will consider each payment as a present value and find its future value at the compounded rate i per period. Obviously, this approach would be extremely tedious if there were a large number of payments. We are looking for a pattern in order to find a mathematical way to add all the future values without doing a lot of work. First, we summarize the meaning of the symbols used.

Summary of Basic Definitions with Notation

i **interest rate/period**	nominal rate divided by periods per year, $i = \frac{i(m)}{m}$
n **number of payments**	number of payments in the term of the annuity
R **payment**	dollar value of the periodic payment or rent
S_n **future value**	sum of all the payments valued at the date of the last payment

The following time line diagram represents a generalized ordinary annuity with n payments each of value R. The diagram shows how each payment is valued at the date of the last payment using compound interest. When adding these future values recognize that they form a geometric series whose sum is the future value of the annuity.

Geometric series: $S_n = a + ar + ar^2 + \cdots + ar^{n-1} = \dfrac{a(1-r^n)}{1-r}$

The derivation of this formula is at the bottom of the page.

TIME LINE DIAGRAM 4.1.1

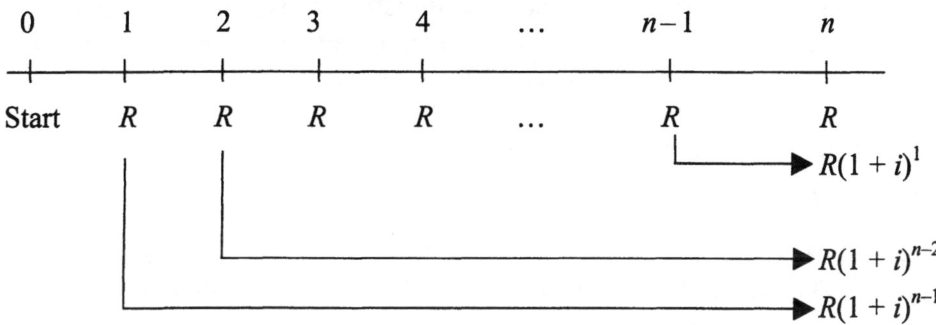

$$S_n = R + R(1+i) + R(1+i)^2 + \ldots + R(1+i)^{n-2} + R(1+i)^{n-1}$$

The first term is R and the ratio $r = (1 + i)$. Substitute into the geometric series formula.

$$S_n = \frac{R[1-(1+i)^n]}{1-(1+i)} = \frac{R[1-(1+i)^n]}{-i} = \frac{R[(1+i)^n-1]}{i}$$

$$\boldsymbol{S_n = \frac{R[(1+i)^n-1]}{i}}$$ **Amount of an Ordinary Annuity (Future Value)**

$$\boldsymbol{S_n = Rs_{\overline{n}|i}}$$ **Compact Notation for the Future Value** **(4.1)**

The notation $s_{\overline{n}|i}$ is read *s angle n at i* and is called the *amount of 1 per period.*

Finding the number of payments for an annuity can be challenging. We learned that when you subtract serial numbers for dates you lose a day. A similar situation occurs when you subtract the dates of the first and last payments in an annuity. Generally, the dates are subtracted using denominate numbers. This is often called date arithmetic. For example, (2008 – 6 – 4) minus (2004 – 3 – 4) gives 4 years and 3 months, which would be 17 quarters or 51 months.

Derivation:
$S_n = a + ar + ar^2 + ar^3 + \ldots + ar^{n-1}$
$rS_n = ar + ar^2 + ar^3 + ar^4 + \ldots + ar^n$ Multiply by r and subtract.
$S_n - rS_n = a + (ar - ar) + (ar^2 - ar^2) + \ldots + (ar^{n-1} - ar^{n-1}) - ar^n$
$S_n(1-r) = a - ar^n$
$S_n = \dfrac{a(1-r^n)}{1-r}$ where $r \neq 1$

If the annuity calls for quarterly payments starting on March 4, 2004, and ending on June 4, 2008, there are 17 interest periods but 18 payments. From a different viewpoint, we can say that between the first and last of 18 payments, there are 17 interest periods.

An even simpler example would place the first payment on January 1 of one year and the last on January 1 of the next year. It is obvious that there is exactly one year or 12 months between them, but the twelfth payment is on December 1, so the last one (on January 1) must be the thirteenth payment. If you build a 100-foot-long fence with posts spaced 10 feet apart, it will take 11 posts. The **Fence Post Principle** says that between every $n+1$ payments in an annuity there are n interest or payment intervals. The denominate number arithmetic always gives the number of interest periods, so applying the Fence Post Principle typically means we have to add 1 to get the correct number of payments. When given an initial payment with its date and a final payment with its date, finding the number of payments will always be an application of the Fence Post Principle.

Example 4.1.1

A man has \$75 per month deposited in his company's credit union. His credit union pays 7.5%(12) on employees' deposits. What will his account be worth in 5 years?

■ We are looking for the future value of 60 payments ($n = 5 \times 12$). The monthly rate $i = 0.625\%$. Using the TVM registers on the EL 733A financial calculator, we will let $n = 60$, $i = 0.625$, PMT = \$75, and compute FV (future value). Before you start, do a 2nd CE (clear) or put PV (present value) = 0. See Appendix B for the TI 83 or BA II.

TIME LINE DIAGRAM 4.1.2

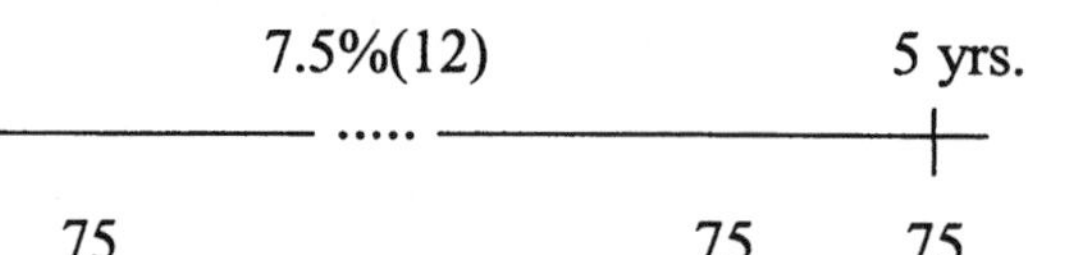

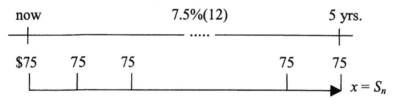

$$S_n = Rs_{\overline{n}|i} = 75s_{\overline{60}|0.625\%}$$

$$S_n = \$5439.53$$

Example 4.1.2

A wise father begins an education fund for his infant daughter by depositing \$125 on March 15, 1986. If he continues to make quarterly payments of \$125 and the fund pays 6%(4), what amount is available when the payment is made on September 15, 2004?

■ Use denominate numbers to find the number of payments. (2004 – 9 – 15) minus (1986 – 3 – 15) gives 18 years and 6 months. The number of quarters is $4 \times 18 + 2 = 74$. Because there is a payment on each of the dates, the Fence Post Principle will come into play, and $n = 74+1=75$. We will use the future value formula S_n (4.1) since we are looking for the amount at the end.

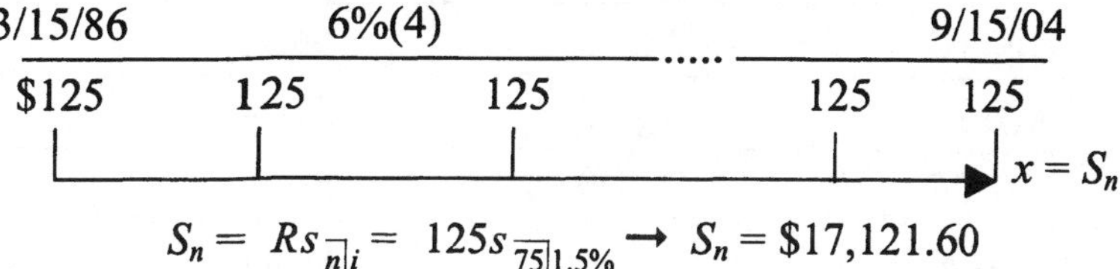

$$S_n = Rs_{\overline{n}|i} = 125s_{\overline{75}|1.5\%} \rightarrow S_n = \$17{,}121.60$$

Example 4.1.3

A man starts an IRA at age 40 by making a $2000 contribution into a mutual fund. If he continues to deposit $2000 per year until his last one at age 65, how much will be in his fund at that time? Assume the stock market yields 11.5%(1) on the long run.

■ The starting and ending ages of the man behave just like yearly dates. The number of years is 65 – 40 = 25, but the Fence Post Principle requires us to add 1, so $n = 26$ payments. Again the future value of this annuity is needed.

TIME LINE DIAGRAM 4.1.4

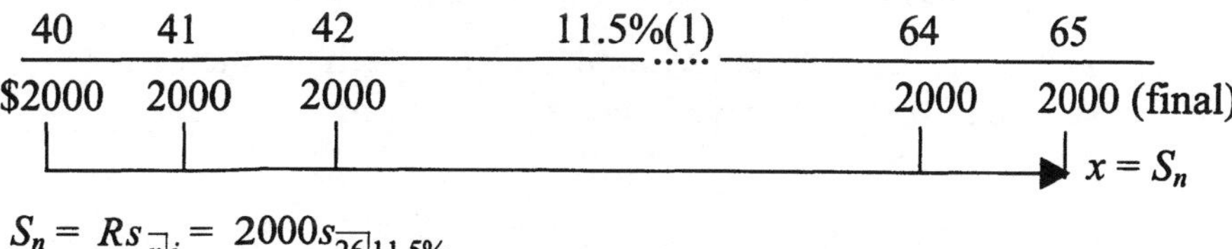

$$S_n = Rs_{\overline{n}|i} = 2000s_{\overline{26}|11.5\%}$$

$S_n = \$277{,}375.59$ available at age 65 (includes the $2000 deposit that year)

◀ EXERCISES 4.1 ▶

Concept and Short Answer Exercises

1. An annuity must have which of the following to be an *ordinary annuity*?
   a. Payment of equal value at regular intervals.
   b. Interest compounding period the same as the payment period.
   c. Present value located one period before the first payment.
   d. Future value located on the period of the last payment.
2. Which of the following illustrates the Fence Post Principle (*fpp*)?
   a. Subtract the first payment date from the last payment date and add 1.
   b. Subtract the PV date from the FV date.

Find n, the number of payments in Exercises 3–13. Each illustrates the Fence Post Principle.

	First Payment	Last Payment	rate = $i(m)$	Number of Payments n
3.	12/1/00	12/1/05	8%(12)	
4.	12/1/00	12/1/05	8%(2)	
5.	5/1/04	11/1/20	9%(12)	

6.	5/1/04	11/1/20	9%(2)	
7.	Age 12	Age 21	5%(1)	
8.	Age 25	Age 65	5%(4)	
9.	12/1/00	12/1/05	8%(4)	
10.	12/1/00	12/1/05	8%(1)	
11.	5/1/04	11/1/20	9%(4)	
12.	Age 12	Age 21	5%(4)	
13.	Age 25	Age 65	12%(2)	

14. If \$100 is invested each year for 5 years and if money is worth 8%(1), then the formula $FV = 100(1.08)^4 + 100(1.08)^3 + 100(1.08)^2 + 100(1.08)^1 + 100$ is equivalent to what annuity formula?

15. If $S_5 = 100s_{\overline{5}|8\%}$, then

a. How many regular payments of \$100 each are there?
b. Each \$100 payment is matured by moving it to the ________ period.
c. All of the values in **b** are ________.

16. Repeat Exercise 15 with the following change: $S_{12} = 100s_{\overline{12}|8\%}$.

Calculation Exercises

17. Find the future value of 3 yearly deposits of \$100 each at 10%(1)

a. Using the compound interest formula three times
b. Using the future value of an annuity once

18. Find the future value of 4 semiannual deposits of \$1000 each at 10%(2)

a. Using the compound interest formula four times
b. Using the future value of an annuity once

19. Find the future value of 20 semiannual payments of \$500 each at 8%(2).

20. Find the future value of 20 quarterly payments of \$200 each at 8%(4).

21. Find the future value of 52 quarterly payments of \$25 each at 6.5%(4).

22. Find the future value of 48 monthly deposits of \$25 each at 6%(12).

23. On Sarah's 10th birthday, her mother deposited \$100 into a savings account earning 7%. Her mother continued such \$100 deposits, making the last one on Sarah's 23rd birthday. At that time Mom withdrew it all for a wedding gift for Sarah. How large was the gift?

24. On Susan's 1st birthday, her mother deposited \$100 into a savings account earning 7%. Her mother continued such \$100 deposits until Susan's 23rd birthday when she made the last one. At that time Mom withdrew it all to help Susan pay for a new car. How large was the gift?

25. Silas has paid \$2000 per year into his personal IRA from ages 30 to 65 inclusive. If his fund is earning 12%, how much is in his IRA at age 65?

26. Aaron and Eppie have each paid \$2000 per year into their personal IRAs from ages 40 to 70 inclusive. If both of their funds are earning 6.5%, how much is in their IRAs at age 70?

Theory and Extension Exercises

27. The Z Corporation needs \$180,000 in 60 months. If they deposit \$2000 per month for the first 20 months, \$2500 for the next 20 months, and \$2000 + R for the last 20 months, what is R if they can invest at 7%(12)?

28. A company needs to accumulate \$$X$ in 36 months. If they deposit \$$R$ the first 12 months, \$2R the next 6 months, and \$3R the last 18 months, find a solution for R as a function of X and $s_{\overline{n}|i}$ where i is the rate per month.

4.2 Present Value of an Ordinary Annuity

The **present value** (or discounted value) of an *ordinary annuity* (*annuity immediate*) is a sum of money at the beginning of the term that is equivalent to the sequence of payments that follow. Any loan repaid with a sequence of payments requires a calculation that uses the present value of an annuity. The money borrowed is the *present value* and the payments made on the loan are the *periodic rent.* Typically, with a loan the amount of money to be borrowed is known and the payment is calculated for a given rate and term. Occasionally the borrower knows the size of the payment he can afford and then must calculate the present value to find out how much he can borrow. Present value calculations have a number of other applications such as income annuities, asset evaluation, the sale of coupon bonds, capital budgeting, and insurance premiums.

There are two ways to find a formula for the present value of an ordinary annuity. First, in a fashion similar to the development of the future value formula, we can find the sum of the present values of the individual periodic payments of the annuity. These present values form a geometric series and can be evaluated by the series sum formula. The second approach is to find the present value of the amount of the annuity as expressed by the future value formula. We will use this method, and, as before, we first summarize the meaning of the symbols used.

Summary of Basic Definitions with Notation

i	**interest rate/period**	nominal rate divided by periods per year, $i = \frac{i(m)}{m}$
n	**number of payments**	number of payments in the term of the annuity
R	**payment**	dollar value of the periodic payment or rent
A_n	**present value**	sum of the present values of all the payments

Time line diagram 4.2.1 represents a generalized **ordinary annuity** (*annuity immediate*) with n payments. Note carefully the location of the present value and future values. The present value is located at the beginning of the first payment period; or, considered another way, it is valued one period before the first payment. The future value is located at the date of the last payment.

TIME LINE DIAGRAM 4.2.1

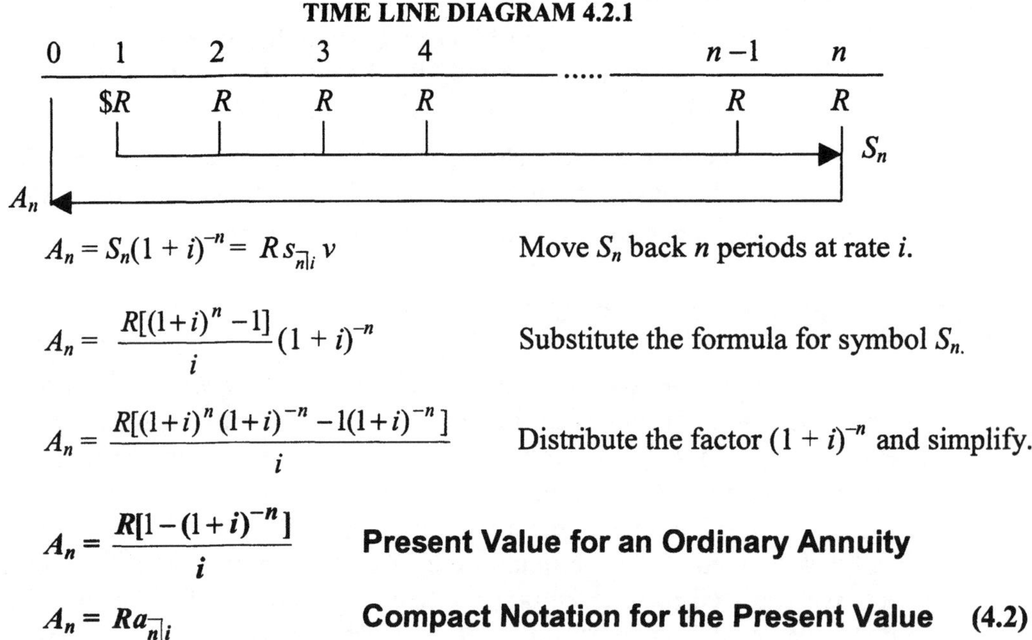

$A_n = S_n(1+i)^{-n} = R s_{\overline{n}|i} v$ Move S_n back n periods at rate i.

$$A_n = \frac{R[(1+i)^n - 1]}{i}(1+i)^{-n}$$ Substitute the formula for symbol S_n.

$$A_n = \frac{R[(1+i)^n(1+i)^{-n} - 1(1+i)^{-n}]}{i}$$ Distribute the factor $(1+i)^{-n}$ and simplify.

$$A_n = \frac{R[1-(1+i)^{-n}]}{i}$$ **Present Value for an Ordinary Annuity**

$$A_n = Ra_{\overline{n}|i}$$ **Compact Notation for the Present Value** (4.2)

The notation $a_{\overline{n}|i}$ is read *a angle n at i* and called the *present worth of 1 per period.* This means that the payment is \$1 each period (i.e., the initial value of the geometric series is 1). We have also shown that $s_{\overline{n}|i}\, v^n = a_{\overline{n}|i}$ or that $s_{\overline{n}|i} = a_{\overline{n}|i}(1+i)^n$.

Example 4.2.1

Find the investment needed on December 1, 2004, to produce a \$1200 per month income starting on January 1, 2005, for 15 years. Assume the average rate of return to be 9.5%(12).

■ Make a time line diagram with the dates and money. The number of payments $n = 12 \times 15 = 180$. The Fence Post Principle does not come into play because there is not a payment at both the beginning and ending dates.

TIME LINE DIAGRAM 4.2.2

12/1/04 1/1/05 2/1/05 3/1/05 ..... 15 yr.

\$1200 1200 1200 1200

$x = A_n$

$A_n = Ra_{\overline{n}|i}$

$A_n = 1200a_{\overline{180}|\frac{9.5}{12}\%} = \$114{,}917.80$

Example 4.2.2

CarMax advertises a vehicle for $2000 down and $400 per month for 2 years financed at 10.5%(12). What is the cash price of this vehicle?

■ Make a time line diagram with the dates and money. The $2000 down payment is a cash value that we will add after we have figured the present value of the payment annuity. The 2-year term with monthly interest will give $n = 2 \times 12 = 24$, while $i = 10.5 \div 12 = .875\%$.

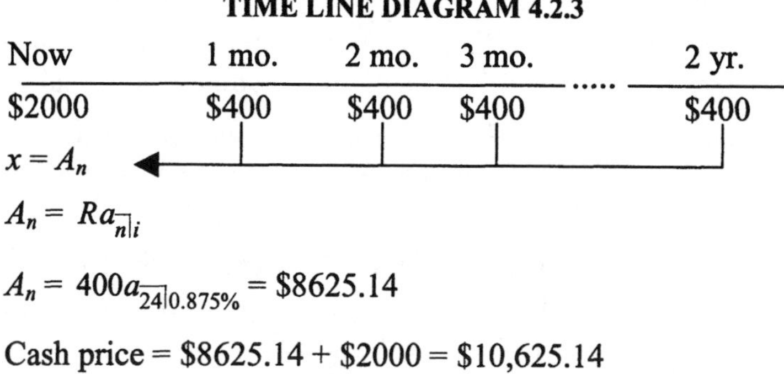

$$A_n = Ra_{\overline{n}|i}$$

$$A_n = 400a_{\overline{24}|0.875\%} = \$8625.14$$

Cash price = $8625.14 + $2000 = $10,625.14

Example 4.2.3

A 30-year mortgage on a home has a monthly payment of $586.75. If this mortgage is sold at the end of the 9th year to a buyer desiring a yield of 14%(12), what did the purchase cost the buyer?

■ In this problem we need to find the present value of the remaining payments. The problem is similar to discounting a promissory note, except the future value is a sequence of payments instead of a maturity value at some one date. There are $30 - 9 = 21$ years remaining, so $n = 21 \times 12 = 252$. The interest rate of the original mortgage is not important, because the buyer wants to find the present value at a rate $i = 14 \div 12 = 1.1\overline{6}\,\%$.

$A_n = Ra_{\overline{n}|i} = 586.75a_{\overline{252}|\frac{14}{12}\%} = \$47{,}588.46$ purchase price (provided it is accepted)

◀ EXERCISES 4.2 ▶

Concept and Short Answer Exercises

1. If a home costs $100,000 and 20% is paid down, how much is financed?
2. If a home has $100,000 financed and $20,000 down, what is the cash price of the home?
3. If a car costs $30,000, the trade-in is worth $5000, and an additional $7000 is paid down, how much is left to be financed?
4. If you buy a car with $8000 down, a $12,000 trade-in, and finance $30,000, how much was the cash price of the car?

Calculation Exercises

5. John is earning enough to pay $500 per month on a house. If the loan will have a term of 20 years at 9%(12), how large of a home loan is John able to get?

6. Francie is earning enough to pay $1500 per month on a house. If the loan will have a term of 25 years at 6%(12), for how large of a home loan will Francie qualify?

7. If for Exercise 5 John has saved $15,000 toward a down payment for a home, what will be the cash price of a home that John can afford?

8. If for Exercise 6 Francie has saved $20,000 toward a down payment for her home, what will be the cash price of a home that Francie can afford?

9. John has found a $120,000 home that he wants. Using the same down payment as in Exercise 5 ($15,000) but changing the payments to $800 per month for 30 years at 9%(12), can John afford this home?

10. Francie finds a $250,000 chalet that she wants. Using the same down payment as in Exercise 8 ($20,000) but changing the payments to $2000 per month for 30 years at 6%(12), can she afford this chalet?

11. Is it better to pay $10,000 in cash or to pay $852.49 per month for a year at 8%(12)?

12. Is it better to pay $20,000 in cash or to pay $1700 per month for a year at 8%(12)?

13. Is it better to pay $400 cash for a washing machine or to pay $20.56 per month for 2 years at 9%(12)?

14. Is it better to pay $4000 cash for a side-by-side refrigerator or to pay $200 per month for 2 years at 9%(12)?

15. Joshua has a home loan on which he pays $660 per month for 15 years at 7.5%(12). What did he borrow for this home? If his down payment were $12,000, find the cash price of the home.

16. Fiona has a home loan on which she pays $1600 per month for 15 years at 6.5%(12). What did she borrow for this home? If her down payment were $30,000, find the cash price of the home.

17. Is it better to pay $1000 cash or $92 per month for 1 year at 8%(12)?

18. Is it better to pay $1000 cash or $92 per month for 1 year at 10%(12)?

19. A home can be very expensive. Suppose Kent has a 20-year loan with monthly payments of $700 at 6.2% compounded monthly.
    a. Find the cash value of Kent's original loan.
    b. If Kent paid $30,000 down, what was the cash value of the home?
    c. If Kent wishes to pay off the loan after 15 years, find the payoff. (*Hint*: He has 5 years of $700 monthly payments left.)

20. Suppose Theodore has a 25-year loan with monthly payments of $1720 at 5.2% compounded monthly.

a. Find the cash value of his original loan.
b. If he paid $200,000 down, what was the cash value of the home?
c. If Tim wishes to pay off the loan after 16 years, find the payoff. (*Hint*: He has 9 years of monthly payments left.)

21. Suppose your folks are paying $500 per month on their new home and they have a 15-year loan with a mortgage company that is charging 7.3%(12).
a. Find the value of your dad's loan.
b. If your dad paid $50,000 down, what was the cash price of his home?
c. Suppose now that your dad has 6 years left on his loan. Find his payoff.

22. Your neighbors, who just bought a new house, are paying $500 per month on a 20-year loan, and the Tennessee Mortgage Company is charging 7.3%(12).
a. Find the cash value of your neighbors' loan.
b. If your neighbors paid $100,000 down, what was the cash price of their home?
c. Suppose now that your neighbors have 8 years left on their loan. Find their payoff.

23. Renee's car loan is costing her $900 per month for 3 years at 2.8%(12).
a. Find the cash value of Renee's loan.
b. If Renee had a trade-in worth $4000 and paid an additional $2000 down payment, find the sticker price of the car.
c. Suppose that after 1 year Renee's loan was sold to Jason, who required 8%(12) on his money. Find the amount that Jason was willing to pay for Renee's loan.

24. Suppose Helmut's car loan is costing him $450 per month for 4 years at 5.8%(12).
a. Find the cash value of Helmut's loan.
b. If Helmut had a trade-in worth $7000 and paid an additional $5000 down payment, find the sticker price of the car.
c. Suppose that after 1 year Helmut's loan was sold to Tamanya, who requires 8%(12) on her money. Find the amount that Tamanya is willing to pay for Helmut's loan.

Theory and Extension Exercises

25. ♦Justin, Demi, and Carlos each borrow $7500 for 6 years at 6%(4). Justin pays back his loan via a lump sum of principal and interest at the end of the term. Demi pays the interest each quarter it accrues and pays the principal at the end. Carlos pays his loan with equal payments at the end of each quarter. Find the total interest paid by the three borrowers.

26. Let the present value of a loan with $1 payments be $a_{\overline{n}|i}$. Find an expression for the sum of the interest paid in period k plus the principal paid in period $k+1$.

27. Derive the formula $Ra_{\overline{n}|i}$ using the sum of a geometric sequence.

4.3 The Periodic Payment or Rent for an Ordinary Annuity

We often know the present value of a loan or the amount of a savings program, and we want to find the periodic payment (or rent). Because of the number of loans transacted in the world of finance, finding the payment may be the single most repeated financial calculation. Besides the tricky little Fence Post Principle, deciding if a problem involves the present value or future value formula can be quite annoying to those learning math of finance.

Certain clue words will indicate that the problem requires the bundle of money to be at the present. Look for the words *loan, cash value, now, estate, money to produce income*, and *selling price*. On the other hand, problems that require the bundle of money in the future will use words like *amount, future value, accumulate, save, balance*, and *settlement*. A word like *payoff* might be either, and it sometimes involves both present value and future value in the same problem.

When using either of the annuity formulas with the TVM registers of the financial calculator, we typically do not solve the formulas for R. The formula is chosen and the parameters of the problem are substituted. The value of R is found by computing PMT on the calculator. When using the exponential formula, it is best to compute the value of the annuity accumulation factor $s_{\overline{n}|i} = \left[\frac{(1+i)^n - 1}{i}\right]$ and then solve for R.

It is interesting to address the question of how the payment to borrow compares to the payment to save for the same amount of money. The relationship can be motivated by comparisons of several cases involving different rates and terms.

Case I. Use 5%(1) for 10 years:	Payment to borrow \$1	= \$0.1295
	Payment to save \$1	= \$0.0795
	difference	$= \$0.05 = .05 \times \$1$
Case II. Use 7%(1) for 5 years:	Payment to borrow \$1	= \$0.2439
	Payment to save \$1	= \$0.1739
	difference	$= \$0.07 = .07 \times \$1$

Using $S_n = \$1$ we have $R = \frac{1}{s_{\overline{n}|i}}$, and using $A_n = \$1$ we have $R = \frac{1}{a_{\overline{n}|i}}$.

The case study above suggests the following relationship: $\frac{1}{a_{\overline{n}|i}} = \frac{1}{s_{\overline{n}|i}} + i$.

The proof follows from an expansion of the right side using the definition. It is left as an exercise.

Example 4.3.1

If a \$150,000 insurance settlement is invested at 8%(12) in order to provide monthly income for 15 years, what will the monthly income be?

■ The key idea that identifies this as a present value problem is that it must produce income. There must be money now (cash) in order to produce income from the investment. Banks will not pay interest unless the money is deposited with them. We will do this problem with the formula instead of the TVM registers.

TIME LINE DIAGRAM 4.3.1

Now ..... 15 years

\$150,000   \$*R*   *R*   *R* = unknown

$$A_n = R\left[\frac{1-(1+i)^{-n}}{i}\right] \quad \text{Use } n = 12\times 15 = 180 \text{ and } i = \tfrac{.08}{12} = .00\overline{6}.$$

$$150{,}000 = R(104.6405972)$$

$$R = 150{,}000 \div 104.6405972$$

$$R = \$1433.48 \text{ per month}$$

Example 4.3.2

An employee wisely chose to have a certain amount per month automatically transferred from his paycheck into a money market account paying 6.5%(12). His goal was to have \$10,000 for a down payment on June 30, 2008. The first automatic deposit was made on September 30, 2004. What would the monthly deposit have to be to reach his goal?

■ Since this is a savings account, we use the future value formula. The Fence Post Principle will come into play since there is a payment on each date. $(2008-6-30)$ minus $(2004-9-30)$ gives 3 years and 9 months. Therefore, $n = 3\times 12 + 9 + 1 = 46$.

TIME LINE DIAGRAM 4.3.2

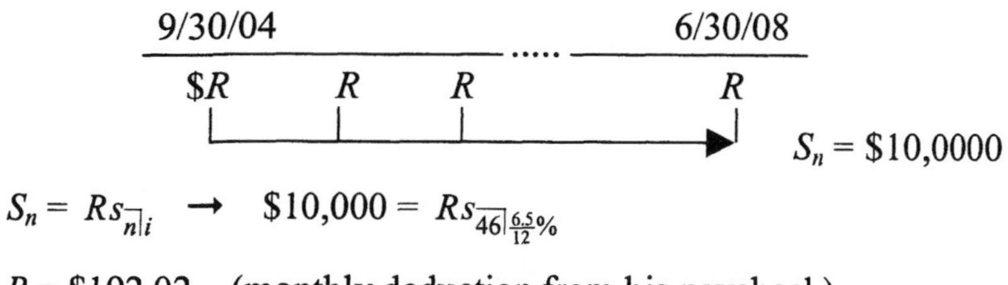

$$S_n = Rs_{\overline{n}|i} \rightarrow \$10{,}000 = Rs_{\overline{46}|\frac{6.5}{12}\%}$$

$R = \$192.02$ (monthly deduction from his paycheck)

Example 4.3.3

A home mortgage for \$86,000 is financed for 20 years at 8.75%(12). Find the monthly payment and the total interest charges over the life (term) of the loan.

■ This is a present value problem because it is a loan for which we know the principal (present value) and need to find the payment. The total interest is the difference between the sum of all the payments and the principal. Remember that each payment includes two amounts: part of the principal and the interest due from the preceding interest period.

$$n = 12\times 20 = 240, \quad i = 8.75 \div 12 = .72916666\%$$

TIME LINE DIAGRAM 4.3.3

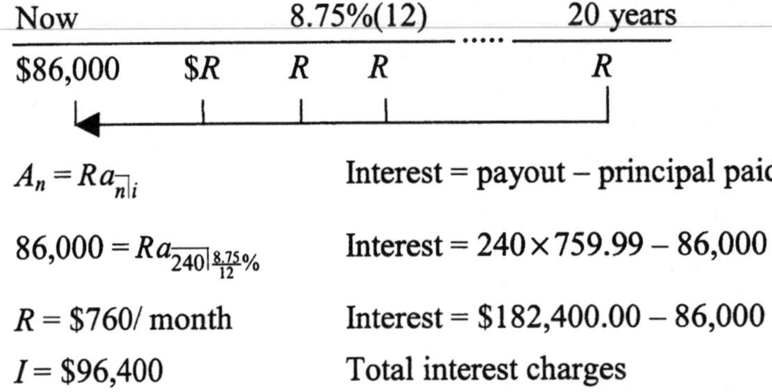

$A_n = Ra_{\overline{n}|i}$ Interest = payout – principal paid

$86{,}000 = Ra_{\overline{240}|\frac{8.75}{12}\%}$ Interest = $240 \times 759.99 - 86{,}000$

$R = \$760/\text{ month}$ Interest = \$182,400.00 – 86,000

$I = \$96{,}400$ Total interest charges

Example 4.3.4

A saver has a long-term investment opportunity that pays 10.25%(4). What quarterly payments will accumulate \$580,000 if the first one is on October 1, 2004 and the last on January 1, 2030?

■ This is a future value problem since we are accumulating assets to reach a future goal. Use denominate numbers to find n. (2030 – 1 – 1) minus (2004 – 10 – 1) = 25 years and 3 months, or 101 periods. Since there is a payment on each date, the Fence Post Principle comes into play and $n = 102$.

TIME LINE DIAGRAM 4.3.4

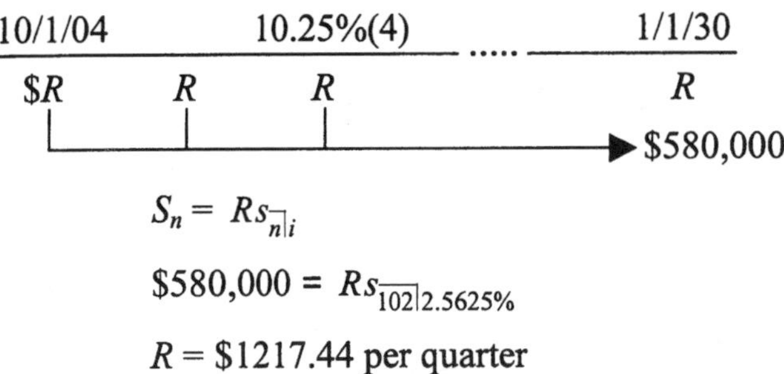

$S_n = Rs_{\overline{n}|i}$

$\$580{,}000 = Rs_{\overline{102}|2.5625\%}$

$R = \$1217.44$ per quarter

EXERCISES 4.3

Payments or deposits will be rounded up to the next penny unless the problem says otherwise. This approach avoids the last payment being a balloon payment (larger than the others). For example, the values \$123.467 and \$123.461 would both be rounded to \$123.47. In Excel this operation is the ceiling function.

Concept and Short Answer Exercises

1. The payment or deposit is calculated to be \$671.4267. You reenter the payment as ______.

2. The payment or deposit is calculated to be \$459.7216. You reenter the payment as ______.

3. Explain the differences in loans and savings accounts for each of these:
   a. The interest
   b. The waiting
   c. The security
4. Assume a $20,000 credit card debt and an effective rate of 15%. What is the minimum yearly payment that will cover the interest? If the yearly payment does not exceed this minimum, what happens to the debt?
5. If the Johansons have an $80,000 first mortgage at 6%(12) and a $36,000 second mortgage for a home improvement loan at 9%(12), then find the minimum monthly payment they can make to cover the interest. If the Johansons cannot make that minimum monthly payment, what can happen to their home?
6. Tell how to use each of the following to effectively lower each payment or the total of all payments:
   a. The interest rate
   b. The down payment
   c. The term of the loan
   d. The payment interval
   e. The price
   f. Tax considerations

Calculation Exercises

7. Within 5 years, Vladimir wishes to save $10,000 for a down payment on a home. What would his monthly deposit be if his savings account is paying 4%(12)?
8. Within 3 years, Jolene wishes to save $20,000 for a down payment on some property. What would Jolene's monthly deposit be if her savings account is paying 4%(12)?
9. Jan borrows $30,000 at 10%(2) for her college education and wants to repay it within 10 years by making semiannual payments. Find the semiannual payment.
10. Max borrows $45,000 at 12%(2) for a nice boat and wants to repay it within 3 years by making semiannual payments. Find the semiannual payment.
11. If in Exercise 9 Jan can find someone to lend her the money at 8%(2), how much would she save per payment and what would be her total savings?
12. If in Exercise 10 Max can find someone to lend him the money at 6%(2), how much would he save per payment and what would be his total savings?
13. Emil is buying new appliances for his kitchen and finds a double oven that costs $800. After a $200 down payment it can be financed over 1 year with monthly payments at a rate of only 1.4%(12). Find Emil's monthly payments.
14. Jurgen is buying a new HVAC system costing $5200. After a $2000 down payment he can finance the rest over 2 years with monthly payments at a rate of only 3.4%(12). Find his monthly payments.

15. Preston is looking at a new motorcycle that sells for $12,500 and decides to save the money rather than going into debt to buy it now. His goal is to have all the money in hand within 3 years. His savings account is paying 4%(12). Find his monthly deposit.

16. Roza is considering a new mountain bike that sells for $3500 but decides to save the money to buy it. Her goal is to have all the money saved within 3 years. Her savings account is paying 3%(12). Find her monthly deposit.

17. After 2 years, Preston in Exercise 15 has a medical emergency and finds that the money saved for the street bike will be needed for bills. How much does he have on hand to pay for the hospital bills?

18. After 2 years, Roza in Exercise 16 decides to use the money for a vacation instead of the mountain bike. How much does she have on hand to pay toward her vacation?

Theory and Extension Exercises

19. A $10,000 loan for 36 months at 6%(12) is arranged for the customer to make payments R for the first year, $2R$ for the second year and $3R$ for the third year. Find the payments for each of the three years.

20. How much needs to be in an education fund on August 1 in order to provide $800 per month for 9 months for each of the following 4 years of college with payments made at the beginning of each month starting in September? Assume the fund earns 5.5%(12).

21. Prove the following relationship: $\dfrac{1}{a_{\overline{n}|i}} = \dfrac{1}{s_{\overline{n}|i}} + i.$

22. If $1 is invested for n periods at rate i per period with interest paid out at the end of each period, find an expression showing that the present value of the interest payments plus the present value of the $1 returned after n periods equals $1. Use the definition of $a_{\overline{n}|i}$ to justify your formula.

4.4 The Number of Payments or the Term of an Ordinary Annuity

Whenever a sizable sum of money is invested to provide a regular income, the number of payments it will provide must be calculated. Retirement accounts, insurance settlements, estates, and the sale of property can all provide regular income. If the income continues without ending, it is a perpetuity since a perpetuity pays out only interest and never the principal. The income will last only so long if the recipient needs a level of income that requires the use of the principal. Knowing the present value and the size of the withdrawals, we can find out the number of withdrawals (payments) and the smaller last payment when the account is closed once the money is gone.

There is a second situation, which requires calculating the number of payments. If both the highest affordable payment and the target sum are known, then the number of required payments can be found. Accumulating a certain sum this way may require a smaller last payment to complete the needed fund balance. On the other hand, the interest accrued during the last payment period may provide sufficient growth so that no smaller last payment will be needed.

When the number of payments is calculated on the financial calculator, the decimal part of the n will give us information about the smaller last payment. If you multiply the decimal part of n times the payment, it will give an estimate of the smaller last payment. The examples will illustrate how the actual last payment is found, so do not use the estimate for anything but an indicator.

Example 4.4.1

From a \$250,000 insurance settlement, a widow wants to take an income of \$3000 per month. If the money can be invested at 10.75%(12), how many months of income can she receive, and what will the smaller last payment be?

■ We know that the \$250,000 is the present value because it is deposited in the bank to produce income. This procedure is like a reverse loan: You give the bank money instead of receiving it, and the bank makes payments to you instead of your making the payments to the bank.

TIME LINE DIAGRAM 4.4.1

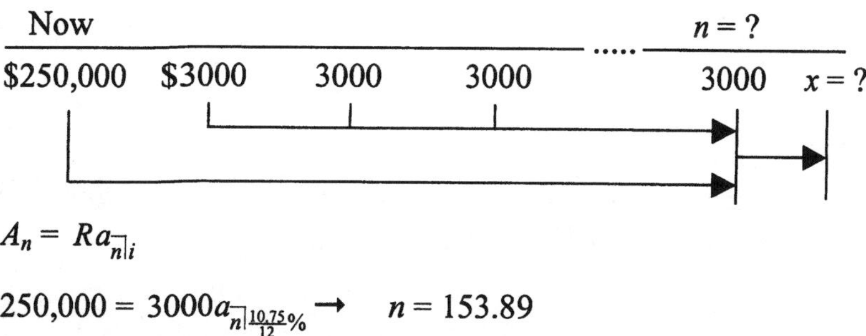

$$A_n = Ra_{\overline{n}|i}$$

$$250{,}000 = 3000a_{\overline{n}|\frac{10.75}{12}\%} \rightarrow \quad n = 153.89$$

There are 153 full-size payments of \$3000 each.

$$x = [250{,}000(1.00895833..)^{153} - 3000s_{\overline{153}|\frac{10.75}{12}\%}](1.008958333) = \$2685.21$$

This calculation is done by entering the whole number of payments 153 for N and then doing a compute FV. The calculator solves for what is in the [ ] brackets; then you multiply by the $(1+i)$ factor to move the balance to the next payment position. Did you check the fractional part of n times the payment as an indicator of the smaller last payment? \$3000(.8946..) = \$2683.95. This fractional part of n gives a very good estimate.

Example 4.4.2

In order to save for an equipment purchase costing \$55,000, a company deposits \$6000 every quarter into a fund paying 7%(4). How many deposits will it need to make before the equipment can be purchased? If the company needs a smaller last payment, what will it be?

■ This is a future value problem because it is a savings account with $55,000 as the future value, a target balance to be accumulated. The smaller last payment problem will require us to do a comparison between the accumulated money and the target value at a focal date one period after the last full-sized payment.

TIME LINE DIAGRAM 4.4.2

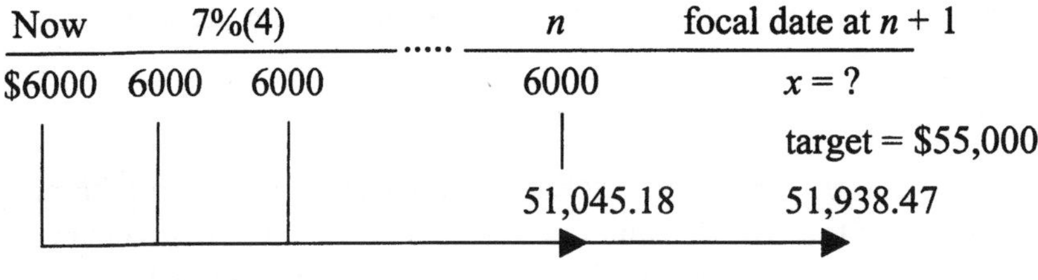

$S_n = Rs_{\overline{n}|i}$

$55{,}000 = 6000s_{\overline{n}|1.75\%}$ → $n = 8.575$ or 8 full $6000 payments (2 years)

$S_n = 6000s_{\overline{8}|1.75\%} = \$51{,}045.18$ at the time of the last full payment (8th)

$x = \$55{,}000 - \$51{,}045.18(1.0175)$ Move the bundle forward 1 period.

$x = \$55{,}000 - 51{,}938.47 = \$3061.53$ the smaller last payment (9th)

Example 4.4.3

A college student withdraws $1500 per month from her $56,000 education fund. If the fund is invested at 8%(12), how many months of income can she expect?

■ Income is being taken from a sum of money, so this is a present value problem. Notice that the value of her fund will not allow her to go to school year-round for 4 years. But if she does not make withdrawals during the summer holidays, her fund can grow during those months.

$A_n = Ra_{\overline{n}|i}$

$56{,}000 = 1500a_{\overline{n}|\frac{8}{12}\%}$ → $n = 43.07$ or 43 months of income

◀ EXERCISES 4.4 ▶

Problems computing the term n of an annuity with a target future value involve three possible cases:

a. Rounding the n to the nearest value

b. Rounding n up to the next whole period on problems where *no interest is posted between periods* or where we desire *at least a certain amount*

c. Letting the whole number part of n be the number of full-sized payments and then finding the smaller last payment or deposit

Concept and Short Answer Exercises

1. When calculating n and the final payment for a loan, the final payment is always needed. But when calculating n and the final deposit for a savings account (sinking fund), the final deposit may or may not be needed. Explain this.
2. The payments must always cover the interest on a loan, but there is no minimum deposit to cover the interest on a savings account (sinking fund). Why?
3. Most financial calculators as well as Excel express their "displeasure" in calculating n when the payment does not cover the interest on a loan. What will be displayed on the screen?
4. Most financial calculators as well as Excel express their "displeasure" at computing n when you forget to make either the payment or the PV a negative. What will be displayed on the screen?

Calculation Exercises

5. How many quarters will it take a deposit of $100 per quarter to accumulate to $5000 at 6%(4) if we
   a. Round to the nearest quarter?
   b. Get no interest for part of a quarter—hence at least $5000?
   c. Compute the number of full $100 deposits and find the final deposit?
6. How many half-years will it take a deposit of $300 per half-year to accumulate to $5000 at 6%(2) if we
   a. Round to the nearest half-year?
   b. Get no interest for part of a half-year—hence at least $5000?
   c. Compute the number of full $300 deposits and find the final deposit?
7. How many months of $200 payments will be needed to retire a MasterCard™ debt of $5020.40 at 12.3%(12)? Answer all three ways.
8. How many months of $500 payments will be needed to retire a VISA™ card debt of $5020.40 at 12.3%(12)? Answer all three ways.
9. How long will it take parents who are depositing $25 per month into a trust fund earning 5.1%(12) to accumulate the $10,000 needed for their 10-year-old daughter's schooling?
10. How long will it take a business that is depositing $250 per month into a sinking fund earning 5.1%(12) to accumulate $10,000 needed for a business expansion?
11. Since the time calculated in Exercise 9 is a little long, act as a financial planner for the family and set up a monthly deposit plan that will have the necessary money by the time the daughter is 18 if they start when she is 10.
12. For Exercise 10 act as a financial planner for that business and set up a monthly deposit plan that will have the necessary money within 15 months.
13. The settlement on a $150,000 life insurance policy is invested at 8.5%(12). How many $2500 monthly payments could the beneficiary expect to receive from this bequest? What will the smaller last payment be?

14. The settlement on a workman's compensation policy of $1,000,000 is invested at 6.5%(1). How many $200,000 yearly payments could the beneficiary expect to receive from this settlement? What will the smaller last payment be?

15. A prospective homeowner assumes a $68,540 mortgage at 7.75%(12) by agreeing to pay $700 per month. How many $700 payments will he need to make and what will the last smaller payment be?

16. A family assumes an $80,000 mortgage at 7%(12) by agreeing to pay $1000 per month. How many $1000 payments will they need to make and what will their last smaller payment be?

17. A small businessman has $50,000 for a down payment and can afford payments of $2500 per month. How long will it take the businessman to pay off a $250,000 building at 12% converted monthly?

18. An executive has $100,000 for a down payment and can afford $2000-per-month house payments. How long will it take her to pay off a $250,000 home at 8% converted monthly?

19. How long would it take you to accumulate $3600 by depositing $150 every 6 months at 5% compounded semiannually?

20. How long would it take Kathy to accumulate $5000 by depositing $500 every 6 months at 5% compounded semiannually?

21. A university receives an endowment of $2.5 million and invests it at 6.5%(1) for a scholarship fund. For how many years will the fund provide $192,000 per year for scholarships if the first ones are paid out 1 year after the fund is started? After the last year of full scholarships, how much money is left over for partial scholarships to be granted the next year?

22. A university receives an endowment of $5 million that it invests at 8.5%(1) in a scholarship fund. For how many years will the fund provide $200,000 per year for scholarships if the first ones are paid out 1 year after the fund is started? After the last year of full scholarships, how much money is left over for partial scholarships to be granted the next year?

Theory and Extension Exercises

23. If a college student has $56,000 in her education fund on September 1 of her freshman year, find her monthly income from this fund under the following set of conditions: The fund is earning 6%(12), she only takes income from the fund from September 1 to May 1 of each school year, and she attends college 4 years prior to graduating.

24. Éomer is preparing for retirement and wants to deposit $\$X$ per month at a rate i per month for n years. In turn he wants to withdraw $\$6X$ per month at the same rate for n years. For how many years will he need to make his deposit? If he can invest at 6%(12), how many years of deposits will he need to make?

25. Éowyn wishes to withdraw $\$X/24$ per month from an account with a present worth of $\$X$. How many months of income can she receive and what will the smaller last payment be if the fund earns 8%(12)?

4.5 The Interest Rate of an Ordinary Annuity

To this point we have been able to calculate the future value, present value, payment, and number of payments when the other parameters are known. But we still need to find the interest rate at which an annuity is compounding interest. Knowing the rate of an annuity provides a realistic way to compare different investments or loan rates. Many lending agencies advertise sums that can be borrowed along with the required payment and term, but they do not bother to tell their interest rates. When loan papers are finally processed, the truth-in-lending law requires that the true annual percentage rate be given. However, long before a loan ever reaches the stage of signing papers, a knowledgeable person can quickly calculate the actual rate.

We have already found that rates of return on a simple interest or discount basis are quite useful in making judgments about investments and capital expenditures. Since many investments give periodic returns that are annuities, it will be valuable to discern the rate of return for making financial decisions.

The value of i in the annuity formulas does not have an algebraic solution, because in the FV factor $s_{\overline{n}|i} = \left[\frac{(1+i)^n - 1}{i}\right]$ the i is in both the exponential term and the denominator. Without the power of the financial calculator, the only simple method of solving for i is by interpolation. Calculators use an iterative method that gives accurate results, but expect some calculators to take a little while to get the answer.

Example 4.5.1

A financial institution advertises an annuity that costs $150,000 and gives a quarterly return of $5500 for 10 years. What is the nominal rate of return compounded quarterly?

■ This is a present value problem because you are depositing $150,000 with the institution and receiving income in subsequent years. Note that $n = 10 \times 4 = 40$ payments.

$$A_n = Ra_{\overline{n}|i} \quad \rightarrow \quad 150{,}000 = 5500a_{\overline{40}|i} \quad \rightarrow \quad i = 2.01728703\%$$

Since i is the quarterly rate, multiply by 4.

$i(4) = 4(2.01728703) \approx 8.069\%(4)$

Example 4.5.2

A life insurance company offers a 20-year $100,000 paid-up policy for $3250 per year. The same company, as well as its competitors, sells $100,000 of term insurance at the same age bracket for $225 per year. What is the company's nominal rate of return on deposits?

■ The paid-up policy will be worth $100,000 in 20 years, so this is a future value problem. Since the company also sells term insurance, which has no cash-value after 20 years, the difference in the two premiums represents the periodic charge or payment for the "savings" account that grows to $100,000 in 20 years.

$$S_n = Rs_{\overline{n}|i}$$

$$100{,}000 = 3025s_{\overline{20}|i}$$

$$i = i(1) = 4.998\% \approx 5\%$$

◀ EXERCISES 4.5 ▶

Concept and Short Answer Exercises

1. In computing $i\%(m)$ on a loan of \$1000 with 12 monthly payments of \$100, show how each value is entered in many calculators and in Excel.

   Rate _____ PV _____ FV _____ PMT _____ Term _____

2. In Exercise 1, $i = 2.922854\%$. $i\%(m)$ is found by multiplying i by ___.
3. In computing $i\%(m)$ on a savings account of \$1000 with 4 semiannual deposits of \$200, show how each value is entered in many calculators and in Excel.

   Rate _____ PV _____ FV _____ PMT _____ Term _____

4. In Exercise 3, $i = 15.0911\%$. $i\%(m)$ is found by multiplying i by ___.

Calculation Exercises

Give answers as rate per period and as a nominal rate to two decimal places.

5. At what rate of interest will \$100 per month be worth \$3000 in 2 years?
6. At what rate of interest will \$100 per month be worth \$2500 in 2 years?
7. At what rate of interest will \$100 per month pay off a loan of \$2000 in 2 years?
8. At what rate of interest will \$600 per half-year satisfy a loan of \$2000 in 2 years?
9. If Nienna buys a \$10,000 car by making two \$6000 semiannual payments, what is the rate she is being charged?
10. If I buy a \$10,000 car by making 24 \$500 monthly payments, what is the rate I am being charged?
11. If Manney can save \$12,000 over 2 years by depositing \$1300 per quarter, what rate of return is he getting?
12. If you can accumulate \$10,000 over 2 years by investing \$1000 per quarter, what rate of return are you getting?
13. A washer and dryer set that costs \$1055.20 can be bought with nothing down and \$50 per month for 2 years. Is this a good deal if the bank will lend you money on an unsecured note at 10%?
14. A \$30,000 car can be bought with 20% down, a \$5000 trade-in, and a loan requiring \$600 per month for 3 years. Find the APR of the loan.
15. A man invests \$20,000 in the Roof Clean Corp. For his investment he gets a \$6000 annual return for each of the next 4 years. Find his ROR.

16. A young couple saved the 15% down payment on their new $150,000 home by making $300 monthly deposits over the last 5 years. Find the rate their investment account is paying.

17. Luba has $5000 in a savings account that pays 3.4%(4). In 5 years she anticipates doing a $30,000 addition to her home. Hence she deposits $350 a month into a money market fund to cover the rest of what the savings account does not cover. Find the ROR on the money market.

18. Many financial advisors promote the 70% rule for retirement: your yearly retirement income needs to be at least 70% of the average of your last five years of full time work. To achieve that goal Nicole feels she will need to save an additional $200,000 by age 65. At age 51 she begins to deposit $9000 per year into a savings account. Find the APR necessary for Nicole to reach her goal at age 65.

19. Kyla's wedding will be in a year and a half. Her father plans to save $800 per month in a money market account to fund the $15,000 event. What ROR is her father getting in this account?

20. A $100,000 whole life insurance policy has a cash value of $50,000 after 40 years and an annual premium of $1050. The same company will sell the same individual a 40-year guaranteed $100,000 term policy for $325 per year. What is the nominal rate of return this insurance company is paying?

Theory and Extension Exercises

21. An investor needs $28,000 in 8 years to meet an obligation. He plans to deposit $2000 per year for 5 years and $3000 per year for the last 3 years. What rate of return will he need in order to meet his obligation?

22. Jean Paul finds a lender who will advance him $2600 to be repaid with 5 quarterly payments of $1000, $800, $600, $400, $200. Find the quarterly rate and the nominal rate he is paying.

23. Suppose the lender in Exercise 22 agrees for Jean Paul to repay the loan with 5 quarterly payments of $200, $400, $600, $800, $1000. Find the quarterly rate and the nominal rate he will pay and explain the difference in rates for the two payment plans.

4.6 Truth in Lending and the Annual Percentage Rate

Money lenders have historically tried to hide the true rate that they are charging for lending money. Some people, however, are not concerned that a lender charges 25% because they do not think a cost of $10 to $20 is too much to pay for a small loan for a few months. Many types of institutions lend money, and their lending practices vary considerably. We can borrow money from the cash value of life insurance or from credit unions, banks, finance companies, automobile dealers, automobile companies, retail stores, credit cards, or the infamous loan sharks at the local pawnshops. With so many different institutions lending money, there needs to be a way to make reasonable comparisons of their lending rates. In July of 1969

Congress passed the Truth in Lending Act. This law requires the **annual percentage rate** (APR) to be stated on the loan papers or other contract documents issued by the lender. In addition, the stated finance charge and the subsequent interest rate have to include all the costs involved in obtaining the loan. The law also makes it possible for someone with second thoughts about borrowing the money to change his or her mind within three business days.

Definition 4.6.1 *The annual percentage rate (APR) is the rate at which the cash value of the loan equals the present value of the payments. The APR is the nominal rate.*

An APR situation is created when a simple interest or discount loan is paid back on a payment schedule rather than with a lump sum at the end of the term. We learned in Chapters 1 and 2 that simple interest and discount loans have a certain term and the balance is paid at the end of that term in one lump sum. The interest is computed at the start of the loan and is either added to the principal (simple interest loan) or subtracted from the face value (discount loan). If these loans were actually based on the structure of an annuity, the interest for each month would be computed on the loan balance during that month. Because the lender has part of his or her money back after several payments were made, the true rate must be much higher than the stated rate. Simple interest loans repaid with a payment structure are called **add-on loans** because the interest is calculated, added to the principal, and then the total is divided into equal payments.

Retail stores or chains of stores have for years made offers of a little down and a little per month to buy their products. Customers often fail to see that the interest is being charged in a subtle way. The truth-in-lending requirements seldom address these deceptive practices; however, if a customer can calculate the APR when the same item can be purchased for different cash prices (or payment plans), then he or she will be able to make the appropriate comparisons.

Example 4.6.1

The Autohaus uses 8% simple interest for add-on loans to customers who purchase its preowned vehicles. If \$2400 is financed for 18 months, what is the APR?

■ There are 2 steps to the solution of this problem. The *first* is to complete the simple interest loan (add-on) calculation in order to find the payment. The *second* is to apply the APR principle: *The cash value of the loan equals the present value of the payments.*

$$S = P(1+it) = 2400(1 + (.08)(\tfrac{18}{12})) = \$2688$$

$$\text{Payment} = \frac{2688}{18} = \$149.34 \text{ per month}$$

Cash value of loan = present value of the payments, so use $A_n = Ra_{\overline{n}|i}$

$$\$2400 = 149.34a_{\overline{18}|i}$$

$$i = 1.22\% \rightarrow i(12) = 12\times(1.22) \rightarrow \text{APR} = 14.64\%(12)$$

What happens when a person pays off his or her add-on or discount loan ahead of schedule? A common practice at one time was for the lender to rebate the unearned finance charge on the basis of the Rule of 78s. (This practice does not apply to a mortgage or other debt instrument where the interest is based on the previous month's balance.) The rise of the credit card industry has made this method of returning unearned interest more of historical interest than a current practice. The Rule of 78s applies to loans in which the finance charge is added to or subtracted from the principal at the beginning of the loan. The **Rule of 78s** says that unearned finance charges are to the total finance charges as the sum of the numbers of the remaining payments is to the sum of the numbers of all the payments. This ratio proportion will be clearer if written as the following equation:

$$\frac{\text{Rebate}}{\text{Finance charge}} = \frac{1+2+3+\cdots+n}{1+2+3+\cdots+m}.$$

If five payments are left out of a total of twelve, the numerator becomes $1 + 2 + 3 + 4 + 5 = 15$, and the denominator becomes $1 + 2 + 3 + \cdots + 12 = 78$. Many loans are for one year, so the sum of the first twelve numbers became the name of the rule. Gauss's formula for the sum of n numbers helps perform the addition when the numbers being added are larger: $1 + 2 + 3 + \cdots + n = ½[n(n+1)]$.

Example 4.6.2

If the borrower in Example 4.6.1 paid the loan off with 5 payments left, how much should the rebate be if based on the Rule of 78s?

■ Note that the finance charge = \$2688 – \$2400 = \$288. Now substitute into the Rule of 78s formula.

$$\frac{\text{Rebate}}{\text{Finance charge}} = \frac{1+2+3+\cdots+n}{1+2+3+\cdots+m} \rightarrow \frac{x}{288} = \frac{1+2+\cdots+5}{1+2+\cdots+18}$$

$$1 + 2 + \ldots + 5 = \frac{5}{2}(5+1) = 15 \text{ and } 1 + 2 + \ldots + 18 = \frac{18}{2}(18+1) = 171$$

$$\frac{x}{288} = \frac{15}{171} \rightarrow x = 288\left(\frac{15}{171}\right) = \$25.26$$

Example 4.6.3

A homeowner got a \$3600 home improvement loan for 2 years from a bank that charges 9% simple discount for such loans. If the loan called for monthly payments and he needed the entire \$3600, what was the APR?

■ Again, there are two steps: Figure the loan information and then apply the APR principle. Since the owner needs the whole \$3600, this becomes the proceeds, and we must figure the amount of the loan using the amount formula for discount interest.

$$S = \frac{P}{1-dt} = \frac{3600}{1-(.09)(2)} = \$4390.24 \quad \text{amount of the discount loan}$$

$$\text{Payment} = \frac{4390.24}{24} = \$182.93 \text{ per month}$$

Cash value of the loan = present value of the payments

$$A_n = Ra_{\overline{n}|i}$$

$$\$3600 = 182.93a_{\overline{24}|i}$$

$$i \approx 1.6527\% \rightarrow i(12) = 12\times(1.6527) \rightarrow \text{APR} \approx 19.8\%(12)$$

Example 4.6.4

If the homeowner in Example 4.6.3 paid his loan off with 8 payments remaining, what rebate on the finance charge did he get using the Rule of 78s?

■ Calculate the total finance charge as $4390.24 − $3600 = $790.24. Substitute into the Rule of 78s formula.

$$\frac{\text{Rebate}}{\text{Finance charge}} = \frac{1+2+3+\cdots+n}{1+2+3+\cdots+m} \rightarrow \frac{x}{790.24} = \frac{1+2+...+8}{1+2+...+24}$$

$$1+2+\cdots+8 = \frac{8}{2}(8+1) = 36 \text{ and } 1+2+\cdots+24 = \frac{24}{2}(24+1) = 300$$

$$\frac{x}{790.24} = \frac{36}{300} \rightarrow x = (790.24)\left(\frac{36}{300}\right) = \$94.83 \quad \text{Rebate for early payoff}$$

◀ EXERCISES 4.6 ▶

Concept and Short Answer Exercises

When the stated rate is less than the actual rate for a loan, that loan can deceive the unwary borrower. Explain the deceptions in Exercises 1–4.

1. There will be little or no interest charged on a loan for an item, but the price is discounted if cash is paid.
2. This is an 8% add-on loan for $3000 for 3 years.
3. This is an 8% discount loan for $3000 for 3 years.
4. You are paying off a 36-month car loan a year early. The lender will be glad to reimburse you the rebate on the interest using the Rule of 78s.

Calculation Exercises

5. The Vadalia Appliance Center claims that it charges no interest. Hence, a $1200 refrigerator will cost you $100 per month for a year. However, if you pay cash, you can have the refrigerator for $1000. Find the actual interest rate.
6. A $2400 bedroom suite will cost you $100 per month for 2 years. However, if you pay cash, you can have the suite for $2160. Find the actual interest rate.

7. If you pay by credit, the Rough Diamond used car dealer is charging \$200 down and only \$150 per month for 2 years for a "nearly new" 1994 Ranger. If you pay cash, you can have the same Ranger for \$3000. Find the rate you are being charged.

8. The Buy-Here-Pay-Here used car dealer is charging \$300 down and only \$300 per month for 1 year for a "nearly new" 1989 VW van. If you pay cash, you can have the same VW van for \$3500. Find the rate you are being charged.

9. If we buy a \$3000 Universal Widget with an 8% add-on loan and monthly payments for 2 years, find the APR.

10. A \$3000 fishing boat can be financed with an 8% add-on loan and monthly payments for 3 years. Find the APR.

11. If we can pay off the Universal Widget in Exercise 9 with 6 months left, find the rebate of the finance charge using the Rule of 78s.

12. If we can pay off the fishing boat in Exercise 10 with 8 months left, find the rebate of the finance charge using the Rule of 78s.

13. A \$9000 car is purchased using a 4% add-on loan and monthly payments over 3 years. What is the actual APR?

14. Repeat Exercise 13 with a 12% add-on loan.

15. The car in Exercise 13 is paid off after 2 years. Find the interest rebate using the Rule of 78s.

16. If the loan in Exercise 14 is paid off after 15 months, find the interest rebate using the Rule of 78s.

17. We purchase a \$3000 Lawn-Mower® with an 8% discount loan and monthly payments for 2 years. Find the APR.

18. Find the APR if we buy a \$5000 Weed-Mower® with an 8% discount loan and monthly payments for 3 years.

19. If we can pay off the Lawn-Mower® in Exercise 17 with 6 months left, find the rebate of interest using the Rule of 78s.

20. Find the rebate of interest using the Rule of 78s if we can pay off the Weed-Mower® in Exercise 18 with 6 months left.

21. If a \$9000 truck is purchased with a 4% discount loan and monthly payments over 3 years, what is the actual APR?

22. What is the actual APR if a \$9000 ATV is purchased with a 7% discount loan and monthly payments over 3 years?

23. If the truck in Exercise 21 is paid off after 2 years, find the rebate of interest using the Rule of 78s.

24. Find the rebate of interest using the Rule of 78s if the ATV in Exercise 22 is paid off after 2 years.

Chapter 4 Summary of Concepts

Future Value of an Ordinary Annuity: $S_n = Rs_{\overline{n}|i}$

Present Value of an Ordinary Annuity: $A_n = Ra_{\overline{n}|i}$

Annual Percentage Rate (APR)

Rule of 78s: $\dfrac{\text{Rebate}}{\text{Finance chg.}} = \dfrac{1+2+3+\cdots+n}{1+2+3+\cdots+m}$

Gauss's Formula: $1+2+3+\cdots+n = \dfrac{n}{2}(n+1)$

Chapter 4 Vocabulary Check

Annuity	*Fence Post Principle*
Annuity Certain	*Number of Payments*
Contingent Annuity	*Payment Interval*
Ordinary Annuity	*Periodic Interest Rate*
Simple Annuity	*Periodic Rent or Payment*
Term of an Annuity	*Smaller Last Payment*

Chapter 4 Skills Check

1. Find the number of payments and the rate per period; then compute the future value of an ordinary annuity.

   Section 4.1 Examples 1, 2, 3; Exercises 2, 5, 23, 25

2. Find the number of payments and the rate per period; then compute the present value of an ordinary annuity.

   Section 4.2 Examples 1, 2, 3; Exercises 5, 9, 11, 15

3. Find the number of payments and the rate per period; then compute the payment for a known present value or future value of an ordinary annuity.

   Section 4.3 Examples 1, 2, 3, 4; Exercises 5, 7, 13

4. From a known bundle of money, determine if it is present value or future value, and find the number of payments of a known size that is equivalent to the bundle. Determine if a smaller last payment is needed and find what it is.

   Section 4.4 Examples 1–3; Exercises 5, 9, 13, 19

5. Determine the nominal rate of return for an annuity with known term, payment, and either present value or future value bundle.

   Section 4.5 Examples 1, 2; Exercises 5, 9, 15

6. Find the annual percentage rate (APR) for add-on and discount loans. Based on the Rule of 78s find the rebate from an add-on or discount loan that is paid off early.

Section 4.6 Examples 1–4; Exercises 5, 13, 17

Review Test for Annuities

1. On Mariah's 8th birthday, her mother deposited \$150 into a savings account earning 7%. Her mother continued the yearly \$150 deposits including the one on Mariah's 23rd birthday. At that time her mom withdrew it all for a wedding gift for Mariah. How large was the gift?
2. Francie is earning enough to pay \$2500 per month on a house. If the loan will have a term of 20 years at 6.5%(12), how large of a home loan is Francie able to get?
3. If for Exercise 2 Francie could pay \$20,000 as a down payment for his home, what would be the cash price of a home that Francie buys?
4. Is it better to pay \$10,000 in cash or to pay \$852.49 per month for a year at 8%(12)?
5. **a.** Suppose Hildegard's car loan is costing her \$900 per month for 3 years at 2.8%(12). Find the cash value of her loan.

   b. If Hildegard had a trade-in worth \$4000 and paid an additional \$2000 down payment, find the sticker price of the car.

   c. Suppose that after 1 year Hildegard's loan was sold to Juan, who required 8%(12) on his money. Find the amount that Juan was willing to pay for her loan.
6. Eduardo is buying new power tools for his garage and finds an air compressor that costs \$800. After a \$200 down payment it can be financed over 1 year with monthly payments at a rate of only 1.4%(12). Find his monthly payments.
7. How long will it take parents who are depositing \$25 per month into a trust fund earning 5.1%(12) to accumulate \$10,000 needed for their first daughter's schooling?
8. The settlement on a life insurance policy of \$150,000 is invested at 8.5%(12). How many \$2500 monthly payments could the beneficiary expect to receive from this bequest? What will the smaller last payment be?
9. If Grendel can accumulate \$12,000 over 2 years by investing \$1300 per quarter, what rate of return is he getting?
10. If a \$9000 car is purchased using a 4% add-on loan and monthly payments over 3 years, what is the actual APR?
11. If the car in Exercise 10 is paid off after 2 years, find the interest rebate using the Rule of 78s.

12. A $12,600 kitchen renovation is financed at a bank that charges 7.25% discount. If the loan is paid off monthly over 30 months, what is the APR?

Chapter 5

Other Annuities Certain

5.1 Overview of All the Annuities

The ordinary annuities of Chapter 4 are the foundation upon which the other annuities are built. We will modify the formulas so that the value of an annuity can occur at various places on the time line. In fact, the best way to identify an annuity is to note where the present or future value is located relative to the sequence of payments. We have already distinguished ordinary annuities from annuities due by the location of the payment either at the end or the beginning of the payment period. For example, the present value of an ordinary annuity is at the beginning of the first payment period, but this is also the beginning of the term of the annuity. Since we also know that each payment is at the end of the payment period, then the present value of an ordinary annuity is located one period before the first payment. The future value will then be located at the last payment. With these locations for the "bundle," we always know that the annuity is ordinary, and we can choose the formula appropriately. In summary, an annuity with the present value located one period before the first payment and the future value located at the last payment is called an **ordinary annuity** or an **annuity immediate**.

An annuity with the present value located at the first payment and the future value located one period after the last payment is called an **annuity due**. The name implies that something is owed, like an invoice or a bill. Insurance premiums come due at regular intervals, and they must be paid at the beginning of each payment period. Because of this requirement, annual insurance premiums converted to equivalent monthly premiums provide a good example of an *annuity due* present value. Any of these annuities could also be contingent annuities whose beginning or ending dates depend on some event. A life insurance annuity would be a good example of a contingent annuity since payments cease at the annuitant's death.

An annuity with the present value located two or more periods before the first payment is called a **deferred annuity**. The name implies that someone has an amount of money, like an insurance settlement or inheritance, which will provide income in the form of an annuity, but he defers starting those payments until a later date. The deferred use of the money will allow the fund to grow at compound interest and thus increase the size of the income payment.

An annuity with the future value located two or more periods after the last payment is sometimes called a **forborne annuity**. *Forborne* is the past participle of *forbear*, which means to refrain from a certain action. The payment structure and delayed use of a retirement fund, for example, could be a forborne annuity. A person regularly saves money during the working years but refrains from using it for a period of time after retirement. The accumulated money in the fund will grow at compound interest and consequently be worth much more when it is finally needed.

Time line diagram 5.1.1 shows a sequence of n payments with numbers identifying the six possible locations (date of valuation) of the bundle of money. Each number corresponds to the present or future value of one of the annuities we have described. After the diagram we have listed the annuities that correspond to each number. Getting a formula for each of these annuities will be a matter of moving the present or future value of an ordinary annuity to the necessary location.

TIME LINE DIAGRAM 5.1.1

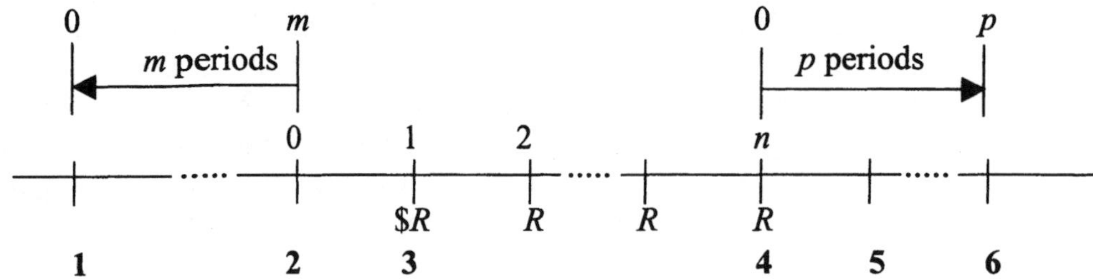

Type of Annuity		Symbol	Location on Time Line
Deferred	PV	A_n(def)	**1** two or more periods before the 1st payment
Ordinary	PV	A_n(ord)	**2** one period before the 1st payment
Due	PV	A_n(due)	**3** at the time of the 1st payment
Ordinary	FV	S_n(ord)	**4** at the time of the last payment
Due	FV	S_n(due)	**5** one period after the last payment
Forborne	FV	S_n(for)	**6** two or more periods after the last payment

FORMULAS

The more compact notation of the Society of Actuaries (SOA) is also given.

Deferred Annuity PV The present value of a deferred annuity is located m periods before the present value of an ordinary annuity, so we move A_n(ord) back m periods at compound interest. The value m is the number of intervals of deferment and is measured from the present value of an ordinary annuity and not from the first payment. If the number of periods between the present value of the deferred annuity and the first payment has been calculated, the value of m is one less than that value.

$$A_n(\text{def}) = R\, a_{\overline{n}|i}(1+i)^{-m} = R\, a_{\overline{n}|i} v^m \qquad \text{SOA notation: } R\,{}_{m|}a_{\overline{n}|i} \qquad \textbf{(5.1)}$$

Annuity Due PV The present value of an annuity due is located at the first payment (or one period after the present value of an ordinary annuity), so we move A_n(ord) forward one period at compound interest.

$$A_n(\text{due}) = R\, a_{\overline{n}|i}(1+i) \qquad \text{SOA notation: } R\ddot{a}_{\overline{n}|i} \qquad \textbf{(5.2)}$$

Annuity Due FV The future value of an annuity due is located one period after the last payment, so we move S_n(ord) forward one period at compound interest.

$$S_n(\text{due}) = R\, s_{\overline{n}|i}(1+i) \qquad \text{SOA notation: } R\ddot{s}_{\overline{n}|i} \qquad \textbf{(5.3)}$$

Forborne Annuity FV The future value of a forborne annuity is located p periods after the last payment, so we move S_n(ord) forward p periods at compound interest.

$$S_n(\text{for}) = R s_{\overline{n}|i}(1+i)^p \qquad \text{SOA notation: } R s_{\overline{n}|i} v^{-p} \qquad \textbf{(5.4)}$$

◀ EXERCISES 5.1 ▶

Concept and Short Answer Exercises

For each of the following situations, give the position (use a, b, …, f from the time line), the name, and the formula of the single bundle of money, assuming an annuity with n payments of R dollars each has been or will be made to equal that "bundle."

Deferred →		Annuity Period →			Forborne →		
0 ..	m			0	1 ..		p
	0	1	2 ..	n			
		R	R ..	R			
a	b	c		d	e		f

1. I get a loan and start making payments in 1 period.
2. I get a loan and start making payments after 6 periods.
3. I get a loan and no payments will be made for a whole year of periods.
4. I get a loan and payments will be made for a whole year of periods starting immediately.
5. I get a loan and payments begin immediately.
6. I get a loan and payments begin next period.
7. I start a savings account with regular deposits and want to know the amount in the savings account as of the last deposit.
8. I start an education fund with regular deposits and want to know the amount in the fund 1 period after the last deposit.
9. I start a savings account with regular deposits and want to know the amount in the savings account 1 period after the final deposit.
10. I start a savings account with regular deposits and want to know the amount in the savings account 3 years after the final deposit.
11. I start a retirement savings account with regular deposits and want to know the amount in the savings account 20 periods after the final deposit.
12. I start a savings account with regular deposits and want to know the amount in the savings account at the date of the final deposit.
13. I deposit regularly, let the money sit for several periods, then take out a bundle.
14. I deposit regularly, let the money sit for 1 period, then take out a bundle.

15. I invest a bundle and immediately start taking out monthly stipends.
16. I buy furniture but make no monthly payments for a year.
17. I invest a bundle, let it sit one period, and take out periodic rents.
18. I buy furniture, and monthly payments begin next month.
19. I deposit regularly and take out the bundle on the last payment.
20. I make monthly savings deposits toward a car and let the money sit for a year before taking out the bundle.
21. I invest a bundle, let it mature for a long time, and take out periodic rent.
22. I invest monthly, let the bundle mature for a time, then take out periodic rent.
23. I deposit regularly, let the money sit for one period, then take out the bundle.

5.2 Annuities Due with Applications

As we noted in Section 5.1, the name **annuity due** suggests that we owe something. Insurance premiums and apartment rent are annuities due because the payment is due at the beginning of each rent period. People who sell insurance want a premium before they write an insurance policy, and people who rent apartments want at least one month's rent before the renter moves in. It is clear that the premiums and rent are at the beginning of each rent period, but what does the present value represent? We know that the present value of an annuity due is a "bundle" of money at the date of the first payment, so we can think of this present value as an equivalent premium with a longer rent period. For example, if the car insurance premiums are being paid monthly, the present value could be an equivalent single premium covering a year or a quarter.

Refinancing or other changes in amortized loans will usually entail the calculation of the outstanding balance. If this balance is needed on a payment date but before the payment is made, the situation will require the use of the future value of an annuity due. In the context of saving money for accumulation of some future target value, the future value of an annuity due is used to get the smaller last payment, if one is needed.

Most financial calculators have a function key that can be turned on to compute the various parameters of an annuity due. On some calculators this function goes by the name DUE while on others it is called the BEGIN or BGN key. (See Appendix B.) The problems can be worked without ever using this key if you remember to change the information given or needed into an ordinary annuity. For example, if you are calculating the present value of an annuity due, just find the present value of an ordinary annuity and move it forward one period. On the other hand, if the present value is given and the payment is needed, let the point of valuation be one period before the payment, and then compute the payment. In that case, we are simply discounting the given present value one period at compound interest. These computations will be made quite clear by using a time line diagram with the parameters correctly located.

Example 5.2.1

Find the annual premium on a life insurance policy that is equivalent to a \$38 monthly premium if the insurance company charges 7%(12) for making monthly payments. What is the interest savings by paying annually instead of monthly?

■ This is an annuity due because premiums are at the beginning of the payment periods. The term of this annuity is one year.

TIME LINE DIAGRAM 5.2.1

1	2	3	.....	11	12
\$38	38	38		38	38

$x = A_n(\text{due})$

$$A_n(\text{due}) = R\ddot{a}_{\overline{n}|i} = R\,a_{\overline{n}|i}(1+i) = 38\,a_{\overline{12}|7/12\%}(1.0058\overline{3})$$

$$x = \$441.73 \qquad \text{Interest savings} = 12(38) - 441.73 = \$14.27$$

When we refer to various sums of money as being *equivalent*, we are typically seeking a bundle of money that is the present or future value of a sequence of payments in an annuity. We could reverse the perspective and seek the payments that are equivalent to a known bundle of money. In general these are equations of value based on the time value of money. The unknown may also be the interest rate or the number of payments. Some equations of value may not have a real solution, just as some algebraic equations may not have a solution. This can occur, for example, when the equation is a quadratic with a negative discriminant.

Example 5.2.2

An annuity due pays \$1 per year for 4 years and is invested at i per quarter. Show that the present value of this annuity can be expressed as the following quotient:

$$\frac{a_{\overline{16}|i}}{a_{\overline{4}|i}}.$$

■ $$\frac{a_{\overline{16}|i}}{a_{\overline{4}|i}} = \frac{1-(1+i)^{-16}}{1-(1+i)^{-4}}; \text{ let } x = v^4 = (1+i)^{-4}$$

$$= \frac{1-x^4}{1-x} = \frac{(1-x)(1+x+x^2+x^3)}{(1-x)} = 1+x+x^2+x^3$$

$$= 1+(1+i)^{-4}+(1+i)^{-8}+(1+i)^{-12} = 1+v^4+v^8+v^{12}$$

$$= \ddot{a}_{\overline{n}|j} \text{ where } j = (1+i)^4 - 1 \text{ is the rate per year}$$

Example 5.2.3

A piece of commercial real estate is sold for \$175,000 with \$50,000 down and the balance financed for 10 years at 8.5%(12). The buyer agrees to pay \$1200 per month with the final payment a balloon payment. Find the size of the balloon payment.

■ The usual approach to this problem is very much like a Merchant's Rule calculation. Note that the loan will be \$175,000 – \$50,000 = \$125,000. We find the difference in the values of 119 \$1200 payments at the date of the 120th, which is S_n(due), and the future value of the \$125,000 loan principal at the 120th payment.

TIME LINE DIAGRAM 5.2.2

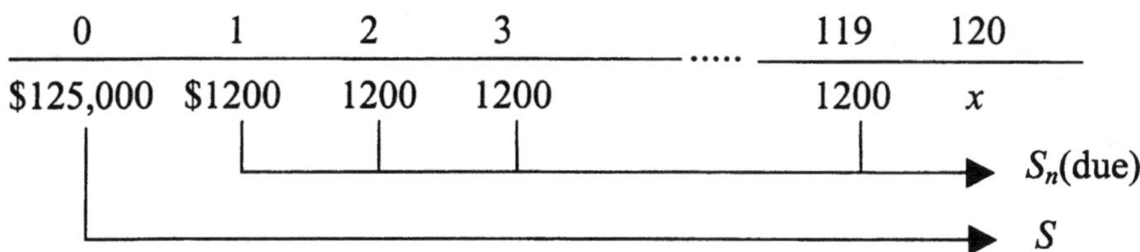

The 120th payment, x = FV of the loan principal – FV of the payment annuity

$S = P(1+i)^n = \$125{,}000(1.0070833..)^{120} =$ \$291,580.89

$S_n(\text{due}) = R s_{\overline{n}|i}(1+i) = 1200\, s_{\overline{119}|8.5/12\%}(1+.085/12) =$ \$224,566.10

Balloon payment, x = \$67,014.79

A little bit of algebra and the built-in capacities of the financial calculator allow us to simplify the outstanding balance calculation. If we use the method of Example 5.2.3 and express it as an equation, it is

$$x = A_n(1+i)^n - R s_{\overline{n-1}|i}(1+i) \rightarrow x = [A_n(1+i)^{n-1} - R s_{\overline{n-1}|i}](1+i).$$

Now the compound interest calculation and the ordinary annuity calculation have the same number of periods and payments, $n-1$. The calculator will compute the expression in the brackets [ ] when we press comp FV. All that remains is to multiply it by $(1+i)$ if we want it one period later; otherwise we have the outstanding balance at the $(n-1)$st payment.

Example 5.2.4

A couple begins a savings program to accumulate \$40,000 for the down payment on a new home. If they can earn 7%(12) on their investment, and they deposit \$550 every month, how many deposits will they need to make? Will they need a smaller last payment? If so, what will it be?

■ Finding the number of monthly payments will be an S_n(ord) calculation. Finding the smaller last payment will require the future value of an annuity due with 60 payments. This payment will be located at the 61st position, and the amount that it is short of \$40,000 will be the smaller last payment.

TIME LINE DIAGRAM 5.2.3

1 2 3 ..... $n = ?$ $n+1$

\$550 550 550 550 x

\$40,000 (target)

S_n(due)

$S_n(\text{ord}) = R s_{\overline{n}|i} \rightarrow 40{,}000 = 550 s_{\overline{n}|7/12\%} \rightarrow n =$ 60 monthly payments @ 550

$S_n(\text{due}) = R s_{\overline{n}|i}(1+i) \rightarrow S_n(\text{due}) = 550 s_{\overline{60}|\frac{7}{12}\%}(1+.07/12) = \$39{,}605.79$

The smaller last payment $x = \$40{,}000 - 39{,}605.79 = \$394.21$

Example 5.2.5

A home mortgage for \$80,000 is financed at 9%(12) for 30 years. Find the payment and the outstanding balance after 10 years.

■ Use an ordinary annuity to find the payment. Round the payment up to the cent and then replace n by $10(12)=120$. Be sure that the payment is negative, so that the calculator will find the difference. Now do a comp FV, and the calculator will give you the outstanding balance at the 120th payment.

$A_n(\text{ord}) = R a_{\overline{n}|i} \rightarrow \$80{,}000 = R a_{\overline{360}|\frac{9}{12}} \rightarrow R = \$643.70$

We know the outstanding balance $= 80{,}000(1.0075)^{120} - 643.70 s_{\overline{120}|\frac{9}{12}\%}$.

On the calculator we let $n = 120$ and compute FV, to give $S_n = \$71{,}543.43$.

We can summarize the concepts of these last payment problems into two procedures:

1. If we are finding the last payment in a problem involving a *future value* or *accumulation* of money to reach a target number, we use

   Last payment, x = Target Value – S_n(due).

2. If we are finding the last payment in a problem involving a known *present value* that is being distributed as n income payments of \$$R$, we use

   Last payment, $x = [A_n(1 + i)^n - R s_{\overline{n}|i}](1 + i)$.

◀ EXERCISES 5.2 ▶

Concept and Short Answer Exercises

1. How do you recognize an annuity due problem?
2. What words are used to specify an annuity due problem?
3. What does the formula $Rs_{\overline{n+1}|i} - R$ calculate?
4. What does the formula $Ra_{\overline{n-1}|i} + R$ calculate?
5. In an annuity due savings account, when does the rent start to earn interest?
6. The FV of an annuity due is larger than the FV of an ordinary annuity with the same number of payments because _____.

Calculation Exercises

7. On 2/3/02 Joe begins depositing \$100 per month into a savings account earning 4%(12), with the last deposit on 5/3/04. Find the value of the savings account on 6/3/04.

8. Find the value of Jolene's savings account on 2/3/05 if she deposits $500 per half year into a savings account earning 4%(2) with the first deposit on 2/3/02 and the last on 8/3/04.

9. Pierre deposits $100 per month into a savings account earning 4%(12) starting on 2/3/02 and ending on 5/3/04. Find the equivalent value (bundle) of the savings account on 2/3/02.

10. Find the equivalent value of Bruce's savings account on 2/3/02 if he deposits $1000 per quarter into a savings account earning 4%(4), starting on 2/3/02 and ending on 5/3/04.

11. Surgai wants to be able to withdraw $2000 every quarter from an account with the first withdrawal on 4/1/03 and last on 1/1/10. Give the date and the size of the present value of an annuity due at 8%(4).

12. Give the date and the present value of Patty's proposed annuity due at 8%(12) if she wants to be able to withdraw $2000 every month from an account with the first withdrawal on 4/1/03 and last on 1/1/10.

13. Suppose in Exercise 11 that Surgai is saving $2000 per quarter instead of withdrawing it. Find the future value of this annuity due.

14. Suppose in Exercise 12 that Patty is saving $2000 per month instead of withdrawing it. Find the future value of the annuity due and its date.

15. A man has an inheritance of $200,000 from which he wants to withdraw money quarterly, starting immediately, for the next 10 years. If money earns 9% compounded quarterly, compute the quarterly stipends.

16. If money earns 9% compounded monthly, compute the monthly stipend for a woman who inherited $200,000 from which she wants to withdraw money monthly, starting immediately, for the next 10 years.

17. A man has an inheritance of $200,000 from which he wants to withdraw $10,000 quarterly, starting immediately. If money earns 9% compounded quarterly, compute the number of full quarterly stipends and the final stipend.

18. If money earns 9% compounded monthly, compute the number of full monthly stipends and the final stipend paid to a man who has an inheritance of $200,000 from which he wants to withdraw $1000 monthly, starting immediately.

19. Margaret wants to save $20,000 within the next 5 years. If her monthly deposits are made at the beginning of each month and if her savings is making 5%(12), find the monthly deposit upped to the next full dollar.

20. Find the necessary deposit rounded to the next full dollar if Roy wants to save $10,000 within the next 5 years and if his semiannual deposits are made at the beginning of each half-year. His savings account is earning 5%(2).

21. Virginia wants to save $20,000 by making $500 monthly deposits. If her monthly deposits are made starting immediately and her savings is making 5%(12), find the number of full monthly deposits and find the last partial deposit.

22. Jose wants to save $10,000 by making $1000 quarterly deposits. If his quarterly deposits start immediately and if his savings is making 5%(4), find the number of full monthly deposits and the last partial deposit.

Theory and Extension Exercises

23. Assuming a level payment of $1, prove the following equivalent relationships:

a. $\ddot{a}_{\overline{n}|i} = \dfrac{1-v^n}{d}$ b. $\ddot{a}_{\overline{n}|i} = a_{\overline{n-1}|i} + 1$ c. $\ddot{a}_{\overline{n}|i} = a_{\overline{n}|i} + 1 - v^n$

24. Assuming a level payment of $1, prove the following equivalent relationships:

a. $\ddot{s}_{\overline{n}|i} = \dfrac{v^{-n}-1}{d}$ b. $\ddot{s}_{\overline{n}|i} = s_{\overline{n+1}|i} - 1$ c. $\ddot{s}_{\overline{n}|i} = s_{\overline{n}|i} - 1 + v^{-n}$

25. Assuming a level payment of $1, show that a sequence of n payments paid at the end of every 2 years at rate i per year will have the following present value: $\dfrac{a_{\overline{2n}|i}}{a_{\overline{2}|i}}$. Where is this present value located?

26. Applying your results from Exercise 25, what is $\dfrac{a_{\overline{45}|i}}{a_{\overline{9}|i}}$?

27. Show that $a_{\overline{10}|i}(1+i)^5 = \ddot{s}_{\overline{5}|i} + \ddot{a}_{\overline{5}|i}$.

28. Prove that $\dfrac{1}{\ddot{a}_{\overline{n}|i}} = \dfrac{1}{\ddot{s}_{\overline{n}|i}} + d$.

29. If an insurance premium is $65 per month, find the equivalent annual premium at 9%(12) compound discount. Use Exercise 23 instead of effective rate.

30. If an investor saves $50 per month for 2 years in an account paying 6%(12) compound discount, how much will be in the account at the end of 2 years?

5.3 Deferred Annuities

In Section 5.1 we defined a **deferred annuity** as an annuity in which the present value is located two or more periods before the first payment. We also showed that the formula comes from moving the present value of an ordinary annuity back on the time line the m periods of deferment. For example, the present value of a deferred annuity tells how much must be invested now in a retirement fund in order to provide a sequence of income payments starting at some future date two or more periods away. An inheritance, whole life annuity, or insurance settlement may be the present value of a deferred annuity, for which we calculate the payments with the first starting in several years. On the other hand, someone may know the size of the payment she needs to receive but must calculate how many payments she can withdraw from the inheritance or insurance. It is important to remember that we are adjusting the location or valuation date of the bundle of money in order to use the ordinary annuity capacity of the financial calculator. Using a well-drawn time line diagram will make it clear what has to be done.

Example 5.3.1

Find the sum of money to be invested on October 18, 2003, at 6%(12) in order to receive 5 years of payments of \$500 per month, if the first is on August 18, 2009.

■ Use denominate numbers to find the interval of deferment m. (2009 − 8 − 18) − (2003 − 10 − 18) is 5 years and 10 months; therefore, $m = 5 \times 12 + 10 - 1 = 69$. Note that we subtract 1 because the present value of an ordinary annuity is one period before the first payment. The number of payments $n = 5 \times 12 = 60$. Calculate and store the factor $(1 + i)^{-m} = (1.005)^{-69}$ before doing the ordinary annuity.

TIME LINE DIAGRAM 5.3.1

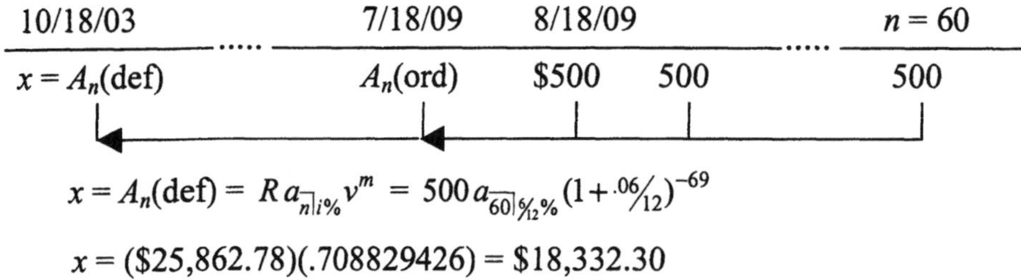

$$x = A_n(\text{def}) = R\,a_{\overline{n}|i\%}\,v^m = 500\,a_{\overline{60}|\frac{6}{12}\%}\,(1 + .06/12)^{-69}$$

$$x = (\$25{,}862.78)(.708829426) = \$18{,}332.30$$

Example 5.3.2

An inheritance worth \$65,350 received at age 55 is invested at 8.5%(12). If the recipient desires 10 years of income starting at age 61 in the same month as the inheritance was received, what will the monthly payment be?

■ Since the payment is needed, the present value will need to be located at the present value of an ordinary annuity. Move the \$65,350 with compound interest for m periods, followed by an ordinary annuity calculation. We can accomplish the same thing by solving the formula to eliminate the factor $v^m = (1 + i)^{-m}$ from the right side of the equation. *Note*: $m = 12(61 - 55) - 1 = 71$.

TIME LINE DIAGRAM 5.3.2

Age 55		Age 61		Age 71
\$65,350		\$$R$	R	R
$m = 71$			$n = 120$	

$$A_n(\text{def}) = R\,a_{\overline{n}|i\%}(1+i)^{-m} \rightarrow A_n(\text{def})(1 + i)^m = R\,a_{\overline{n}|i}$$

$$65{,}350(1.0070833..)^{71} = R\,a_{\overline{120}|\frac{8.5}{12}\%} \rightarrow R = \$1337.40$$

Example 5.3.3

A future college student received a \$100,000 insurance settlement. If this money is invested at 6%(12), for how many months can she receive an income of \$2500 when she starts school in 23 months?

■ This is a deferred annuity with $m = 22$ because the present value of an ordinary annuity is located one period (month) before the first payment (which is 23 months away). We need to find the number of payments n, so move the \$100,000 forward 22 months and use an ordinary annuity. Remember to make either the present value or the payment negative before computing n with your calculator.

TIME LINE DIAGRAM 5.3.3

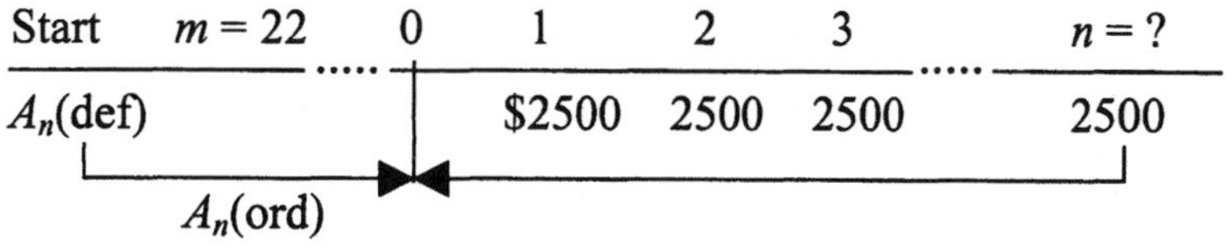

Start	$m = 22$	0	1	2	3	.....	$n = ?$
A_n(def)			\$2500	2500	2500		2500
	A_n(ord)						

$$A_n(\text{def}) = R\,a_{\overline{n}|i}(1+i)^{-m} \rightarrow A_n(\text{def})(1+i)^m = R\,a_{\overline{n}|i}$$

$$100{,}000(1.005)^{22} = 2500\,a_{\overline{n}|\frac{1}{2}\%} \rightarrow \$111{,}597.22 = 2500\,a_{\overline{n}|\frac{1}{2}\%} \rightarrow n = 50.639$$

The student can receive 50 monthly payments of \$2500. If we do a comp FV with $n = 50$, times (1.005), we will find the smaller 51st payment to be \$1599.48. (See the last payment calculation, summary 2, on page 153.)

◀ EXERCISES 5.3 ▶

Concept and Short Answer Exercises

1. If a time line diagram indicates an equation of value different from an ordinary annuity, give the two steps used to calculate a bundle of money equivalent to a sequence of payments.
2. If a time line diagram indicates an equation of value different from an ordinary annuity, give the two steps used to calculate the payments equivalent to a bundle of money.
3. If a time line diagram indicates an equation of value different from an ordinary annuity, give the three steps used to calculate the number of payments and the final partial payment equivalent to a bundle of money.
4. If the PV = \$2000 is paid off by 24 payments of \$100, then the total interest paid on the loan is _____.
5. If the FV = \$3000 is earned by 24 deposits of \$100, then the total interest earned by the savings account (sinking fund) is _____.
6. If Rachel receives her first yearly stipend at age 21 and her last at age 28, give her age where the following bundles of money would be located:
   a. PV deferred 5 years
   b. PV of ordinary annuity
   c. PV due
   d. FV of ordinary annuity
   e. FV due
   f. FV forborne 8 years

Calculation Exercises

7. Find the value at 9% on 3/4/02 of yearly rents of $2000 with the first on 3/4/06 and last on 3/4/20.

8. Find the value at 18%(2) on 3/4/02 of semiannual rents of $2000 with the first on 3/4/06 and last on 3/4/20.

9. A popular furniture store advertises that payments are deferred for 2 years. If we can afford to pay $200/month for 3 years at 9%(12), what is the maximum cash price of the furniture that we can afford?

10. If we can afford to pay $100/month for 2 years at 6%(12), what is the maximum cash price of a stereo system that we can afford if payments are deferred for 2 years?

11. How much interest did we pay in Exercise 9?

12. How much interest did we pay in Exercise 10?

13. Aunt Elma dies leaving Jill's dad $10,000. He wants to use it for 4 yearly stipends for Jill's college expense. If Jill is 10 when Aunt Elma dies and if Jill begins college at the young age of 17, find Jill's yearly stipend. Money is earning 8%.

14. When JD was 13 Uncle Carlos died, leaving him $20,000, which will be used for 4 yearly stipends starting when JD reaches age 18. If money is making 6%, find his yearly stipend.

15. Uncle Bill dies, leaving his family $10,000. They want to use the gift for $3000 yearly stipends for Jason starting at age 17. If Jason is 10 when Uncle Bill dies and if money is earning 8%, find the number of full stipends and the final partial stipend.

16. When Marie was 13 she received an insurance settlement for $20,000. The money will be used for a number of $4000 yearly stipends starting when she reaches age 18. If money is making 6%, find the number of full stipends and the final partial stipend.

17. You plan to retire on July 1, 2050, with $2,000,000 in hand. To achieve your goal you plan on making monthly deposits into a money market account making 5.5% (12) with the first deposit on July 1, 2004 and the last on July 1, 2044. Find your monthly deposit.

18. A couple sold a lakefront home that paid them $200,000 on September 1, 2002. They deposited the money at a bank paying 5% and plan to receive yearly income from this investment with the first on September 1, 2005, and the last on September 1, 2035. Find the size of their yearly income payment.

19. Find the total interest earned in Exercise 17.

20. Find the total interest earned in Exercise 18.

Theory and Extension Exercises

21. Prove that $a_{\overline{n+m}|i} = v^n a_{\overline{m}|i} + a_{\overline{n}|i}$, for $n<m$.

22. Prove that $a_{\overline{n}|i}(1+i)^m = s_{\overline{m}|i} + a_{\overline{n-m}|i}$, for $n>m$.

23. At age 55 Michael invests $175,000 at rate i per year. At age 65 he wants to begin 20 years of income at $20,000 per year. What is the minimum annual rate he needs to earn on this fund? At what rate can he earn $40,000 per year?

5.4 Forborne Annuities

In Section 5.1 we defined a **forborne annuity** as an annuity whose future value is positioned two or more periods after the last payment. We showed that the formula comes from moving the future value of an ordinary annuity forward p periods. From another perspective we are using compound interest to change the focal date. As we noted in Section 5.1, the word *forbear* means to wait or refrain from doing something. In this case we are waiting p periods before using the money so it can grow or because we do not need it yet. For example, saving money regularly for a future expense like a college education may entail putting money aside for 10 or 12 years but not using it for another 5 or 6 years when the student is ready for college. Remember that we are just moving the future value "bundle" of an ordinary annuity forward p periods at compound interest where $(1+i)^p$ is the accumulation factor. The financial calculator will give us only the future value of an ordinary annuity or an annuity due. Example 5.4.1 will suggest how to find the future value of a forborne annuity quickly on the financial calculator.

Example 5.4.1

At age 23, one year after graduating from college, a young man begins to make $2000 per year contributions to an Individual Retirement Account (IRA). He does this for 6 years, but when new family obligations arise, he never makes another contribution to the IRA. Assume that the fund is in the stock market and that it averages 11%(1) on the long run. Find the value of this fund when the man is 65.

■ This is clearly a forborne annuity with 6 payments and a forbearance interval of 36 years. On the calculator we find the FV of 6 payments of $2000 each, then move this amount into the PV, zero the payment, let $n=36$, and compute the FV.

TIME LINE DIAGRAM 5.4.1

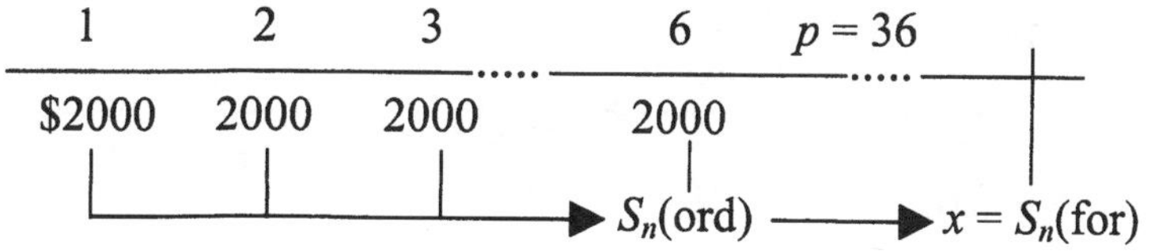

1	2	3	.....	6	$p=36$	.....	
$2000	2000	2000		2000			
			→	S_n(ord)	→		$x = S_n$(for)

$$x = S_n(\text{for}) = R s_{\overline{n}|i}(1+i)^p \rightarrow$$

$$x = 2000 s_{\overline{6}|11\%}(1.11)^{36} = \$15{,}825.72(1.11)^{36} = \$677{,}626.98$$

While Example 5.4.1 illustrated the value of starting young, Figure 5.1 further demonstrates the effect of time on the growth of a retirement account at various starting ages. The fund was built at \$100 per month earning a conservative 4%(12).

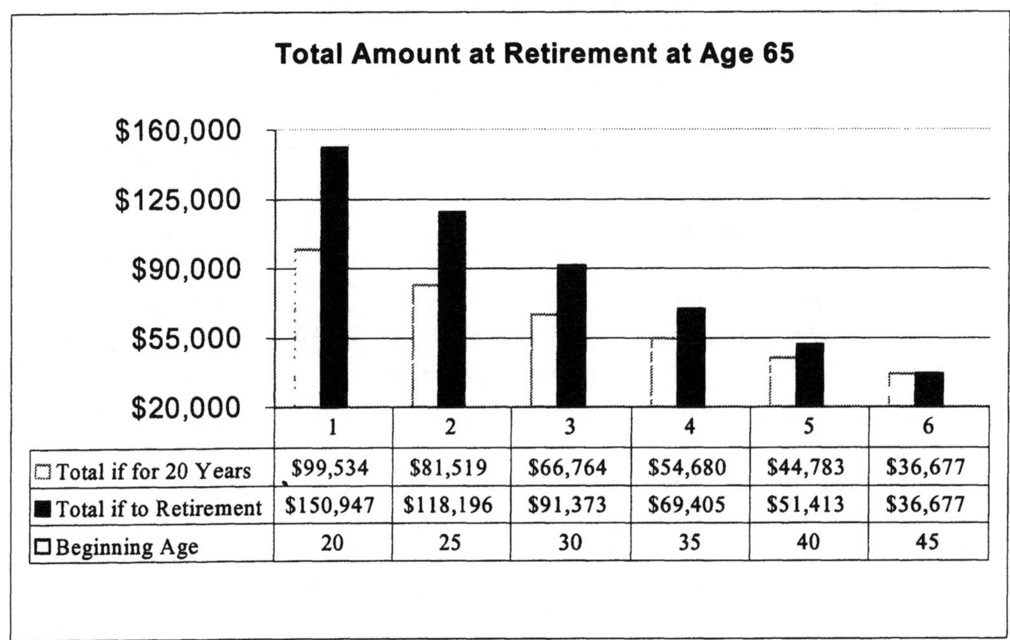

	1	2	3	4	5	6
□ Total if for 20 Years	\$99,534	\$81,519	\$66,764	\$54,680	\$44,783	\$36,677
■ Total if to Retirement	\$150,947	\$118,196	\$91,373	\$69,405	\$51,413	\$36,677
□ Beginning Age	20	25	30	35	40	45

FIGURE 5.1

Example 5.4.2

A thoughtful father begins a college education fund when his twins are 1 year old. He deposits \$35 per month in his company's credit union, which pays an average of 7%(12). His last deposit to this fund is on their 12th birthday. What will the education fund be worth when the twins are 18 years old?

■ This is a forborne annuity with $n = 12(11) + 1 = 133$, and $p = 12(6) = 72$. Remember that n is the number of payments while p is the number of interest periods after the last payment. The Fence Post Principle applies only to the payments, since there is a payment at the 1st birthday and at the 12th birthday. We added one payment to 12(11).

TIME LINE DIAGRAM 5.4.2

1 2 3 ..... 133 $p = 72$ ..... Age 18

\$35 35 35 35

→ S_n(ord) → $S_n(\text{for}) = x$

$$x = S_n(\text{for}) = R s_{\overline{n}|i}(1+i)^p \rightarrow$$

$$x = 35 s_{\overline{133}|7/12\%}(1+.07/12)^{72} = \$7005.06(1.00583\ldots)^{72}$$

$x = \$10,648.43$, amount in the fund at age 18

◀ EXERCISES 5.4 ▶

Concept and Short Answer Exercises

1. It is fairly common for someone to pay many years into a retirement account such as an IRA or a 401(k), after which there are several forborne years. What happens to the bundle of money during that forborne period?

2. Starting your retirement program early is wise. Why? (See Exercises 7 and 8 for good examples of this concept.)

Calculation Exercises

3. 240 monthly deposits of $100 are forborne 5 years. Find the amount at 8%(12).

4. 30 semiannual deposits of $500 at 9%(2) are forborne 3 years. Find the amount.

5. 180 monthly deposits at 6%(12) are forborne 2.5 years to give a bundle worth $800,000. Find the monthly deposit.

6. 60 quarterly deposits at 6.2%(4) are forborne 4 years to give a bundle worth $60,000. Find the quarterly deposit.

7. Marci, age 20, invests $100 per month at 4%(12) for 40 years and then carries that bundle forward 10 years to her retirement at age 70. Glenda, age 50, invests the same total amount by depositing $400 per month for 10 years at 4%(12) and then she carries that total forward 10 years until her retirement. Both are 70 when they retire.
   a. Show that the total amount invested is the same for Marci and Glenda.
   b. Compute the amount of the forborne annuity for each.
   c. Comment on why Marci has more than twice Glenda's total.

8. Monique, age 18, invests $1000 every half-year at 7%(2) for 30 years and then carries that bundle forward 22 years to her retirement. Megan, age 48, invests the same total amount by depositing $3000 every 6 months for 10 years at 7%(2), and she carries the total forward 22 years to the same retirement date.
   a. Show that the total amount invested is the same for Monique and Megan.
   b. Compute the amount of the forborne annuity for each.
   c. Comment on why Monique has more than twice Megan's total.

9. Dirk's granddad has been saving $25 per month at 4%(12) for him since he was born. Dirk is now getting married at age 22 and his granddad would like to present him with a cash wedding gift from that account. If for the last 2 years Granddad has not been able to save any money due to failing health, what is the amount of the wedding gift?

10. Miles's grandmother has been saving $100 per month for him since he was 1 month old. Miles is now 25 and is looking to buy a home, and Grandmother would like to present him with cash from that account to help with the down payment. If we know that for the last 4 years Grandmother has not contributed any additional money and that the fund is earning 5%(12), what is the amount of Grandmother's gift?

11. Joan invests $2000 a year into her IRA with the first investment at age 25 and the last at age 65. How much money does Joan remove at age 70? Money is worth 9%.

12. Myron and his wife each invests $3000 a year into their IRAs with the first investment at age 25 and the last at age 65. How much money do they have when they retire at age 70? Money is worth 6%.

13. When planning your retirement, you anticipate that you will be able to invest $150 every month with the first deposit on 2/1/02 and the last on 4/1/42. How much is in your retirement fund on 1/1/50? Money is worth 8%(12).

14. How much is in your retirement fund on 11/1/50 if you invest $1000 every quarter with the first deposit on 2/1/02 and the last on 5/1/42? Money is worth 8%(4).

15. You plan to make semiannual deposits into a savings account with the first deposit at age 25 and last at age 50. If the goal is to have $400,000 in your savings when you reach age 60, and if money is worth 8% compounded semiannually, find the semiannual deposit.

16. Find the monthly deposit necessary to raise $1,400,000 by age 60 if you make the first deposit at age 20 and last at age 50. Money is worth 6% compounded monthly.

17. Find the total interest earned in Exercise 13.

18. Find the total interest earned in Exercise 14.

19. Find the total interest earned in Exercise 15.

20. Find the total interest earned in Exercise 16.

Theory and Extension Exercises

21. Prove that $s_{\overline{n+m}|i} = v^{-n} s_{\overline{m}|i} + s_{\overline{n}|i}$.

22. A father invests $75 per month in an education fund during his son's first 12 years. He then stops making payments and invests in another fund earning 2.4%(12) more per year. What rate nominal rate $i(12)$ must he earn on the first 12 years of savings payments in order to have $28,000 available when the son turns 18?

5.5 Perpetuities—Income Without Using the Principal

The interest earned on an investment is typically compounded, and the fund would continue to grow. However, the interest earned at each interest interval could be paid out as an income payment to the investor. As long as the principal is left unchanged and the interest paying institution survives, this process can go on without ending, or in perpetuity. A **perpetuity** is an annuity with an infinite term in which the periodic payments are the interest earned during the previous interest period. A perpetuity has only a present value. Payments are made from the fund, and hence there is a bundle of money preceding a sequence of payments that theoretically go on infinitely. In Chapter 7 we will find that most preferred stock issues pay dividends in perpetuity. When universities set up endowment funds for scholarships, the interest from the funds generates the periodic scholarships in perpetuity. Many foundations have vast sums of money invested in various securities, bonds, and stocks. The philanthropic efforts of these foundations are all funded by the interest earned as a perpetuity.

Calculation of a perpetuity's parameters is quite simple because all we have is a present value "bundle," a payment, and an interest rate. The payment is always the rate per period times the present value. As long as we know any two of the parameters, the other can be found. Because the payments theoretically go on forever, we subscript the present value symbol A with an infinity symbol (∞) instead of the usual n.

Perpetuity Formulas: $R = iA_\infty \quad A_\infty = \dfrac{R}{i} \quad i = \dfrac{R}{A_\infty}$ **(5.5)**

It is possible to think of a perpetuity as an ordinary annuity with a large number of payments but not necessarily infinite. If we find the present value of a perpetuity paying \$250 per month, when invested at 8%(12), it will be \$37,500. The present value of an ordinary annuity paying \$250 monthly for 200 years at the same investment rate is also \$37,500. In fact, the only difference between the present values using 200 years and 300 years is \$.005. Although it may be no easier than the formulas above, we can always find the values of the perpetuity's parameters by using the annuity formulas and a reasonably large n, like 3000. These ideas lead us to the following derivation of an alternate notation and to an examination of the exact relationship between an ordinary annuity and an ordinary perpetuity (*perpetuity immediate*).

By definition we know $Ra_{\overline{\infty}|i} = \lim\limits_{n\to\infty} Ra_{\overline{n}|i} = \lim\limits_{n\to\infty} R\left[\dfrac{1-(1+i)^{-n}}{i}\right] = R\left[\dfrac{1}{i}\right] = \dfrac{R}{i} = A_\infty.$

From this we can conclude that $Ra_{\overline{\infty}|i}$ is an optional symbol to A_∞.

If the perpetuity present value is located at the time of the first payment, then we can also consider it a perpetuity due and use our annuity due formula with a large value for n. The notation would be $a_{\overline{\infty}|i}(1+i)$ or $\ddot{a}_{\overline{\infty}|i}$ in SOA notation.

We could also discount the present value one period to give $R\ddot{a}_{\overline{\infty}|i}(1+i)^{-1} = \dfrac{R}{i}$.

In the exercises in Section 5.2 we saw that $\ddot{a}_{\overline{n}|i} = \dfrac{1-v^n}{d}$. Taking the limit ($n \to \infty$) gives $\ddot{a}_{\overline{\infty}|i} = \dfrac{1}{d}$. In summary, we have shown the following relationships between perpetuities and the annuity formulas.

Annuity Forms of Perpetuities: $A_\infty(\text{ord}) = Ra_{\overline{\infty}|i}$, $A_\infty(\text{due}) = R\ddot{a}_{\overline{\infty}|i} = \dfrac{R}{d}$ **(5.6)**

If a perpetuity has a deferred period before the payments actually start, move the present value bundle so it is valued one payment period before the first payment and then use the ordinary perpetuity (*perpetuity immediate*) formula for the parameter needed. If we let the interest accrue for several periods between payments, the interest rate will have to be adjusted to an equivalent rate that matches the payment interval. Perpetuities in which the interest accrues more often than the payment is made will be addressed in the following derivation, which in effect converts the interest to an effective rate between payment periods.

Let k be the number of conversion periods between payments.

Perpetuity with Effective Rate: $R = A_\infty(1+i)^k - A_\infty \rightarrow R = A_\infty[(1+i)^k - 1]$ **(5.7)**

A perpetuity could have a changing periodic payment. Consider the dividends from a stock issue where the stock realizes regular growth over time. Although the growth rate may fluctuate slightly it is likely to have some average increase that gives a reasonable representation of the growth. Income from a rental property with regular build-in increases shows the same structure as perpetuity with an increasing payment. Although most variable payment annuities are presented in Chapter 9, the simplicity of this perpetuity case and its value in Chapter 7 give us an important reason to consider it at this point. Let the yield rate be i and the growth rate g. Presently we will see why we also need $i > g$.

PV of a fixed payment perpetuity: $A_\infty = Rv + Rv^2 + Rv^3 + \ldots$

As the infinite sum of a geometric series: $A_\infty =$

$$\frac{Rv}{1-v} = \frac{R(1+i)^{-1}}{1-(1+i)^{-1}} = \frac{R}{(1+i)-1} = \frac{R}{i}$$

PV of a perpetuity with growth rate g: $A_\infty = Rv + R(1+g)v^2 + R(1+g)^2v^3 + \ldots$

Again as an infinite sum:

$$A_\infty = \frac{Rv}{1-v(1+g)} = \frac{R(1+i)^{-1}}{1-(1+i)^{-1}(1+g)} = \frac{R}{(1+i)-(1+g)} = \frac{R}{i-g}, \; i > g \qquad \textbf{(5.8)}$$

Note that the geometric series ratio $v(1+g) < 1$ gives $i > g$.

Example 5.5.1

What monthly income in perpetuity can be expected from \$58,000 invested at 8.5%(12)?

■ We are looking for the payment, so use the payment formula from (5.5).

Note $i = .085/12 = .0070833333$. $\qquad R = .007083333(\$58,000) = \$410.83$

Example 5.5.2

A University receives an Alumni gift of \$278,900 on August 1, 2004. It invests the money at 9%(1) and wants to provide yearly scholarships with the first beginning right away.

■ This is a perpetuity due. The first step is to find the payment (since we cannot make a cash disbursement of an unknown payment until it is found). Since the first payment is located at the same date as the present value, we need to move the bundle back 1 year to match the payment interval and use the payment formula from (5.5).

TIME LINE DIAGRAM 5.5.1

0	1	2	3	→ ∞
	$R	R	R	……

$A_\infty \longleftarrow$ \$278,900

$$A_\infty = 278{,}900(1.09)^{-1} = \$255{,}871.56$$

$$R = iA_\infty \rightarrow R = (.09)(255{,}871.56) = \$23{,}028.44 \text{ (annual scholarship)}$$

Using an annuity due (5.6) gives 278,000 = $R\ddot{a}_{\overline{1000}|9\%}$ and R = \$28,028.44.

$$278{,}999 = \frac{R}{d} \rightarrow R = 278{,}900d = 278{,}900(.082568807) = \$28{,}028.44$$

Note that we find the compound discount rate from $d = \dfrac{i}{1+i}$.

An important observation needs to be made concerning this calculation. If we find the difference between the original gift and the discounted gift at 1 year earlier, it will be the payment we calculated. \$278,900 − \$255,871.56 = \$23,028.44. This result is easily shown by letting the gift = G and noting that $G(1+i)^{-1} = A_\infty$. Now substitute into (5.7) with $k = 1$ to get $R = G - G(1+i)^{-1}$.

Example 5.5.3

Find the value of an investment at 7.5%(4) that will provide \$4500 quarterly payments in perpetuity. Use both formulas (5.5) and (5.6).

■ We are looking for a present value 1 quarter before the first payment.

$$A_\infty = \frac{R}{i} \rightarrow A_\infty = \frac{4500}{.075/4} = \frac{4500}{.01875} = \$240{,}000$$

$$A_\infty = Ra_{\overline{\infty}|i} \rightarrow A_\infty = 4500a_{\overline{2000}|1.875\%} = \$240{,}000$$

Example 5.5.4

How much should a man invest at age 40 in a fund paying 9%(12) if he wants \$4000 per month in perpetuity, starting at age 65?

■ Keeping with the principle that the "bundle" of money must be 1 payment period before the first payment, we will find the present value of a perpetuity yielding \$4000 per month when invested at 9%(12). We will then find the period of deferment between age 40 and age 64 years 11 months. (12)(64 − 40) + 11 = 299 periods (months).

$$A_\infty = \frac{R}{i} \rightarrow A_\infty = \frac{4000}{.09/12} = \frac{4000}{.0075} = \$533{,}333.33 \text{ (bundle 1 month before)}$$

Now move this back 299 months. $x = \$533{,}333.33(1.0075)^{-299} = \$57{,}112$

◀ EXERCISES 5.5 ▶

Concept and Short Answer Exercises

1. The essence of all perpetuities is that you can distribute the _____ forever if you do not touch the _____.
2. If a grant of $2,000,000 distributed yearly over the next 20 years is compared to a perpetuity with the same $2,000,000 at the same rate, which would yield the higher yearly grant? Why?
3. Locate the present value of a yearly perpetuity with the first rent on 1/1/08.
4. Locate the present value of a monthly perpetuity with the first rent on 1/1/08.

Calculation Exercises

5. Calculate and locate the PV of a perpetuity yielding a monthly rent of $400 forever at 4.6%(12) with the first rent on 5/7/06.
6. A perpetuity yields a quarterly stipend of $2500 forever at 6%(4) with the first rent on 5/7/06. Calculate and locate the monies necessary to fund this perpetuity.
7. Calculate and locate the semiannual rents of a perpetuity funded by a $200,000 grant given on 8/12/05 if money is worth 6%(2).
8. If money is worth 5%(1), calculate and locate the yearly rent of a perpetuity funded by a $10,000 life insurance policy on 6/6/05.
9. Find the single value that will fund $2000 per year in perpetuity at 10%(1). Locate that value on the time line.
10. Find the single value that will fund $2000 per quarter in perpetuity at 10%(4). Locate that value on the time line.
11. Repeat Exercise 9 with the $2000 yearly stipend starting immediately.
12. Repeat Exercise 10 with the $2000 quarterly stipend starting immediately and each successive stipend increased for an annual inflation rate of 5.25%.
13. A $100,000 grant results in a $1000 per month scholarship forever with the first scholarship given at the end of 1 month. Find the interest rate.
14. A $200,000 grant results in a $10,000 per quarter scholarship forever with the first scholarship given at the end of 1 quarter. Find the interest rate.
15. A $100,000 grant results in a $1000 per month scholarship forever with the first scholarship given at the end of 1 year. Find the interest rate. (This is a hard one: Guess the interest rate, starting at a rate slightly lower than that of the previous problem. Try it, and then adjust.)
16. A $200,000 grant results in a $10,000 per quarter scholarship forever with the first scholarship given immediately. Find the interest rate.
17. A man wants an insurance policy that will result in $10,000 per year for his wife to live from for the rest of her life after he dies. If money is paying 5%(1), how

large of an insurance policy is needed? We assume a perpetuity, so that the wife will not run out of money and the principal is left to the heirs.

18. If money is paying 5.75%(1), how large of an insurance policy is needed to fund a perpetuity that will result in $20,000 per year plus inflationary increases for a man's widow for the rest of her life? Assume the average inflation is 4%(1).

19. Generex, Inc. makes a grant to a university of $1,000,000 on 1/1/03. Starting on 1/1/05, semiannual stipends will be made to a math scholarship fund. At 7%(2), how large will these stipends be if

a. The last is on 1/1/15?

b. The grants continue in perpetuity?

20. The Heritage Foundation endows a university with $2,000,000 on 1/1/03. Starting on 1/1/03, semiannual grants will be paid to a minority student fund. At 6%(2), how large will these grants be if

a. The last is on 1/1/20?

b. The grants continue in perpetuity?

Theory and Extension Exercises

21. MSU has three perpetuities each paying yearly into the faculty endowment fund. The first was endowed with $2 million at 8%(1), the second with $0.4 million at 6%(1), and the third with $1 million at 4%(1). These are to be combined into one equivalent perpetuity at $i(1)$. Find $i(1)$.

22. A grant of $1,000,000 is made to USC in 1970 to give scholarships totaling $50,000 per year with the first scholarships to be given in 2005. Find the rate $i(1)$ that will make it possible to fund these scholarships in perpetuity.

23. Show that the present value of an annuity of n unit payments is the difference between an ordinary perpetuity (immediate) and a perpetuity starting at time $n+1$.

5.6 General Case Annuities Using Effective Interest

In Chapter 4 we introduced the classification of annuities. **Simple annuities** have the interest compounded at the same frequency as the payments are made. **General annuities** have the interest compounded at a frequency different from the payment frequency. The most straightforward approach to general annuities is to change them into simple annuities. Various methods have been used that include subannuities and equivalent payments, but they all lack the simplicity and ease we find by using effective interest to convert general annuities into simple annuities. The use of effective interest when interest is less frequent than payments will require that compound interest be paid for part of a period. If only simple interest were paid for part of a period, we would have to use the equivalent payment method. However, experience has shown that the answers using either method differ by very little.

General annuities are fairly common. Most of us do not let the interest conversion frequency used by a bank or investment fund dictate when we make deposits into an account. We just make our deposit and go on with life. Institutions that have endowment funds for scholarships generally withdraw payments once a year, but it is highly unlikely that all those investments are earning at a rate converted yearly. For example, if the money is in bonds, then the interest is typically paid semiannually.

The interest being paid in a general annuity may accrue more frequently or less frequently than the payments, so there are two cases to consider. The formula for effective interest from Chapter 3 will be our basic tool to compute effective rates, and it will need only a slight modification in the way we compute the exponent. Once the effective rate has been calculated for a given problem, the computations will be like all other simple annuities. The following derivation gives a modified formula that will change a nominal rate $i(m)$ to a nominal rate $i(p)$, where m is the number of interest periods per year and p is the number of payments per year. This assures us that the interest rate compounds at the same frequency as the payments, and it thus reverts a general annuity into a simple annuity.

We need the following notation in order to develop the modified formula.

Given rate per period: $i = i(m)/m$
Required rate per period: $j = i(p)/p$

Start with the assumption that the accumulation factors are equivalent and solve for j. Let $(1 + j)^p = (1 + i)^m$, and take the $1/p$ power of each side and subtract 1 from each side to give the modified formula.

$$\left[(1+j)^p\right]^{\frac{1}{p}} = \left[(1+i)^m\right]^{\frac{1}{p}} \rightarrow (1+j)^{\frac{p}{p}} = (1+i)^{\frac{m}{p}} \rightarrow \boldsymbol{j = (1+i)^{\frac{m}{p}} - 1} \qquad \textbf{(5.9)}$$

Another form of this formula lets $k = m/p$ to give $\boldsymbol{j = (1 + \frac{i(m)}{m})^k - 1}$.

We now consider the two cases for interest more often and less often than payments.

Case I *Interest paid more frequently than payments are made.*

In the modified formula for effective interest, $j = (1 + \frac{i(m)}{m})^k - 1$, the value of k will be m interest periods per year over p payments per year. When there are more interest periods, k will be a whole number. The value of i that we use will be based on the given rate and interval of compounding. For example, if the interest rate is 8%(12) and the payments are quarterly, we find that $k = \frac{12}{4} = 3$ and $i = \frac{i(m)}{m} = \frac{8}{12} = \frac{2}{3}\%$. Thus, $j = (1.006666666)^3 - 1 = 2.0133627\%$ per quarter. This can be interpreted: 2/3% compounded three times per quarter is equivalent to 2.0133627% once a quarter.

Case II *Interest paid less frequently than payments are made.*

We still define the value of k as m interest periods per year over p payments per year, but since there are fewer interest periods than payments, k will be a fraction. The interest-paying institution must pay compound interest for part of a period. For example, if the interest is 8%(4) and the payments are monthly, we find that

$k=\frac{m}{p}=\frac{4}{12}=\frac{1}{3}$ and $i=\frac{8}{4}=2\%$. Thus, $j=(1.02)^{\frac{1}{3}}-1=.6622709\%$. This can be interpreted: 2% compounded per quarter is equivalent to .6622707% compounded three times per quarter.

Example 5.6.1

An employee has $50 per month deposited in his company's credit union, which pays 8%(4) on deposits. What is his balance after 4 years of saving?

■ We identify the annuity as a general case II where interest is less frequent than payments, and we are looking for the future value of an ordinary annuity with 48 payments. Calculate the effective rate first, and then substitute the parameters into the S_n(ord) formula.

1. Find the effective rate:

$$k=\frac{m}{p}=\frac{4}{12}=\frac{1}{3} \text{ and } i=\frac{8}{4}=2\%\text{, so } j=(1.02)^{\frac{1}{3}}-1=.6622709\%.$$

2. Find the balance after 4 years: $S_n(\text{ord}) = R s_{\overline{n}|i} = 50 s_{\overline{48}|.6622709\%} = \$2814.45$

Example 5.6.2

An executive's life insurance premiums are $325 per year. If the company charges 6%(12) for the privilege of making more frequent payments, what will the quarterly payments be?

■ Monthly interest with quarterly payments indicates that we have a Case I general annuity. Insurance premiums are paid at the beginning of the payment periods, so this is an annuity due present value problem, and we are looking for the quarterly payment. Calculate the effective rate first; then substitute the parameters into the A_n(due) formula.

1. Find the effective interest:

$$k=\frac{12}{4}=3 \text{ and } i=\frac{6}{12}=\frac{1}{2}\%\text{, so } j=(1.005)^3-1=1.507512499\%.$$

2. $A_n(\text{due}) = R a_{\overline{n}|i}(1+i) \rightarrow 325 = R a_{\overline{4}|1.5075..\%}(1.015075..)$

$$R = \$83.08 \text{ per quarter}$$

Example 5.6.3

At age 50 a woman received $48,500 from an inheritance settlement. If she invests the money in an account paying 8.5%(4) and wants to receive monthly income for 10 years starting at age 65, find her payment. Assume compound interest is paid for part of a period.

■ This is a deferred annuity and it is a Case II general annuity, since interest is less frequent than payments. The deferred part of the problem could be done with monthly interest or quarterly interest. From age 50 to age 65 there are 180 months. Using monthly interest, we can take the bundle forward 179 periods to 1 month before the first payment. Using quarterly interest, we will have to take the bundle forward 59 periods to 1 quarter before the first payment. This second approach creates a problem in trying to find the monthly payments. We could solve this problem by taking the bundle to the first payment and using an annuity due to find the payments, but this is less complicated than the first approach.

TIME LINE DIAGRAM 5.6.1

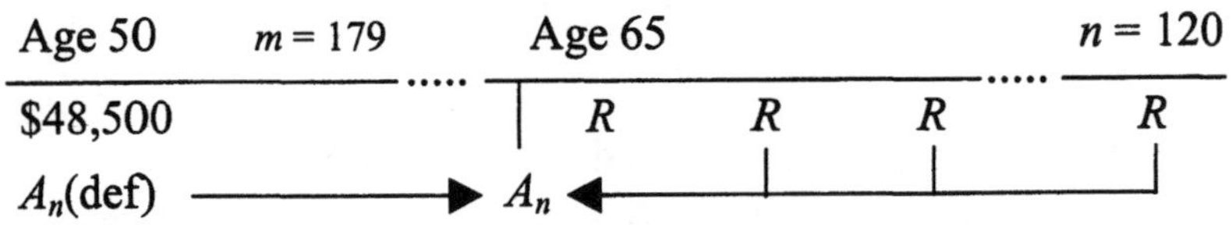

Age 50	$m = 179$	Age 65			$n = 120$
\$48,500	.....	R	R	R	..... R
A_n(def) ⟶		A_n ⟵			

Find the effective rate first.

$$k = \frac{4}{12} = \frac{1}{3} \text{ and } i = \frac{8.5}{4} = 2.125\%\text{, so } j = (1.02125)^{\frac{1}{3}} - 1$$

$j = 0.703374378\%$ per month

Find the value 1 month before age 65.

$$S = P(1+i)^n = 48{,}500(1.00703374378)^{179} = \$170{,}067.72$$

Find the payments.

$$A_n = Ra_{\overline{n}|i} \rightarrow \$170{,}067.72 = Ra_{\overline{120}|.703\cdots\%}$$

Now compute: PMT. $R = \$2103.19$ (her monthly income)

Example 5.6.4

Find the yearly scholarship that can be provided in perpetuity from a \$350,000 endowment invested at 8.25%(12). Assume that the first scholarship is paid out 1 year after the money is invested.

▪ The fund will compound 12 times before the interest is withdrawn as a scholarship payment. Compute the effective annual rate since the rate of compounding must match the payment frequency in order to use the perpetuity formula. Note that $k = \frac{12}{1} = 12$ and $i = \frac{8.25}{12} = .6875\%$.

$$j = (1+i)^k - 1 \quad \rightarrow j = (1.006875)^{12} - 1 = 8.569\ldots\%$$

$$R = iA_\infty \quad \rightarrow R = (.085692138)(350{,}000) = \$29{,}992.25 \text{ (scholarship)}$$

$$A_\infty = Ra_{\overline{\infty}|i} \rightarrow 350{,}000 = Ra_{\overline{1000}|8.56\cdots\%} \quad \rightarrow R = \$29{,}992.25$$

Example 5.6.5

A saver deposits \$65 per month into an account paying 6%(∞) for 12 years. After 8 more years the money is applied toward a property purchase. What amount is available?

▪ Finding the monthly effective rate takes two steps. First find the annual effective rate for 6%(∞) and then find the equivalent monthly effective rate. Since we are looking for the savings program's future value and there is a sitting period, it will be a forborne annuity.

$$i = e^{\delta} - 1 \text{ gives } i = e^{.06} - 1 = 6.183654653\%(1),\ k = \frac{m}{p} = \frac{1}{12} \text{ and } i = .061836\ldots$$

$$\text{so } j = (1.06183654653)^{\frac{1}{12}} - 1 = 0.501252085\% \text{ monthly}$$

$S_n(\text{for}) = R s_{\overline{n}|i}\,(1+i)^p = 65 s_{\overline{144}|.50125\%}(1.00501252)^{96} = \$13{,}673.39(1.6160744)$

Value of the fund after 20 years is $22,097.22

Example 5.6.6

Find the payment for a Canadian mortgage written for a $54,000 loan with monthly payments for 20 years at 7%(2).

■ Monthly payments with semiannual interest is case II where interest is computed less often than payments are made.

1. Find the effective rate:

$$k = \tfrac{2}{12} = \tfrac{1}{6} \text{ and } i = \tfrac{7}{2} = 3.5\%, \text{ so } j = (1.035)^{\frac{1}{6}} - 1 = .00575\%$$

2. Find the payment: $A_n = R a_{\overline{n}|i} \rightarrow 54{,}000 = R a_{\overline{240}|.575\%}$

$$R = \$415.43$$

◀ EXERCISES 5.6 ▶

Assume that compound interest is paid for part of a period.

Concept and Short Answer Exercises

1. 8%(4) ≈ ___%(12)?
2. 9%(12) ≈ ___%(2)?
3. 6.8%(1) ≈ ___%(4)?
4. 5.2%(4) ≈ ___ %(2)?
5. Give the three steps used to calculate a bundle of money equivalent to a sequence of payments for a general annuity. (Remember that checking the interest compounding periods against the payment periods is also a step.)
6. Give the three steps used to calculate the payments equivalent to a bundle of money.
7. Give the four steps used to calculate the number of payments and the final partial payment equivalent to a bundle of money.
8. Which of the following must be true for the general annuity problem?
   a. Payment of equal values at regular intervals.
   b. Interest compounding period the same as the payment period.
   c. Present value located one period before the first payment.
   d. Future value located on the period of the last payment.

Calculation Exercises

9. A popular carpet store advertises that payments are deferred for 2 years. If we can afford to pay $200/month for 3 years at 9%(2), what is the maximum price of the carpet that we can afford?
10. What is the maximum price of the furniture that a customer can afford if he can pay $200/month for 3 years at 9%(4) with payments deferred for 2 years?

11. A man has an inheritance of $200,000 from which he wants to withdraw $10,000 quarterly starting immediately. If money earns 9% compounded monthly, compute the number of full quarterly stipends and the final stipend.

12. Repeat Exercise 11, but assume that money earns 9% compounded yearly.

13. Dr. Evans leaves a university $1,000,000 on 1/1/03. Starting on 1/1/05, semiannual grants will be paid to the MacArthur Life Science student fund. At 7%(12), how large will these grants be if

    a. The last is on 1/1/15?

    b. The grants continue in perpetuity?

14. Repeat Exercise 13 at 7%.

15. Jenny wants to save $20,000 within the next 5 years. If her monthly deposits are made at the beginning of each month and if her savings is making 5%, find the monthly deposit upped to the next full dollar.

16. Repeat Exercise 15 at 5%(4).

17. Victoria wants to save $20,000 by making $500 monthly deposits. If her monthly deposits are made starting immediately and if her savings is making 5%, find the number of full monthly deposit and the last partial deposit.

18. Repeat Exercise 17 at 5%(4).

Theory and Extension Exercises

Note: These problems anticipate Section 5.7. The derivations in Exercises 19 and 20 use the equivalent rate of the force interest, δ, if there are p payments per year. Exercises 19 and 20 will be derived again in Section 5.7 using another approach. It is instructive to do these problems on your own before reading Section 5.7.

19. We have an annuity that is compounding continuously with a force of interest δ and with p payments per year. Derive the formula for S_n, the future value of the annuity with n payments.

20. We have an annuity that is compounding continuously with a force of interest δ and with p payments per year. Derive the formula for A_n, the present value of the annuity with n payments.

21. Use the formula derived in Exercise 20 to calculate the monthly payment for a 30-year annuity whose present value is $50,000 costing $\delta = .045$.

22. Use the formula derived in Exercise 19 to calculate the future value of a 7-year annuity with quarterly payments of $90 earning at $\delta = .0525$.

5.7 Annuities with Continuous Compounding

In Chapter 3 we developed formulas for computing future and present values at a rate compounded continuously. In this section we will consider the existence of similar formulas for annuities with interest compounded continuously. In Chapter 9 we will study continuous income streams in situations where there is an infinite number of payments to match the continuous compounding. For now we are interested in level payments at p times per year but with continuously compounded interest. There are two approaches to arrive at a method of evaluating annuities in the context of continuous rates. The first is to apply our equivalent rate structure and then revert the problem to one in which the interest rate and payment period coincide. The second is a more classical approach where the annuity is modeled as a geometric sequence in order to find the future and present values.

The first approach uses a two-step interest rate computation. The continuous rate δ is first converted to an equivalent annual rate $i(1)$. The annual rate is then changed to an equivalent effective rate $i(p)$ that matches the payment periods per year. This method was used to do Example 5.6.5 of Section 5.6.

Example 5.7.1

A homeowner saves \$70 per month for the replacement of his furnace and air conditioning system in 3 years. If the money is deposited into a fund paying 6% compounded continuously, how much will be available for the project in 3 years?

■ The effective annual rate is found as $i(1) = e^{.06} - 1 = .061836547$. The effective monthly rate is found as $j = (1+i)^{1/12} - 1 = (1.061836547)^{1/12} - 1 = .501252085\%/\text{mo}$.

$$S_n = R s_{\overline{n}|i} = 70 s_{\overline{36}|.5012\cdots} = \$2754.15$$

In the second approach we model the annuity as a geometric sequence where each term is the periodic payment valued at either the location of the future value or present value. This development will deal with just ordinary annuities. We will assume p payments per year for t years at a continuous compound rate δ. We also know from Section 3.7 that the future value of each payment is found by the following formula: $S = Pe^{\delta t}$. Let R be \$1 to simplify the derivation. Note that $n = pt$.

TIME LINE DIAGRAM 5.7.1

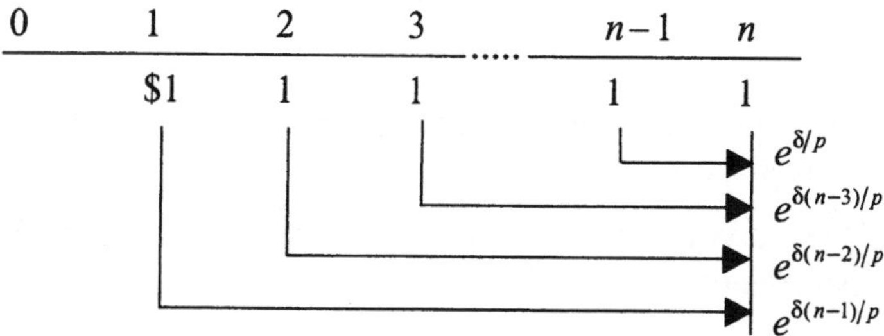

Adding the future values of the individual payments will give the following geometric series, which is summed with the general geometric series formula.

$$s_{\overline{n}|} = 1 + e^{\delta/p} + e^{2\delta/p} + \cdots + e^{\delta(n-3)/p} + e^{\delta(n-2)/p} + e^{\delta(n-1)/p}$$

Substitute into the general geometric series formula, noting that the ratio is $e^{\delta/p}$. The present value formula is found easily by multiplying by $e^{-n\delta/p}$.

$$s_{\overline{n}|} = \frac{1-(e^{\delta/p})^n}{1-e^{\delta/p}} = \frac{1-e^{n\delta/p}}{1-e^{\delta/p}} = \frac{e^{n\delta/p}-1}{e^{\delta/p}-1} \quad \text{and} \quad a_{\overline{n}|} = \left[\frac{e^{n\delta/p}-1}{e^{\delta/p}-1}\right]e^{-n\delta/p} = \frac{1-e^{-n\delta/p}}{e^{\delta/p}-1} \ \blacksquare$$

We have proved the following theorem for the future and present values of a continuous compounded annuity with n level payments.

Theorem 5.7.1 If \$$R$ is the level periodic payment of an ordinary annuity of n payments invested at a continuously compounded rate δ and paid p times per year, then the future and present values are given by

$$\textbf{FV: } S_n = R\left[\frac{e^{\delta n/p}-1}{e^{\delta/p}-1}\right] \qquad \textbf{PV: } A_n = R\left[\frac{1-e^{-\delta n/p}}{e^{\delta/p}-1}\right] \tag{5.10}$$

Example 5.7.2

Repeat Example 5.7.1 using formula (5.10).

■ From the information in Example 5.7.1 we have $R=70$, $\delta=.06$, and $n=36$.

$$S_n = R\left[\frac{e^{\delta n/p}-1}{e^{\delta/p}-1}\right] \rightarrow 70\left[\frac{e^{.06(36)/12}-1}{e^{.06/12}-1}\right] = 70\left[\frac{.197217363}{.00501252}\right] = \$2754.15$$

Example 5.7.3

What is the present worth of an investment that returns quarterly payments of \$2000 each for a period of 5 years when invested at 7% compounded continuously?

■ $$A_n = R\frac{1-e^{-n\delta/p}}{e^{\delta/p}-1} = 2000\frac{1-e^{-20(.07)/4}}{e^{.07/4}-1} = \$33{,}455.48$$

◀ EXERCISES 5.7 ▶

Concept and Short Answer Exercises

1. Prove that $j = \dfrac{i(p)}{p} = e^{\delta/p} - 1$.

2. Find the equivalent rate $i(4)$ to the force of interest $\delta = .08$ when there are 4 payments per year.

3. Find the equivalent rate $i(12)$ to the force of interest 5.32%(∞) when there are 12 payments per year.

4. Prove that $S_n = Rs_{\overline{n}|i} = R\dfrac{e^{\delta n/p}-1}{e^{\delta/p}-1}$ using the results of Exercise 1.

5. Prove that $A_n = Ra_{\overline{n}|i} = R\dfrac{1-e^{-\delta n/p}}{e^{\delta/p}-1}$ using the results of Exercise 1.

Calculation Exercises

6. A \$50,000 inheritance is invested in a fund paying 4.5%(∞). The beneficiary wishes to receive monthly payments from the fund for 30 years. How much will the monthly stipend be?

7. If an employee makes deposits of \$90 per quarter into a credit union that pays 5.25%(∞), what will the employee have after 7 years of saving?

8. Calculate the force of interest δ necessary to make the present value of \$2000 semiannual payments over 5 years worth \$18,000

a. Without finding a semiannual rate
b. By finding a semiannual rate and then converting it to the force of interest δ

9. Calculate the force of interest δ necessary to make the future value of \$2000 semiannual payments over 5 years of worth \$22,000

a. Without finding a semiannual rate
b. By finding a semiannual rate and then converting it to the force of interest δ

10. Money is worth 8%(∞). \$20,000 is invested on 1/1/04. On 7/1/08 the first quarterly withdrawal of \$500 is made. Find the number of withdrawals and the final partial withdrawal

a. Without finding a quarterly rate
b. By converting the force of interest δ to a quarterly rate

11. Money is worth 8%(∞). To save \$20,000 by 1/1/10 make the first quarterly deposit on 4/1/05 and the last quarterly deposit and on 10/1/08. Find the size of the quarterly deposits

a. Without finding a quarterly rate
b. By converting the force of interest δ to a quarterly rate

Chapter 5 Summary of Concepts

Future Value of an Annuity Due: $S_n(\text{due}) = R\,s_{\overline{n}|i}(1+i) = R\ddot{s}_{\overline{n}|i}$

Present Value of an Annuity Due: $A_n(\text{due}) = R\,a_{\overline{n}|i}(1+i) = R\ddot{a}_{\overline{n}|i}$

Present Value of a Deferred Annuity: $A_n(\text{def}) = R\,a_{\overline{n}|i}(1+i)^{-m}$

Future Value of a Forborne Annuity: $S_n(\text{for}) = R\,s_{\overline{n}|i}(1+i)^{p}$

Last Payment for Accumulation: $x = \text{Target Value} - S_n(\text{due})$

Last Payment for Withdrawal: $x = [A_n(1+i)^n - R\,s_{\overline{n}|i}](1+i)$

Ordinary Perpetuity: $R = iA_\infty$ or $A_\infty = Ra_{\overline{\infty}|i}$

Perpetuity Due: $R = dA_\infty$ or $A_\infty = R\ddot{a}_{\overline{\infty}|i}$

Perpetuity with Growing Payment: $R = (i-g)A_\infty$

Effective Interest Rate: $j = (1+i)^{\frac{m}{p}} - 1$

Ordinary Annuity–Continuous

Future Value: $S_n = R\left[\dfrac{e^{\delta n/p} - 1}{e^{\delta/p} - 1}\right]$

Present Value: $$A_n = R\left[\frac{1-e^{-\delta n/p}}{e^{\delta/p}-1}\right]$$

Chapter 5 Vocabulary Check

Annuity Due	*Interval of Forbearance*
Balloon Payment	*Insurance Premium*
Continuous Compounding	*Number of Withdrawals*
Deferred Annuity	*Ordinary (Annuity Immediate)*
Endowment	*Perpetuity*
Equivalent Values	*Perpetuity Due*
Forborne Annuity	*Perpetuity Immediate*
General Annuity	*Simple Annuity*
Interval of Deferment	*Stipend*

Chapter 5 Skills Check

1. Classify annuities by where the "bundle" is located.

   Section 5.1 Exercise 5.1

2. Find future and present values of annuities due.

   Section 5.2 Examples 1, 2; Exercises 7, 9

3. Find the last partial payment and outstanding balance.

   Section 5.2 Examples 3, 4; Exercises 17, 24

4. Find the number of deferment intervals and the payment or present value of a deferred annuity.

   Section 5.3 Examples 1, 2; Exercises 7, 9, 13

5. Find the number of periods of forbearance and the payment or future value of a forborne annuity.

   Section 5.4 Examples 1, 2; Exercises 9, 13

6. Find the regular perpetual income from a perpetuity.

   Section 5.5 Examples 1, 2; Exercise 7

7. Find the equivalent effective rate for general case annuities.

   Section 5.6 Examples 1, 2; Exercises 1, 3

8. Find the future and present values and the payment for ordinary annuities with continuous compound interest.

   Section 5.6 Examples 1, 2, 3; Exercises 6, 7, 11

Review Test for Other Annuities Certain

In-annuity period: During this time a person will save for a future need by making deposits (generally during the years that he is earning a regular income) to accumulate a bundle of money.

Sitting period: The bundle of money will sit for a period of time while the money is not needed, in order to grow at compound interest to a larger bundle of money.

Out-annuity or **perpetuity period:** This bundle of money is then distributed in periodic rents to meet some future need for regular income.

1. Joseph pays $100 per month into a savings account earning 5%(4), with the first deposit on 5/1/99 and the last on 8/1/03. Then the money sits until 10/1/05 when Joseph takes out his first semiannual retirement payment. Find the semiannual retirement payment if

   a. The last one is on 4/1/10.

   b. The retirement payments are to last indefinitely.

2. Repeat Exercise 1 at 5%(2).

3. To cover repairs on their building, a church has a sinking fund that earns 8%(2). Quarterly payments of $15,000 are paid to this sinking fund with the first on 6/1/99 and the last on 9/1/10. On 9/1/10 the money is reinvested at an interest rate of 9%(1). On 10/1/12 the church votes to use this money to give monthly support to missionaries. Find the available monthly support if the first withdrawal is to be made immediately (i.e., on 10/1/12) and

   a. The last is on 8/1/20.

   b. The support money continues indefinitely.

4. A small business makes $15,000 quarterly payments into an equity fund that earns an average return of 8%(12). The fund was started on 6/1/99 and payments will continue until 9/1/10. Suppose the fund is reinvested on 9/1/10 at 9%(4), and starting on 10/1/12 monthly payments will be made from the account to help cover the employees' benefits. With payments starting on 10/1/12, how much is available monthly if

   a. Payments continue until 8/1/20?

   b. Payments continue indefinitely?

5. From 9/1/66 until 11/1/99 a rich philanthropist, Dr. Dotcom, gave his favorite university $1000 per month. The university invested the income in a fund earning 7%(2). Suppose that on 11/1/42 the fund is reinvested at 10%(4). On 11/1/43 the university will start distributing yearly scholarships. Find the amount available for the yearly scholarships if

   a. The last is on 11/1/3043.

   b. They are paid indefinitely.

6. The Third Planet Foundation gives a university astronomy department \$1000 per month, with the first on 9/1/66 and the last on 11/1/99. The money is invested at 7%(4). To celebrate the 100th anniversary of TPF, the astronomy department starts distributing yearly scholarships on 11/1/43. If the interest rate is changed to 10%(2) on 11/1/42, find the amount available for the yearly scholarships if

   a. The last is on 11/1/3043.

   b. They go on in perpetuity.

Chapter 6

Debt Retirement Methods

6.1 Amortization of Debts and Amortization Schedules

An important innovation in the structure of long-term debt retirement occurred during the early 1830s. The typical loan structure until that time had used simple or compound interest paid off in one lump sum at the end of the term. The wealthy and the commercial establishments made most of these large loans, and foreclosure was common since the debtors needed to pay back such large sums. Oxford Provident Building Association of Frankford, Pennsylvania, established in 1831, was the first banking association to use the deposits of its members to provide financing for the purchase of a home. The first loan on April 11, 1831 was for $375 and helped Mr. Comly Rich purchase and finance a three-room house in Frankford. Oxford Provident encouraged workers to save part of their earnings, which in turn made it possible for the lending institution to finance home ownership for the families of the association members [tempobank.com]. This new loan structure, called the *amortization method*, quickly spread into every area of business. The amortization method made it possible to finance large capital expenditures and use the resulting income to pay the debt with a sequence of payments.

To **amortize a debt** is to pay a sequence of equal-size payments, each of which is composed of the interest due plus a portion of the principal. The payments are structured to match the conversion frequency of the compound interest rate. If the loan were financed at 12% compounded monthly, then the interest due each month would be 1% of the previous balance. The term of the loan and the payment frequency determine the total number of payments. A 30-year loan financed with monthly payments will require 360 payments over the life of the loan. Because the principal is reduced each month, the interest at each payment will slowly decrease while the portion going to the principal will slowly increase. Early in the life of a loan, when the principal is large, the amount going to pay interest will make up most of the payment. Near the end of the loan, when the principal is quite small, the amount going to the principal will make up most of the payment. The lending institution will often provide the borrower with an **amortization schedule** that details every payment and how it is split between principal and interest. The schedule also gives the outstanding balance at any given payment. Several of the examples will illustrate the construction of an amortization table and how the numbers are calculated.

In this chapter we will come to understand the structure of amortized mortgages and the costs associated with borrowing. Knowing how interest rates and loan terms affect the long-term cost of borrowing money can help us make wise decisions about the choice of a lender and the terms offered. Many of our examples and exercises are going to deal with home or automobile mortgages. Commercial loans are often similar, but they may use other methods, like the sinking fund method introduced in Section 6.6.

We now consider a list of terms that need to be understood in order to set up a home mortgage. These terms would also apply to most commercial loans for capital expenditures.

1. The *cash price* of a home or automobile is the price you actually pay (including taxes). A home may be advertised for \$129,000, but if you can buy it with an offer of \$125,000, that is the cash price. When an individual sells the real property, it usually will not involve taxes in most states. An automobile for which you pay \$14,400 will have some state taxes added to give the cash price. Remember that cash is always present value or current value.

2. The *down payment* for a home loan is the actual amount of money you pay on the home before borrowing any money. Conventional loans through banks often require that 20% of the cash price be paid as a down payment. Hence, a \$125,000 house might require a \$25,000 down payment. If this is all you pay up front, then you will need to finance \$100,000. Unless related costs are added to the loan, this will be the present value of the loan annuity.

3. The *closing costs* for a loan are charges associated with the borrowing process. The lending institution will charge an origination fee to process the paperwork and to pay their staff. In the legal area there will be a lawyer's fee, a filing fee, document stamps, a title search, and title insurance. Sometimes the lender will charge a percent of the principal as "discount points." This cost will be taken up in Section 6.2. Depending on the buyer's financial situation, some or all of these costs may have to be added to the amount of money borrowed. On a \$100,000 loan, closing costs and points may amount to \$4000 or more.

4. The *payment* for a loan is based on the compounded interest rate and the term of the loan. The principal borrowed is simply the present value of an ordinary annuity, from which we calculate the resulting payment. A \$100,000 loan financed at 8%(12) over 30 years will require 360 monthly payments of \$733.77 each. Most lending institutions require the borrower to pay a monthly fee into an escrow account. This money is held by the lender until real estate taxes and homeowner's insurance premiums come due. If the real estate taxes are about \$1500 per year and the insurance about \$800, the escrow cost will be nearly \$200 per month. That makes the actual payment for the \$100,000 loan \$933.77 per month. We are going to concentrate on the principal and interest part of the loan in this chapter. As we go on, it may also prove to be eye opening to compute interest costs and changes in the APR resulting from charges for discount points.

5. An *amortization schedule* is a table giving five entries at each payment: the number of the payment (or date), the dollar value of the payment, the interest due at that payment, the amount that will go to principal, and the balance. The main purpose of

the table is to show how the payment is split between principal and interest, and the balance left on the loan. The key to any line of an amortization table is to understand that the interest entry on that line is the balance from the previous line times the rate per period. Table 6.1.1 below gives the first few lines of an amortization table for a $100,000 loan at 8%(12) for 30 years. The payment has been rounded up to the whole cent.

TABLE 6.1.1

Payment No.	Payment	Interest Paid	Principal Paid	Balance
0				$100,000.00
1	$733.77	$666.67	$67.10	$99,932.90
2	$733.77	$666.22	$67.55	$99,865.35
3	$733.77	$665.77	$68.00	$99,797.35

Example 6.1.1

Find the loan payment for an $84,000 house requiring 20% down that is financed at 8%(12) for 15 years. Find the payment for a rate of 7%(12) and give both the savings per month and the savings over the life of the loan that the lower rate provides.

■ The principal to be financed must be found by first subtracting 20% of $84,000 from $84,000. The down payment is $(.2)\times(\$84{,}000) = \$16{,}800$. The principal $=$ $\$84{,}000 - \$16{,}800 = \$67{,}200$. Now find the payments using an ordinary annuity. Note that $n = 12\times 15 = 180$.

Formula: $A_n = R\,a_{\overline{n|}i}$

$67{,}200 = R\,a_{\overline{180|}8/12} \rightarrow R = \$642.20$ Payment for 8%(12)

$67{,}200 = R\,a_{\overline{180|}7/12\%} \rightarrow R = \$604.02$ Payment for 7%(12)

The savings per month with the lower rate: $\$642.20 - \$604.02 = \$38.18$

The savings over the life of the loan: $180(\$38.18) = \$6872.40$

Example 6.1.2

Give the first three lines of the amortization table for the mortgage in Example 6.1.1 using the 8%(12) rate.

■ The interest due at the first payment will be $i = .\overline{6}$ times the balance 1 month earlier, which is the actual amount of the loan. The difference between the interest and the payment of $642.20 will be the amount paid on the principal.

TABLE 6.1.2

Payment No.	Payment	Interest Paid	Principal Paid	Balance
0				$67,200.00
1	$642.20	$448.00	$194.20	$67,005.80
2	$642.20	$446.71	$195.49	$66,810.31

Example 6.1.3

An automobile is purchased for $12,500, and a $3500 trade-in allowance is given. If the balance is financed at 10.5%(12) for 3 years and the 5% sales tax has a $300 cap, find the monthly payment.

■ The tax on $12,500 at 5% would be $625, so we use the $300 cap value for a total of $12,800. Subtracting the trade-in allowance of $3500 leaves a balance of $9300 to finance. We are finding the payment for an ordinary annuity with 36 payments.

Formula: $A_n = R a_{\overline{n}|i}$

$9300 = R a_{\overline{36}|10.5/12\%} \rightarrow R = \$302.28$ Monthly payment

◀ EXERCISES 6.1 ▶

Concept and Short Answer Exercises

1. An item cost $20,000, and the trade-in is worth $3000. Find the amount financed.
2. Why are payments often rounded up to the next penny or next dollar?
3. Give the formula(s) for the final payment of a loan. It is worth your time to compare the several equivalent methods given in the answer key.
4. A 2-year loan on $20,000 has 24 monthly payments of $1000 each. Find the total interest.
5. An 8%(12), $10,000 loan has monthly payments of $300. Find the payoff immediately after making the 14th payment.
6. Show how to use the amortization button on your financial calculator to find the answer to Exercise 5.
7. The payoff immediately after making the *n*th payment is also called by which of these terms?
   a. The outstanding balance of the loan
   b. The amount still owed on the loan
   c. The amount left on the loan
   d. The payoff on the loan
8. What's the purpose of an amortization schedule (table)?
9. If your financial calculator has an amortization button, tell how to use it to find the 14th line of the amortization table for an 8%(12), $10,000 loan with monthly payments of $300. Find the 14th line of the amortization table in Exercise 5.
10. Use a financial program like Quicken, MS Money, or Excel to print the amortization schedule for an 8%(12), $10,000 loan with 2 years of monthly payments.

Calculation Exercises

11. Susannah buys a $20,000 car with a $5000 trade-in and an additional $2000 down. The balance is financed over 2 years at 6%(12).

a. Find the payment rounded up to the nearest dollar.
b. Find the final payment.
c. Find the total amount paid in interest.
d. Give an amortization schedule for the first three lines of the loan.
e. Give the 12th line of the amortization table. (*Hint*: See Example 6.3.3)

12. Karen buys a $30,000 car with a $5000 trade-in and an additional $2000 down. The balance is financed over 3 years at 3.8%(12).
    a. Find the payment rounded up to the nearest dollar.
    b. Find the final payment.
    c. Find the total amount paid in interest.
    d. Give an amortization schedule for the first three lines of the loan.
    e. Give the 30th line of the amortization table.

13. Find the loan payment for a $65,000 house requiring 15% down, financed at 9%(12) for 30 years. Give the savings per month and the savings over the life of the loan if the rate were 8.5%(12).

14. Find the loan payment for a $165,000 house requiring 20% down, financed at 6.5%(12) for 30 years. Give the savings per month and over the life of the loan if the rate were 5.5%(12).

15. A Lexus can be purchased for $38,500. If the buyer trades in a Ford Explorer to receive an $8900 trade in allowance and then finances the balance at 9.5%(12) for 48 months, find the monthly payment.

16. A BMW can be purchased for $32,000. If the buyer trades in a Chevy Blazer to receive an $8200 allowance and then finances the balance at a force of interest of .055 for 60 months, find the monthly payment. *(The rate has been changed.)*

Theory and Extension Exercises

17. Randy borrows $$L$ to be repaid in 6 level yearly payments at an annual effective rate of 6%. Knowing that the outstanding balance at the end of the 2nd year is $3523.36, calculate how much principal is repaid on the 1st payment and on the 6th payment.

18. ♦Given that a loan has a present value of $a_{\overline{n|}}$, show that the sum of the interest repaid in the kth period plus the principal paid in the $k+1$st period is $1+v^{n-k}d$.

19. Kathryn needs $9400 to finance an automobile purchase. If the loan company charges 7%(12) compound discount for 3 years, what will her payment be?

20. R Corporation borrows $$W$ for n years at rate i per year. If the contract calls for them to pay $1/n$th of the principal per year plus interest, what is the kth payment?

6.2 Discount Points and Annual Percentage Rate

Because lending institutions operate under certain government regulations, they are restricted as to what rates they may charge. The regulating government agencies are usually the ones that guarantee or insure loans, like the Federal Housing

Administration (FHA). The lending institution is also in competition with other lenders, so its rates need to be competitive. The need to earn more revenue from mortgage loans during times of low rates brought into existence a type of up-front charge called **discount points**. A *point* is 1% of the amount of money being lent. It works like discount interest in that the lender subtracts the points from the loan amount before the borrower receives the money. For example, a bank charging 2 points on a $100,000 loan will subtract (.02)($100,000) or $2000 from the face value of the loan and give the borrower $98,000. However, the borrower must repay the whole $100,000 loan. This obviously increases the effective rate being charged for this loan. Before the truth-in-lending laws required the annual percentage rate (APR) to be stated on all loans, the points system could hide the true rate of borrowing. In this section we want to learn how to calculate the APR when discount points are charged. We must note that the seller of the real estate sometimes pays the points, and thus the rate of interest to the borrower would not increase. Of course, the seller can foresee the cost of paying points and increase the price of the real estate to include this cost.

If the borrower in a mortgage contract cannot afford to pay cash for the discount points, he or she can have them added to the loan. The mortgage then becomes a combined loan that includes both the points and the real estate. If the points are added to the loan, the size of the loan must be increased so that the borrower gets the amount of money needed to complete the real estate buying process. We must be cautious because just adding the $2000 to the $100,000 loan from the example above will not work. It is clear that 2% of $102,000 is $2040 and the borrower will receive only $99,960. If we think of it as an equation with a variable x, where x is the amount to be borrowed, we get $x - .02x = \$100{,}000$. This means that $.98x = \$100{,}000$, and so $x = \$100{,}000 \div .98 = \$102{,}040.82$. The actual discount to be paid when the points are added to the loan is $2040.82 rather than $2000. The result of all this can be summarized by noting that the loan amount = proceeds needed ÷ (1 − points rate).

The **annual percentage rate** (APR) is the rate that makes the cash value of the loan equal to the present value of the payments. This is equivalent to equating the proceeds from the loan to the present value of the payment annuity. There are two steps involved with this calculation, just like the steps we took in Chapter 4 with add-on loans.

▶1. Add the points to the loan and compute the payment based on the stated compound rate.

▶2. Set the cash value of the loan (loan minus points) equal to the present value of the payments using the formula for an ordinary annuity, $A_n = R\,a_{\overline{n}|i}$.

What happens if the borrower can afford to pay the points and does not need to add them to the loan? The APR calculation will still use the second step above, but the cash value of the loan will be the amount the lender advances after subtracting the points from the original amount of the loan. The payment will still be based on whatever amount of money the loan was written for. The APR rate will be the same even if the points are charged but not added to the loan. The following examples will illustrate finding the new loan with points, added or not added, and computing the APR.

Example 6.2.1

Find the annual percentage rate (APR) for a home loan of \$55,600 for 15 years at 7.25%(12) where the lender charges 2¼ points that are added to the loan.

■ First compute the amount of the loan with points added. Then find the payment based on the result and the loan parameters.

$$\text{Loan with points} = \frac{\$55,600}{1-.0225} = \frac{\$55,600}{.9775} = \$56,879.80 \quad \text{Points} = \$1,279.80$$

$$\text{Payment formula: } A_n = R\,a_{\overline{n}|i} \rightarrow 56,879.80 = R\,a_{\overline{180}|7.25/12\%} \rightarrow R = \$519.24$$

Find the APR by setting the cash value of the loan equal to the present value of the payments.

Formula: $A_n = R\,a_{\overline{n}|i}$

$$55,600 = 519.24\,a_{\overline{180}|i} \rightarrow i = .635\% \quad \text{Rate per month}$$

APR $= 12\times(.635\%) = 7.62\%(12)$. Not adding the points also gives 7.62%(12).

Example 6.2.2

A house priced at \$135,500 can be financed for 20% down, at 6.75%(12) for 30 years, with 3 points. If the points are added to the loan, and insurance and taxes amount to \$2583 per year, find the APR and the monthly payment including escrow.

■ To find the amount the buyer needs to net from the loan, subtract the down payment. Then find the amount of the loan with points added and compute the loan payment.

$$\text{Net amount to borrow} = \$135,500 - 20\%(\$135,500) = .8(135,500) = \$108,400$$

$$\text{Loan with points} = \frac{108,400}{1-.03} = \frac{108,400}{.97} = \$111,752.58 \text{ (the points} = \$3352.58)$$

Payment formula: $A_n = R\,a_{\overline{n}|i}$

$$111,752.58 = R\,a_{\overline{360}|6.75/12\%} \rightarrow R = \$724.83$$

Find the APR by setting the cash value of the loan equal to the present value of the payments.

Formula: $A_n = R\,a_{\overline{n}|i}$

$$108,400 = 724.83\,a_{\overline{360}|i} \rightarrow i = .587\% \quad \text{Rate per month}$$

APR $= 12\times(.587\%) = 7.05\%(12)$

$$\text{The monthly payment with escrow} = 724.83 + \frac{2583}{12} = \$940.08$$

Example 6.2.3

Find the annual percentage rate (APR) for a home loan of \$95,600 financed for 30 years at 8.25%(12) where the lender charges 1¾ points that are not added to the loan.

■ Compute the payment and find the amount advanced after the points are subtracted.

Payment formula: $A_n = R\,a_{\overline{n}|i}$

$95{,}600 = R\,a_{\overline{360}|8.25/12\%} \rightarrow R = \$718.21$

Amount advanced after points: \$95,600 – (.0175)(\$95,600) = \$93,927

Find the APR by setting the cash value of the loan equal to the present value of the payments.

Formula: $A_n = R\,a_{\overline{n}|i}$

$93{,}927 = 718.21\,a_{\overline{360}|i} \rightarrow i = .7033\%$ Rate per month

$\text{APR} = 12 \times (.7033\%) = 8.44\%(12)$. Adding the points also gives 8.44%(12).

◀ EXERCISES 6.2 ▶

Concept and Short Answer Exercises

1. What are points in a home loan?
2. In financing a \$100,000 home with 20% down and 3 points, the amount financed is _____.
3. In financing a \$250,000 loan with 10% down and 2 points, the amount financed is _____.
4. Find the APR for a \$20,000 loan that is paid off with 24 monthly payments of \$1000.
5. Find the APR for a \$100,000 home loan with a term of 30 years and with \$733.76 monthly payments.
6. Find the APR for a \$30,000 car loan with a term of 5 years and with \$625.67 monthly payments.
7. When getting a loan, it is wise to inquire at several possible loan institutions to see which has the best overall rate. Different institutions may have loans with different stated rates and different points. If the term of the loan stays the same, to argue which loan institution has the better overall rate we should
   a. Compute the APR for each and see which is _____.
   b. Compute the monthly payments for each and see which is _____.
8. In Exercise 7, if the terms are different, which one of **a** or **b** still gives a valid comparison?

Calculation Exercises

9. To secure a 20-year 9%(12) loan on their $200,000 home, a couple must pay 10% down and 3.2 points, which will be added to the loan.
   a. Find the amount of the loan.
   b. Find the payment.
   c. Find the actual APR.
10. To secure a 30-year 7%(12) loan on her $300,000 home, Victoria must pay 20% down and 5.2 points, which will be added to the loan.
    a. Find the amount of the loan.
    b. Find the payment.
    c. Find the actual APR.
11. To secure a 15-year 10.3%(12) loan on his $100,000 home, Albert must pay 20% down and 2 points.
    a. Find the amount of the loan.
    b. Find the payment.
    c. Find the actual APR.
12. To secure a 22-year 6.3%(12) loan on their $150,000 home, a couple must pay 20% down and 1.5 points.
    a. Find the amount of the loan.
    b. Find the payment.
    c. Find the actual APR.
13. Assuming points are financed over the term of the loan, would you do better with a 20-year 6%(12) $100,000 loan or a 20-year 5.8%(12) $100,000 loan with 2 points? Why is no loan value needed to make the comparison?
14. Assuming points are financed over the term of the loan, which is better, a 30-year 7%(12) loan or a 30-year 6.5%(12) loan with 4 points?
15. Assuming points are financed over the term of the loan, would you do better with a 25-year 8%(12) $200,000 loan with 2 points or a 25-year 7.9%(12) $200,000 loan with 4 points?
16. Assuming points are financed over the term of the loan, which is better, a 30-year 7%(12) loan with 1.5 points or a 30-year 6.9%(12) loan with 4 points?

Theory and Extension Exercises

17. If a 15-year loan for $40,000 is financed at 8%(12) with 1.75 points, how many points would a person have to pay to create an equivalent APR on a the loan that is financed at 7.5%(12)?
18. $*M* financed at 7%(12) for 20 years with 2 points has the same APR as what force of interest for the same loan?
19. Roger gets a $60,000 loan at 6.5%(12) for 15 years with 1.75 points. If he can finance the points with a separate loan with the same term at 5%(12), what will the APR be?
20. Write a general solution in terms of $a_{\overline{n}|}$ for finding the rate per period i to get the APR when the given rate is j per period and the points are given as r%.

6.3 Outstanding Balance during the Term of a Loan

Most home mortgages are not continued for the entire term, because either they are refinanced or the property is sold. In order to refinance a loan, the outstanding balance at the time of refinancing must be known. The **outstanding balance** is the principal still to be paid, and it is often the amount of the new loan. The most common reason people refinance their mortgage is to lower the interest rate. If the mortgage was taken out during a time of high rates but current rates are now lower, refinancing might be an excellent choice. If current rates are at least 2% lower, refinancing would be a wise financial decision. The cost of refinancing will usually include all the typical closing costs (and possibly points), so these must be deducted from the actual savings in interest charges.

The length of a loan's term that remains after refinancing will also have a bearing on the choice to refinance. If a number of years in the term remain, even rates with less than a 2% difference may realize a significant saving to the borrower. Some people refinance in order to change the term of their loan. They may now be able to afford a larger payment and therefore want to save interest by paying the loan off more quickly. Other people want to increase the term of their loan when they find that their payment is too large for their income level. Others may want to remove equity from the real estate to finance some business adventure or make significant improvements to the property.

We have two approaches for finding the outstanding balance:

▶1. We can find the present value of the remaining payments. However, the common practice of rounding all payments up to the cent, dime, or dollar makes this method less accurate. Finding the present value of the remaining payments is often referred to as the **prospective method**. The present value formula is used, and n will be the number of remaining payments.

The **outstanding balance** of the n remaining payments: $A_n = R\,a_{\overline{n|}i}$.

▶2. We can find the difference between the accumulated value of what has actually been paid and the original principal accumulated to the date of the refinancing. This method is often referred to as the **retrospective method**. This method is a little more complicated if done by figuring the parts; however, the financial calculator is set up to do this computation quickly while you only punch a couple of buttons. The following formula was presented in Section 5.2 on page 153 with last payment problems. It takes the present value A_n forward for n periods at the compound interest rate i and subtracts the future value of n payments each of value R at the same rate i.

The **outstanding balance** after n payments have been made:

$$\text{OB} = A_n(1+i)^n - R\,s_{\overline{n|}i}\,.$$

Using the financial calculator, we compute the payment with the given parameters of principal, compound rate, and term (number of payments). We then round the payment (keeping the negative) and enter it in PMT, replace n by the payment number at which we are finding the balance, and compute the FV. The calculator will give us the outstanding balance. We can also use this method to find the smaller last payment that results when the original payment is rounded up. The following examples will illustrate finding the outstanding balance.

Example 6.3.1

Find the outstanding balance at the end of 8 years for the following loan for \$85,000 financed at 8.5%(12) for 15 years.

▪ First find the payment using the present value formula for an ordinary annuity. Then round the payment up and replace n by $8 \times 12 = 96$ and compute the future value.

Payment formula: $A_n = R\,a_{\overline{n}|i}$

$85{,}000 = R\,a_{\overline{180}|8.5/12\%} \rightarrow R = \$837.03 \;\; (\$837.0286)$

Outstanding balance formula: $A_n(1+i)^n - R\,s_{\overline{n}|i}$ Retrospective

(with $n = 96$) OB = \$52,854.26

Now use the present value of the remaining payments method.

Present value of the remaining 84 payments: $A_n = R\,a_{\overline{n}|i}$ Prospective

$A_n = 837.03\,a_{\overline{84}|8.5/12\%} = \$52{,}854.53$

Note that the difference yielded by the two methods is only \$0.27.

Example 6.3.2

A home costing \$180,000 was financed for 30 years with 20% down at 7%(12) and 2 points. If the points are added to the loan, what is the outstanding balance at the end of 18 years?

▪ There are two preliminary steps before computing the outstanding balance information. First find the amount to borrow after the down payment and then the size of the loan with points added.

Net amount to borrow = \$180,000 – 20%(\$180,000) = \$144,000

Loan with points added: $= \dfrac{\$144{,}000}{1-.02} = \dfrac{\$144{,}000}{.98} = \$146{,}938.78$ Points = \$2938.78

Payment formula: $A_n = R\,a_{\overline{n}|i}$

$\$146{,}938.78 = R\,a_{\overline{360}|7/12\%} \rightarrow R = \$977.59 \; (\$977.587)$

Outstanding balance formula: $A_n(1+i)^n - R\,s_{\overline{n}|i}$ (with $n = 216$) → OB = \$95,059.67

One very useful application of outstanding balance is finding the split between principal and interest for any payment in a loan. Finding this information would typically require having the amortization table printed out so any line could be read.

The key is to remember that the interest paid at any payment is the rate per period times the outstanding balance from the previous payment period. For example, if we want to know the amount of interest paid at the 84th payment of a loan, we will need the outstanding balance at the 83rd payment. Once we know the interest, the principal paid is found by subtracting the interest from the payment. To complete the 84th line of the amortization table will require us to subtract the principal paid from the outstanding balance at the 83rd payment.

Example 6.3.3

Find the 84th line of the amortization table for a $64,000 home loan financed at 9%(12) for 15 years.

■ First find the payment required for this loan; then find the outstanding balance at the 83rd payment. This balance is then multiplied by the rate $i = .75\% = .0075$ to give the interest due at the 84th payment.

Payment formula: $A_n = R\,a_{\overline{n}|i}$

$$64{,}000 = R\,a_{\overline{180}|\frac{9}{12}\%} \rightarrow R = \$649.13 \quad (649.1306)$$

Outstanding balance formula: $A_n(1+i)^n - R\,s_{\overline{n}|i}$

$$\text{OB} = \$44{,}623.17 \text{ at the 83rd payment}$$

Interest paid at the 84th payment $= .0075 \times (\$44{,}623.17) = \$334.67$

Principal paid at the 84th payment $= \$649.13 - \$334.67 = \$314.46$

The outstanding balance at the 84th payment $= \$44{,}623.17 - \$314.46 = \$44{,}308.71$

TABLE 6.3.1

Payment No.	Payment	Interest Paid	Principal Paid	Balance
83				$44,623.17
84	$649.13	$334.67	$314.46	$44,308.71

◀ EXERCISES 6.3 ▶

Concept and Short Answer Exercises

1. Use your financial calculator to find the 24th line of the amortization table on a $50,000 loan with monthly payments of $500 at 6%(12).
2. Give the formulas necessary to do Exercise 1.
3. Use your financial calculator to find the 30th line of the amortization table on a $5000 loan with monthly payments of $100 at 9%(12).
4. Give the formulas to do Exercise 3.

Calculation Exercises

5. Find the outstanding balance at the end of 6 years for a \$55,600 loan financed at 7.5%(12) for 15 years.

6. Find the outstanding balance at the end of 8 years for a \$55,600 loan financed at 7.5%(12) for 15 years.

7. A home costing \$115,800 was financed for 30 years with 20% down at 8.8%(12) and 1.25 points. If the points are added to the loan, what is the outstanding balance after 16 years and 8 months?

8. A home costing \$166,000 was financed for 20 years with 25% down at 10.8%(12) and 2.4 points. If the points are added to the loan, what is the outstanding balance after 16 years and 8 months?

9. Find the 56th line of the amortization table for a \$75,000 loan financed at 6.75%(12) for 15 years.

10. Find the 30th line of the amortization table for a \$55,000 loan financed at 6.8%(12) for 20 years.

Theory and Extension Exercises

11. Prove that the retrospective method and the prospective method for the outstanding balance of an annuity are equivalent. Establish your results at the kth payment using an annuity of n level payments of \$1 at rate i per period.

12. ♦Assume that the present value of a loan is $a_{\overline{n}|i}$ and show that the sum of the interest paid for any 2 consecutive payments kth and $(k+1)$st is given by $2-(v+1)v^{n-k}$.

13. Assume that the present value of a loan is $a_{\overline{n}|i}$ and show the kth line of the amortization schedule.

14. The Jackson family has a loan for \$82,000 financed at 8%(12) for 30 years. At the end of the 7th year they start paying an additional \$70 per month toward the principal of the loan. If they continue to do this what will the new term be and what will their last payment be?

6.4 Refinancing Loans and the Resulting Savings

Now that we have established a way to find the outstanding balance for a loan, we are ready to see how much interest savings can be realized by refinancing at a lower rate or by decreasing the term of the loan. The comparison is made between the *existing* payment for the remainder of the term and the *new* payment for the remainder of the term. Since the remaining principal will be the same either way, the difference in the two payments must be the interest saved per month. We can also now find the total amount of interest paid for the term of a loan. Many people are shocked to find that the total interest over the life of a loan may equal or exceed the actual principal borrowed. In effect, a \$100,000 house may cost \$200,000 before it is paid for. Of course, there are some offsetting benefits like property value appreciation and tax deductions, and these will be taken up in the next section.

Any time a borrower can decrease the term of the loan, considerable savings in interest charges will be realized. In fact, the loan could even be refinanced at a higher rate, and yet thousands of dollars are saved. The reason lies in the fact that a larger payment and a shorter term pay much more principal each payment. For example, a \$60,000 loan at 7%(12) for 30 years will cost \$45,895 more in interest charges than a \$60,000 loan at 8%(12) for 15 years. This difference assumes the loan in each case is kept to the end of the term.

Besides decreasing the term as shown above, observe in Figure 6.1, that paying more frequently will also reduce the total amount paid over the life of a loan.

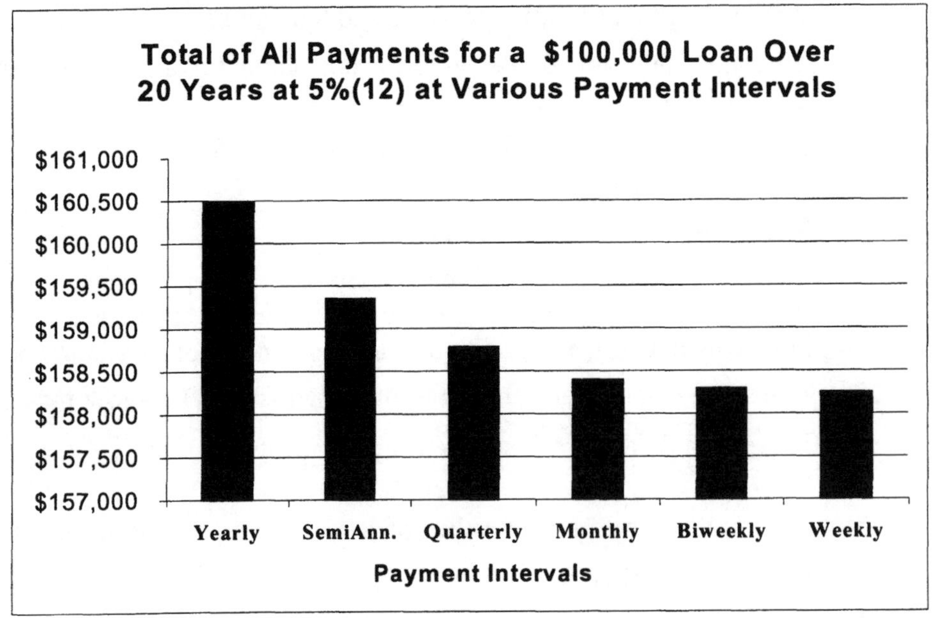

FIGURE 6.1

Example 6.4.1

A home loan for \$52,000 is financed at 8.5%(12) for 30 years and no points. Find the interest saved if this loan is refinanced at 7.0%(12) at the end of the 10th year, leaving the remaining term unchanged. Assuming that no other refinancing takes place, how much interest was paid during the 8.5% loan, and how much was paid during the 7% loan?

■ The first step is to find the payment for the original loan and then compute the outstanding balance at the 120th payment. This balance will be the loan principal for the 7% loan. The savings realized will be the difference in the payments times the number of payments, 360 – 120 = 240.

Payment formula: $A_n = R\, a_{\overline{n}|i}$

$$52{,}000 = R\, a_{\overline{360}|8.5/12\%} \quad \rightarrow \quad R = \$399.84 \text{ First payment}$$

Outstanding balance formula: $A_n(1+i)^n - R\,s_{\overline{n}|i}$

$$OB = \$46{,}072.39 \quad (n = 120)$$

New payment: $\$46{,}072.39 = R\,a_{\overline{240}|7/12\%} \rightarrow R = \$357.20$

Refinancing savings: $240 \times (\$399.84 - \$357.20) = 240 \times (\$42.64) = \$10{,}233.60$

Interest paid at 8%: total paid out in payments minus principal paid off

$$= 120 \times (\$399.84) - (\$52{,}000 - \$46{,}072.39)$$

$$= \$47{,}980.80 - \$5927.61 = \$42{,}053.19$$

Interest paid at 7%: total paid out in payments minus principal paid off

$$= 240 \times (\$357.20) - \$46{,}072.39$$

$$= \$85{,}728.00 - \$46{,}072.39 = \$39{,}655.61$$

Interest paid over the 30 year life of the loan = $81,708.80

Example 6.4.2

A $75,500 home loan was originally financed for 30 years at 7%(12). At the end of 8 years and 5 months the mortgage is refinanced at 8%(12) for 15 years. Find the total savings in interest if the new 15-year loan is paid off as scheduled.

■ First find the payment for the 30-year loan and then find the outstanding balance at the 101st payment ($8 \times 12 + 5$). Use the outstanding balance as the present value of the new 15-year loan. The savings in this case will be the difference between the total interest that would have accrued by keeping the 30-year loan and the total interest that will accrue during the new 15-year loan.

Payment formula: $A_n = R\,a_{\overline{n}|i}$

$$75{,}500 = R\,a_{\overline{360}|7/12\%} \rightarrow R = \$502.31 \text{ First payment}$$

Outstanding balance: $A_n(1+i)^n - R\,s_{\overline{n}|i}$

$$OB = \$67{,}018.11 \quad (n = 101)$$

New payment: $A_n = R\,a_{\overline{n}|i}$

$$67{,}018.11 = R\,a_{\overline{180}|8/12\%} \rightarrow R = \$640.46 \text{ New payment}$$

Interest charges if the remaining 259 payments had been paid off at 7%(12):

$$\text{Total paid out} - \text{principal paid off} = 259 \times (\$502.31) - \$67{,}018.11 = \$63{,}080.18$$

Interest charges that resulted from paying all the payments for the new 15-year loan:

$$\text{Total paid out} - \text{principal paid off} = 180 \times (\$640.46) - \$67{,}018.11 = \$48{,}264.69$$

Savings realized using a 15-year loan $= \$63{,}080.18 - \$48{,}264.69 = \$14{,}815.49$

◀ EXERCISE 6.4 ▶

Concept and Short Answer Exercises

1. When is refinancing a home worthwhile?
2. What are closing costs and what do they have to do with a loan or with refinancing a loan?
3. Internet topic: Discuss variable rate loans. What are they? When are they better/worse than fixed rate loans? Why does this text discuss fixed rate loans but not variable rate loans?
4. Tell how to calculate the refinanced
   a. Term
   b. Balance
   c. Payment
5. Assume your old payments on a 30-year loan were $1000 per month and suppose that after refinancing in 10 years your new payments are $900. Give the total savings if:
   a. The term is unchanged. b. The refinanced term is 15 years.
6. Assume your old payments on a 20-year loan were $1500 per month and suppose that after refinancing in 5 years your new payments are $1200. Give the total savings if
   a. The term is unchanged. b. The refinanced term is 10 years.

Calculation Exercises

Use the results from Exercises 6.2, items 9–12, to complete the following:

7. To secure a 20-year 9%(12) loan on their $200,000 home, a couple must pay 10% down and 3.2 points that will be added to the loan.
   a. Find the outstanding balance after 5 years.
   b. If they can refinance after 5 years at 7%(12) with no points, keeping the same total term, what would their new payment be?
   c. Find the total savings in **b** because of refinancing.
   d. If they can refinance after 5 years at 7%(12) with no points, changing the new term to 10 years, what would their new payment be?
   e. Find the total savings in **d** because of refinancing.
8. To secure a 30-year 7%(12) loan on her $300,000 home, Victoria must pay 20% down and 5.2 points that will be added to the loan.
   a. Find the outstanding balance after 5 years.
   b. If she can refinance after 5 years at 5.2%(12) with no points and the same total term, what would her new payment be?
   c. Find the total savings because of refinancing.
9. To secure a 15-year 10.3%(12) loan on his $100,000 home, Albert must pay 20% down and 2 points.
   a. Find the outstanding balance after 7 years.

b. Find the new payment if he refinances after 7 years at 7.1%(12) with 3 points, keeping the same total term.
c. Find the total savings.
d. Find the 120th line of the amortization table.

10. To secure a 22-year 6.3%(12) loan on their $150,000 home, a couple must pay 20% down and 1.5 points.
 a. Find the outstanding balance after 7 years.
 b. Find the new payment if they refinance after 7 years at 4.1%(12) with 3 points.
 c. Find the total savings.
 d. Find the 120th line of the amortization table.

Theory and Extension Exercises

11. A schoolteacher arranges for his $50,000 home mortgage to be paid with 9 payments from October 1 through June 1 but no payments during the 3 months of the summer. Find the payment if this is a 15-year mortgage at 9%(12).

12. Develop a general formula for Exercise 11 where the loan is $\$X$, there are $p < 12$ payments per year, rate i per period, and a term of n years.

6.5 Owner's Equity, Real Estate Appreciation, and Taxes

The **owner's equity** in a piece of real estate is the current value minus any indebtedness. Most property appreciates in value over time. This is not always true, but it is the general trend. Situations like an economic downturn or changing neighborhood conditions may seriously lower property values. Barring these negative factors, the long-term rate of inflation can be used to make a good estimate of the increase in value of a piece of property. The second factor that increases the value of a piece of real estate is the reduction of principal owed in the mortgage contract. This reduction takes place slowly at the beginning of a loan when more of the payment goes to interest and less to principal. Later in the loan, the amount going to principal makes up the larger part of each payment. The expected increase in property values gives a little relief from the heavy burden of interest costs that result from a long-term mortgage contract. The fact that the Internal Revenue Service currently allows a Schedule A deduction on form 1040 for interest paid on a home mortgage provides another relief from the interest costs. While appreciation and tax deductions give a positive aspect to borrowing for a home, the depreciation of automobiles gives a definite negative aspect to borrowing for a car.

If you borrow to pay for an automobile using a long-term loan (like 5 years) and make a minimal down payment, the mortgage could be larger than the value of the automobile for part of the time. This means you could have an accident that totals the car and still owe some money on the loan after the insurance has paid for the value of the vehicle.

The calculations for owner's equity problems will require us to

1. find the future value of the property at an annual compound rate of appreciation (inflation)

2. find the outstanding balance at a given payment or date
3. find their difference.

The calculations for interest deductions on schedule A will require us to find the outstanding balance at the beginning and end of the year in question. The difference will represent principal paid off. The principal paid off is then subtracted from the total paid out = 12×(payment). Loan companies are required by law to send their customers a 1099 form that tells the amount of interest paid by the borrower during the previous year. Our calculation will let us get this number early and provide a check on the loan company.

Example 6.5.1

A \$58,600 home loan is financed at 8%(12) for 15 years with a \$14,650 down payment. Find the owner's equity at the end of 7 years if the average appreciation rate during that time was 4.5%(1).

■ First we find the payment and compute the outstanding balance at the 84th payment. We then use compound amount to find the appreciated value of the property. The difference between the value of the home and the indebtedness will be the owner's equity.

Payment formula: $A_n = R\,a_{\overline{n|}i}$

$$58{,}600 = R\,a_{\overline{180|}8/12\%} \rightarrow R = \$560.02 \text{ Monthly payment}$$

Outstanding balance: $\text{OB} = A_n(1+i)^n - R\,s_{\overline{n|}i}$

$$\text{OB} = \$39{,}613.24 \text{ (at } n = 84)$$

Appreciated value of home = (\$58,600 + \$14,650)$(1.045)^7$ = \$99,683.13

Owner's equity after 7 years = \$99,683.13 – \$39,613.24 = \$60,069.89

Note: The \$28,054.92 in interest paid is almost offset by a \$26,433.13 increase in value.

Example 6.5.2

A buyer gets a conventional 30-year loan, with 20% down, to buy a \$128,000 home. The loan is financed at 6.8%(12) with 2½ points, which are added to the loan. If the home appreciates at 5%(12), find the owner's equity after 12 years and 8 months.

■ The first step is to calculate the amount to be borrowed by subtracting the down payment and adding the points. First figure the payment and outstanding balance; then figure the appreciated value of the home. Subtract the outstanding balance from the appreciated value to find the owner's equity.

$$\text{Amount financed} + \text{points} = \frac{128{,}000 - 20\%(128{,}000)}{1 - .025} = \frac{102{,}400}{.975} = \$105{,}025.64$$

Payment formula: $A_n = R\,a_{\overline{n|}i}$

$$105{,}025.64 = R\,a_{\overline{360}|6.8/12\%} \quad \rightarrow \quad R = \$684.69 \text{ Payment}$$

Outstanding balance: $A_n(1+i)^n - R\,s_{\overline{n}|i}$

$$\text{OB} = \$83{,}525.94 \quad (\text{at } n = 152)$$

Appreciated value of house: $128{,}000(1.0041\overline{6})^{152} = \$240{,}819.53$

Owner's equity at 12 years 8 months = $240,819.53 – $83,525.94 = $157,293.59

Note: The points loan for $2625.64 was not part of the original value of the house, so it is not used to figure the appreciated value. However, the outstanding balance of this points loan constitutes an obligation that must be considered in reducing the appreciated value.

Example 6.5.3

In Example 6.5.2 find the allowable interest deduction on the Federal 1040 Schedule A tax form for the 14th year of the loan.

■ We need the total paid to the loan company during the 14th year (12 times the payment) and the part of this total that was just principal. The principal paid off during that year will be the difference between the outstanding balances at the beginning and the end of the year. First, get the two outstanding balances.

Outstanding balance at the end of the 13th year, $n = 156$:

$$A_n(1+i)^n - R\,s_{\overline{n}|i} \rightarrow \text{OB} = \$82{,}673.22$$

Outstanding balance at the end of the 14th year, $n = 168$:

$$A_n(1+i)^n - R\,s_{\overline{n}|i} \rightarrow \text{OB} = \underline{\$79{,}996.31}$$

Amount of principal paid off during the 14th year: $2676.91

Total paid during the 14th year = 12 × ($684.69) = $8216.28

Allowable tax deduction on Schedule A = $8216.28 – $2676.91 = $5539.37

◀ EXERCISES 6.5 ▶

Concept and Short Answer Exercises

1. Calculate the appreciated (depreciated) home value in 10 years for a $200,000 home if home values are growing at 3% per year in that area.
2. Find the home equity for the home in Exercise 1 if $150,000 is still owed on the home.
3. Calculate the appreciated (depreciated) car value in 3 years for a $20,000 car if automobile values decrease at 15% per year.
4. Find the equity you have in the car in Exercise 3 if you still owe $6000 on the car.
5. Tell how to use your financial calculator to find the total interest for the third year on a $50,000 loan with monthly payments of $500 at 6%(12).

6. Give the necessary formulas to do Exercise 5.

Calculation Exercises

7. Mr. and Mrs. Williams would like to buy a $150,000 home and have found financing at 7.74%(12) with 2 points for a 20-year loan if they pay 10% down.
   a. Find the amount financed including points.
   b. Find their monthly payment. Be sure to round up to the next penny.
   c. Find the actual APR.
   d. Give the 60th line of the amortization table.
   e. Find how much of the 60th payment goes to interest.
   f. Find how much of the 5th year of payments goes to interest. You can usually take this as a Schedule A deduction on your federal income taxes.
   g. If homes are appreciating at 4%(1), find the Williams's equity immediately after the 60th payment.

   After the Williams make their 60th payment, they find that the interest rates on home loans have dropped to as low as 6.01%(12) with no points, so they decide to refinance keeping the same term.

   h. Find the amount refinanced.
   i. Find the new payment.
   j. Find the total saved in payments.
   k. Find the total saved in interest.
   l. Should the Williams have refinanced?
   m. Find the total of the payments, the total of the "toward principal," and the total of the "toward interest" for the original loan.
   n. Find the total of the payments, the total of the "toward principal," and the total of the "toward interest" for the refinanced loan.
   o. Give the total interest paid for the 15th year, which is the ___ year of the new loan.
   p. Give the 180th line of the amortization schedule, which is the ___ line of the new loan.

8. Mr. and Mrs. Halos would like to buy a $250,000 home and have found financing at 7%(12) with 2 points for a 30-year loan if they pay 20% down.
   a. Find the amount financed including points.
   b. Find their monthly payment—be sure to round up to the next penny.
   c. Find the actual APR.
   d. Give the 60th line of the amortization table.
   e. Find how much of the 60th payment goes to interest.
   f. Find how much of the 5th year of payments goes to interest. You can usually take this as a Schedule A deduction on your federal income taxes.
   g. If homes are appreciating at 4%(1), find the Halos's equity immediately after the 60th payment.

After the Halos make their 120th payment, they find that the interest rates on home loans have dropped to as low as 5%(12) with no points, so they decide to refinance.

h. Find the amount refinanced.

i. Find the new payment.

j. Find the total saved in payments.

k. Find the total saved in interest.

l. Should the Halos have refinanced?

m. Find the total of the payments, the total of the "toward principal," and the total of the "toward interest" for the original loan.

n. Find the total of the payments, the total of the "toward principal," and the total of the "toward interest" for the refinanced loan.

o. Give the total interest paid for the 15th year, which is the _____ year of the new loan.

p. Give the 180th line of the amortization schedule, which is the _____ line of the new loan.

6.6 Sinking Funds to Retire Debt

When a municipality, a corporation, or a church prepares to redeem a bond issue, it generally makes systematic payments into a fund in order to accumulate the needed money at some future date (the redemption date). If the bonds have varying maturities, like 10, 15, or 20 years, a large portion of the fund will deplete (sink) at the two earlier due dates, before the bond issue is completely discharged at the end. So a **sinking fund** is just an ordinary annuity with a known future value that represents some debt or obligation that is coming due. Like any other debt retirement instrument, the size and frequency of the payment are of primary concern in our calculations.

It would be most unusual for an individual to retire a debt by any method other than amortization, because creditors do not expect individuals to have enough self-discipline to save for a future obligation. The risk of default would be quite high for individuals using the sinking fund method of debt retirement. Corporations, on the other hand, which have much greater cash flows and more structured financial controls, often use sinking funds to retire debt or save for large capital expenditures like equipment, upgrades, or renovations. Occasionally, a sinking fund schedule is set up just like an amortization schedule. The schedule shows each payment, the interest earned during that period, and the balances at the beginning and end. A sample of a sinking fund schedule is given in Example 6.6.1 below.

Even though a loan may require the payment of the entire principal at one point in the future, the interest charges are usually computed monthly or quarterly. The lender will require the borrower to pay the interest every time it accrues; otherwise the entire principal comes due. The loan will usually have a higher interest rate than the sinking fund investment pays. The reason is that it usually costs more to borrow than one can earn with savings or investment accounts. When the borrower makes his sinking fund payment into the savings account he will also make an interest payment toward the loan. Typically, these two payments would go to different financial institutions. The sum of the sinking fund payment and the interest charges on the loan is called the **total periodic charge** and is comparable to an amortized loan payment.

Example 6.6.1

A corporation issues a $2,000,000 piece of commercial paper that comes due in 2 years. If it sets up a sinking fund with an institution that pays 7%(4), what will its quarterly payment be? Set up a schedule showing the accumulation of the assets in this sinking fund.

■ The sinking fund has a future value of $2,000,000, and we need to find the payment if the investment earns 7%(4). Note that $n = 4\times 2 = 8$ payments.

Payment formula: $S_n = R s_{\overline{n}|i}$

$$2{,}000{,}000 = R s_{\overline{8}|1\frac{3}{4}\%} \rightarrow R = \$235{,}085.85 \text{ quarterly}$$

Table 6.6.1 is similar to an amortization schedule but with the fund increasing to meet the required total at the end. This is a good application of an Excel spreadsheet.

TABLE 6.6.1

Period	Beginning Balance	Interest Earned This Period	Deposit At The End of Period	Ending Balance
1	—	—	$235,085.85	$235,085.85
2	$235,085.85	$4,114.00	$235,085.85	$474,285.70
3	$474,285.70	$8,300.00	$235,085.85	$717,671.55
4	$717,671.55	$12,559.25	$235,085.85	$965,316.65
5	$965,316.65	$16,893.04	$235,085.85	$1,217,295.55
6	$1,217,295.55	$21,302.67	$235,085.85	$1,473,684.07
7	$1,473,684.07	$25,789.47	$235,085.85	$1,734,559.39
8	$1,734,559.39	$30,354.79	$235,085.85	$2,000,000.03
Totals		**$119,313.23**	**$1,880,686.80**	

Example 6.6.2

A construction company has a construction loan for $350,000 that is due in 30 months with interest at 9%(12). The company sets up a sinking fund with an institution that pays 7%(4). Find the total monthly cost of retiring this debt if compound interest is paid for part of a period.

■ Since the construction loan requires monthly interest payments, the sinking fund should be set up with monthly payments even though it earns only quarterly interest. Find the effective monthly rate for 7%(4) and compute the monthly sinking fund payment as well as the monthly interest payment on the loan.

Effective rate: $j = (1+i)^k - 1 \rightarrow j = (1.0175)^{\frac{4}{12}} - 1 = 0.579963...\%$

Sinking fund payment: $S_n = R s_{\overline{n}|i}$

$$350{,}000 = R s_{\overline{30}|0.5799...\%} \rightarrow R = \$10{,}714.87$$

Periodic loan interest: .0075($350,000) = $2625

Total monthly cost: $10,714.87 + $2625 = $13,339.87

Note that the lower savings rate for the sinking fund compared to the loan makes the sinking fund method slightly more expensive than an amortized loan, which would have been $13,071.86 per month.

Example 6.6.3

A church uses a bond issue to borrow $400,000 for a building program. The bonds pay 7%(2) and mature in 15 years. In order to redeem the bonds in 15 years, the church sets up a sinking fund with a local bank that pays 6%(12) on deposits. Find the monthly cost of retiring this debt with a sinking fund.

■ The sinking fund will have two future obligations to meet: (1) the $400,000 due in 15 years, plus (2) the interest payment every 6 months. Since the church is making monthly payments, it will make 6 payments that will need to amount to the interest due on the bonds.

Semiannual bond interest: .035($400,000) = $14,000

Monthly payment for bond interest: $S_n = R s_{\overline{n}|i}$

$$14{,}000 = R s_{\overline{6}|\frac{1}{2}\%} \rightarrow R = \$2304.34$$

Monthly payment for loan: $S_n = R s_{\overline{n}|i}$

$$\$400{,}000 = R s_{\overline{180}|\frac{1}{2}\%} \rightarrow R = \$1375.43$$

Total monthly payment: debt and interest, $2304.34 + $1375.43 ≈ $3680.

◀ EXERCISES 6.6 ▶

Concept and Short Answer Exercises

1. Find the interest gained if you deposit $100 a month for a year and the savings account is worth $1300 after the 12th deposit.
2. Find the interest if a sinking fund is worth $20,000 after making semiannual deposits of $2400 for 4 years.
3. What is a sinking fund?
4. What is a sinking fund table or schedule?
5. How much is in a savings account after 20 monthly $200 deposits at 4%(12)?

6. How much is in a sinking fund after 5 years of annual $20,000 deposits at 8%(1)?
7. Name at least four sinking funds nearly every home will need. (*Hint*: Think of yearly bills.)
8. Name at least four sinking funds nearly every school will need. (*Hint*: What wears out?)
9. Name at least four sinking funds nearly every business will need.
10. Give an example of a forborne sinking fund.

Calculation Exercises

11. Janet makes her first semiannual savings deposit of $500 on 12/1/01 and her last one on 12/1/04.
    a. If money is earning 6%(2), then how much is in her account on 12/1/04?
    b. Give a sinking fund table for Janet's savings plan.
    c. Show how to compute just the 4th line of the sinking fund table; give all formulas.
12. Lynne makes her first quarterly savings deposit of $500 on 6/1/02 and her last one on 12/1/04.
    a. If money is earning 6%(2), then how much is in her account on 12/1/04? Be sure to change the rate.
    b. Give a sinking fund table for Lynne's savings.
    c. Show how to compute just the 8th line of the sinking fund table; give all formulas.
13. Kathy plans to buy a new car every 3 years and wisely saves by depositing monthly until she has enough money. The Chevy Cavalier she buys will cost approximately $13,000, and her used Cavalier with only 30,000 miles on it will have a trade-in value of $6000. Her savings account is paying 3.8%(12).
    a. Find her monthly deposit.
    b. Find her final deposit.
    c. Find the 20th line of the sinking fund table.
14. You plan to buy a new truck every 5 years, and you wisely save by making monthly deposits until you have enough money. The new truck you will buy costs approximately $33,000, and your used truck with only 48,000 miles on it will have a trade-in value of $12,000. Your savings account is paying 3.1%(12).
    a. Find your monthly deposit.
    b. Find your final deposit.
    c. Find the 40th line of the sinking fund table.
15. The Leatherwood Corporation sets up a bond issue for $2,000,000 with 10 years to maturity. The bonds pay interest at 6.5%(2). The Corporation opens a sinking fund with Southwest Life that pays 5.75%(12). Find the total monthly cost that will build the sinking fund and pay the coupons (bond interest).

16. A church sets up a bond issue for $2,000,000 with 10 years to maturity. The bonds pay interest at 8.5%(2). The church opens a sinking fund that pays 4.2%(12). Find the total monthly cost that will build the sinking fund and pay the coupons (bond interest).

17. The East Coast Development Company (ECDC) has a $650,000 loan that comes due in 2 years, and interest charges accrue at 7.5%(4). What will ECDC's total quarterly cost be if its money market–based sinking fund earns 6.8%(4)?

18. The West Coast Development Company (WCDC) has a $6,050,000 loan that comes due in 2 years, and interest charges accrue at 7.5%(12). What will WCDC's total monthly cost be if its money market–based sinking fund earns 6.8%(4)?

Theory and Extension Exercises

19. Assume a sequence of n level payments of $1 paid at the end of every 2 years at rate i per year. If the 2-year effective rate is j, show that the future value of this annuity is given by $s_{\overline{n}|j} = \dfrac{s_{\overline{2n}|i}}{s_{\overline{2}|i}}$. Where is this future value located?

20. A schoolteacher wants to save $40,000 for his children's education in 15 years. He plans to make monthly deposits from October 1 through June 1 each year, but not make deposits during the three summer months. Find the payment needed if he can earn 6%(12) through his credit union.

21. Develop a general formula for Exercise 20 where the amount to be saved is $$E$, there are $p < 12$ payments each year, the rate is i per month, and the term is n years.

22. The B Corporation borrows $3,000,000 using a bond issue paying 8%(2) for 20 years. One-third of the bonds are redeemed at 10 years, one-third at 15 years, and one-third at 20 years. Find the level semiannual payment into a sinking fund paying 6%(12) to redeem these bonds at 10, 15, and 20 years. Also find the semiannual funding to pay the coupon for each of the blocks of time.

6.7 Comparing Amortization to Sinking Fund Methods

We learned that when a debt is amortized, the principal is repaid through a sequence of equal payments, each consisting of the accrued interest and some of the principal. The structure of an amortized debt matches the present value of an ordinary annuity. We further learned that when a sinking fund is used to discharge a loan, the loan's principal is not repaid until the due date. The loan requires only that the borrower pay the accrued interest when it comes due. The sinking fund is actually a separate savings account that will accumulate until it is needed to pay off the loan principal at some future date. The structure of a sinking fund matches the future value of an ordinary annuity. With the exception of bond issues, sinking fund methods are not generally used for long-term debts on the order of 10 years or more.

It is quite easy to tell which method is the least expensive. If the loan rate is the same for either amortization or lump sum payback, then the rate of interest that the sinking fund earns will be the deciding factor. If the sinking fund earns a higher rate than the loan rate, then the sinking fund method is the least expensive. If the sinking fund and the loan rate are the same, the methods will cost exactly the same. If the sinking fund rate is lower than the loan rate, then the amortized loan will be the least expensive. The following examples illustrate the comparison of amortization to sinking fund methods.

Example 6.7.1

Find the total periodic cost for borrowing \$56,400 for 2 years and 6 months at 7%(4). Use an amortized loan and a sinking fund that earns 6%(4).

■ Find the quarterly payment using both methods. Remember to include the interest payment as well as the sinking fund payment when finding the total periodic cost via a sinking fund.

Payment formula via amortization: $A_n = R\,a_{\overline{n}|i}$

$$56{,}400 = R\,a_{\overline{10}|7/4\%} \rightarrow R = \$6196.97$$

Payment formula via a sinking fund: $S_n = R\,s_{\overline{n}|i}$

$$56{,}400 = R\,s_{\overline{10}|6/4\%} \rightarrow R = \$5269.69$$

Payment for loan interest: .0175(\$56,400) = \$987

Total periodic cost using a sinking fund: \$5269.69 + \$987 = \$6256.69

The sinking fund method costs \$59.72 more per quarter.

Example 6.7.2

Find the total periodic charge to retire a \$38,600 debt with quarterly payments for 5 years, using the following plans:

a. Amortized at 8%(4)
b. Loan at 8%(4) with a sinking fund at 5%(4)
c. Loan at 8%(4) with a sinking fund at 8%(4)
d. Loan at 8%(4) with a sinking fund at 9%(4)

■ **a.** Payment formula: $A_n = R\,a_{\overline{n}|i} \rightarrow 38{,}600 = R\,a_{\overline{20}|2\%} \rightarrow R = \$2360.65$

b. Payment formula: $S_n = R\,s_{\overline{n}|i} \rightarrow 38{,}600 = R\,s_{\overline{20}|1.25\%} \rightarrow R = \$1710.77$

Loan interest: $I = .02\,(\$38{,}600) = \$772$, Total periodic charge = \$2482.77

c. Payment formula: $S_n = R\,s_{\overline{n}|i} \rightarrow 38{,}600 = R\,s_{\overline{20}|2\%} \rightarrow R = \$1588.65$

Loan interest: $I = .02\,(\$38{,}600) = \$772$, Total periodic charge = \$2360.65

d. Payment formula: $S_n = R\,s_{\overline{n}|i} \rightarrow 38{,}600 = R\,s_{\overline{20}|2.25\%} \rightarrow R = \$1549.49$

Loan interest: $I = .02\,(\$38{,}600) = \$772$, Total periodic charge = \$2321.49

We can make a couple of observations about the comparison between amortized loans and those retired with a sinking fund. Parts **a** and **c** show that the two methods are equivalent if the savings rate for the sinking fund is the same as the loan rate for the amortized loan. In practice, the savings rate is almost always less than the loan rate, so part **b** is the norm.

EXERCISES 6.7

Concept and Short Answer Exercises

1. What does mean it for a sinking fund to cover a loan?
2. Give two reasons that a company might use a sinking fund to cover a loan.
3. A \$1000, 12%(12) loan would require an interest payment of ____ each month.
4. A \$1000, 7%(12) sinking fund over 1 year would require monthly deposits of _____.
5. If both 3 and 4 were to happen, the total of the monthly interest payment and the monthly deposit would be _____.
6. A \$20,000, 8%(2) loan would require an interest payment of _____ each half-year.
7. A \$20,000, 9%(2) sinking fund over 1 year would require semiannual deposits of _____.
8. If both 6 and 7 were to happen, the total of the monthly interest payment and the monthly deposit would be _____.
9. Without calculating anything and assuming that the term and principal are the same, will the monthly payment be less for a 10%(4) loan or for an 8%(4) sinking fund to cover a 10%(4) loan? Why?
10. Without calculating anything and assuming that the term and principal are the same, will the monthly payment be less for a 8%(2) loan or for a 9%(2) sinking fund to cover an 8%(2) loan? Why?

Calculation Exercises

11. Suppose you need \$2000 for 6 months.
    - **a.** If you can get a loan at 10%(12), what will your payment be?
    - **b.** If your savings account is paying 5%(12), your loan is charging 10%(12), and you use a sinking fund to pay off the loan, what would your payment be?
    - **c.** Comparing **a** and **b**, which is the better deal? Before you ever compute the payments, how can you tell which is better? Why would you ever do the sinking fund in this case?
    - **d.** Give the table for the sinking fund. Include the month, beginning balance, sinking fund interest, sinking fund payment, ending balance, loan interest, and total periodic charge.

12. Suppose you need $2000 for 12 months.
    a. If you can get a loan at 10%(12), what will your payment be?
    b. If your savings account is paying 5%(12), your loan is charging 10%(12), and you set up a sinking fund to pay off the loan, what is your payment?
    c. Comparing **a** and **b**, which is the better deal? Before you ever compute the payments, how can you tell which is better? Why might you still do the second one in this case?
    d. Give the table for the sinking fund. Include the month, beginning balance, sinking fund interest, sinking fund payment, ending balance, loan interest, and total periodic charge.
13. Suppose you need an $8000 loan over 3 years and can borrow the money from your father's life insurance policy at 6%(12). Also suppose that you can get 8%(12) on a savings account.
    a. Compute and compare the payments for an amortized loan and for a sinking fund to cover the loan principal at 3 years.
    b. Give the 25th line of the sinking fund table.
14. Suppose your company needs a $50,000 loan over 3 years and can qualify for a small business loan at 4%(12). Also suppose you can get 5%(12) on a savings account.
    a. Compute and compare the payments for an amortized loan and for a sinking fund to cover the loan principal at 3 years.
    b. Give the 20th line of the sinking fund table.
15. Suppose the Bar Harbor Corporation issues $20,000,000 worth of bonds that pay interest (coupons) at 6.75%(2). Assume that the bonds mature in 20 years and that the company can make 7%(2) on deposits to a sinking fund to redeem this bond issue.
    a. Find the semiannual deposit to the bond redemption sinking fund.
    b. Find the semiannual payment for the coupons.
    c. Find the amount of interest earned by the sinking fund over the 20 years.
    d. Find the amount of interest paid for the bond issue interest (coupons).
16. Jensen and Son Publishers issues $20,000,000 worth of bonds that pay interest at 6.75%(4). Assume that the bonds mature in 20 years and that the company can make 7%(4) on deposits to a sinking fund to redeem this bond issue.
    a. Find the quarterly deposit to the bond redemption sinking fund.
    b. Find the quarterly payment for the coupons.
    c. Find the amount of interest earned by the sinking fund over the 20 years.
    d. Find the amount of interest paid for the bond issue interest (coupons).

Theory and Extension Exercises

17. ♦A 15-year loan for $40,000 can be financed as an amortized loan at 7.5%(1) or as a sinking fund where the lender charges 7%(1) and the fund earns an annual rate of *i*%. If both methods require the same annual payment, what is the sinking fund rate *i*?

18. If the rate per period for the loan is i and the rate per period for the sinking fund is j, develop a formula relating the payment using amortization to the payment using a sinking fund to discharge a debt.

Chapter 6 Summary of Concepts

Outstanding Balance (Retrospective): $\text{OB} = A_n(1+i)^n - R\,s_{\overline{n}|i}$

Outstanding Balance (Prospective): $\text{OB} = A_n = R\,a_{\overline{n}|i}$

Chapter 6 Vocabulary Check

Amortize	*Escrow Account*
Amortization Schedule	*Mortgage*
Annual Percentage Rate (APR)	*Owner's Equity*
Appreciation	*Refinance*
Closing Costs	*Sinking Fund*
Discount Points	*Total Periodic Charge*

Chapter 6 Skills Check

1. Find the payment for a loan and construct an amortization table.
   Section 6.1 Examples 1, 2; Exercises 11, 13
2. Find the APR when the lender charges discount points.
   Section 6.2 Examples 1, 3; Exercises 9, 15
3. Find outstanding balance and find how the interest and principal are split for a given payment. Find any line of an amortization table.
   Section 6.3 Examples 1, 3; Exercises 5, 9
4. Use outstanding balance to refinance a loan and find all the interest costs.
   Section 6.4 Examples 1, 2; Exercises 7, 9
5. Find owner's equity using outstanding balance and property appreciation.
   Section 6.5 Examples 1, 2; Exercise 7
6. Find sinking fund payments to retire debt, make a sinking fund schedule, and compare sinking fund loans to amortized loans.
   Section 6.6 Examples 1, 2; Exercises 11, 13
   Section 6.7 Examples 1, 2; Exercises 11, 13

Review Test for Debt Retirement Methods

1. Gary wants to buy a new BMW worth $50,000. BMW is willing to finance his loan at 4%(12) for 5 years. Assume the sales tax is 5% and Gary can afford $3000 down either with cash or a trade-in.
   a. Find the amount financed.
   b. Find the monthly payment.
   c. Give the 10th line of the amortization schedule.

d. Give the amount spent on interest for the second year of the loan. This interest is usually not tax deductible.

e. If Gary needs $10,000 minimum for a down payment on a home and he has $1000 per month discretionary money that he can save or pay toward the BMW, how long will it take Gary before he has the necessary money for a down payment for a home? Assume the rate is 4%(12).

f. How long would it take him to save up the down payment at $1000 per month if he forgoes the car purchase for a while? Assume the rate is 4%(12).

g. What are Gary's choices in this situation?

h. If Gary made payments on the BMW every 2 weeks instead of every month, how much would the new payment be, and how much would be saved? Assume the rate is 4%(26).

i. Assume taxes, upkeep, gas, and parking for the car cost Gary an additional $3600 per year. What is Gary's real monthly payment for the BMW?

2. Establish a sinking fund to accumulate $20,000 in 5 years using monthly deposits at 8%(12).

   a. Find the monthly deposit.

   b. Find the amount in the account immediately after making the 24th deposit.

   c. Give the 25th line of the sinking fund table.

3. Suppose your credit card has a $20,000 balance due on it. You decide to get a 5-year amortized loan for $20,000 with monthly payments at 8%(12) to discharge the credit card debt.

   a. Find the monthly payment.

   b. Find the monthly payment if you were to use a sinking fund earning 5%(12) to retire the debt and the loan accrues interest at 8%(12).

4. A 1955 T-Bird worth $50,000 is financed with 20% down over 5 years with monthly payments at 10%(12).

   a. If the owner is charged 5 points and the points are added to the loan, find the payment and the APR.

   b. Give the 10th line of the amortization schedule.

   c. Find the total interest charged during the 2nd year of the loan.

   d. If the T-Bird is appreciating at 8%(1), find the owner's equity at the end of the second year.

   e. If the owner refinances the loan at the end of the 2nd year at 8%(4):

      i. Find the new monthly payment.

      ii. Find the savings in interest because of refinancing.

      iii. Find the total interest charges over the last 3 years of the loan.

Chapter 7

Investing in Stocks and Bonds

7.1 Valuation of Bonds and Their Yield Rates

Many corporations, governments, and public service institutions must borrow large sums of money to finance capital improvements. But a loan for $200 million to build a new water treatment plant would probably be too large for any one lending institution to advance. The corporations or government agencies that need these large sums often issue bonds that are purchased by a wide variety of investors such as insurance companies, pension funds, mutual fund managers, and individuals. A **bond** is a long-term debt instrument that pays interest at regular intervals and that matures at some specified date in the future. The lender buys the bond from the corporation, for maybe $1000, and every six months he receives a guaranteed interest payment, called the **coupon**. The term of the bond can be as short as several months or more than thirty years. Short-term securities are also called notes or bills. Like a promissory note, the value of the bond at the end of its term is called the maturity value or **redemption value**. When the bond holder receives his principal back at the maturity date, the process is called **redeeming the bond**. The redemption value at the maturity date is typically the face value of the bond. The amount the holder originally paid for it could be less than face value if it was purchased at auction.

An important consideration for bond issues is how the corporation will redeem the bonds at the maturity date. The corporation or government agency will use regular earnings or revenue fees to pay the coupon, but it will also establish a sinking fund to plan for the redemption of the bond issue at the maturity date. Setting up a serial bond issue so the maturity dates will be staggered over a period of time—say, 15, 20, and 25 years—also helps the company retire the debt in a more manageable way.

The actual bond that the investor buys is just a fancy piece of paper with a very official look. The information on the bond includes the face value (or par value), the issuing corporation, the bond rate (coupon rate), a serial number, the maturity date, the terms of issuance, the trustee that oversees the payment of interest and redemption of the bond, and the corporate seal. The trustee is usually a commercial bank. The bond will state whether it is registered in the name of a particular owner or unregistered. Unregistered bonds are called **coupon bonds** because they have coupons attached that are presented to the trustee for payment of interest. Coupon bonds are bearer instruments, just like Federal Reserve Notes, and they are very seldom issued anymore because current laws require all new bond issues by corporations and municipalities to be registered in the owner's or broker's name.

Besides the issue of registration, bonds may be classified in other ways. **Mortgage bonds** pledge certain fixed assets as security or collateral for the debt. A **debenture** offers no collateral except the good name of the issuing company. **Convertible bonds** provide all of the regular features of a bond, like interest coupons and a maturity date, but there is an embedded option, giving the investor the option to convert the bond into a specific number of shares of common stock. The investor in convertible bonds could realize significant capital gain if the price of the stock were to increase. Another embedded option is termed a **call provision.** This allows the issuer of the bonds to redeem them at a specified price before maturity. Bonds with a call provision must pay higher rates to be competitive. **Zero coupon** or **discount bonds** pay no interest but are sold like treasury bills. The investor buys them at a discount and receives the face value at maturity.

In the late 1990s a new type of bond called an *indexed bond* became available in the United States. An **indexed bond** has an interest payment structure tied to inflation so that the returns are increased as the Consumer Price Index increases. The U.S. Treasury issues indexed bonds known as Inflation-Protected Securities (TIPS). Most bonds pay a *nominal* yield that does not compensate for inflation. A rate of return that is indexed for inflation is called a *real* rate of return. In Chapter 9 we will address the effect of inflation on interest theory.[1]

Bonds have a significant place in the day-to-day trading of the securities secondary market. By watching the bond tables in newspapers like the *Wall Street Journal*, you can see that their prices fluctuate much like stock prices, although not as much. Bond prices fluctuate less because their value is related to the rise and fall of prime interest rates. The Federal Reserve System does not change interest rates very often or in large increments, except in times of economic crises. Bond prices rise and fall with interest rates because bonds are paying interest to their owners. If other securities are paying a higher rate, then bonds will have to sell at a lower price in order for an investor to make the same return. Likewise, in times of low prime rates, bonds that are paying interest at a higher rate will be a more attractive investment and can sell for a higher price. In summary, there is an inverse relationship between bond prices and the prime interest rate.

The anticipated return to an investor in bonds is called the yield. Unless a bond is called early, the **yield to maturity** is the rate of return the buyer gets if he buys and holds the bond until its maturity date when it is redeemed at par. Yield to maturity assumes that *all interest payments are reinvested at the yield rate*, although this is somewhat idealistic. This reinvestment is very important because doing nothing but spending the interest paid will change the real earnings for the investment. **Current yield** is the rate of return for a given year; it is simply the annual interest earned divided by the cost to the buyer. A $1000 bond paying 8%(2) and purchased for $950 would have a current yield of $80/$950 = 8.4%.

An investor desiring a certain yield to maturity from a bond purchase must calculate the price he can pay for the bond to achieve the desired yield. Valuing a bond and finding the yield to maturity are two important calculations in this chapter.

---

[1]The relationship between the real yield rate, i_{real}, and the nominal yield rate, i_{nom}, due to inflation, r, can be seen by the relationship $1 + i_{nom} = (1 + i_{real})(1 + r)$.

Remember that there are two rates involved in a bond price calculation. The **bond rate** determines the coupon or amount of interest the bond pays. The coupon typically pays semiannually over the life of a bond. We call this sequence of payments the **coupon annuity**. The second rate is the yield rate. The **yield rate** is used to find the present value of the coupon annuity and the present value of the redemption value. These two present values are added to give the current price of the bond that will return the desired yield to the buyer. Some texts use C instead of S for the future value or redemption value of a bond. You will also see P for the value or purchase price instead of V_n. If you understand the concept, notation should not cause any difficulty.

Formula for the Value of a Bond

F	face value or par value of a bond
S	the redemption value of a bond (future value)
r	interest rate paid by the bond each period
Fr	interest paid by the bond (the face value times the bond rate)
n	number of interest periods to the maturity date
i	current yield (or investor's desired rate of return per period)
V_n	value (or price which will give the desired yield)

Value of a bond = PV of the redemption price + PV of the coupon annuity

TIME LINE DIAGRAM 7.1.1

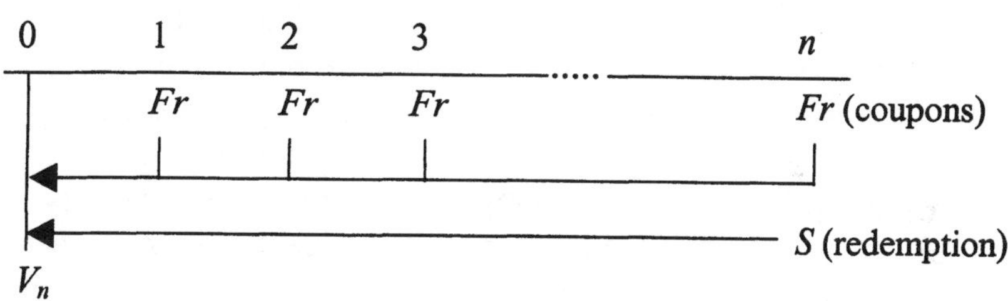

$$V_n = S(1+i)^{-n} + Fr\,a_{\overline{n}|i} = Sv^n + Fr\,a_{\overline{n}|i} \qquad (7.1)$$

The basic tool used to establish the above formula is often called the *method of discounted cash flows*. We first introduced this concept in Section 1.7, Equations of Value. The cash flows in the present context are all equal except the redemption value S. This makes the present values of the cash flows easy to represent with a nice compact formula made up of other familiar valuation formulas. Analysis of our bond formula will show that for a given bond the time to maturity n and the yield rate i will both significantly effect the value of the bond. The relationship between the time to maturity and the interest rate is called the **term structure of interest rates.** Besides the yield to maturity approach there are at least two other theories of the term structure of interest that are used to value bonds. Francis and Ibbotson, in their text *INVESTMENTS: A Global Perspective*, present the methods of *spot rates* and *forward rates* as well as *yield to maturity* in an appendix to Chapter 20.

Figure 7.1 illustrates the effect of yield rates on bond prices relative to years to maturity for two $100 bonds each paying 6%(2). One bond is valued 16 years before its due date and the other is valued 8 years before its due date.

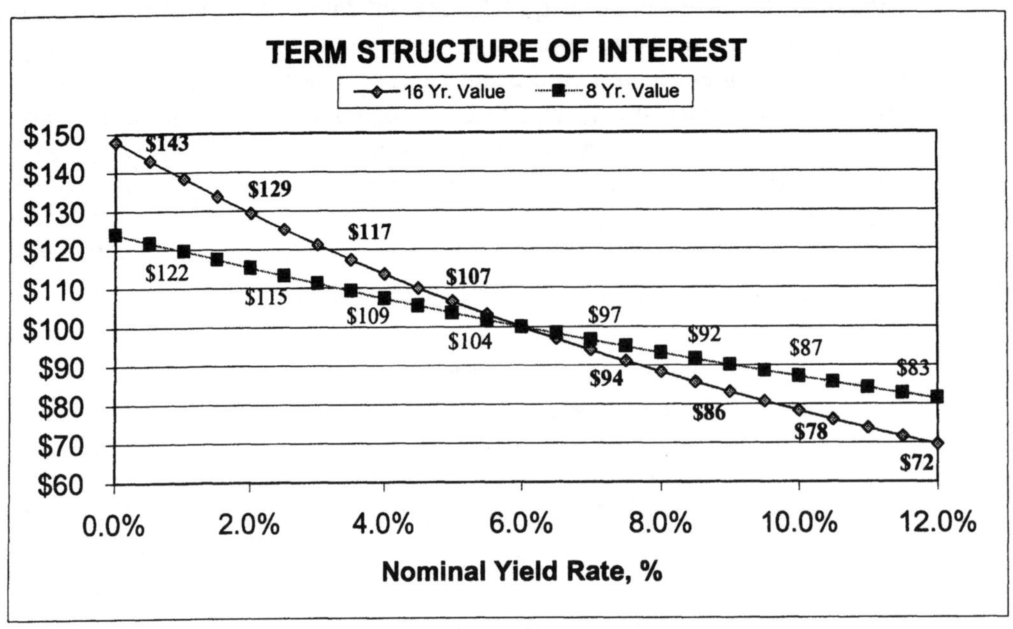

FIGURE 7.1

Potential investors must be aware that some bonds are issued with an embedded provision that lets the issuer redeem the bonds long before the maturity date. A **call provision** gives the bond issuer the legal right to speed up repayment of the debt by refunding the principal to the bondholders at certain specified call dates. Calling in bonds provides the borrowing corporation more flexibility to use improved profits to decrease the interest burden. A decline in interest rates would also warrant a company's paying off the old, higher-rate bonds and issuing new bonds at a more favorable rate. To make a bond issue with a call provision more attractive, a premium of 2 to 5% is offered whenever bonds are called. The bond prospectus will typically state this premium as "the bond is redeemable at 103" on the call date or within a certain window of time around the call date. The holder of a $1000 bond redeemable at 103 would receive $1030. Redeeming $5,000,000 worth of bonds at 103 would cost the company calling in the bonds an additional $150,000. On the other hand, if the coupon rate is 7%(2), the interest alone on $5,000,000 worth of bonds is $350,000 per year.

Example 7.1.1

Find the price to yield 9%(2) for a $1000 bond paying 7%(2) and maturing at par in 12 years.

■ Note that the yield rate $i = 9\% \div 2 = 4.5\%$ and the bond rate $r = 7\% \div 2 = 3.5\%$. The number of periods to maturity $n = 2 \times 12 = 24$. The coupon $Fr = .035 \times 1000 =$

\$35. On a financial calculator \$35 goes in Pmt, \$1000 in FV, 4.5% in i, and 24 in n. Compute PV.

$$V_n = S(1+i)^{-n} + Fra_{\overline{n}|i} = 1000(1.045)^{-24} + 35a_{\overline{24}|4\frac{1}{2}\%} = \$855.05$$

Since the price of the bond in Example 7.1.1 was below face value (\$1000), this is called a **discount bond**. The difference between the face value and the selling price is \$144.95 and is called the *discount*. The investor who buys the bond at \$855.05 will earn \$70 per year in interest and \$144.95 in capital gains over 12 years, for a total annual return of 9%. It is important to note that when the yield rate is higher than the coupon rate, the bond will sell at discount or below face value. The value of this bond will gradually increase until it is worth \$1000; therefore, we can assume that the value increases linearly at \$12.08 per year. Looking at this as the return per year, we get a return of \$70 + \$12.08 = \$82.50. The **adjusted current yield** is therefore \$82.08/\$855.05 ≈ 9.6%. Not taking into account the \$12 increase in capital gives a current yield of 8.2%, which does not give a true picture of the return.

Example 7.1.2

A \$10,000 R Corporation 9%(2) debenture matures on November 1, 2018. Coupon dates are May 1 and November 1. Find the value of this bond on May 1, 2004, to yield 7.5%(2).

■ First find the semiannual yield rate i = 7.5% ÷ 2 = 3.75% and the semiannual bond rate r = 9% ÷ 2 = 4.5%. You can use denominate number arithmetic to find the interest periods as n = 29. The coupon Fr = .045 × \$10,000 = \$450. On the financial calculator 450 goes in Pmt, 10,000 goes in FV, 3.75 goes in i, and 29 goes in n. The value is found by computing PV.

$$V_n = S(1+i)^{-n} + Fra_{\overline{n}|i} = 10{,}000(1.0375)^{-29} + 450a_{\overline{29}|3.75\%} = \$11{,}312.34$$

Since the price of the bond in Example 7.1.2 is above face value (\$10,000), this is called a **premium bond**. The difference between the face value and the selling price is called the premium and equals \$1312.34. Since the bond will mature at par, the investor will actually lose the \$1312.34 over the 14.5 years until maturity. If one uses a linear relationship, the loss is \$90.51 per year. However, this bond will pay \$900 per year in interest. The combination of interest gained and value lost will realize a total annual return of 7.5% for the investor. Calculating the return per year as \$900 − \$90.51 = \$809.49 allows us to find the adjusted current yield as \$809.49/\$11,312.34 = 7.2%. If we calculate the current yield without taking into account the loss of principal, the rate is about 8%.

Figure 7.2 illustrates how the value of a bond converges towards its par value as the years to maturity decrease. The bonds each have a par value of \$1000 with the premium bond paying 8%(2) and the discount bond paying 4%(2). The bonds are valued at a yield rate of 6%(2).

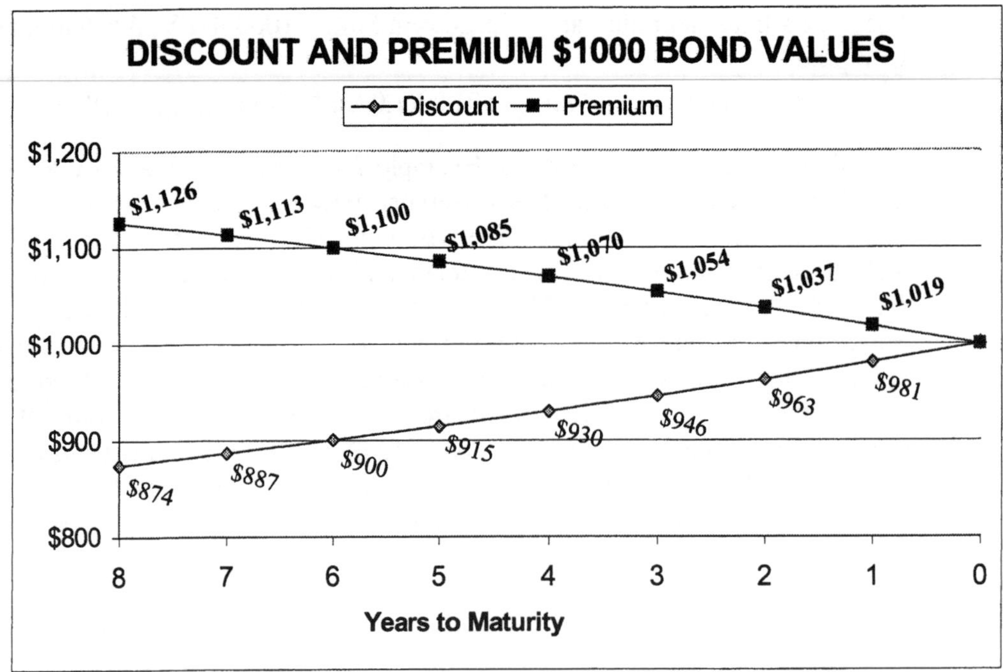

FIGURE 7.2

Example 7.1.3

A Micro-Chip Corporation $1000, 8%(2) debenture matures at par on September 1, 2015. The interest dates are September 1 and March 1. The bond has a call provision at 104 on March 1, 2008. Find the value of this bond on March 1, 2004, to yield 10%(2), if

a. The bond is called at 104 on 3/1/08.

b. The bond is redeemed at par on 9/1/15.

■ Find the yield rate $i = 10\% \div 2 = 5\%$ and the bond rate $r = 8\% \div 2 = 4\%$. The coupon $Fr = .04 \times 1000 = \$40$. If the bond is called, the number of interest periods $n = 2 \times 4 = 8$, and if it is held to maturity, the number of interest periods $n = 2 \times 11 + 1 = 23$. We can anticipate that the bond is a discount bond because the yield rate is higher than the bond rate.

a. $V_n = S(1 + i)^{-n} + Fra_{\overline{n}|i}$

$$V_8 = 1040(1.05)^{-8} + 40a_{\overline{8}|5\%} = \$962.44 \text{ price if called in 2008}$$

b. $V_{23} = 1000(1.05)^{-23} + 40a_{\overline{23}|5\%} = \$865.11$ price if held to 2015

Example 7.1.4

A $5000 Twenty Brothers Corporation 6%(2) bond matures at par on May 1, 2013. The bond may be called on May 1, 2008, at 103. What is the value of this bond on November 1, 2005, to a buyer who wants a yield of 8.5%(2) if

a. The bond is called at 103 on 5/1/08?

b. The bond is redeemed at par on 5/1/13?

■ Find the yield rate $i = 8.5\% \div 2 = 4.25\%$ and the bond rate $r = 6\% \div 2 = 3\%$. The coupon $Fr = .03 \times \$5000 = \$150$. The number of interest periods to the call date is $n = 2\times2 + 1 = 5$, while the number of interest periods to maturity is $n = 2\times7 + 1 = 15$. This is a discount bond because the yield rate is higher than the bond rate.

a. $V_n = Sv^n + Fra_{\overline{n|}i}$

$$V_5 = 5150(1.0425)^{-5} + 150a_{\overline{5|}4.25\%} = \$4845.52$$

b. $V_{15} = 5000(1.0425)^{-15} + 150a_{\overline{15|}4.25\%} = \$4317.09$

Example 7.1.5

What is the value of a \$1000 zero coupon bond maturing in 10 years if the investor requires a 7%(2) return?

■ Find the yield rate $i = 7.5\% \div 2 = 3.75\%$ and the periods to maturity $n = 2\times10 = 20$. The bond is sold at discount, so we are looking for the present value (proceeds). There are no coupons, so the coupon annuity is omitted from the formula.

$$V_n = Sv^n = S(1+i)^{-n} \rightarrow 1000(1.035)^{-20} = \$502.57$$

◀ EXERCISES 7.1 ▶

Assume that all coupons are paid semiannually.

Concept and Short Answer Exercises

1. You can make money on a bond from the coupon. Explain.
2. You can make money on a bond from the bid. Explain.
3. You can make money on a bond from the call provision. Explain.
4. You can make money on a bond from the resale of the bond in a secondary market. Explain.
5. When the bid is 94.2, a \$1000 bond is sold for \$_____ and matures to \$_____. Hence it is sold at a (discount/premium) of \$_____.
6. When the bid is 103.67, a \$5000 bond is sold for \$_____ and matures to \$_____. Hence it is sold at a (discount/premium) of \$_____.
7. Explain why a call provision is often written into a bond agreement.
8. When the bid is 101.3 and when the call provision is 103.2 in 2 years, a \$4000 bond is sold for \$_____ and matures to \$_____.

Calculation Exercises

9. A \$1000, 8% bond matures in 4 years.
   a. What would an investor who desires a 10%(2) yield bid for the bond?
   b. Was the bond sold at a premium or a discount and by how much?
   c. What is the bid for the bond if it is called in 2 years at 103?
10. A \$10,000, 6% bond matures in 5 years.
    a. What would an investor who desires a 6%(2) yield bid for the bond?

b. Was the bond sold at a premium or a discount and by how much?
c. What is the bid for the bond if it is called in 2 years at 102.5?

11. A $500, 9% bond maturing on 10/1/20 is sold to Barton on 4/1/04.
    a. If Barton desires 8%(2) on his money, what will he pay for the bond?
    b. Was the bond sold at a premium or a discount and by how much?
    c. If the bond has a call provision of 105 that may be taken on 10/1/10, what is its value?

12. A $5000, 8% bond maturing on 10/1/20 is sold to Sanilla on 10/1/04.
    a. If Sanilla desires 10%(2) on her money, what will she pay for the bond?
    b. Was the bond sold at a premium or a discount and by how much?
    c. If the bond has a call provision of 103 that may be taken on 10/1/10, what is its value?

13. Suppose in the following cases that the bond is called at face value.
    a. If the coupon rate is 8% and the yield bid rate is 6%, is the bond sold at a premium or a discount?
    b. If the coupon rate is 6% and the yield bid rate is 8%, is the bond sold at a premium or a discount?
    c. If the coupon rate is 8% and the yield bid rate is 8%, is the bond sold at a premium or a discount?

14. Suppose in the following cases that the bond is called at face value.
    a. If the coupon rate is 5% and the bid rate is 6%, is the bond sold at a premium or a discount?
    b. If the coupon rate is 8.5% and the bid rate is 8%, is the bond sold at a premium or a discount?
    c. If the coupon rate is 8.8% and the bid rate is 8.8%, is the bond sold at a premium or a discount?

15. A $1000, 10% bond maturing in 10 years is sold to Baxter, who requires 8%(2) on his investment. Baxter holds the bond for 2 years and sells it to William, who requires 9%(2) on his investment. How much did each pay?

16. A $5000, 7% bond maturing in 8 years is sold to Marla, who requires 8%(2) on her investment. Marla holds the bond for 2 years and sells it to Maylynn, who requires 7%(2) on her investment. How much did each pay?

17. A $5000, 9.2%(2) bond maturing in 5 years is sold to Jerry, who requires 10.6%(2) on his investment. Jerry sells the bond in 3 years to Khadija, who requires 7.8%(2) on her money. How much did each pay?

18. A $5000, 4.6%(2) bond maturing in 5 years is sold to Benito, who requires 10%(2) on his investment. Benito sells the bond in 3 years to Carmen, who requires 7%(2) on her money. How much did each pay?

Theory and Extension Exercises

19. If a $1000 bond paying 6%(2) matures in 8 years and is selling at par, what is the percentage change in the value of the bond if market yield rates increase 2%(2)?

20. Derive the following formula that gives the value of a bond redeemable at par as the face value F plus the premium or minus the discount based on the bond rate r and yield rate i. $V_n = F + (Fr - Fi)a_{\overline{n}|i}$.

21. Solve the basic bond value formula (7.1) for the number of interest periods to maturity.

22. Use the formula from Exercise 21 to find the number of interest periods to maturity for a $1000 bond paying 6%(2) to yield 8%(2) that can be purchased for $900.

23. Use the formula from Exercise 20 to show that doubling the periods to maturity of a premium bond maturing at par will increase the value by an amount less than or equal to $(Fr - Fi)/4i$. Note that for discount bonds it will be a decrease in value.

24. A $1000 U.S. Treasury indexed bond (TIPS) paying 4.25%(2) matures at par in 5 years. Assume an annual inflation rate of 3.5% and find the value to yield 6%(2).

7.2 Purchasing Bonds between Coupon Dates

In the previous section we found the value of bonds on the coupon dates. Practically speaking, people purchasing bonds do not wait around for the interest date to arrive before making their purchase. To establish a bond's selling price between interest dates, we must find the value of two pieces of money. We will need the quoted price (also net price or market price) of the bond plus the portion of the interest coupon that rightfully belongs to the seller. Some texts call the quoted price the *and interest* price. The coupon pays only on interest dates, so the buyer and seller split the coupon at the time of purchase. The split is based on the fractional part of the interest period during which each of them holds ownership of the bond. If a bond is sold 2 months into the 6-month interest period, the seller will get 2/6th of the coupon, and the buyer will get 4/6th of the coupon. The part of the coupon retained by the seller is called the **accrued interest** or **accrued coupon**. The **quoted price** of the bond also includes a fractional part of the change in value between two interest dates. We simply interpolate between values based on the fractional part of the interest period when the sale takes place. Since discount bonds sell below par and are gradually increasing in value, the fractional change will have to be added to the earlier value. A discount bond that increases $4.80 between coupon dates and is sold 2 months into a 6-month interest period would have 2/6th of $4.80 = $1.60 added to the earlier price. Premium bonds, on the other hand, sell above par and are gradually decreasing in value, so the fractional change will have to be subtracted from the earlier value. In summary, *the purchase price of a bond = the quoted price + accrued interest.* We will illustrate the calculation of the value of a bond between coupon dates in the next example and then introduce a simplifying procedure.

Example 7.2.1

A \$1000, 7.5%(2) Spam-Electric debenture matures at par on July 15, 2019. Find the purchase price of the bond if it is sold on November 15, 2004, to yield 9%(2).

■ The selling date falls between coupon dates 7/15/04 and 1/15/05, which is 4/6th of the way through the interest period. Calculate the values at the two coupon dates and use interpolation to get the quoted (net) price. The coupon $Fr = .0375 \times \$1000 = \$37.50$.

TIME LINE DIAGRAM 7.2.1

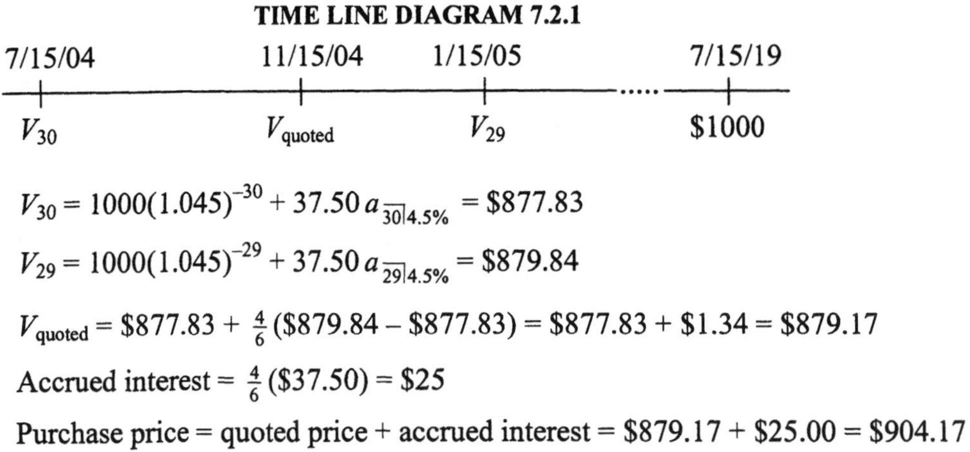

$$V_{30} = 1000(1.045)^{-30} + 37.50\, a_{\overline{30}|4.5\%} = \$877.83$$

$$V_{29} = 1000(1.045)^{-29} + 37.50\, a_{\overline{29}|4.5\%} = \$879.84$$

$$V_{quoted} = \$877.83 + \tfrac{4}{6}(\$879.84 - \$877.83) = \$877.83 + \$1.34 = \$879.17$$

$$\text{Accrued interest} = \tfrac{4}{6}(\$37.50) = \$25$$

$$\text{Purchase price} = \text{quoted price} + \text{accrued interest} = \$879.17 + \$25.00 = \$904.17$$

If we approach the above calculation from the perspective of the buyer who wants a return on investment of 9%(2), we can calculate the purchase price directly using simple interest. With this method the value of the bond at the first date is the principal that earns interest for 4 months at 9%. We may ask, "Why does this *practical method* work?" Remember that the value V_{30} is the present value of the redemption value, \$1000, plus the present value of the coupon annuity, so we are simply going forward on the time line for part of a period. Since compound interest for one period is identical to simple interest, the process works nicely, using simple interest for part of a period. You can check that it works by figuring the value of V_{29}. Just take $\$877.8\overline{3}$ forward for one period using the factor 1.045, subtract the coupon of \$37.50, and you will get \$879.84.

$$\text{Purchase price} = P(1 + it) = \$877.83(1 + (.09)(\tfrac{4}{12})) = \$904.17$$

We used approximate time and ordinary interest because they were employed in the calculation with the interpolation procedure.

Example 7.2.2

Big River Power Co. \$5000 bonds, paying 6%(2), mature at par on February 1, 2019. Find the purchase price and the quoted price (net price) of a bond if an investor desiring an 8%(2) yield to maturity buys on November 16, 2004.

■ The coupon date immediately preceding the date of sale is 8/1/04, and the number of interest periods from this date is 29. We first calculate V_{29} using a coupon of $Fr = .03 \times \$5000 = \$150$ and a yield rate $i = 4\%$. We then use Banker's Rule to get the future value of V_{29} at simple interest for 107 days (day 320 – day 213). Subtracting the accrued interest will give the quoted price.

$$V_n = S(1+i)^{-n} + Fra_{\overline{n}|i}$$

$$V_{29} = 5000(1.04)^{-29} + 150a_{\overline{29}|4\%} = \$4150.81$$

$$\text{Purchase price} = P(1+it) = 4150.81(1+(.08)(\tfrac{107}{360})) = \$4249.51$$

$$\text{Quoted price} = \$4249.51 - (\tfrac{107}{180})(\$150) = \$4249.51 - \$89.17 = \$4160.34$$

Note: The time fraction for the simple interest calculation changes days to years via Banker's Rule, but the time fraction for the accrued interest is expressing what part of the 180 days (6 months) the seller held the bond.

Example 7.2.3

An Inter-City Water Company $1000 debenture, paying 8.5%(2), matures on June 1, 2011. Find the purchase price and the quoted price on October 16, 2004, if the buyer wants a yield rate of 7%(12).

■ The coupon date just preceding the date of sale is 6/1/04, which gives 14 interest periods to maturity. The yield rate is compounded monthly, so we will have to change it to an equivalent rate compounded semiannually because the interest rate must correspond to the frequency of the coupon payments. We will then calculate V_{14}, using a coupon of $Fr = .0425 \times \$1000 = \$42.50$ and the equivalent yield rate. We use Banker's Rule to find the future value of V_{14} at simple interest for 137 days (day 289 – day 152). The quoted price (net) will be the purchase price minus the accrued interest.

$$\text{Effective rate: } j = (1+i)^k - 1 = (1.0058\overline{3})^{\frac{12}{2}} - 1 = 3.551..\% \rightarrow 7.10288038\%(2)$$

$$V_n = S(1+i)^{-n} + Fra_{\overline{n}|i}$$

$$V_{14} = 1000(1.03551..)^{-14} + 42.50a_{\overline{14}|3.5514...\%} = \$1076.02$$

$$\text{Purchase price} = P(1+it) = 1076.02(1+(.0710288..)(\tfrac{137}{360})) = \$1105.11$$

$$\text{Accrued interest} = \tfrac{137}{180}(\$42.50) = \$32.35$$

$$\text{Quoted price} = \$1105.11 - \$32.35 = \$1072.76$$

Example 7.2.4

A Southwest SolarTec $1000 revenue bond pays 8%(2) and matures at par on June 1, 2023. The bond issue may be called at 104 on December 1, 2008. Find the quoted price on February 10, 2004 to yield 12%(4), if

a. The bond is called.

b. The bond is held to maturity.

■ The equivalent semiannual rate for the yield rate is $j = [(1.03)^2 - 1] \times 100 = 6.09\%$ and the coupon $Fr = .04 \times \$1000 = \$40$.

a. The number of interest periods from 12/1/03 to the call date is $n = 10$, and the number of days in the fractional part via exact time is 71 (30 days in 2003 and 41 days in 2004).

TIME LINE DIAGRAM 7.2.2

12/1/03	2/10/04	6/1/04	12/1/08	6/1/23
V_{10}	V_{quoted}	V_9	Called at 104	S (at par)

$$V_n = S(1 + i)^{-n} + Fra_{\overline{n|}i} \rightarrow V_{10} = 1040(1.0609)^{-10} + 40\,a_{\overline{10|}6.09\%} = \$868.97$$

$$\text{Purchase price} = S(1 + it) = 868.97(1 + (.1218)(\tfrac{71}{360})) = \$889.84$$

Quoted price: purchase price – accrued interest = $\$889.84 - \left(\frac{71}{180}\right)(40) = \$874.06$

b. The fractional part of the period stays the same but the number of interest periods from 12/1/03 to the maturity date is $n = 39$.

$$V_n = S(1 + i)^{-n} + Fra_{\overline{n|}i} \rightarrow V_{39} = 1000(1.0609)^{-39} + 40\,a_{\overline{39|}6.09\%} = \$691.03$$

$$\text{Purchase price} = S(1 + it) = 691.03(1 + (.1218)(\tfrac{71}{360})) = \$707.63$$

Quoted price: purchase price – accrued interest = \$707.63 – \$15.78 = \$691.85

◀ EXERCISES 7.2 ▶

Concept and Short Answer Exercises

Exercises 2 through 5 all use the information in Exercise 1.

1. V_{30} at 8%(2) is \$827.08 for a \$1000 6%(2) bond. Interpret the symbols and values in this sentence by drawing a time line and filling in the values and equations. Be sure to locate all monies correctly on the time line.
2. Where is V_{30} located compared to the first coupon date?
3. On the time line V_{20} is located on which side of V_{21}?
4. Find V_{20} at a yield of 9%(2) for a \$10,000, 8%(2) bond.
5. Find V_{21} at a yield of 9%(2) for a \$10,000, 8%(2) bond.
6. Interpolate the value for 1 of 6 months between successive values \$1000 and \$1120.
7. Interpolate the value for 5 of 6 months between the successive values \$2000 and \$1700.
8. In Exercises 4 and 5, interpolate the value for 2 of 6 months between the successive values V_{21} and V_{20} to find the quoted price.
9. Repeat Exercise 8 using the technique of Example 7.2.2 to find the purchase price.
10. Find the quoted price for Exercise 9 by subtracting the interpolated coupon.

Calculation Exercises

11. A \$1000, 8%(2) bond matures in 4 years and 2 months. Find the *quoted price = and interest price* and the *purchase price = price with accrued interest* for a yield rate of 10%(2).

12. A \$5000, 6%(2) bond matures in 8 years and 8 months. Find the *and interest price* and the *price with accrued interest* for a yield rate of 9.2%(2).

13. A \$500, 9%(2) bond maturing on 10/1/20 is sold on 5/1/04 to Randall who gets a yield of 8%(2). Find the *quoted* or *net price* and the *price with accrued interest* = *purchase price*.

14. A \$500, 8%(2) bond maturing on 10/1/20 is sold to Juan on 5/1/04, who gets a yield of 9%(2). Find the purchase and the quoted price.

15. Angela buys a \$5000, 10%(2) bond that matures in 10 years. After 5 years and 2 months, Angela sells the bond to Rachel, who requires 12%(2) on her investment. Find the price that Rachel paid for Angela's bond as both a quoted and purchase price.

16. Phillip buys a \$5000, 6%(2) bond that matures in 14 years. After 5 years and 2 months he sells the bond to Francie, who requires 12%(2) on her investment. Find the price that Francie paid for Phillip's bond as both a purchase and quoted price

17. A \$10,000, 8%(2) bond that matures at par on 6/1/10 is sold on 11/12/03 to a man requiring 10%(4) on his money. Find the quoted and the purchased price.

18. A \$100,000 6%(2) bond that matures at par on 7/1/08 is sold on 11/12/03 to a woman requiring 10%(12) on her money. Find the net price and the purchase price.

Theory and Extension Exercises

19. A \$1000, 6.5%(2) debenture that matures at par on 3/1/12 is offered for sale on 7/15/04. The bond can be called at 103 on 3/1/08. Find the purchase price to yield 9%(2) if

    a. The bond is called on 3/1/08.

    b. The bond is held to maturity.

20. A \$1000, 12%(2) bond matures on 5/1/11 at \$*X*. The bond can be purchased on 9/19/05 for \$1110 to yield 11%(2). What is the redemption value \$*X*?

7.3 Finding the Yield Rate by Two Methods

When investor's purchase bonds, they may have several choices that are being offered at about the same quoted price. They can find the value of each bond using their anticipated rate of return and compare the resulting price to the quoted price in the bond market. If the quoted price is less than or equal to what they calculate, they know that the investment will return a yield equal to or better than what they want. The calculations from the previous two sections would provide the investor the tools to do this price comparison. On the other hand, investors could simply find the current yield and/or the yield to maturity that the quoted price would return if purchased at that price. In this section we will find the yield to maturity by an approximate method called the *Bond Salesman's Method* as well as by the application of the TVM keys of the financial calculator, using the value of a bond formula.

The **Bond Salesman's Method** is derived from the principle that the yield rate per period equals the return per period divided by the average price. The return per period adjusts the coupon up or down by the per period gain or loss of the bond value over the time remaining to maturity. Since a premium bond loses value between the purchase date and the maturity date, this loss will be divided equally among each of the remaining interest periods. We have already used this technique for computing the adjusted current yield. For example, a premium bond purchased for \$1200 and maturing at \$1000 in 16 periods would lose \$200 over 16 periods or \$12.50 per period. A \$50 coupon for this bond would return an average of \$50.00 – \$12.50 = \$37.50 per period. The following is our formula for the *Bond Salesman's Method*:

Bond Salesman's Formula (BSF): $i = \dfrac{\text{return per period}}{\text{average price}} = \dfrac{Fr - (V_{\text{quote}} - S)/n}{\frac{1}{2}(V_{\text{quote}} + S)}$ **(7.2)**

n = interest periods to maturity
S = redemption value
Fr = coupon interest payment
V_{quote} = quoted price

Example 7.3.1

A Steven's Corporation \$1000 debenture, paying 9%(2), matures at par on December 1, 2013. If this bond is quoted at \$1180 on June 1, 2005, what are the current yield, the adjusted current yield, and the yield to maturity (YTM) using the BSF (7.2)?

■ There are 17 periods to the maturity date, and the bond pays a coupon Fr = .045(\$1000) = \$45.

$$\text{BSF: } i = \frac{Fr - (V_{\text{quote}} - S)/n}{\frac{1}{2}(V_{\text{quote}} + S)}$$

$$\frac{45 - (1180 - 1000)/17}{\frac{1}{2}(1180 + 1000)} = \frac{45 - 10.59}{1090} = .03157 \rightarrow \text{YTM} \approx 6.3\%$$

$$\text{Current yield (CY)} = \frac{90}{1180} = .07627 \rightarrow \text{CY} = 7.63\%$$

$$\text{Adjusted current yield (ACY)} = \frac{2(45 - 10.59)}{1180} = .0583 \rightarrow \text{ACY} = 5.83\%$$

Note that even though the adjusted current yield is slightly low, it is much more in line with the yield to maturity.

Our second method of computing the yield to maturity uses the power of the financial calculator and renders the Bond Salesman's Method obsolete—unless you do not own a financial calculator. Our calculations of interest rates for the various annuities have already demonstrated how valuable the calculator can be for finding the rate. The annuity formulas were such that the rate i could not be isolated in the formula, and hence other methods would be necessary. Without the capacity of the financial calculator to iterate the values rapidly, it would require many trial-and-error steps or an approximation method like interpolation. In the following examples we will use the value of a bond formula and substitute the known parameters and compute the rate i. Most financial calculators require the quote (PV) to have the opposite sign from the coupon (Pmt) and the redemption value (FV).

Example 7.3.2

A TnT Corporation $1000 bond was quoted at $890 on July 1, 2000. The bond rate is 6.25%(2), and it matures January 1, 2015. Find the adjusted current yield (ACY) and the yield to maturity (YTM).

■ There are 29 periods to maturity, and the bond pays a coupon $Fr = .03125 \times \$1000 = \$31.25$.

$$V_n = S(1+i)^{-n} + Fra_{\overline{n}|i}$$

$$890 = 1000(1+i)^{-29} + 31.25a_{\overline{29}|i} \rightarrow \text{YTM} = 7.51\%$$

$$\text{Adjusted current yield} = \frac{31.25 + \frac{110}{29}}{890} = \frac{31.25 + 3.79}{890} = \frac{35.04}{890} = .0394$$

$$\text{ACY} = 7.9\%$$

Calculating the value of a bond between coupon dates fits the real world of the bond market, since most bonds are not sold on the coupon dates. However, finding the yield to maturity for a bond quoted between coupon dates at first seems impossible. Our method of moving the value at a coupon date to a date between coupons required us to know the yield rate, but in this section we are looking for the yield rate. Since the financial calculators allow us to compute the yield rate for a quote at a coupon date, we can adjust this process slightly. Our method will require us to express the fractional part of the interest period that remains at the selling date. For example, a bond sold 2/3 of the way between the 30th and 29th interest periods to maturity will be taken as 29-1/3 periods to maturity. The financial calculator can handle fractional periods just fine and will still give us the required yield rate.

Example 7.3.3

The Pax Mountain Fire District $1000, 6%(2) general obligation bonds were quoted at $785 on January 15, 2004. The bonds mature at par September 15, 2026. Find the yield to maturity if the bonds were purchased at the quoted price.

■ The time to maturity from September 15, 2003 is 46 periods, so from January 15, 2004, it is $45.\overline{3}$ periods. The coupon $Fr = .03 \times \$1000 = \$30$. Do not truncate the repeated n.

$$V_n = S(1+i)^{-n} + Fra_{\overline{n}|i}$$

$$785 = 1000(1+i)^{-45.333} + 30a_{\overline{45.\overline{3}}|i} \rightarrow \text{YTM} = 8.08\%(2)$$

Example 7.3.4

The Southern Connector $5000 revenue bonds pay 7.5%(2) and mature at par on March 30, 2029. If these bonds are quoted at $4000 on January 5, 2005, what yield to maturity could an investor expect?

■ It is 84 days from January 5 to March 30 and 48 periods from March 30, 2005 to March 30, 2029. Using Banker's Rule, the fractional part $^{84}/_{180} = .4\bar{6}$. The coupon is $Fr = .0375 \times \$5000 = \$187.50$.

$$V_n = S(1+i)^{-n} + Fra_{\overline{n}|i}$$

$$4000 = 5000(1+i)^{-48.4666} + 187.50a_{\overline{48.466}|i} \rightarrow \text{YTM} = 9.65\%(2)$$

◀ EXERCISES 7.3 ▶

Concept and Short Answer Exercises

Exercises 1 through 9 all refer to Example 7.3.1.

1. What is $Fr = .045 \times 1000 = \$45$ and where is it placed?
2. What is *average per period return on bid* $= \dfrac{S - V_{quote}}{n} = \dfrac{1000-1180}{17} = -\$10.59$?
3. The per period return from the coupon and from the bid $= \$45 - 10.59 = \$34.41$ has what formula?
4. (\$1180+1000)/2 could be called the *average worth* of the bond. Explain why and give its formula.
5. In the BSF, $i = \dfrac{\text{the per period return on coupon and bid}}{\text{average worth of the bond}}$. Explain why this is reasonable.
6. Explain YTM $= 2 \times i$.
7. Explain current yield $= 2\times45/1180$.
8. Explain adjusted current yield $= 2(45-10.59)/1180$.
9. Adjusted current yield could have been $= 2(45-10.59)/1090$. Explain why.
10. *Try this calculus problem*: Start with the formula for V_n, substitute the tangent line approximation equation $1 - ni$ for $(1+i)^{-n}$ and solve for i. You will get the BSF (almost). Explain the BSF in light of this approximation.

Calculation Exercises

For Exercises 11–14, use the Bond Salesman's Method.

11. If a \$2000 debenture, paying 8%(2) and maturing at par in 5 years, has the quoted price (bid) of \$1920, find the yield to maturity, the current yield, and the adjusted current yield. Compare your answers to the calculator value.
12. If a \$20,000 debenture, paying 6%(2) and maturing at par in 4 years, has the quoted price (bid) of \$19,000, find the yield to maturity, the current yield, and the adjusted current yield. Compare your answers to the calculator value.
13. If a \$500 school bond, paying 7%(2) and called at 102 on 10/1/12, is quoted at \$530 on 4/1/05, find the yield to maturity, the current yield, and the adjusted current yield.

14. If a \$50,000,000 school bond, paying 7%(2) and called at 102.4 on 10/1/11, is quoted at \$53,500,000 on 4/1/04, find the yield to maturity, the current yield, and the adjusted current yield.

Use a financial calculator or Excel to find the following yield rates.

15. If a \$1000, 8%(2) municipal bond matures in 12 years and sells for \$950, find the yield rate.

16. If a \$10,000, 6%(2) municipal bond matures in 7 years and sells for \$9750, find the yield rate.

17. A \$1000, 10%(2) bond maturing in 10 years is sold to Jason, who requires 8%(2) on his investment. Jason holds the bond for 2 years and sells it to Wan, who requires 9%(2) on his investment. Find what each paid and the ROR Jason made on his investment.

18. A \$5000, 7%(2) bond maturing in 8 years is sold to Juanita, who requires 8%(2) on her investment. Juanita holds the bond for two years and sells it to Lihn, who requires 7%(2) on her investment. How much did each pay and what ROR did Juanita make on her investment?

19. A \$5000, 9.2%(2) bond maturing in 5 years is sold to Peng, who requires 10.6%(2) on his investment. Peng sells the bond in 3 years to Ge Su, who requires 7.8% on her money. Find what each paid and the ROR Peng made on his investment.

20. A \$5000, 4.6%(2) bond maturing in 5 years is sold to Simon, who requires 10%(2) on his investment. Simon sells the bond in 3 years to Teresa, who requires 7%(2) on her money. How much did each pay and what ROR did Simon make on his investment?

Theory and Extension Exercises

21. A \$1000 bond with semiannual coupons matures at par in 8 years. At a purchase price of \$1210 the yield rate is 2% per half year less than the bond rate. Find the yield rate for this bond.

22. A \$1000 bond with semiannual coupons matures at par in 11 years. At a purchase price of \$812 the yield rate is 3%(2) higher than the bond rate. Find the yield rate.

23. A \$1000, 6.5%(2) bond matures at par on 6/15/16. If the bond is quoted at \$800 on 9/1/06 what yield to maturity would a investor expect to earn? Use compound interest for part of a period.

24. An issue of 20-year, \$1000 bonds paying 7%(2) is called at 5 years with a 5% call premium. What is the yield to call for an investor who purchased original issue bonds at par?

25. A \$1000, 6%(2) bond maturing at par in 8 years has a current yield of 7.32%. What is the yield to maturity?

7.4 The Valuation of Stocks

Our main interest in this chapter is learning how to find the price or value of securities such as stocks and bonds. In this section we will calculate the value of common and preferred stock, as we did for bonds in Sections 7.1 and 7.2. Finding the value of stock poses a more complicated problem than bonds, so we will only deal with some very basic methods. Herbert Mayo, in his fine investment text, remarks that "finding the value of common stock is elusive and perplexing." [Mayo, 6th edition]

When a company is incorporated by the laws of a given state, a certain number of shares of common stock are authorized. **Common stock** is a security representing ownership in a corporation. A stock certificate is issued as evidence of this ownership. Common stock does not mature at some future date like a bond would. The owner of common stock expects to get a return on his investment either through dividends (share of profits) or by the increase in value called capital gain or by both.

Besides common stock, a corporation may also issue preferred stock. **Preferred stock** is an equity instrument that usually pays a fixed dividend, although it is not guaranteed. Preferred stock is generally issued at a price of $100, and the fixed dividend will be given on the stock certificate. Preferred stock dividends are paid from the corporation's earnings, provided they are sufficient. As the name *preferred* suggests, this type of stock will take preference over common stock in the paying of dividends or the distribution of assets if the company "folds." A corporation may have several issues of preferred stock, but it can have only one issue of common stock. Most preferred stock is like a perpetuity because it has no future maturity value. The value or price is like A_∞, the dividend is like the rent R, and the yield rate is the i. The equation for both preferred stock and common stock if they pay a fixed dividend (assuming no growth) is given by

$V = \dfrac{D}{k}$, where D is the dividend and k is the yield rate.[2]

$$\text{Therefore, } \boldsymbol{k = \frac{D}{V}} \qquad \textbf{(7.4)}$$

Compare this to the perpetuity formulas: $A_\infty = \dfrac{R}{i}$ and $i = \dfrac{R}{A_\infty}$.

An investor who wants a yield of 12% for a preferred stock that pays a fixed dividend of $10 would be willing to pay only $83 or less for it, or he will not reach his yield goal. Some preferred stock has a maturity date or call date when the company closes out the issue and returns the stockholder's money. In such cases the value of preferred stock will be found just like the value of a bond. Its value will be the sum of the present value of the fixed dividend annuity plus the present value of the face value of the stock. In the larger picture of stocks, preferred stock could be

[2]We have chosen to simplify the conventional notation by using V instead of P_0 for *market price*, $\hat{P}_0$ for the *theoretical price*, or $\hat{P}_1$ for the *expected price*. Some texts use r instead of k for the market capitalization rate. The rate k can also be further identified by *required*, *expected* or *actual* rate of return. It also goes by *risk-adjusted discount rate*.

classified as a *zero growth* stock and hence the perpetuity structure. The discounted cash flow representation any stock's value of as an infinite stream of future dividends lets us give a simplified form representing the sum of the present values.

$$V = D_1(1+k)^{-1} + D_2(1+k)^{-2} + D_3(1+k)^{-3} + \cdots + D_t(1+k)^{-t} + \cdots$$

$$= \sum_{t=1}^{\infty} D_t(1+k)^{-t} \tag{7.5}$$

If every dividend is the same—as with preferred stock—we see the following simplification to our perpetuity formula. Let D be the expected dividend at the end of one year and each year thereafter, let $v = (1+k)^{-1}$, and use the infinite sum of a geometric series.[3]

$$V = Dv + Dv^2 + Dv^3 + \cdots = D(v + v^2 + v^3 + \cdots) = D\left(\frac{v}{1-v}\right) = D\left(\frac{1}{k}\right) = \frac{D}{k}$$

Common stock may or may not pay dividends, and when it does, it may vary considerably from year to year. The capital gain of common stock is subject not only to the rise and fall of the stock market but also to the growth in earnings of the corporation. Let us first consider a common stock that is expected to experience a regular growth in dividends (even if it only modestly tracks the inflation rate). If the growth rate of the perpetual dividend stream is some constant rate g, equation (7.5) can be modified to the following. See (5.8) for the justification of this result.

$$V = Dv + D(1+g)v^2 + D(1+g)^2v^3 + \cdots \rightarrow V = \frac{D}{k-g}, \text{ where } k > g \tag{7.6}$$

The **expected return** k on investment is the sum of the next year's dividend yield and the growth rate. This follows easily by solving (7.6) for the expected return k. The following equation expresses the resulting relationship.

$$k = \frac{D}{V} + g \qquad \text{alternate form: } k = \frac{D_0(1+g)}{P_0} + g \tag{7.7}$$

For example, a stock priced at \$48 and returning a dividend of \$1.40 with an anticipated growth of 6% will give an expected return of $k = \$1.40/\$48 + .06 = .089$ or 8.9%. Because this is only an expected return, the typical stock prospectus will say, "Past performance does not guarantee future performance." If this stock did not reach the anticipated growth of 6%, then the expected return would be as low as 2.9%. If we note that the next dividend will be (1.06)(\$1.40) ≈ \$1.48, equation (7.6) will give the next year's stock price as 1.48/(.089 – .06) = \$51.03. This is about a 6% growth in the stock price, and hence the dividend growth equals the stock growth.

In order to avoid most of the "elusive" and "perplexing" difficulties of finding the value of common stock, we will consider only one other special case. As with the previous case, we will assume that the dividend grows at some rate g, and we can value the dividends as the sum of a geometric series. If we modify the sequence of growing dividends and let D_0 be the current dividend, then the sequence of expected dividends growing at rate g will be seen as follows.

---

[3]Preferred stock would typically pay dividends quarterly, so we would need to use our effective rate tools to express the equivalent annual rate.

Dividend sequence: $D_0(1+g), D_0(1+g)^2, D_0(1+g)^3, D_0(1+g)^4, \ldots$

Value: $V = D_0(1+g)(1+k)^{-1} + D_0(1+g)^2(1+k)^{-2} + D_0(1+g)^3(1+k)^{-3} + \cdots$

$$V = \frac{D_0(1+g)(1+k)^{-1}}{1-(1+g)(1+k)^{-1}} = \left[\frac{D_0(1+g)(1+k)^{-1}}{1-(1+g)(1+k)^{-1}}\right]\left[\frac{(1+k)}{(1+k)}\right] = \left[\frac{D_0(1+g)}{(1+k)-(1+g)}\right]$$

$$V = \frac{D_0(1+g)}{k-g} \qquad \textbf{(7.8)}$$

D_0 = current dividend
k = yield rate
g = growth rate

We observe that at one year substituting the dividend $D = D_0(1+g)$ gives (7.6).

The above valuation model is called the **dividend-growth valuation model**. Its usefulness is limited to situations where $k > g$, since any growth rate g that is larger than the desired yield rate k is a good buy regardless of the price. The calculation of the value of a stock only serves as an indicator of whether the offered market price is going to return the investor's desired yield rate. A number of other indicators can also be used to make investment decisions. Among these are the "price to earnings per share" ratio (P/E) and the risk-adjusted rate of return. Regardless of the technique used, valuation is always the process of finding the present value of future dividends including growth in earnings or dividends at an appropriate yield rate. The following examples illustrate a few of these calculations.

Example 7.4.1

The Quality Plus Corporation common stock is paying \$2.60 per share, but the corporation only distributes 55% of its earnings as cash dividends. The anticipated growth of this stock is 6%. What is the value of the stock if an investor wants a yield of 11%? If this stock were selling for \$32, what is the expected yield?

■ This is an application of the dividend-growth valuation model (7.8). Substitute the parameters into the formula, remembering to use decimals for the rates. The dividend will be 55%(\$2.60) = \$1.43. Use the expected return formula for the second question.

$$V = \frac{D(1+g)}{k-g} \rightarrow \frac{1.43(1.06)}{.11-.06} = \$30.32$$

$$k = \frac{D}{V} + g \rightarrow \frac{1.43}{32} + .06 = .1047 = 10.47\%$$

Example 7.4.2

What would an investor be willing to pay for each share of New South Gas & Electric preferred stock if it pays a fixed dividend of \$3.50 and the investor wants a 10% yield?

■ This preferred stock is a fixed dividend instrument without a call provision, so it is perpetual and will require formula (7.4).

$$V = \frac{D}{k} = \frac{\$3.50}{.10} = \$35$$

Example 7.4.3

The BCF Corporation pays a \$5.50 per year dividend on its Series 2 preferred stock issue. If this stock matures in 12 years at par, what is the value today to yield 14%?

■ Use a time line diagram to see the time-value structure of this security. Use the present value of an ordinary annuity to find the present value of the dividend annuity. Then use the compound discount formula to find the present value of the redemption value (par value).

TIME LINE DIAGRAM 7.4.1

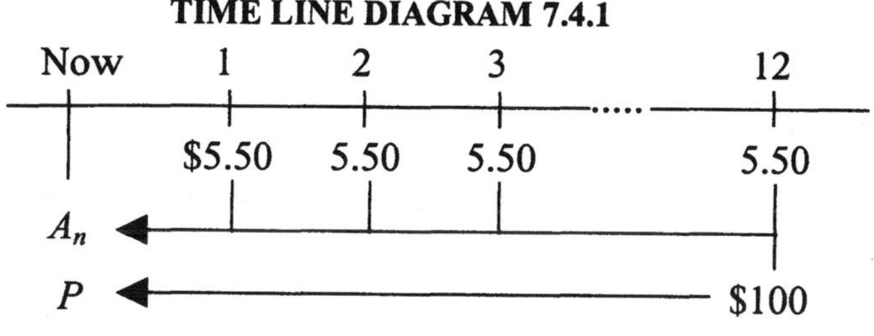

$$V_n = A_n + P$$

$$V_n = Da_{\overline{n}|i} + S(1+i)^{-n}$$

$$V_n = 5.50a_{\overline{12}|14\%} + 100(1.14)^{-12}$$

$$V_n = \$31.13 + \$20.76 = \$51.89$$

Example 7.4.4

The R Corporation's projected earnings and dividends for its common stock are given in Table 7.4.1. Find the current value for this stock to yield 12%.

TABLE 7.4.1

Year	Earnings \$	Dividend \$	Growth Rate %
1	0.80	0.36	—
2	1.28	0.58	60.0
3	1.65	0.75	30.0
4	1.91	0.86	15.0
5	2.06	0.93	8.0
6	2.16	0.97	5.0
7	2.27	1.02	5.0
8	2.38	1.07	5.0

■ The value of the first 5 years, when the high growth occurs, can be found by compound interest using the desired yield rate. Since the growth levels off at 5%, we can apply the dividend-growth model to the dividends from year 6 and beyond. The value of these later dividends will be located at the end of the 5th year, so this value will have to be brought back to the present with compound interest at the yield rate.

$$V_{1\text{-}5} = 0.36(1.12)^{-1} + 0.58(1.12)^{-2} + 0.75(1.12)^{-3} + 0.86(1.12)^{-4} + 0.93(1.12)^{-5}$$
$$= \$0.32 + \$0.46 + \$0.53 + \$0.55 + \$0.53 = \$2.39$$

$$V_{6+} = \frac{D(1+g)}{k-g}(1.12)^{-5} = \frac{0.93(1.05)}{.12-.05}(1.12)^{-5} = \$13.95(1.12)^{-5} = \$7.92$$

$$V = V_{1\text{-}5} + V_{6+} = \$10.31$$

Example 7.4.5

If the BCF stock in Example 7.4.3 is selling for \$62, what is the yield rate?

■ Use the same formula as in Example 7.4.3, but solve for i. Most financial calculators will require that the present value have the opposite sign from the future value and the payment.

$$V_n = D a_{\overline{n}|i} + S(1+i)^{-n}$$

$$62 = 5.50 a_{\overline{12}|i} + 100(1+i)^{-12} \rightarrow i = 11.49\% \text{ Yield rate}$$

One other method of evaluating stock looks at each dividend and the expected selling price in several years. Example 7.4.4 illustrated that short-term or long-term dividend income stream from a stock need not be uniform or grow at some fixed rate. Stock prices are easily seen as the present value of the dividends plus the present value of the future selling price. The method of discounted cash flows provides the basic tool and will help us find the price to reach a desired yield rate or find the yield rate to expect when the stock is purchased at a certain price and sold a while later at hopefully a better price. The discounted cash flow tools of the financial calculator make these calculations relatively painless. These are also calculations that anticipate the cash flow analysis work needed in Chapter 8 for capital budgeting. The price of a piece of stock as the present value of a stream of cash flows parallels the same process illustrated in Time Line Diagram 7.1.1 for bonds. Note that $v = (1+k)^{-t}$, where k is the yield rate.

$$\text{Value of the stock} = V_0 = D_1 v + D_2 v^2 + D_3 v^3 + \cdots + D_T v^T + V_T v^T$$
$$= \sum_{t=1}^{T} D_t v^t + V_T v^T \text{ or } \sum_{t=1}^{T} D_t (1+k)^{-t} + V_T (1+k)^{-T} \quad \textbf{(7.9)}$$

Example 7.4.6

L Corporation stock is currently selling for \$26.50 with expected dividends over the next three years of \$2.05, \$2.10, and \$2.20. If purchased at \$26.50 and sold in three years at \$31, what rate of return will the investor realize?

■ Use the CF registers on the financial calculator to solve the following equation of value resulting from substituting into (7.9). This is an IRR calculation.

$$26.50 = 2.05(1+k)^{-1} + 2.10(1+k)^{-2} + (2.20 + 31.00)(1+k)^{-3}$$
$$k = 12.95\%$$

Example 7.4.7

If the investor in Example 7.4.6 wants to make 14%, what is the highest price he or she would be willing to pay for the stock?

■ Using the same information in the CF registers, calculate the NPV at 14%. We can anticipate that the price will need to be lower to produce a higher yield. The NPV calculation gives –.6768, which we round to –.68. This indicates that the price in Example 7.4.6 is \$0.68 too high, so the highest price to realize a 14% yield is \$26.50 – \$0.68 = \$25.82.

Example 7.4.8

If the investor in Example 7.4.6 buys the stock at \$26.50, what is the minimum price he can sell the stock for in 3 years and make 14%?

■ This question requires us to find the selling price from the following equation of value, which is like the equation in Example 7.4.6 but with a different unknown.

$$\begin{aligned}26.50 &= 2.05(1.14)^{-1} + 2.10(1.14)^{-2} + (2.20 + V_3)(1.14)^{-3}\\ &= 2.05(1.14)^{-1} + 2.10(1.14)^{-2} + 2.20(1.14)^{-3} + V_3(1.14)^{-3}\\ &= 1.80 + 1.62 + 1.48 + V_3(1.14)^{-3}\\ 21.60 &= V_3(1.14)^{-3}\\ V_3 &= 21.60(1.14)^3 = \$32\end{aligned}$$

◀ EXERCISES 7.4 ▶

Concept and Short Answer Exercises

1. The formula for expected return on a stock is $k = \frac{D}{P} + g$ and requires a constant dividend and a constant growth for the stock. Why are stocks inherently hard to analyze in the short run?
2. Compare $V = D/k$ with the perpetuity formula and explain why it is used to compute the value of a stock.
3. If the growth rate equals the yield rate ($g = k$), the formula for the dividend-growth valuation model, V, will become _____.
4. How does the analysis of stock change if the earnings, dividends, or the growth rates have no apparent pattern in them?

Calculation Exercises

5. What is the expected return on investment for a share of All Grow, Inc. common stock selling at \$45, paying a \$2.15 dividend, with an expected growth of 5.5%?
6. What is the expected return on investment for a share of CTF common stock selling at \$108, paying a \$4.15 dividend, with an anticipated growth of 5%?
7. What should an investor be willing to pay for a share of X-Seed preferred stock with a fixed dividend of \$10.50 if she wants a yield of 12%?
8. What should an investor be willing to pay for a share of Greenville Municipal stock with a fixed dividend of \$12.50 if he wants a yield of 8%?
9. A share of Tex Corporation common stock is paying \$2.45 per share, but the corporation only pays 45% of its earning as cash dividends. The anticipated growth of this stock is 4.5%. Find the value of this stock if an investor wants a yield of 10.5%. If the stock is selling for \$22, what is the expected yield?

10. A share of Zytex Corporation common stock is paying $4.50 per share, but the corporation only pays 30% of its earnings as cash dividends. The anticipated growth of this stock is 6%. Find the value of this stock if an investor wants a yield of 8%. If the stock is selling for $35, what is the expected yield?

11. Big Sky Petroleum pays a $4.85 dividend on its E-Series preferred stock. If this stock matures in 8 years at par, what is the value today that will yield 12%?

12. Up East Industrials pays a $4.25 dividend on its F-Series preferred stock. If this stock matures in 12 years at par, what is the value today that will yield 10%?

13. If the Big Sky Petroleum stock in Exercise 11 can be purchased for $60 per share, what is the yield rate?

14. If the Up East Industrials stock in Exercise 12 can be purchased for $72 per share, what is the yield rate?

15. What yield can an investor expect if he pays $50 for a share of Greentank, Inc. preferred stock that has a fixed dividend of $8 per share?

16. What yield can an investor expect if she pays $500 for a share of SamCO, Inc. preferred stock that has a fixed dividend of $58 per share?

17. Omega Security common stock has had earnings of $3.05 per share, and the corporation pays 80% of its earnings in cash dividends. The stock shows a growth trend of about 7%. What is the value of this stock to an investor who wants a yield of 15%?

18. Beta Testing Corp common stock has had earnings of $4.56 per share, and the corporation pays 40% of its earnings in cash dividends. The stock shows a growth trend of about 10%. What is the value of this stock to an investor who wants a yield of 12%?

19. What is the expected return on investment for a share of common stock that pays a $4.05 dividend and is being offered for $62? The growth of this stock is expected to be slightly more than 6.5%.

20. What is the expected return on investment for a share of common stock that pays a $4.78 dividend and is being offered for $65.24? The growth of this stock is expected to be slightly more than 7.5%.

21. What dividend would an investor need to get from a share of common stock that sells for $76 if she wants a 9.5% yield?

22. What dividend would an investor need to get from a share of common stock that sells for $79 if he wants a 7.5% yield?

23. A share of Skytec common stock currently sells for $44.75 with expected dividends over the next 4 years of $1.10, $1.35, $1.55, and $1.70. What yield rate can an investor expect if she is able to sell the stock in 4 years at $54.75?

24. What would an investor desiring a 12% yield be willing to pay for a share of common stock with expected dividends of $2.65, $2.80, and $3.05 and a selling price after 3 years of $38.50?

25. A share of TLC common stock selling at \$78.30 has expected dividends of \$2.20, \$2.20, \$2.20, and \$3.10 over the next 4 years. What price would an investor need in 4 years in order to realize a 15% yield?

26. The projected earnings, dividends, and growth for Datatronics, Inc. common stock are given in Table 7.4.2. Find the current value of this stock to yield 11%.

TABLE 7.4.2

Year	Earnings $	Dividend $	Growth Rate %
1	0.65	0.39	0.0
2	1.03	0.62	59
3	1.28	0.77	24
4	1.42	0.85	10.5
5	1.52	0.91	7.5
6	1.63	0.98	7.5

Chapter 7 Summary of Concepts

Value of a Bond: $V_n = S(1+i)^{-n} + Fra_{\overline{n}|i}$

Value of a Bond between Coupon Dates

Bond Salesman's Method: $i = \dfrac{Fr - (V_{quote} - S)/n}{\frac{1}{2}(V_{quote} + S)}$

Expected Return on Stock: $k = D/V + g$

Preferred Stock Dividend: $D = kV$

Dividend-Growth Valuation Model: $V = \dfrac{D(1+g)}{k-g}$

Discounted Cash Flow Model: $\sum_{t=1}^{T} D_t(1+k)^{-t} + V_T(1+k)^{-T}$

Chapter 7 Vocabulary Check

Accrued Interest
Adjusted Current Yield
Average Price
Bond
Bond Rate
Call Provision
Common Stock
Convertible Bond
Coupon
Coupon Bond
Current Yield
Debenture
Mortgage Bond
P/E Ratio
Preferred Stock
Premium Bond
Purchase Price
Quoted Price
(Net Price)
(And Interest Price)
Redemption Price
Registered Bond
Return per Period
Yield Rate

Discount Bond	*Yield to Maturity*
Growth Rate	*Zero Coupon Bond*

Chapter 7 Skills Check

1. Find the value of a bond on either coupon dates or between coupon dates.

   Section 7.1 Examples 2, 3; Exercises 11, 13
   Section 7.2 Examples 1, 2, 4; Exercises 13, 15

2. Find the yield rate of a bond if purchased at a quoted price, using either the Bond Salesman's Method or the financial calculator. Also find the current yield and the adjusted current yield.

   Section 7.3 Examples 1, 2, 4; Exercises 11, 15, 17

3. Find the expected return on an issue of common stock knowing the price, dividend, and growth in earnings. Find the value of an issue of preferred stock knowing the dividend and desired yield.

   Section 7.3 Examples 1, 2; Exercises 5, 7

4. Find the value of a common stock issue based on the dividend-growth valuation model or the discounted cash flow model.

   Section 7.4 Examples 1, 5, 7; Exercises 9, 24

Review Test for Investing in Stocks and Bonds

1. A Helix-Tec Corporation \$1000, 7%(2) debenture matures at par on 10/15/18. The bond has a call provision paying 103 on 4/15/08. Find the value of this bond on 4/15/04 to yield 9.5%(2) if

   a. The bond is called at 103 on 4/15/08.
   b. The bond is redeemed at par on 10/15/18.

2. What should be bid for a \$5000 zero coupon bond maturing in 78 months if the investor wants a return of 8%(2)?

3. Mount Carmel municipal \$10,000 revenue bonds pay 6%(2) and mature at par on March 30, 2020. Find the quoted price and purchase price on August 15, 2005 to yield 7.5%(4) if held to maturity.

4. A Dynamic Oil \$1000, 5.5%(2) bond matures at par on December 5, 2012. Find the yield to maturity and the adjusted current yield if the bond is quoted at \$840 on June 5, 2005.

5. On April 8, 2004, a Rockford Bios \$1000, 8%(2) bond was quoted at \$1185. If this bond matures at par on August 8, 2022, find the yield to maturity if purchased at the quoted price. Use compound interest for part of a period.

6. Falcon Star, Inc. pays \$8.20 per year dividend on its Series E preferred stock issue. What should an investor be willing to pay per share of this stock if he or she needs a 9% yield?

7. Cross Country Systems common stock is paying \$2.38 per share on a 65% distribution of earnings. The stock is predicted to continue a 5% growth for several years. What is the value of this stock to an investor wanting a 10% yield? If the stock is selling for \$34.50, what is the expected yield?
8. An issue of preferred stock pays dividends of \$6.25 per year. If the stock matures in 10 years at par, what is its value today to yield 12%?
9. If the preferred stock in exercise 8 is sold for \$70.50, what is the yield rate?

7.5 The Cost of Capital—An Appendix to Chapter 7

The need to have some background on the cost of capital for Chapter 8 and its close connection to the ideas of Chapter 7 leads us to this brief discussion.

Every firm must raise money (capital) to continue expansion, make upgrades, and seek investment opportunities. Besides their profits, the three primary ways companies raise capital are by debt (such as bonds and loans), by issuing preferred stock, and by selling common stock. Issuing new shares of common stock provides one source of *equity capital,* and additions to retained earnings provide a second source. All of these sources of capital cost the firm money that we call the **cost of capital**. Bonds pay coupons that must be paid regularly, while preferred stock requires dividend payments. New shares of common stock will involve flotation costs to issue new shares, and they often pay dividends as well. Even retained earnings have an associated *opportunity cost* by which the return from some project replaces another source of return from securities that have a similar degree of risk. The cost of capital becomes quite significant in capital budgeting—a topic we shall address shortly in Chapter 8. There are a number of ideas related to the cost of capital for which we will give brief overviews. For an in-depth study of these ideas consult a corporate finance or investment text. Several are noted in Appendix A.

The **marginal cost of capital** (MCC) is the cost to obtain another dollar of new capital. The mathematical concept involved uses the rate of change of the cost as a derivative at x to estimate the increase in cost at $x+1$. Another important approach in dealing with the cost of capital (for, say, capital budgeting) is to calculate it as a weighted average of the various components. If we consider debt, preferred stock, and common equity as the three main capital components, then the **weighted average cost of capital** (WACC) can be defined as the percent of debt times the after-tax cost of debt plus the percent of preferred stock times the rate of return plus the percent of common equity times the required rate of return on equity.

- Debt
  - k_1 is the interest rate
  - $(1-\text{tax rate})k_1$ is the after-tax cost of debt
  - w_1 is the weight as a percent, usually based on book value
- Preferred stock
  - $k_2 = \text{dividend/current price}$
  - w_2 is the weight as a percent
- Common stock
  - $k_3 = D/V + g$ (i.e., the dividend yield plus the growth rate)
  - w_3 is the weight as a percent

$$\textbf{WACC} = w_1(1-T)k_1 + w_2k_2 + w_3k_3 \qquad \textbf{(7.10)}$$

The weights and the values of k generate a percent of each dollar of capital that it costs to raise these three components, thus WACC is also the marginal cost of capital.

Example 7.5.1

Find the weighted average cost of capital for the Brown Corporation, whose capital structure calls for 35% debt, 8% preferred stock, and 57% common equity (retained earnings and common stock). They borrow at 7%, pay 6.5% on preferred stock with a current price of \$90, and their cost of equity is 10.5%. The marginal tax rate including state and federal is 42%.

■ Note that the rate of return for the preferred stock is $6.50/90 \approx 7.2\%$.

$$\text{WACC} = w_1(1 - T)k_1 + w_2k_2 + w_3k_3$$

$$\text{WACC} = .35(.58)(.07) + .08(.072) + .57(.105)$$

$$\approx 6.06\%$$

One other topic of concern is the need to make adjustments to the cost of capital to allow for risk. The **risk-adjusted cost of capital** makes allowance for the amount of risk associated with a given project so that the greater the risk the higher the cost. Risk will be addressed in greater detail in Chapter 9, but for now we will only note the need and suggest a relevant model. The Capital Asset Pricing Model infers that the riskiness of a given stock relates to its effect on the riskiness of a diversified portfolio. The **beta measure** of a stock measures how volatile it is in comparison to the general market. In Chapter 9 we will see how the regression line for a stock with some history has a slope which has been defined as the *beta coefficient.* A stock with a beta of 1 moves pretty much with the general market, whereas a stock with a beta of 2 would be quite volatile, and one with a beta of .5 would be relatively unvolatile. The security market line equation gives a means of defining the risk-adjusted cost of capital.

Required return on stock A = the risk-free rate + (market risk premium)(beta)

k(stock A) = k(risk free) + [k(market) – k(risk free)](beta)

$$\mathbf{k_A = k_{RF} + (k_M - k_{RF})b} \qquad \text{where } b = \text{beta} \tag{7.11}$$

To see this equation in the context of a regression line, solve it for b as a slope.

$$b = \frac{k_A - k_{RF}}{k_M - k_{RF}}$$

Example 7.5.2

Find the Wood Tectonic Corporation's risk-adjusted cost of capital if their b =.9, the risk-free rate is 4.9%, and the market yield is 6.8%.

■ $k_A = k_{RF} + (k_M - k_{RF})b$

$k = 4.9\% + (6.8\% - 4.9\%)(.90)$

$k = 4.9\% + 1.9(.90)$

$k = 6.61\%$

Appendix A

References and Endnotes

References

Brealey, Richard A., and Stewart C. Myers. *Principles of Corporate Finance*, 7th ed. Boston: McGraw-Hill/Irwin, 2003.

Brigham, Eugene F., and Joel F. Houston. *Fundamentals of Financial Management*, concise 2nd ed. Orlando: Harcourt Brace, 1999.

Federal Reserve Bank of New York Statistics. "Prime Rate History: 1921–Present." ftp://ftp.ny.frb.org/prime/Prime.txt (20 June 2002).

Federal Reserve Markets Group. "Domestic Open Market Operations During 2001." http://www.newyorkfed.org/pihome/omo/omo2001.pdf (9 July 2002).

Francis, Jack Clark, and Roger G. Ibbotson. *Investments: A Global Perspective*. Upper Saddle River, NJ: Prentice Hall, 2000, Chapter 5.

Friedman, D. H. , *Money and Banking*, 4th ed. American Banker's Association, Washington, DC, 1998.

Hawawini, Gabriel, and Claude Viallet. *Finance for Executives*. Cincinnati: South-Western College Publ., 1999. Chapter 7.

Kellison, Stephen G. *Theory of Interest*, 2nd ed. Homewood, IL: Irwin, 1991.

Latorre, Don R., et al. *Calculus Concepts: An Informal Approach to the Mathematics of Change*, 2nd ed. Boston: Houghton Mifflin, 2002, pp. 487–95.

Lester, Robert M. *Forty Years of Carnegie Giving*. New York: Scribner's, 1941.

Mayo, Herbert. *Investments*, 6th ed. Fort Worth: Dryden, 2000.

Nikolai, Loren A., and John D. Bazley. *Intermediate Accounting*, 5th ed. Boston: PWS-Kent, 1991.

Parmenter, Michael M. *Theory of Interest and Life Contingencies*, 3rd ed. Winsted, CT: ACTEX, 1999.

Shao, Stephen P., and Lawrence P. Shao. *Mathematics for Management and Finance*, 8th ed. Cincinnati: South-Western College Publ., 1998.

Tempo Bank dot Com. "Mutual Savings Institutions: A Community Banking Charter that Works." http://www.tempobank.com/whatsamutual.htm (25 July 2002).

Zima, Petr, and Robert L. Brown. *Mathematics of Finance*, 5th ed. Boston: McGraw-Hill, 2001.

Endnotes

1. In the early 1990s there were about 3400 member banks in the Federal Reserve System. An Internet search in mid-2002 shows 954. One possible explanation for this shrinkage is the large number of bank mergers and acquisitions that have placed a number of banks under a single bank holding company.

2. A convenient way to distinguish a *life annuity* from *life insurance* is to note that the purchaser of the life annuity (*annuitant*) will receive a sequence of payments if still living at a given age. On the other hand, the purchaser of life insurance (*insured*) designates beneficiaries that receive the insurance settlement if he dies while the policy is in force.

   A *life annuity* provides for the accrual of financial assets from the premiums of a number of annuitants under the assumption that those that die before the payout date will not need the income and those that are living will be the only ones to collect the income. The living annuitants will continue to collect income as long as they live. The premium structure of both life annuities and life insurance is based on life expectancy information from a mortality table.

   Whole life annuities continue to pay the annuitant periodic income from some starting date (maybe age 65) until the person dies. These annuities are classified on the basis of when the first payment occurs relative to the purchase date. If the first payment is made one year after the date of purchase, then the life annuity is called an *ordinary whole life annuity* (*immediate whole life annuity*). If the first payment is made at the date of purchase, it is called a *whole life annuity due*. If the first payment is made two or more years after the purchase date, it is called a *deferred whole life annuity*.

   A *temporary life annuity* pays benefits for a fixed number of years regardless of whether the annuitant is living. These annuities can also be classified as ordinary, due, and deferred.

Appendix B

Using Financial Calculators and Spreadsheets

B.1 The Texas Instruments TI 83 Plus and TI 83 Solutions

This calculator is representative of all menu-driven calculators, including the Texas Instruments' financial calculator and Casio's financial calculator. If you are using the TI 83, enter the financial mode by using [2nd] [x^{-1}]. If you are using the TI 83 Plus, enter the financial mode by using [APPS] 1:Finance, 1:TVM Solver. When you are not sure about how to approach a problem, use your graphing calculator handbook. There are some very helpful tree diagrams in the appendix that show which functions are under the numerous menus at the different levels.

A. Chapters 1 and 2 — Simple Interest and Bank Discount Problems

1. The usual algebraic calculations are displayed on the screen of the TI 83 so that you can see the formula before completing the calculation. The [ENTER] key completes all computations just like the = key on a simple calculator. The sequence [ALPHA] [ENTER] completes financial mode calculations.
2. NPV and IRR at Simple Interest:
   Invest \$1000 and get returns of \$600 in 1 year and \$800 in 2 years. Hence the NPV @ r% = −1000 + 600/(1+r) + 800/(1+2r). Find the NPV@15% and the IRR.
   (a) We will use the [MATH] 0:Solver to find the NPV and IRR.
   (b) SOLVER solves equations for zero. The TI 83 prefers single letter variable names, so we will use N for NPV and x for the rate since it is a variable name quickly written using [X,T,Θ,*n*]. Rewrite the NPV equation as: 0=N+1000−600/(1+X)−800/(1+2X). You can also use the [Y=] menu to define your function as: $0 = N - Y_1$.
   (c) To find the NPV @ 15% enter .15 ➔ x field, place the cursor on the N field, and press the [ALPHA] [ENTER] (SOLVE) to solve for N. In this case NPV @ 15%=\$137.12.
   (d) To find the IRR, enter 0 ➔ N field, place the cursor on the x field, and press the [ALPHA] [ENTER] to find x. In this case the IRR=.2623=26.23%.

B. Chapter 3—Compound Interest

1. [2nd] [x^{-1}] enters the finance routines on the TI 83. Use [APPS] on the 83 Plus.
2. Select option 1: TVM Solver.
3. Compute the value of $S = 1000(1+6\%/4)^{10}$.
   (a) 10 ➔ N; 6 ➔ I%; 1000 ➔ PV; 0 ➔ PMT; 4 ➔ P/Y; 4 ➔ C/Y. Move the cursor to FV field and press [ALPHA] [ENTER]. Answer: FV = 1160.54.
   (b) Caution: On this type of calculator the I% is the yearly rate. You must also enter the P/Y (payments per year) and C/Y (compounding periods per year). Keep these the same for this problem.
4. Compute the value of $P = 1000(1+6\%/4)^{-10}$.
   (a) 10➔ N; 6➔ I%; 1000➔ FV; 0➔ PMT; 4➔ P/Y. Move the cursor to the PV field and press the [ALPHA] [ENTER]. Answer: PV = 861.67.
   (b) Caution: Same as 3b above.
   (c) Caution: The N is never entered as a negative for any problem. When you calculate the PV the financial program displays it as a negative.
5. Compute the value of N in $2050 = -1000(1+9\%/12)^{N}$.
   (a) –1000 ➔ PV; 9 ➔ I%; 2050 ➔ FV; 0 ➔ PMT; 12 ➔ P/Y. Move cursor to the N field and press the [ALPHA] [ENTER]. Answer: N = 96.07 months.
   (b) Caution: Same as 3b and 4c above.
6. Compute the value of I in $3 = -1(1+I\%/4)^{20}$.
   (a) 20➔ N; –1➔ PV; 3➔ FV; 0➔ PMT; 4➔ P/Y. Move the cursor to I field and press the [ALPHA] [ENTER]. Answer: I = 22.59%(4).
   (b) Caution: I on this calculator is the same as $j\%(m)$ in the text.
7. Compute NPV and IRR at compound interest: Compute the NPV at 15% for an expenditure of $1000 now with a return of $600 in 1 year and $800 in 2 years and find the IRR.
   (a) Use Finance CALC 7:npv, which is the NPV function. The menu has the following structure: npv(*interest rate*, *CFO*, *CFList*, *CFFreq*). The default for *CFFreq* is 1 and does not need to be given.
   (b) npv(15,–1000,{600,800}) yields NPV = 126.65.
   (c) irr(–1000,{600,800}) yields IRR = 24.34%.
   (d) Caution: If monies were compounded semiannually with annual payments, you would need to enter monies for each period. Suppose that the rate were 15%(2) with the yearly returns as shown, then use the following format for NPV: npv(15/2,–1000,{0,600,0,800}). This yields $118.24. Furthermore, 2*irr(–1000,{0,600,0,800}) yields 23.02%(2).

C. Chapter 4—Ordinary Annuities

As in compound interest, you may enter all of the other fields and solve for the one needed. In annuities, we enter or solve for *n* payments.

1. [2nd] [x^{-1}] enters the finance routines on the TI 83. Use [APPS] on the 83 Plus.
2. Select option 1: TVM Solver.
3. Compute FV: $S_n = Rs_{\overline{n}|i} = 1000s_{\overline{20}|8\%/2}$ is the return on investing $1000 every half-year for 10 years at 8%(2).
   (a) 20➧N; 8➧I; 0➧PV; 1000➧PMT; 2➧P/Y; place the cursor on FV and press [ALPHA] [ENTER]. Answer: FV = $29,778.08.
   (b) Note: Suppose the investor already had $20,000 in his account and then made the deposits of $1000 every half year for 10 years at 8%(2). To find the FV of the bundle and the payments in step a) above, also put 20,000➧PV. You should get –$73,600.54.
4. PV, PMT, I, or N use the same approach: Fill in all the other fields and then solve for the appropriate field.
   (a) Caution: When solving for I or for N, one of the monies must be positive and the other negative.
   (b) Caution: N is never negative.
   (c) If you need one of the data fields to compute with, you may set up the problem in TVM SOLVER and then go back one level to [2nd] (or [APPS]) FINANCE CALC and use options 2, 3, 4, 5, or 6 to get the value.

D. Chapter 5—Other Annuities Certain

1. FV Forborne Annuity: $S_n(\text{for}) = Rs_{\overline{n}|i} = 1000s_{\overline{20}|8\%/2}(1+8\%/2)^6$ is the return on investing $1000 every half year for 10 years at 8%(2), then letting the bundle sit for 3 more years at the same rate. These problems are done in stages on this calculator.
   (a) Stage 1: Do the ordinary part by 20➧N; 8➧I; 0➧PV; –1000➧PMT; 2➧P/Y; place the cursor on FV and press [ALPHA] [ENTER]. FV= 29,778.08.
   (b) Stage 2: Do the compound interest:
      (1) Change 6➧N.
      (2) Put the cursor on the PV field and press 2nd (or [APPS]) FINANCE 6:tvm_FV [ENTER] (places the 29,778.08➧PV).
      (3) 0➧PMT.
      (4) Put the cursor on FV and press [ALPHA] [ENTER]. FV= –37,678.77.
   (c) PV, R, and N are similar.
   (d) There are no I problems in this chapter except for perpetuities.

(e) Caution: To solve for N or R, check the outline in the text.

2. Perpetuities are simple interest problems, provided you have found the ffective rate that matches the payment interval.

3. Conversion of rates to match payment: \$100/month for 12 months at 8%(2).

   (a) 12➔N; 8➔I; 0➔PV; 100➔PMT; 12➔P/Y; 2➔C/Y and solve for the FV with [ALPHA] [ENTER]. FV = 1244.24.

   (b) Note that the payments per year and the compounding periods per year are different, and each must be entered.

   (c) If you want to compute the effective rate first using $j=(1+i)^k-1$, it can be done on the main screen or in I%= register. You will then have to let 1➔P/Y and 1➔C/Y.

E. Chapter 6—Debt Retirement Methods

Home loans and savings accounts are the same as ordinary annuities and compound interest, with the following two often-used applications:

1. Outstanding balances for loans:

   $OB_n = P(1+i)^n - Rs_{\overline{n}|i} = 50{,}000(1+6\%/12)^{60} - 1000s_{\overline{60}|6\%/12}$ is the formula for how much you owe on a \$50,000 loan after 60 monthly payments of \$1000 each at 6%(12).

   (a) 20➔N; 6➔I; 50,000➔PV; –1000➔PMT; 12➔P/Y; place the cursor on FV and press [ALPHA] [ENTER]. OB_{60} = \$2327.52.

   (b) Caution: PV must be a +50,000 and PMT must be a –1000.

2. Find the appreciated worth of a \$150,000 home after 10 years if home values are growing at 3% per year: Value = $150{,}000(1+3\%)^{10}$.

   (a) Note that this is just compound interest on the original price of the home.

   (b) 10➔N; 3➔I; 150,000➔PV; 0➔PMT; 1➔P/Y; place the cursor on FV and press [ALPHA] [ENTER]. Value = \$201,587.46.

F. Chapter 7—Stocks and Bonds

1. Find the value of a \$1000, 8%(2) bond that matures in 6 years if you want a yield 10%(2) on your investment.

   $$V_n = S(1+i)^{-n} + Fra_{\overline{n}|i} = 1000(1+10\%/2)^{-12} + (1000*.04)a_{\overline{12}|10\%/2}$$

   (a) 12➔N; 10➔I; 40➔PMT; 1000➔FV; 2➔P/Y; place the cursor on PV and press [ALPHA] [ENTER]. V = 911.37.

   (b) Caution: 1000*.04 = 40 is the coupon and is entered as +40, as is the 1000.

2. If the yield rate were 6%(2), the value of the premium bond would equal \$1099.54.

B.2 The Sharp EL-733A Solutions

The Sharp financial calculator is inexpensive and has nearly all of the financial functions you will need for this basic form of this text. However, the financial buttons are for compound interest and annuities, which do not start until Chapter 3.

A. Chapters 1 and 2—Simple Interest and Bank Discount problems

1. Usual calculations are a bit cumbersome on the Sharp EL-733A since there is no hierarchy of operations built in and there are no parentheses. Example: Calculate 1000/(1+3×(.04)). You will need to do the operations in the correct order, as follows:
   (a) 3×(.04)+1= calculates the denominator.
   (b) $1/x$ button takes its reciprocal. (Multiply by the reciprocal instead of dividing.)
   (c) ×1000= Yields 892.86.
2. NPV and IRR at simple interest are done by finding the values at the required dates using the methods presented in the text. Note that the IRR and NPV buttons are for compound interest and will not give the correct answer for simple interest.

B. Chapter 3—Compound Interest

1. 2ndF Mode enters the finance routines. You need to do this step only if the FIN annotator is not in the upper right of your screen.
2. 2ndF C·CE clears all of the registers by placing a 0 in each one. This step should be done before each new problem.
3. Compute the value of $S = 1000(1+6\%/4)^{10}$.
   (a) 10 ➜ n; 6/4= ➜ I%; 1000 ➜ PV; 0 ➜ PMT; COMP FV. Value = –1160.54.
   (b) Caution: Rates for compound interest and annuities are entered as a % and not as a decimal. Hence 6/4 = 1.5 ➜ i is correct, while .06/4 = .015 ➜ i is incorrect.
4. Compute the value of $P = 1000(1+6\%/4)^{-10}$.
   (a) 10➜ n; 6/4= ➜ i; 1000➜ FV; 0➜ PMT; COMP PV. Value = –861.6672.
   (b) Caution: Same as 3b above.
   (c) Caution: The n is never entered as a negative in any problem. When we calculate the PV, the financial programs will display it as a negative. This will be important when we find outstanding balance.
5. Compute n in $2050 = -1000(1+9\%/12)^n$. This yields $n = 96.07$ months
   (a) –1000 ➜ PV; 9/12= ➜ i; 2050 ➜ FV; 0 ➜ PMT; 12 ➜ P/Y; COMP n.
   (b) Caution: Same as 3b above.
   (c) Caution: The n is never entered as a negative in any problem.

6. Compute i in $3 = -1(1+i)^{20}$, where the nominal rate is quarterly.
   (a) 20➜N; −1➜PV; 3➜FV; 0➜PMT; COMP i; ×4= 22.59%(4).
   (b) Caution: Same as 3b above.
   (c) Caution: i on this calculator is rate per period and must be multiplied by the number of compounding periods/year to get the nominal rate.

7. Compute NPV and IRR at compound interest: Compute the NPV at 15% of a $1000 expenditure now with a return of $600 in 1 year and $800 in 2 years and find the IRR.
   (a) −1000➜CFi; 600➜CFi; 800➜CFi enters the cash flows into registers 0, 1, and 2.
   (b) 15➜i; pressing the NPV button yields NPV = $126.65.
   (c) Pressing the IRR button yields IRR = 24.34%.
   (d) Caution: If monies were compounded semiannually with annual payments, you would need to enter monies for each compounding period. This means 0 at the periods where there is no return. Suppose that the rate were 15%(2) with the yearly returns as shown. Then enter −1000➜CFi; 0➜CFi; 600➜CFi; 0➜CFi; 800➜CFi enters the cash flows into registers 0, 1, 2, 3, and 4. 15/2=➜i enters the correct rate and then press the NPV to yield $118.24. Finally, IRR×2 = yields 23.02%(2).

C. Chapter 4—Ordinary Annuities

As in compound interest you may enter all of the other fields and solve for the one needed. In annuities, you enter or solve for *n* payments.

1. The FIN mode is needed.
2. 2ndF C·CE
3. Compute the value of $S_n = Rs_{\overline{n}|i} = 1000s_{\overline{20}|8\%/2}$. This is the return on investing $1000 every half year for 10 years at 8%(2).
   (a) 20➜n; 8/2=➜i; 0➜PV; 1000➜PMT; COMP FV yields −$29,778.08.
   (b) Note: Suppose that the investor already had $20,000 in his or her account and then made the deposits of $1000 every half-year for 10 years at 8%(2). To find the FV of the bundle and the payments as in step (a) above, also put 20,000➜PV. You should get −$73,600.54.
4. PV, PMT, i, or n uses the same approach: Fill in all the other fields and then solve for the appropriate field.
   (a) Caution: When solving for i or for n, one of the monies must be positive and the other negative.
   (b) Caution: n is never negative.
   (c) If you need a field to calculate with, you may recall that field with 2ndF RCL n or i or any other register.

D. Chapter 5—Other Annuities Certain

1. Find the value of the forborne annuity $S_n = Rs_{\overline{n}|i} = 1000s_{\overline{20}|8\%/2}(1+8\%/2)^6$.

   This is the return on investing \$1000 every half year for 10 years at 8%(2), then letting the bundle sit for 3 more years at the same rate. These problems are done in stages.

   (a) Stage 1: Do the ordinary part by 20 ➜ n; 8/2= ➜ i; 0 ➜ PV; 1000 ➜ PMT; COMP FV. This yields –29,778.08.

   (b) Stage 2: Do the compound interest:

      (1) With the above result (–29,778.08) still on the screen, press the PV.

      (2) Change 6 ➜ n.

      (3) 0 ➜ PMT.

      (4) COMP FV yields –37,678.77.

   (c) PV is similar.

   (d) There are no i problems in this chapter except for perpetuities.

   (e) Caution: To solve for n or PMT, check the outline in the text.

2. Perpetuities are simple interest problems provided you have found the effective rate that matches the payment interval.

3. Conversion of rates to match payment: Convert 8%(4) to *j*%(12).

   (a) Enter the formula $[\$1(1+8\%/4)^{4/12} - 1]\times 100$ ➜ i by b) and c).

   (b) 4/12= ➜ n; 8/4= ➜ i; 1 ➜ PV; 0 ➜ PMT; COMP FV ±– 1×100×12 = ➜ *j*.

   (c) Caution: Do not do the 2ndF CA, since you will lose your results. Use partial clearing by moving 0 into fields not used.

E. Chapter 6—Debt Retirement Methods

Home loans and savings accounts are the same as annuities and compound interest with the following two often-used applications:

1. Outstanding balances for loans:

   $\text{OB}_n = P(1+i)^n - Rs_{\overline{n}|i} = 50{,}000(1+6\%/12)^{60} - 1000s_{\overline{60}|6\%/12} = 2327.52$ is the formula for how much one owes on a \$50,000 loan after 60 monthly payments of \$1000 each at 6%(12).

   (a) 20 ➜ n; 6/12 ➜ i; 50,000 ➜ PV; –1000 ➜ PMT; COMP FV.

   (b) Caution: PV must be a +50,000 and payments must be a negative 1000.

2. Appreciated worth after 10 years of a \$150,000 home if home values are growing at 3% per year is found by $150{,}000(1+3\%)^{10}$.

   (a) Note: This is just compound interest on the original price of the home.

   (b) 10 ➜ n; 3 ➜ i; 150,000 ➜ PV; 0 ➜ PMT; COMP FV. Value = \$201,587.46.

3. You can also do a line-by-line amortization table with the AMORT register.

F. Chapters 7—Stocks and Bonds

1. Find the value of a \$1000, 8%(2) bond that matures in 6 years if you want a yield of 10%(2) on your investment.

   $$V_n = S(1+i)^{-n} + Fra_{\overline{n}|i} = 1000(1+10\%/2)^{-12} + 1000\times.04a_{\overline{12}|10\%/2}$$

   (a) 12 ➜ n, 10/2= ➜ i, 40 ➜ PMT, 1000 ➜ FV, COMP PV. Value = \$911.37.

   (b) Caution: 1000×.04 = 40 is the coupon. Fr = +40 and FV = +1000.

2. If the yield rate were 6%(2), the value of the premium bond would equal \$1099.54.

B.3 The Texas Instruments BA II Plus Solutions

The TI BA II Plus financial calculator has all of the financial functions you will need for the basic form of this text. However, the financial modes are for compound interest and annuities, which we do not discuss until Chapter 3.

A. Chapters 1 and 2—Simple Interest and Bank Discount Problems

1. The usual algebraic/arithmetic calculations are much less cumbersome than on the Sharp EL-733A since there is a hierarchy of operations built in that includes parentheses. The one weakness of the BA II Plus (compared to the TI 83) is that you will not visually see the string of operations. This means you have to remember where you are as you enter the values and operations. Before starting a calculation, it helps to write down what you are doing. For the following example, set the calculator to AOS mode under the FORMAT register. Now calculate 1000/(1+3×(.04)) by entering the following in the correct order:

   1000/(1 + 3×.04) = Yields 892.86.

2. There are 10 storage registers under the number pad. To store a value in memory from the display, use STO 0 or 1 or any of the ten positions. To add a displayed value to a stored value in register 1, use STO + 1.
3. If you prefer not to use a serial table for days of the year, you may use the date arithmetic menu found as 2nd DATE. Enter the two dates using United States format MM.DDYY following by ENTER. Access the next entry by the down arrow and at the DBD =, CPT will give the number of exact days.
4. NPV and IRR at simple interest are done by finding the values at the required dates using the methods presented in the text. Note that the IRR and NPV buttons are for compound interest and will not give the correct answer for simple interest.

B. Chapter 3—Compound Interest

1. The default mode on the BA II is the finance mode. If you are starting a new calculation, you should clear the registers with 2nd CLR TVM. For the submenus such as CF (cash flow calculations) you should perform 2nd CLR WORK. The CE/C button clears the current display.

2. For all the 1st function registers just type your value and press the appropriate button. The 2nd P/Y register will require you to press ENTER after typing your value. You should also do 2nd QUIT before computing the desired parameter.

3. Compute the value of $S = 1000(1+6\%/4)^{10}$.

   (a) 10 ➔ N; 6 ➔ I/Y; 2nd P/Y 4 ➔ ENTER 2nd QUIT; 1000 ➔ PV; 0 ➔ PMT; CPT FV. Value = –1160.54.

   (b) Caution: Rates for compound interest and annuities are entered as a % and not as a decimal. Hence 6% = 6 ➔ I/Y is correct, while .06 ➔ I/Y is incorrect.

4. Compute the value of $P = 1000(1+6\%/4)^{-10}$.

   (a) 10 ➔ N; 6= ➔ I/Y; 2nd P/Y 4 ➔ ENTER 2nd QUIT; 1000 ➔ FV; 0 ➔ PMT; CPT PV. Value = –861.6672.

   (b) Caution: Same as 3b above.

   (c) Caution: The N is never entered as a negative in any problem. When we calculate the PV, the financial programs will display it as a negative if you enter the FV as positive. This indicates they are on the opposite side of the = sign and remembering this will be important when we find outstanding balance.

5. Compute N in $2050 = -1000(1+9\%/12)^N$. This yields $N = 96.07$ months.

   (a) –1000 ➔ PV; 9= ➔ I/Y; 2050 ➔ FV; 0 ➔ PMT; 12 ➔ P/Y; CPT N.

   (b) Caution: Same as 3b above.

   (c) Caution: The N is never entered as a negative in any problem.

6. Compute I/Y in $3 = -1(1+i)^{20}$, where the nominal rate is quarterly.

   (a) 20 ➔ N; –1 ➔ PV; 3 ➔ FV; 0 ➔ PMT; 4 ➔ P/Y; CPT I/Y = 22.59%(4).

   (b) Caution: Same as 3b above.

   (c) Caution: I/Y on this calculator is nominal rate per year and must be divided by P/Y to get the rate per period.

7. Compute NPV and IRR at compound interest: Compute the NPV at 15% for an expenditure of $1000 now with a return of $600 in 1 year and $800 in 2 years. Then find the IRR.

   (a) CF 2nd CLR WORK prepares the cash flow registers for a new problem. The ➔ below will indicate that the value must be followed by ENTER.

   (b) –1000 ➔ CF_0; ↓ 600 ➔ C01; ↓ 1 ➔ FO1; 800 ➔ CO2; ↓ 1 ➔ FO2.

   (c) NPV; 15 ➔ I ↓ NPV = CPT yields NPV = 126.65.

   (d) IRR; CPT yields IRR = 24.34%.

   (e) Caution: If monies were compounded semiannually but with annual returns, you need to enter monies for each compounding period. Suppose that the rate were 15%(2) but with the yearly returns as shown.

Then -1000➜CF_0; 0➜C01; 600➜C02; 0➜C03; 800➜C04 enters the cash flows into registers 0, 1, 2, 3, and 4. 15/2=➜I enters the correct rate and then press the CPT NPV to yield \$118.24. IRR CPT yields 11.508. Finally, IRR×2 = yields 23.02%(2).

C. Chapter 4—Ordinary Annuities

As in compound interest, you may enter all of the other fields and solve for the one needed. In annuities, we enter or solve for *N* payments rather than periods.

1. Compute the value of $S_n = Rs_{\overline{n}|i} = 1000s_{\overline{20}|8\%/2}$. This is the return on investing \$1000 every half year for 10 years at 8%(2).
   (a) 20➜N; 8=➜I/Y, 2➜P/Y; 0➜PV; 1000➜PMT; CPT FV = –\$29,778.08.
   (b) Note: Suppose that the investor already had \$20,000 in his account and then made the deposits of \$1000 every half-year for 10 years at 8%(2). To find the FV of the bundle and the payments as in step (a) above, also enter 20,000➜PV. You should get –\$73,600.54.
2. PV, PMT, I/Y or N use the same approach: Fill in all the other fields and then solve for the appropriate field.
   (a) Caution: When solving for I/Y or for N, one of the monies must be positive and the other negative.
   (b) Caution: N is never negative.
   (c) If you need to recall a value in a field for another calculation or to check its value, you may recall that field with RCL N or I/Y or any other TVM register, as well as the 10 storage registers under the number pad.

D. Chapter 5—Other Annuities Certain

1. Find the value of the forborne annuity $S_n = Rs_{\overline{n}|i} = 1000s_{\overline{20}|8\%/2}(1+8\%/2)^6$. This is the return on investing \$1000 every half-year for 10 years at 8%(2), then letting the bundle sit for 3 more years at the same rate. These problems are done in stages.
   (a) Stage 1: Compute the ordinary annuity by 20➜N; 8➜I/Y; 2➜P/Y; 0➜PV; 1000➜PMT; CPT FV. This yields –29,778.08.
   (b) Stage 2: Compute the compound interest:
      (1) With the above result still on the screen (–29,778.08)➜PV.
      (2) Change 6➜N.
      (3) 0➜PMT.
      (4) CPT FV yields –37,678.77.
   (c) PV is similar.
   (d) There are no I/Y problems in this chapter for deferred or forborne annuities.
   (e) Caution: To solve for N or PMT for a forborne or a deferred annuity, check the procedure in the text.

(f) Annuities due are computed like ordinary annuities but with the BGN switch turned on. This is done by 2nd BGN; 2nd SET; 2nd QUIT.

2. Perpetuities are simple interest problems provided you have found the effective rate that matches the payment interval.

3. Conversion of rates to match payment for general case annuities. Example: Find the amount after 5 years for a savings program paying \$50 per month invested at 8%(4). You must convert 8%(4) to j%(12).

   (a) Enter the formula [\$1(1+8%/4)$^{4/12}$ – 1]×100×12➧I/Y using (b) and (c).

   (b) 4/12=➧N, 8➧I/Y, 4➧P/Y; –1➧PV; 0➧PMT; CPT FV –1×100×12➧j The rate j%(12) = 7.947251464%(12)➧I/Y.

   (c) Caution: Do not do the 2nd CLR TVM, since you will lose your results for I/Y. Use partial clearing by moving 0 into fields not used.

   (d) 60➧N; 12➧P/Y; 0➧PV; 50➧PMT; CPT FV = –3668.80.

E. Chapter 6—Debt Retirement Methods

Home loans and savings accounts are the same as annuities and compound interest with the following additional applications:

1. Outstanding balances for loans (retrospective):
   $OB_n = P(1+i)^n - Rs_{\overline{n}|i} = 50{,}000(1+6\%/12)^{60} - 1000s_{\overline{60}|6\%/12} = 2327.52$ is the formula for how much you owe on a \$50,000 loan after 60 monthly payments of \$1000 with interest at 6%(12).

   (a) 60➧N, 6➧I/Y, 12➧P/Y; 50,000➧PV; –1000➧PMT; CPT FV = 2327.52.

   (b) Caution: PV must be a +50,000 and payments must be a negative 1000.

2. Appreciated worth after 10 years of a \$150,000 home if home values are growing at 3% per year is found by 150,000(1+3%)^{10}.

   (a) Note: This is just compound interest on the original price of the home.

   (b) 10➧N, 3➧I/Y, 1➧P/Y; 150,000➧PV; 0➧PMT; CPT FV = \$201,587.46.

3. We can find any line of the amortization schedule for a loan or we can generate the entire schedule a line at a time. Finding any line lets us determine the way the payment is split between interest and principal. Furthermore, we can find the accumulated interest and/or principal between any two payments as we would need to do when calculating the interest for a given tax year.

   (a) Find the 21st line of the amortization schedule for the loan in 1. Begin with 2nd AMORT; 21➧P1; 21➧P2; ↓BAL = 33,436.99; ↓PRN = 828.67; ↓INT = 171.33.

   (b) Find the interest paid in the 4th year of the loan in 1. Note this will be for payments 37 through 48. 2nd AMORT; 37➧P1; ↓48➧P2; ↓ ↓ ↓ INT = 928.70.

F. Chapters 7—Stocks and Bonds:

1. Find the value of a \$1000, 8%(2) bond that matures in 6 years if you want a yield of 10%(2) on your investment.

   $$V_n = S(1+i)^{-n} + Fra_{\overline{n}|i} = 1000(1+10\%/2)^{-12} + 1000\times.04a_{\overline{12}|10\%/2}$$

   (a) 12 ➜ N; 10 ➜ I/Y; 2 ➜ P/Y; 40 ➜ PMT; 1000 ➜ FV; CPT PV = \$911.37.

   (b) Caution: 1000×.04 = 40 is the coupon. Fr = +40 and FV = +1000. They must both be positive or negative.

2. The BA II Plus also has a bond menu similar to the other menus (such as AMORT and CF). If you want to use the bond worksheet, you will need to consult your user's manual where the 11 registers are defined and explained.

B.4 Microsoft Excel Solutions

A. Chapters 1 and 2—Simple Interest and Bank Discount Problems

1. The usual algebraic calculations for Excel require % and decimals to be the same for a given cell formatting. For a percent format 20% and .20 will both be taken as 20%. Formulas are straightforward to enter in simple interest and bank discount problems using the usual formula entry for Excel.

2. NPV and IRR at simple interest: Invest \$1000 and get returns of \$600 in 1 year and \$800 in 2 years. Hence the NPV@r = $-1000+600/(1+r)$ + $800/(1+2r)$. Find the NPV(15%) and the IRR.

   (a) In Excel enter a table like the following where the formula -1000 + 600/(1+A2) +800/(1+2*A2) is in B2.

   (b) Note that NPV(15%) = 137.12 and the IRR is between 25% and 30%. The IRR could be refined by using smaller increments between 25% and 30%.

R (rate)	NPV
0.00%	\$ 400.00
5.00%	\$ 298.70
10.00%	\$ 212.12
15.00%	\$ 137.12
20.00%	\$ 71.43
25.00%	\$ 13.33
30.00%	\$ (38.46)
35.00%	\$ (84.97)
40.00%	\$(126.98)

B. Chapter 3—Compound interest

1. FV: Computing $S = 1000(1+6\%/4)^{10}$ will yield –1160.5408.

   (a) ➜ here means entering the number or expression in the appropriate field.

   (b) In the appropriate cell type = and pick the FV function. The function genie will prompt for the following values:

(c) = FV(.06/4➧rate, 10➧nper, 0➧pmt, 1000➧PV).

(d) Caution: In Excel % and decimals are the same, except in formatting. Hence 6%/4 is correct, as is .06/4 for the rate. Both give .015.

(e) Note: As is true of all Excel functions, you may enter a function or a value in each field by typing it in or by pointing to a cell containing the info or a combination.

2. PV: Computing $P = 1000(1+6\%/4)^{-10}$ will yield −861.6672.

   (a) In the appropriate cell type = and pick the PV function. The function genie will prompt for the values, which follow:

   (b) = PV(.06/4➧rate, 10➧nper, 0➧pmt, 1000➧FV).

   (c) Caution: The N is never entered as a negative. When you calculate the PV, the financial programs will change it to a negative.

3. Computing n in $2050 = -1000(1+9\%/12)^n$ yields $n = 96.07$ months.

   (a) In the appropriate cell type = and pick the NPER function. The function genie will prompt for the following values:

   (b) = NPER(.06/4➧rate, −1000➧PV, 0➧pmt, 2050➧FV).

   (c) Caution: Either PV or FV must be negative and the other positive.

4. Computing i in $3 = -1(1+i)^{20 \text{ quarters}}$ yields $i = 22.59\%(4)$.

   (a) In the appropriate cell, type = and pick the RATE function. The function genie will prompt for the following values:

   (b) RATE(20➧nper, −1➧PV, 0➧pmt, 3➧FV)*4.

   (c) Caution: i in Excel is rate per period and must be multiplied by the number of compounding periods/year to get the nominal rate.

5. NPV and IRR at compound interest: Compute the NPV at 15% of an expenditure of $1000 now with a return of $600 in 1 year and $800 in 2 years and find the IRR.

   (a) In the appropriate cell, type = and pick the NPV or IRR function. The function genie will prompt for the following values:

   (b) = NPV(.15➧rate, 600➧value1, 800➧value 2) −1000 yields $126.55.

   (c) = IRR({−1000,600,800},20%) yields 24.34%.

   (d) Caution: If monies were compounded semiannually with annual payments, you would need to enter monies for each period. Suppose that the rate were 15%(2) with the yearly returns as shown, then = NPV (.15/2,0,600,0,800)− 1000 yields $118.24. Furthermore, = IRR ({−1000, 0, 600, 0, 800}, 10%)*2 = yields 23.02%(2).

C. Chapter 4—Ordinary Annuities

As in compound interest, you may enter all of the other fields and solve for the one needed. In annuities, we enter or solve for n payments.

1. FV: $S_n = Rs_{\overline{n}|i} = 1000s_{\overline{20}|8\%/2}$ yields –\$30,969.20. This is the return on investing \$1000 every half-year for 10 years at 8%(2).
   (a) = FV(.08/2➔ rate, 20➔ nper, 1000➔ pmt, 0➔ PV).
   (b) Note: If you already had \$20,000 in your account and then made the deposits of \$1000 every half-year for 10 years at 8%(2), then = FV(.08/2➔ rate, 20➔ nper, 1000➔ pmt, 20000➔ PV) yields –\$74,791.66.
2. PV, PMT, i or n are the same attack: Fill in all the other fields in the appropriate function and then solve for the appropriate field.
   - Caution: When solving for i or for n, one of the monies must be positive and the other negative. n is never entered as a negative.

D. Chapter 5—Other Annuity Certain

1. FV: $S_n = Rs_{\overline{n}|i} = 1000s_{\overline{20}|8\%/2}(1+8\%/2)^6$ yields –\$67,857.33. This is the return on investing \$1000 every half-year for 10 years at 8%(2). Let the bundle sit for 3 more years at the same rate. These are nested function problems.
   (a) = FV(.08/2➔ rate, 6➔ nper, 0➔ pmt, FV(.08/2➔ rate, 20➔ nper, 1000➔ pmt, 0➔ PV)➔ PV).
   (b) PV, PMT, and n are similar.
   (c) Caution: To solve for n or PMT, make the two monies opposite signs.
2. Perpetuities are simple interest problems.
3. Conversion of rates to match payment: \$100/month for 12 months at 8%(2) yields 1244.24.
   - = FV((1+8%/2)^(2/12)–1 ➔ rate, 12➔ n, 0➔ PV, 100➔ PMT).

E. Chapter 6—Debt Retirement Methods

Home loans and savings accounts are the same as annuities and compound interest with the following often-used applications:

1. Outstanding balances for loans:
   $\text{OB}_n = P(1+i)^n - Rs_{\overline{n}|i} = 50{,}000(1+6\%/12)^{60} - 1000s_{\overline{60}|6\%/12} = 2327.52$ is the formula for how much you owe on a \$50,000 loan after 60 monthly payments of \$1000 each at 6%(12).
   - = FV(6%/12➔ rate, 60➔ n, 50,000➔ PV, –100➔ PMT).
2. The appreciated worth of a \$150,000 home if home prices are growing at 3% per year after 10 years = $150{,}000(1+3\%)^{10}$.
   (a) Note: This is just compound interest on the original price of the home.
   (b) = FV(3➔ rate, 10➔ n, 150,000➔ PV, 0➔ PMT).
3. Excel is the ideal tool for generating an amortization schedule.

F. Chapters 7—Stocks and Bonds:

1. Find the value of a \$1000, 8%(2) bond that matures in 6 years if you desire 10%(2) on your investment.

   $V_n = S(1+i)^{-n} + Fra_{\overline{n}|i} = 1000(1+10\%/2)^{-12} + 1000\times.04a_{\overline{12}|10\%/2}$

   ■ = PV(10%/2➧rate, 12➧n, 1000➧FV, 40➧PMT). Value = –911.37.

2. If the yield rate were 6%(2), the value of the premium bond would equal \$1099.54.

Appendix C

Glossary

Accrued interest: the part of the bond coupon retained by the seller

Accumulation factor: $(1+i)^n$; the basic tool to move money on the time line using compound interest

Accumulation function: the integral of a rate of change function expressed as a function of time

Adjusted current yield: the current yield with the loss or gain in capital incorporated into the return per period

Amortization schedule: a table that details every payment, shows how it is divided between principal and interest and gives the outstanding balance at every payment

Amortize: to pay a sequence of equal-size payments made up of the interest due plus a portion of the principal

Amount: the value of money at some future date due to the accrual of interest

Annual percentage rate (APR): the rate at which the cash value of the loan equals the present value of the payments

Annuity: a sequence of equal payments, dispersed or received, at equal intervals of time

Annuity certain: an annuity that begins and ends at a set point in time

Annuity due: an annuity with the present value at the first payment and the future value one period after the last payment

Annuity immediate: see *Ordinary annuity*

Appreciation: the increase in market value of an asset such as real estate

Approximate time: the assumption that each month is 30 days, with exact time used for any portion of a month

Average due date: the date at which a single payment equal to the sum of several obligations will discharge those obligations

Average rate of change: the change in the value of a function over an interval

Balloon payment: the last payment of an amortized loan that is larger than all the other payments

Banker's acceptance: a money market security for which one bank promises to pay a specific sum to another bank on some maturity date within a year

Banker's rule: the use of exact time and ordinary interest

Bearer instrument: a security, like a Federal Reserve note, whose value or interest is payable to the person in possession of the security

Beta measure: a gauge of how volatile a stock issue is in comparison to the general market

Bond: a long-term debt instrument that pays interest at regular intervals and that matures at some specified date in the future

Bond rate: the rate that determines the amount of interest (or coupon) the bond pays

Book value: the value that remains of a given asset at any point in time during its life; the difference between the original cost and the accumulated depreciation

Call provision: a provision that allows the bond issuer the legal right to speed up repayment of the debt by refunding the principal to the bondholders at specified call dates

Capital budgeting: planned expenditures for the tools of production that will generate cash flow returns in the future

Capital expenditures: the monies spent by corporations on tools of production

Capitalization: finding the present worth or cash equivalent of an unlimited number of periodic payments

Capitalized cost: the sum of the original cost plus the present worth of an unlimited number of replacements

Certificate of Deposit (CD): a short-term security sold by banks to raise money

Closing costs: charges, such as attorney's fees, associated with the borrowing process which are not due to the accrual of interest

Commercial paper: a type of unsecured promissory note that may have a term anywhere in length from five days to nine months

Common stock: a security representing ownership in a corporation

Composite life: the average life of a collection of assets

Composite rate: the total of the annual depreciation charges divided by the combined cost of the collection of assets

Compound discount: the shrinkage of money resulting from the repeated discounting of the previous proceeds

Compound interest: the growth of money in which interest is added to the principal so that each time interest is computed, it is based on a larger principal than the previous interval of time

Compound rate: the growth rate or interest rate of money invested at compounded interest

Contingent annuity: an annuity with a beginning or ending date that depends on some event

Continuous compounding: compound interest that is computed theoretically an infinite number of times per year so that m in the formula $i = \left(1 + \frac{i(m)}{m}\right)^m - 1$ becomes infinitely large

Continuous income stream: the income of large corporations or utilities where, in the context of annuities, the payments seem to be flowing into the company without interruption

Conversion period: the time between interest computations

Convertible bond: a bond that the investor has the option of converting into a specific number of shares of common stock

Cost of capital: the interest rate a particular company must pay to raise capital through debt, stock issues, or the required return on equity

Coupon: a guaranteed interest payment

Coupon bond: an unregistered bond with attached coupons that are presented to the trustee for payment of interest

Coupon equivalent: the simple interest rate that is equivalent to a given discount rate

Current yield: the rate of return for a given year found by dividing the annual interest earned by the cost

Debenture: a bond that offers no collateral except the good name of the issuing company

Deferred annuity: an annuity with the present value located two or more periods before the first payment

Demand deposits: monies in a bank that are the basis for writing checks and making electronic transfers

Depletion: the gradual using up of a natural resource

Depletion rate: the total depletion divided by the total resource reserves at the time of the asset's purchase

Depreciation: an expense deducted from income representing an asset's loss of value

Depreciation allowances: yearly depreciation charges computed by one of the depreciation methods such as straight line or double declining balance

Discount: the difference between the future value of a loan or security and the actual amount received from the loan or paid for the security

Discount bond: a bond whose price is below face value (par value)

Discount equivalent: the discount rate that is equivalent to a given simple interest rate

Discount interest: interest that is based on the future value and paid up front

Discount points: a percentage of the loan amount subtracted by the lender before the borrower receives the money; one discount point represents one percent of the loan amount

Discount rate: the percent of the amount (future value) that is the basis for the discount

Discounted cash flow: a method of bringing all returns and investments or expenditures to the present value (see *Net present value*)

Discrete income stream: income or interest payments that occur at single points in time rather than being continuous

Double declining balance: the 200% case for the declining balance, a method of depreciation that uses a fixed rate times the book value to get the depreciation allowance

Effective rate of discount: the ratio of the interest earned in a given measurement period to the value of the investment at the end of that period

Effective rate of interest: the ratio of the interest earned in a given measurement period to the principal at the beginning of that period

Endowment: funds invested for scholarships that generally withdraw payments once a year equal to the amount of interest earned during the previous year

Equation of value: a mathematical expression that equates several pieces of money at some chosen date called the focal date

Equivalent rates: rates that produce the same return for a given investment and measurement period.

Equivalent time: a point in time when a single payment equal to the sum of various debts at several other points in time will discharge the obligation

Equivalent values: lump sums or annuities that have the same present value regardless of the term or interest rates

Escrow account: the accumulation of monthly fees paid by the borrower and held by the lender until real estate taxes and homeowner's insurance premiums come due

Exact interest: the assumption in a financial calculation that a year equals 365 days (366 for leap year)

Exact time: every day of the term except the first day

Expected return: the sum of the year's dividend yield and the growth rate

Expected value: the arithmetic mean or average performance of a chance process

Federal funds: loans between commercial banks for terms as short as one day

Fence post principle: the principle that between each of the n payments in an annuity there are $n-1$ interest or payment intervals

Focal date: the point on the time line when several pieces of money are valued in order to compare or add them

Forborne annuity: an annuity with the future value located two or more periods after the last payment

Force of interest: the instantaneous rate of change per unit value in the investment

Future value: the value of money at some future date due to the accrual of interest

General annuity: an annuity for which interest is compounded at a frequency different from the payment frequency

Golden rule of finance: the principle that monies cannot be added or reconciled unless they are valued at the same point in time

Growth rate: the anticipated growth in the value of common stock

Holder: the party that will receive the principal and interest from a promise to pay at maturity

Indexed bond: a bond with an interest payment structure tied to the inflation rate

Inflation-adjusted payments: annuity payments indexed to keep up with inflation

Inflation-adjusted rate: the rate of return indexed to keep up with inflation

Instantaneous rate of change: the derivative at a point; expresses the rate of change at a point rather than over an interval

Interest rate: the percentage of the principal that is the basis for the interest

Internal rate of return (IRR): the rate at which the returns and investments make the NPV zero

Interval of deferment: the time (given in interest periods) between the valuation date of a deferred annuity and the valuation date of an ordinary annuity's present value

Linear regression model: the statistical model used when the payments in an annuity or value of a stock is changing nearly linearly

Maker: the writer of a promissory note who owes the money

Marginal cost of capital: the cost to obtain another dollar of new capital

Maturity date: the date that a promissory note or other maturing security must be repaid

Maturity value: the amount of money the borrower will pay back; the sum of the principal and interest

Merchant's rule: the use of an equation of value technique in which the final settlement date is the focal date

Money market: a network for buying and selling short-term credit or debt instruments with maturities under one year

Mortgage: a contract between a borrower and lender that assigns the assets purchased by the loan as collateral in case of default

Mortgage bond: bonds that pledge certain fixed assets as security or collateral for the debt

Near monies: instruments that may be quickly transferred into liquid assets

Negotiable instrument: a promise to pay such as a note, certificate of deposit, and time deposit, as well as orders to pay like drafts (checks) and bills of exchange (acceptances)

Net annual return: the annual return (profit) on an investment minus protection of capital

Net cash flow: the difference between cash inflows and outflows during a time interval

Net income: gross income less the cost of doing business; in capital budgeting it is income before figuring taxable income using depreciation allowances

Net present value (NPV): the difference between investments and future returns all moved to the present at some given rate of return

Nominal interest rate: the annual rate together with a compounding interval in a compound interest calculation

Opportunity cost: the return from some project that replaces another source of return from securities that have a similar degree of risk

Ordinary annuity (annuity immediate): an annuity with payments at the end of each rent period a present value located one period before the first payment, and a future value located at the last payment

Ordinary interest: the assumption in a financial calculation that a year equals 360 days

Ordinary perpetuity (perpetuity immediate): a perpetuity with the present value located one payment period before the first payment

Outstanding balance: the principal still to be paid on an amortized loan

Owner's equity: the current value minus any indebtedness in a piece of real estate

Partial payment: a payment that is made before the due date to reduce some interest charges

Payee: the party the promissory note is written to; lends the money to the maker

Payment interval: the interval of time between regular payments for an annuity

Percentage change: the change in a function or quantity over an interval divided by the value of the function at the beginning of that interval

Percentage rate of change: the instantaneous rate of change of a function at a point divided by the value of the function at that point (see *Force of interest*)

Periodic interest rate: the nominal rate divided by conversion periods per year

Periodic rent or payment: the rent or payment paid for an annuity or perpetuity

Perpetuity: an annuity with an indefinite term in which the periodic payments equal the interest earned during the previous period

Perpetuity due: a perpetuity whose present value is located at the first payment

Preferred stock: an equity instrument that usually pays a fixed dividend

Premium bond: a bond that is priced above face value (par value)

Present value: the principal initially received from a loan (cash)

Prime rate: the interest rate banks charge their most financially capable corporate customers

Principal: the amount of money invested or borrowed

Proceeds: the money received from a discount loan (present value)

Production units: a method of depreciation that uses a rate of depreciation times the actual number of items produced in a given year to get the depreciation allowances

Profitability index: the ratio of the present value of the cash inflow stream to the original cost of the asset

Promise to pay: a negotiable financial instrument such as a promissory note, a certificate of deposit, and a time deposit

Promissory note: a document on which one party writes his or her promise to pay another party the principal and interest for a loan due at some date in the future

Purchase price: the quoted price plus accrued interest for a bond

Quoted price: a bond price that includes a fractional part of the change in value of the bond between two interest dates (also called *net* price or *and interest* price)

Random variable: a function that takes the periodic payments, the periodic interest rates, or the term into a real number; in the context of annuities, it means that the random variables of the payments, the interest rates, and/or the term are varying according to some statistical probability distributions making the PV or the FV of an annuity a random variable

Rate of return (ROR): the interest earned divided by the cost to the buyer

Rate per period: the nominal rate divided by the interest periods per year (see *Periodic interest rate*)

Redemption Value (price): the value of the bond at the end of its term

Refinance: to pay off an existing mortgage and negotiate a new mortgage for the same asset

Registered bond: a bond registered in the name of a particular owner

Reserve capacity: the estimated amount of a natural resource that remains at a given time

Residual value: the value of equipment when it comes to the end of its life

Risk-adjusted cost of capital: an adjustment to the cost of capital that makes allowance for the amount of risk associated with a given project so that the greater the risk the higher the cost

Risk of default on a loan: the risk to an annuity when a payment is missed, in the present context always implying that all subsequent payments will be missed

Risk of default on a payment: the risk to an annuity when a payment is missed, in the present context not implying that all subsequent payments will be missed

Salvage value or **Scrap value**: the value of equipment when it comes to the end of its life

Secondary market: organized exchanges located in specific places where outstanding securities are traded

Serial number: a number given to each day of the year (see inside back cover)

Service hours: a method of depreciation that uses a rate of depreciation times the actual number of service hours in a given year to get the depreciation allowances

Service life: the length of time a piece of equipment can be kept in service

Simple annuity: an annuity with interest compounded at the same frequency as the payments are made

Simple discount: interest that is based on the future value

Simple interest: interest that is based merely on the original principal

Sinking fund: an ordinary annuity with a known future value that represents some debt or obligation that is coming due

Standard deviation: the average distance of all scores from the mean; in our context, it is a usual measure of dispersion of the PV or FV of an annuity where the payments, interest rates, and/or the term are varying randomly

Stipend: regular income from an investment or endowment

Straight line: a method of depreciation that assumes that the depreciation allowances are the same for each year: wearing value divided by the life expectancy

Stochastic interest: in our context of annuities, a process whereby the interest varies periodically by chance, thus affecting the PV or FV of an annuity

Stochastic payment: in our context of annuities, the process whereby the payments vary periodically by chance, thus affecting the PV or the FV of an annuity

Stochastic processes: chance processes

Sum of the year's digits: a method of depreciation that uses a yearly diminishing rate times the wearing value to get the depreciation allowances

Taxable income: in capital budgeting the net income minus the depreciation allowance

Term of annuity: interval of time for the life of the annuity; often given as the number of payments

Term of a note: the length of time between the signing date and the due date

Term structure of interest rates: the relationship between the time to maturity and the interest rate

Time value of money: the principle that, because of interest, the value of a given piece of money changes as its location in the time line changes, increasing when moved to the future and decreasing when moved to the past

Total periodic charge: the sinking fund payment plus the interest charges on the loan

Trade-in value: the value of equipment when it comes to the end of its life; scrap value

Treasury bill (T-Bill): a short-term security issued by the U.S. treasury department

United States rule (U.S. Rule): a way to compute the interest due and loan balance on any day a partial payment is made

Value of a bond: the value or price that will give the desired yield

Variable blocks of payments: payments used in an annuity for which the payments remain constant for a block of time, and then the payments change to stay constant for another block of time, etc.

Variable payment annuity: an annuity with regular payments that are changing by some regular sequence pattern such as arithmetic or geometric

Variance: the standard deviation squared

Wearing value: the accumulated depreciation at the end of the life of an asset

Yield rate: the rate used to find the present value of the coupon annuity and the present value of the redemption value of a bond; represents the rate of return for an investment

Yield to maturity: the rate of return the buyer gets if he holds the bond until its maturity date

Zero coupon bond: a bond that pays no interest but is sold at discount like a T-bill

Appendix D

Solutions to Odd-Numbered Exercises

Chapter 1 Simple Interest

Section 1.2 Solutions

Concept and Short Answer Exercises

1. The interest increases as the principal increases. Hence, the more you borrow the more interest you will pay.
2. The interest increases as the rate increases. Hence, it will cost more to borrow \$1000 at 10% for 1 year than to borrow \$1000 at 6% for 1 year.
3. The interest increases as the term increases. Hence, it will cost more to borrow \$1000 at 10% for 3 years than for \$1000 at 10% for 2 years.
4. I = Pit expresses that the interest varies directly with the amount borrowed, the rate, and the term.
5. $I = Pit \rightarrow i = I / (Pt)$ and $t = I / (Pi)$
6. "interest." If you do not pay at least the interest each successive period, you will owe the total principal plus the interest.

Odd Exercise Calculations

To shorten time lines and many explanations the authors have chosen to use the first letter of the time unit for the time. Hence in the answer key for time we use the following:

Abbreviations	d	w	m	q	h	y
Time Unit	day	week	month	quarter	half	year

7. $I = Pit$

$= 425 * 0.065 * 8/12 = \$18.42$

0 ——— 8m
425 —@6.5%→ |

9. $I = Pit$

$= 1580 * 0.08 * {}^{14}\!/_{12} = \$147.47$

0 ——— 14m
1580 —@8%→ |

11. $I = Pit$

$= 2950.50 * 0.0775 * 20/12 = \$381.11$

0 — 20m; 2950.50 @7.75% →

13. $I = Pit$

$= 255.35 * 0.12 * \frac{3}{12} = \$7.66 = \$7.66$

0 — 3m; 255.35 @12% →

15. $I = Pit$

$= 640.45 * 0.065 * 7/12 = \$24.28$

0 — 7m; 640.45 @6.5% →

17. $t = 4/2/04 - 11/2/02 = 16/2/03 - 11/2/02 = 5m + 1y = 17m$

$I = Pit = 1000 * 0.05 * 17/12 = \$70.83$

$S = P + I = 1000 + 70.83 = \$1070.83$

11/2/02 — 4/2/04; 5000 @5% → S

19. $t = 5/5/07 - 9/5/03 = 17/5/06 - 9/5/03 = 8m + 3y = 8m + 36m = 44m$

$I = Pit = 5000 * 0.08 * \frac{44}{12} = \$1466.67$

$S = P + I = 5000 + 1466.67 = \$6466.67$

9/5/03 — 5/5/07; 5000 @8% → S

21. $I = Pit$

$= 100{,}000 * 0.12 * 1/12$

$= \$1000$ which equals her payment. Hence up the payment.

0 — 1m; 100,000 @12% →

23. $I = 5 \rightarrow i = \frac{I}{Pt} = \frac{5}{100 * \frac{1}{52}} = 2.6 = 260\%$

0 — 1w; 100 @i → 105

25. $I = 50 \rightarrow i = \frac{I}{Pt} = \frac{50}{1000 * \frac{6}{12}} = 0.10 = 10\%$

1/2/03 — 7/2/03; 1000 @i → 1050

27. $I = 0.50$

$t = \frac{I}{Pi} = \frac{0.50}{1 * 0.08} = 6.25y$

0 — ty; 1 @8% → 1.50

29. $I = \$1$

$t = \frac{I}{Pi} = \frac{1}{1 * 0.6} = 16\frac{2}{3}y = 16y + 8m$

0 — ty; 1 @6% → 2

It takes the same time for \$1 to double as it does for a million dollars.

Section 1.3 Solutions

Concept and Short Answer Exercises

1. 2044 is a leap year because 4 divides into it evenly.

2. 2133 is not a leap year because 4 does not divide into it evenly.

3. Exact time = the ending date serial number − the beginning date serial number. Please take care on leap years for days on or after February 29th.
4. Approximate time = (the number of full months) $\times 30 +$ (exact time for the portion of the month left).
5. Exact interest means the denominator = 365 (or 366 for a leap year).
6. Approximate interest means the denominator = 360.
7. The Banker's Rule uses exact time for numerator and approximate interest (360 for the denominator).
8. The Banker's Rule usually gives the highest interest.

Odd Exercise Calculations

9.

Oct. 15	288	June 1 to October 1 = $4 \times 30 = 120$
June 1	152	Oct. 1 to October 15 = $15 - 1 = 14$
Exact =	136 days	Approximate time = 134 days

11.

Dec. 31	365	Nov. 12 to April 12 = $5 \times 30 = 150$
Nov. 12	316	April 12 to April 15 = $15 - 12 = 3$
	49 (in 2003)	Approximate time = 153 days
April 15	106 (leap yr)	
Exact	155 days	

13.

Nov. 22	326	Sept. 7 to Nov. 7 = $2 \text{x} 30 = 60$
Sept. 7	250	Nov. 7 to Nov. 22 = $22 - 7 = 15$
Exact=	76 days	Approximate time = 75 days

15.

June 9	160	Mar. 5 to June 5 = $3 \text{x} 30 = 90$
March 5	64	June 5 to June 9 = $9 - 5 = 4$
Exact =	96 days	Approximate time = 94 days

Exact: $I = 2000 \times 0.08 \times \frac{96}{365} = \$42.08$ $\qquad I = 2000 \times 0.08 \times \frac{94}{365} = \$41.21$

Ord.: $I = 2000 \times 0.08 \times \frac{96}{360} = \$42.67$ $\qquad I = 2000 \times 0.08 \times \frac{94}{360} = \$41.78$

17. $I = Pit$

$= 15{,}000 * 0.10 * {}^{70}\!/_{360} = \$291.67$

$S = P + I = 15{,}000 + 291.67 = \$15{,}291.67$ payoff

Time line: 6/6(157 d) — 15,000 —@10%→ — 8/15(227 d)

19. $P = 96.2\%$ of $1{,}000{,}000 = 962{,}000$

$I = 1{,}000{,}000 - 962{,}000 = 38{,}000$

$$i = \frac{I}{Pt} = \frac{38{,}000}{962{,}000 * {}^{182}\!/_{360}} = 7.81\%$$

Time line: 0 (962k) —@i→ 182d (1000k)

21. $P = 98.33\% \text{ of } 500{,}000 = 491{,}650$

$I = 500{,}000 - 491{,}650 = 8350$

$$i = \frac{I}{Pt} = \frac{8350}{491{,}650 * 91/360} = 6.72\%$$

0		91d
491,650	$\xrightarrow{@i}$	500,000

23. $I = Pit$

$$= 500 * 0.04 * 92/360 = \$5.11$$

$S = P + I = 500 + 5.11 = \$505.11$ payoff

2/3(34d)	$\xrightarrow{92d}$	5/5(126d)
500	$\xrightarrow{@4\%}$	|

25. Option 1 — Use the loan:

Interest earned on MM = $7000 \times 0.08 \times 1 = \$560$

Interest paid on loan = $5000 \times 0.12 \times 153/360 = \$255$ → Net gain= \$305

Option 2 — Withdraw \$5000:

Amount earning interest = \$7000 – \$5000 = \$2000

Interest earned on MM = $2000 \times .08 \times 1 = \$160$

Option 1 is better by \$145.

27. Option 1 — Use the loan:

Saving's interest earned = $3000 \times 0.0275 \times \frac{184}{360} = \$42.17$

Loan's interest paid = $2000 \times 0.12 \times \frac{88}{360} = \$58.67$ → Net Loss= -\$16.50

Option 2 — Withdraw \$2000

Interest earned on \$1000 balance = $1000 \times 0.0275 \times \frac{184}{360} = \$14.06$

Option 2 is better by \$14.06 – (–\$16.50) = \$30.56.

Section 1.4 Solutions

Concept and Short Answer Exercises

1. I = Pit is used when calculating the interest, the time, or the rate.

   S = P + I and S = P(1+it) are the same numerically finding S given P.

2. Moving money forward means you are computing the FV given the PV. Values on the left are PV and values on the right are FV. Equivalently, values at earlier dates are PV while values at a later date are FV. Money in the future can be called "amount," "future value," or "mature value."

3. If the beginning and ending date have the same day (same day included the jagged end of months), then use t in terms of months and years. If the beginning and ending date have different days, then use the Banker's Rule unless explicitly told to use exact time and exact interest.

4. 3/10, n/45 means that if the bill is paid within 10 days, then a 3% discount will be given; if the bill is paid between the 11th day and the 45th day, then the "net" (full bill) will be paid; and if the bill is paid after 45 days, then there may be a penalty for a late payment.

Odd Exercise Calculations

5. $S = P(1+it)$
$=1000(1+0.08*6/12)$
$=\$1040$

0m	6m
1000	S
@8% →	

7. $S = P(1+it)$
$=800(1+0.06*2)$
$=\$896$

0y	2y
800	S
@6% →	

9. $S = 1000(1+0.07*209/360)$
$+4000(1+0.07*115/360)$

$= 1040.64 + 4089.44 = \$5130.08$

12/5/03 = 339 d	3/8/04 = 68 d	7/1/04 = 183 d
1000	4000	S
	@7% →	

11. $S=1000(1+0.07*7/12)$
$+4000(1+0.07*4/12)$
$=1040.83+4093.33=\$5134.16$

12/5/03 = 0m	3/5/04 = 3m	7/5/04 = 7m
1000	4000	S
	@7% →	

13. $S=P(1+it)$
$= 5000(1+0.082*2/12)$
$= \$5068.33$
Less the $4000 payment leaves a balance of $1068.33

June 3	2m →	Aug. 3
5000	@8.2% →	S
		−4000

15. Discount $=0.02*5520$ from 5520
$= 5409.60$ on 10th day

10d		45d
5409.60	@i →	5520.00

$$I=110.40 \rightarrow i=\frac{I}{Pt}=\frac{110.40}{5409.6*35/360}=0.2099=20.99\%$$

Verbalize: 1. Compute discounted amount on last day possible.
2. Compute nondiscounted amount on last day possible.
3. Compute interest between those two dates.
4. Compute interest rate between those two dates.

17. Discount $= 0.03 * 10\text{k}$ from 10k
$= \$9700$ on 5th day

5d		60d
9700	$\xrightarrow{@i}$	10,000

$$I = 300 \rightarrow i = \frac{I}{Pt} = \frac{300}{9700 * 55/360} = 20.24\%$$

19. Discount $= 0.98 * 59{,}865$
$= \$58{,}667.70$ on 8th day

8d		45d
58,667.70	$\xrightarrow{@i}$	59,865

$$I = 59{,}865 - 58{,}667.70 = 1197.3 \rightarrow i = \frac{I}{Pt} = \frac{1197.3}{58{,}667.70 * 37/360} = 19.86\%$$

21. $x = 2500(1 + 0.08 * 5/12) + 3850(1 + 0.08 * 2/12)$

$x = 2583.33 + 3901.33$

$x = 6484.66$

3/1	6/1	8/1
2500	3850 ↓	x

|————————→|

Section 1.5 Solutions

Concept and Short Answer Exercises

1. A future value will be given and you will solve for the present value. You will be given a money value at a date to the right and asked to solve for the equivalent money on the left. Present values are also called "cash" as in cash equivalent or the cash value. Present values are the value now.

2. I = Pit is used to solve for the interest, the rate or the time.

   S = P(1+it) is used to move monies forward under simple interest

   P = S/(1+it) is used to move monies backward (discounting) under simple interest.

3. While it is true that P = S − I algebraically, computationally the formula is impossible since you are given S to compute P. But I = Pit uses the present value which you do not have. That's a contradiction. Further, when given the P to solve for S or S to solve for P, it's quicker to use S = P(1 + it) or P = S/(1+ i t) than to go through the interest I.

4. Calculate both answers and pick the better of the two. Remember that better is the smaller if you are paying (outflow) and the larger if you are getting paid (inflow).

Odd Exercise Calculations

5. $$P = \frac{S}{1+it} = \frac{12{,}000}{1 + 0.07 * 11/12} = \$11{,}276.43$$

1/1/04	$\xleftarrow{11m}$	12/1/04
P	$\xleftarrow{@7\%}$	12,000

7. $P = \dfrac{3000}{1+0.065*47/360} + \dfrac{2000}{1+0.065*109/360}$

$= 2974.76 + 1961.40 = \$4936.16$

6/15 =166d	8/1 =213d	10/2 =275d
P	3000	2000
← @6.5%		

9. $\text{Payoff} = 3000\left(1+0.065*14/360\right)$

$+\dfrac{2000}{1+0.065*48/360}$

$= 3007.58 + 1982.82 = \$4990.40$

8/1 =213d	8/15 =227d	10/2 =275d
3000	Payoff	2000
@6.5% →	← @6.5%	

11. $P = \dfrac{1000}{1+0.10*1/2} + \dfrac{2500}{1+0.10*14/12}$

$= 952.38 + 2238.81 = \$3191.19$

1/1/03	7/1/03	3/1/04
P	1000	2500
← @10%		

13. Tech 1: $P = \$3000\text{ cash}$

Tech 2: $P = \dfrac{S}{1+it}$

7/10/02		1/10/03
Tech 1: 3000 now		
Tech 2: P	← @8%	3200

$= \dfrac{3200}{1+0.08*1/2} = \$3076.92 \rightarrow \text{Cash is better by } \$76.92.$

Verbalization: 1. Best means least, if we're paying, and most, if we're earning.

2. Compute the PV of all schemes and pick the best.

15. Tech 1: $P = \$2000\text{ cash}$

Tech 2: $P = \dfrac{S}{1+it}$

now = 0		1y
Tech 1: 2000 now		
Tech 2: P	← @18%	2400

$= \dfrac{2400}{1+0.18*1} = \$2033.90 \rightarrow \text{Cash is better by } \$33.90.$

17. $P = \dfrac{25{,}000}{1+0.11*5/12} = \$23{,}904.38$

0		5m
P	← 11%	25,000

19. $P = \dfrac{8525}{1+0.065*15/12} = \$7884.39$

0		15m
P	← 6.5%	8525

21. $P = \dfrac{7{,}849{,}987.43}{1+0.025*5/366} = \$7{,}847{,}307.34$

8/16/04	← 5d	8/21/04
P	← 2.5%	$7 mil$^+$

23. $x(1+0.0525*170/360)+x(1+0.0525*95/360)$
$=568,950$

5/1 121d	7/15 196d	10/18 291d
x	x ↓	568,950
|—		→|

$(1.024...)x+(1.013...)x=568,950$
$2.03864583334x=568,950 \rightarrow x=\$279,082.32$ each

Section 1.6 Solutions

Concept and Short Answer Exercises

1. Since these cannot be cashed in until maturity, the general procedure is to mature at the rate shown on the financial document and discount that matured value at the investment return rate of the buyer.

2. Non-interest-bearing notes mature at face value. Interest-bearing notes mature at face value + interest using the formula $S=P(1+it)$. Interest-bearing notes will say "with interest." Example: a $10,000 note matures with 9% interest in 8 years, or, equivalently, a $10,000, 9% note matures in 8 years. A non-interest-bearing note will not give the rate. Example: a $10,000 note matures in 10 years.

3. There is the note or loan rate at which the loan will mature. There is the return on investment rate for the buyer.

4. To get cash. To make a profit.

Odd Exercise Calculations

5. Mature: $S=\$1000$ (non-interest-bearing)

3/1 =60d	4/20 =110d	5/30 =150d
1000	—90d@0%→	1000
	P←40d@10%—	|

Discount: $P=\dfrac{S}{1+it}=\dfrac{1000}{1+0.10*40/360}=\$989.01$

Verbalize: 1. Matures at face value since non-interest bearing.
2. Discount at the buyer's rate.

7. Mature: $S=P(1+it)=1000\left(1+0.07*90/360\right)$
$=1017.50$

3/1 =60d	4/20 =110d	5/30 =150d
1000	—90d@7%→	1017.50
	P←40d@10%—	|

Discount: $P=\dfrac{S}{1+it}=\dfrac{1017.50}{1+0.10*40/360}=\$1006.32$

Verbalize: 1. Matures with interest at note's rate.
2. Discount at the buyer's rate.

9. Mature: $S = P(1+it) = 4000\left(1+0.05 * \frac{1}{2}\right)$

$= 4100$

Discount: $P = \frac{S}{1+it} = \frac{4100}{1+0.07 * \frac{2}{12}} = 4052.72$

3/5	7/5	9/5
4000	$\xrightarrow{6m@5\%}$	4100
	P $\xleftarrow{2m@7\%}$	|

Original: $I = 52.72$ on \$4000 for $4m \rightarrow i = \frac{I}{Pt} = \frac{52.72}{4000 * \frac{4}{12}} = 0.0395 = 3.95\%$

Reason: He obviously needed the cash.

11. Mature: $S = P(1+it) = 4000\left(1+0.00 * \frac{1}{2}\right)$

$= 4000$

Discount: $P = \frac{S}{1+it} = \frac{4000}{1+0.07 * \frac{2}{12}} = 3953.87$

3/5	7/5	9/5
4000	$\xrightarrow{6m@0\%}$	4000
	P $\xleftarrow{2m@7\%}$	|

Original: $I = 46.13$ loss on \$4000 for $4m \rightarrow i = \frac{I}{Pt} = \frac{-46.13}{4000 * \frac{4}{12}} = -3.46\%$ loss

Reason: He obviously needed the cash.

13. Mature: $S = P(1+it) = 2000\left(1+0.08 * \frac{100}{360}\right)$

$= 2044.44$

1/1 =1d	2/1 =32d	4/10 =101d
2000	$\xrightarrow{100d@8\%}$	2044.44
	1920.60 $\xleftarrow{69d@i}$	|

Interest: $I = 2044.44 - 1920.60 = 123.84$

$i = \frac{I}{Pt} = \frac{123.84}{1920.60 * \frac{69}{360}} = 33.64\%$

Section 1.7 Solutions

Concept and Short Answer Exercises

1. An equation of value.
2. An equation of value.
3. Focal date.
4. The focal date does affect the answer if you are using simple interest.
5. Cash requires that the focal date be now.
6. Unless stated in the problem, the focal date for payoff problems will be the last payment date.

Odd Exercise Calculations

7. a. $\frac{x}{1+0.10*1} = 500 + \frac{1000}{1+0.10*1/2}$

$x/1.1 = 500 + 952.3809 = 1452.3809 \rightarrow x = \$1597.62$

0	6m	12m
500	1000	x

|←—10%—|

b. $\frac{x}{1+.10*1/2} = 500(1+0.10*1/2) + 1000$

$x/1.05 = 1525 \rightarrow x = \$1601.25$

|——→|←——|

c. $x = 500(1+0.10*1) + 1000(1+0.10*1/2)$

$x = 550 + 1050 = \$1600$

|——10%——→|

9. $x = \frac{900}{1+0.08*1} + \frac{9000}{1+0.08*3} = 833.3\overline{3} + 7258.0645$

$x = \$8091.39$

0	1y	3y
x	900	9000

|←—8%—|

11. $x = 2000(1+0.08*23/12) - 1000(1+0.08*1)$

$-1000(1+0.08*7/12)$

$x = 2306.6\overline{6} - 1080 - 1046.6\overline{6} = \$180$

1/04	12/04	5/05	12/05
2000	1000	1000	x

|——8%——→|

13. $x + x(1+0.10*1/2) = 500(1+0.10*1)$

$2.05x = 550 \rightarrow x = \$268.29$

6/04	12/04	6/05
500	x	x

|——10%——→|

15. $x + x/(1+0.10*1/2) = 500(1+0.10*1/2)$

$1.95238x = 525 \rightarrow x = \$268.90$

6/04	12/04	6/05
500	x	x

|——→|←——|

17. $x = 6500 - 1400(1+0.07*195/360)$

$-2550(1+0.07*90/360)$

$x = 6500 - 1453.08\overline{3} - 2594.625 = \$2452.29$

9/1/04	12/15/04	3/15/04
1400	2550	6500 x

|——7%——→|

19. $x = 6800(1+0.075*297/360)$

$+5500(1+0.075*241/360)$

$x = 7220.75 + 5776.15 = \$12,996.90$

11/13/04	1/8/05	9/6/05
6800	5500	x

|——7.5%——→|

21. $x = 1.75(1+0.0525*66/360) + \frac{2.5}{1+0.0525*103/360}$

$x = 1.76684 + 2.46300 = \$4.232984$ million

4/15	6/20	10/1
1.75	x	2.5

|——→|←——|

Section 1.8 Solutions

Concept and Short Answer Exercises

1. We are earning more than 8% by an additional $402.
2. We are earning less than 8% by a deficit of $402.
3. The IRR will be more than 8%.
4. The IRR will be less than 8%.
5. The FD is now, since "present" value means now. In addition, you must investigate the worth of an investment prior to making the investment.
6. IRR with one investment and one return is linear and can be done as we have done simple interest rate problems. IRR with one investment and two returns is quadratic. IRR with one investment and three or more returns is 3rd order or higher and is hard to solve. We solve higher-order ones by repeated guessing (interpolating) between a positive and negative NPV.
7. We will interpolate between the 8% answer and the 9% answer.

$$\text{IRR} \approx 8\% + \frac{402-0}{402-(-75)}(9\%-8\%) = 8.84\%$$

8. We will interpolate between the 8% answer and the 10% answer.

$$\text{IRR} \approx 8\% + \frac{40.50-0}{40.55-(-75.33)}(10\%-8\%) = 8.70\%$$

Odd Exercise Calculations

9. $\text{NPV}@\,\text{i} = -2000 + 3000/(1+2\text{i})$

0	2y
−2000	3000
|← i% |	

$$\text{NPV}@20\% = -2000 + 3000/(1+2*0.2) = \$142.86$$

$$\text{NPV}@30\% = -2000 + 3000/(1+2*0.3) = -\$125.00$$

$$\text{IRR} \doteq 20\% + \frac{\$142.86-\$0}{\$142.86-(-\$125.00)}(30\%-20\%) = 25.33\% \text{ approximately.}$$

Since we have but one investment and one return, we could do the problem as a simple interest as follows:

$$\text{I}=3000-2000=1000 \rightarrow \text{i}=\text{I}/\text{Pt}=1000/(2000*2)=25\%$$

11. $\text{NPV}@\,\text{i} = -500 + 700/(1+\text{i})$

0	1y
− 500	700
|← i% |	

$$\text{NPV}@30\% = -500 + 700/(1+0.3) = \$38.46$$

As a simple interest problem, we get that

$$\text{I} = 200 \rightarrow \text{i} = \text{I}/\text{Pt} = 200/(500*1) = 40.00\%.$$

0	1y	2y
−8000	4000	6000

|← i% →|

13. $NPV@\,i = -8000 + 4000/(1+i) + 6000/(1+2i)$

$NPV@\,10\% = -8000 + 4000/1.1 + 6000/1.2 = \$636.36$

$NPV@\,20\% = -8000 + 4000/1.2 + 6000/1.4 = -\$380.95$

$$IRR \doteq 10\% + \frac{\$636.36 - \$0}{\$636.36 - (-\$380.95)}(20\% - 10\%) = 16.26\%.$$

0	1y	2y
−500	300	800

|← i% →|

15. $NPV@\,i = -500 + 300/(1+i) + 800/(1+2i)$

$NPV@\,70\% = -500 + 300/1.7 + 800/2.4 = \$9.80$

$NPV@\,80\% = -500 + 300/1.8 + 800/2.6 = -\$25.64$

$$IRR \doteq 70\% + \frac{\$9.80 - \$0}{\$9.80 - (-\$25.64)}(80\% - 70\%) = 72.77\%$$

0	9m	18m
−4500	2500	3200

|← i% →|

17. $NPV@\,i = -4500 + 2500/(1 + i * 9/12) + 3200/(1 + i * 18/12)$

$NPV@\,15\% = +359.44$ $\quad NPV@\,20\% = +135.45$

$NPV@\,25\% = -67.46$ $\quad NPV@\,23\% = +11.38$

$NPV@\,23.4\% = -4.63$ $\quad NPV@\,23.3\% = -.64$

Hence the IRR $\doteq$ 23.2%.
Most graphing calculators can solve for i using their "solver" routine.

Section 1.9 Solutions

Concept and Short Answer Exercises

1. The US Rule—the outstanding balance is calculated when each payment is made.
2. The Merchant's Rule—an equation of value with the focal date over the last payment.
3. For the US Rule, the focal date floats to each payment date in turn.
4. Final payment = payoff = what is still owed = balance = outstanding balance.

Odd Exercise Calculations

5. Merchant's Rule:

0	1m	2m	3m
1000	−200	−200	x

20% (from 0 to 3m)

$$x = 1000(1 + 0.2 * \frac{3}{12}) - 200(1 + 0.2 * \frac{2}{12})$$

$$-200(1 + 0.2 * \frac{1}{12}) \rightarrow x = 1050 - 206.\overline{6} - 203.\overline{3} = \$640.$$

US Rule:

1st payment: $1000(1{+}0.2 * 1/12) = 1016.\overline{6}$ less $200 = 816.\overline{6}$

2nd payment: $816.\overline{6}(1{+}0.2 * 1/12) = 830.2\overline{7}$ less $200 = 630.2\overline{7}$

3rd payment: $630.2\overline{7}(1{+}0.2 * 1/12) = \$640.78$

7. Merchant's Rule:

3/10	6/17	8/10
5000	−2000	x

5% (from 3/10 to 8/10)

$$x = 5000\left(1 + 0.05 * \frac{5}{12}\right) - 2000\left(1 + 0.05 * \frac{54}{360}\right)$$

$x = 5014.17 - 2015.00 = \$3089.17.$

US Rule:

1st payment: $5000(1 + 0.05 * 99/360) = 5068.75$ less $2000 = 3068.75$

2nd payment: $3068.75(1 + 0.05 * 54/360) = \$3091.77$

9. 1st: $850(1 + 0.18 * 1/12) = 862.75$ less $0.15 * 850 = 735.25$

0	1m	2m
850	−pmt1	−pmt2

2nd: $735.25(1 + 0.18 * 1/12) = 746.28$ less $0.15 * 735.25 = 635.99$

3rd: $635.99(1 + 0.18 * 1/12) = 645.53$ less $0.15 * 635.99 = \$550.13$

11. US Rule:

7/1	9/15	12/5	2/12
7000	−2000	−2000	x

7% (from 7/1 to 2/12)

1st: $7000(1{+}0.07 * 76/360) = 7103.\overline{4}$ less $2000 = 5103.\overline{4}$

2rd: $5103.\overline{4}(1{+}0.07 * 81/360) = 5183.823$ less $2000 = 3183.823$

3rd: $3183.823(1{+}0.07 * 69/360) = \$3226.54$

13. Merchant's Rule:

2/1	3/15	7/20	9/10
1860	−800	−500	x

6.75% (from 2/1 to 9/10)

$$x = 1860\left(1 + 0.0675 * \frac{221}{360}\right)$$

$$-800\left(1 + 0.0675 * \frac{179}{360}\right) - 500\left(1 + 0.0675 * \frac{52}{360}\right)$$

$x = 1937.07375 - 826.85 - 504.875 = \$605.35$

15. US Rule:

0m	1m	2m	...
15,000	−311.38	−311.38	...

9% →

$$\text{1st}: \quad 15{,}000(1+0.09/12) = 15{,}112.50 \qquad \text{less } 311.38 = 14{,}801.12$$
$$\text{2nd}: \quad 14{,}801.12(1+0.09/12) = 14{,}912.13 \qquad \text{less } 311.38 = 14{,}600.75$$

Hence
$$\sum \text{PMT} = 2 * 311.38 = \$622.76$$
$$\sum \text{PRN} = 15{,}000 - 14{,}600.75 = \$399.25$$
$$\sum \text{INT} = 622.76 - 399.25 = \$223.51$$

Section 1.10 Solutions

Concept and Short Answer Exercises

1. $\$1700 = 300 + 400 + 1000$
2. Average due date is the focal date where the payback = total amount owed.
3. The rate is irrelevant because of the balance of the payments before and after the average due date.
4. Average due date if the dates are weighted by the amount owed.

Odd Exercise Calculations

5. Average due date $= \dfrac{325 * 24 + 680 * 40 + 450 * 60}{325 + 680 + 450} = 42.6$ days

7. Average due date $= \dfrac{1.2 * 5 + 1.6 * 8 + 1.85 * 12}{1.2 + 1.6 + 1.85} = 8.82$ months

9. Average due date $= \dfrac{100 * 1 + 100 * 2 + \cdots + 100 * 12}{1200} = \dfrac{100}{1200}(1 + 2 + \cdots + 12)$
$= \dfrac{1}{12} * \dfrac{12 * 13}{2} = 6.5\,\text{months}$

11. Average due date $= \dfrac{5200 * 3 + 8900 * 5 + 6150 * 9}{5200 + 8900 + 6150} = 5.7\,\text{weeks}$

13. Average due date $= \dfrac{18{,}000 * 86 + 23{,}580 * 119 + 14{,}860 * 126}{18{,}000 + 23{,}580 + 14{,}860}$
$= 110.3$ days into the year = April 21.

15. Assume that payoff P exceeds the sum of the payments by K

$\therefore P = P_1 + P_2 + \ldots + P_n + K$ and P is located at the adjusted average due date, t.

$\therefore P = P_1(1 + i[t - t_1]) + P_2(1 + i[t - t_2]) + \ldots + P_n(1 + i[t - t_n])$

$\therefore P_1 + P_2 + \ldots + P_n + K = P_1(1 + i[t - t_1]) + P_2(1 + i[t - t_2]) + \ldots + P_n(1 + i[t - t_n])$

$\therefore K = P_1 i[t - t_1] + P_2 i[t - t_2] + \ldots + P_n i[t - t_n]$

$\therefore K = (P_1 + P_2 + \ldots + P_n)it - i(P_1t_1 + P_2t_2 + \ldots + P_nt_n)$

$\therefore (P_1 + P_2 + \ldots + P_n)rt = i(P_1t_1 + P_2t_2 + \ldots + P_nt_n) + K$

$$\therefore t = \frac{i(P_1t_1 + P_2t_2 + \ldots + P_nt_n)}{i(P_1 + P_2 + \ldots + P_n)} + \frac{K}{i(P_1 + P_2 + \ldots + P_n)}$$

$$= \frac{P_1t_1 + P_2t_2 + \ldots + P_nt_n}{P_1 + P_2 + \ldots + P_n} + \frac{K}{i(P_1 + P_2 + \ldots + P_n)}$$

17. Adjusted average due date: $K = 1400 - (325 + 680 + 450) = 1450 - 1455 = -5$

$$t = \frac{P_1t_1 + P_2t_2 + \ldots + P_nt_n}{P_1 + P_2 + \ldots + P_n} + \frac{K}{i(P_1 + P_2 + \ldots + P_n)}$$

$$t = \frac{325 * 24 + 680 * 40 + 450 * 60}{325 + 680 + 450} + \frac{-5}{0.08/360(325 + 680 + 450)}$$

$t = 42.6116 - 15.46 \text{ days} = 27.15 \text{days}$

19. Adjusted average due date: $K = 1500 - (500 + 400 + 320 + 256)$
$= 1500 - 1476 = 24$

$$t = \frac{P_1t_1 + P_2t_2 + \ldots + P_nt_n}{P_1 + P_2 + \ldots + P_n} + \frac{K}{i(P_1 + P_2 + \ldots + P_n)}$$

$$t = \frac{500 * 2 + 400 * 3 + 320 * 4 + 256 * 5}{1476} + \frac{24}{0.09/12 * 1476}$$

$t = 3.2249\text{m} + 2.1680\text{m} = 5.39\text{m}\,(161.7\text{d})$

Review Test for Simple Interest Solutions

1. **C.** 7/1/04 – 1/25/04 = 183 – 25 = 158
2. **B.** The 29th in the month before March is Feb. 29 = March 1. Hence $3 \times 30 + 3/15 - 3/1 = 90 + 14 = 104$
3. **B.** $I = Pit = 1500 \times 0.07 \times 13/52 = 26.25$
4. **A.** Scheme 1: Cash: PV = 23,000

   Scheme 2: Loan: $PV = 25{,}000/(1 + .0625 \times 15/12) = 23{,}188.41$

5. D. Discount $= 0.96 * 94{,}580$
$= \$90{,}796.80$ on 10th day

10d		60d
\$90,796.80	@i →	94,580

$$I = 94{,}580 - 90{,}796.80 = 3783.20 \rightarrow i = \frac{I}{Pt} = \frac{3783.20}{\$90{,}796.80 * {}^{50}\!/_{360}} = 30\%$$

6. $I = 0.091$

$$i = \frac{I}{Pt} = \frac{0.091}{0.909 * 182/360} = 19.80\%$$

0d		182d
\$0.909	@i →	\$1

7. Mature: $S = 4000$

$$\text{Discount: } P = \frac{S}{1+it} = \frac{4000}{1 + 0.10 * {}^{40}\!/_{360}}$$

Discount: $P = \$3956.04$

7/1/04	8/20/04	90d
4000	@0% →	4000
	P ← 40d@10%	

6/04	12/04	6/05
5000	x	x
10% →		

8. $x + x(1 + 0.10 * 1/2) = 5000(1 + 0.10 * 1)$

$2.05x = 5500 \rightarrow x = \$2682.93$

0	1y	2y
−80k	40k	60k
← i%		

9. $NPV@\, i = -80k + 40k/(1+i) + 60k/(1+2i)$

$NPV@\, 10\% = -80k + 40k/1.1 + 60k/1.2 = \$63.636k$
$NPV@\, 20\% = -80k + 40k/1.2 + 60k/1.4 = -\$38.095k$

$$IRR \doteq 10\% + \frac{\$63.636k - \$0}{\$63.636k - (-\$38.095k)}(20\% - 10\%) = 16.26\% \text{ approximately.}$$

Get at least a 16% return.

10. US Rule:

3/05	6/05	8/05
5000	−4000	x
5% →		

1st: $5000(1 + 0.05 * 3/12) = 5062.50$
less $4000 = 1062.50$
2nd: $1062.50(1 + 0.05 * 2/12) = \$1071.35$

11. Merchant's Rule:

3/05	6/05	8/05
5000	−4000	x
5% →		

$x = 5000(1 + 0.05 * 5/12) - 4000(1 + 0.05 * 2/12)$
$x = 5140.1\overline{6} - 4033.\overline{3} = \$1106.83$

12. $$\text{Average due date} = \frac{300 * 40 + 600 * 80 + 1000 * 100}{300 + 600 + 1000} = 84.2 \text{ days}$$

Chapter 2 Discount Interest

Section 2.1 Solutions

Concept and Short Answer Exercises

1. Present value, future value
2. Because $D = Sdt$ is based on S. Hence it is impossible to calculate S using D.
3. S the future value. Hence if one asks for a \$2000 loan under a bank discount, the $P = S(1 - dt)$ will be less than \$2000.
4. Discounting means to move money backward. One may discount at simple interest, bank discount, compound interest, or with annuities. Bank discount is just one way to move money backward by $P = S(1 - dt)$.
5. 5% bank discount rate (bd) is based on the larger value, S, while a 5% simple interest rate (si) is based on the smaller value, P. Hence, other values being equal, a 5% bd rate is higher than a 5% si rate.
6. $I = Pit$ is based on P. Hence, it cannot be used to calculate P.

Odd Exercise Calculations

7. $D = Sdt = 1000 * 0.08 * 2 = \$160$

$P = S - D = 1000 - 160 = \$840$

0 — 2y; P ← 8% bd — 1000

9. $D = Sdt$

$= 2000 * 0.078 * 82/360 = \$35.53$

$P = S - D = 2000 - 35.53 = \$1964.47$

2/10/06 = 41d — 5/3/06 = 123d; | ← 7.8% bd — 2000

11. $P = S(1 - dt)$

$= 8000\left(1 - 0.1 * \frac{9}{12}\right) = \$7400$

0 — 9m; P ← 10% bd — 8000

13. $P = S(1 - dt)$

$= 10{,}000\left(1 - 0.05 * \frac{300}{360}\right) = \$9583.33$

2/5/04 = 36d — Leap yr. — 12/1/04 = 336d; | ← 5% bd — 10,000

15. $S = \frac{P}{1 - dt} = \frac{15{,}000}{1 - 0.08 * 3} = \$19{,}736.84$

0 — 3y; 15,000 — 8%bd → |

17. $S = \frac{P}{1 - dt} = \frac{5000}{1 - 0.09 * 1} = \$5494.51$

0 — 1y; 5000 — 9% bd → |

19. $S = \frac{P}{1-dt} = \frac{6500}{1-0.09*15/12} = \$7323.94$

0		15m
6500	9% bd →	|

Section 2.2 Solutions

Concept and Short Answer Exercises

1. Higher
2. Coupon equivalent is the simple interest rate equivalent to a bank discount rate.
3. To calculate the coupon equivalent use the formula $i = d / (1-dt)$.
4. Since $1-dt < 1$ for positive d, $S = P/(1-dt) > P$.
5. $D = I = \$200$; $d = D/St$; $i = I/Pt$; $t = D/Sd$
6. $d = i/(1+it) = 0.08/(1+0.08\times3) = 6.45\%$

Odd Exercise Calculations

7. $d = \frac{i}{1+it} = \frac{0.08}{1+0.08*92/360} = 7.84\%$

9. $i = \frac{d}{1-dt} = \frac{0.08}{1-0.08*92/360} = 8.17\%$

11. $d = \frac{i}{1+it} = \frac{0.10}{1+0.10*2} = 8.33\%$

13. $i = \frac{d}{1-dt} = \frac{0.10}{1-0.10*2} = 12.50\%$

15.

0		8m
5000	i si or d bd →	5400

$I = 400$ $D = 400$

$i = \frac{I}{Pt} = \frac{400}{5000*8/12} = 12.00\%$ $d = \frac{D}{St} = \frac{400}{5400*8/12} = 11.11\%$

17.

$$\begin{array}{ccc} 8/2/03 & \text{leap yr} & 6/1/04 \\ =214\text{d} & & =153\text{d} \\ \hline 14{,}000 & \xrightarrow{\text{i si or d bd}} & 20{,}000 \end{array}$$

$I = 6000$ $D = 6000$

$$i = \frac{I}{Pt} = \frac{6000}{14{,}000 * 304/360} = 50.75\% \qquad d = \frac{D}{St} = \frac{6000}{20{,}000 * 304/360} = 35.53\%$$

19.

$$\begin{array}{ccc} 6/23/00 & \text{leap yr} & 9/11/00 \\ =175\text{d} & & =255\text{d} \\ \hline 125{,}000 & \xrightarrow{\text{i si or d bd}} & 127{,}200 \end{array}$$

$I = 2200$ $D = 2200$

$$i = \frac{I}{Pt} = \frac{2200}{125{,}000 * 80/366} = 8.05\% \qquad d = \frac{D}{St} = \frac{2200}{127{,}200 * 80/366} = 7.91\%$$

21. $D = 6000 - 5886.75 = 113.25$

$$d = \frac{D}{St} = \frac{113.25}{6000 * 90/360} = 7.55\%$$

$$\begin{array}{ccc} 2/28/04 & \xrightarrow{\text{90 days}} & 149\text{d} \\ =59\text{d} & & =5/28/04 \\ \hline 5886.75 & \xrightarrow{\text{d\% bd}} & 6000.00 \end{array}$$

Section 2.3 Solutions

Concept and Short Answer Exercises

1. Since these cannot be redeemed until the maturity date, the two steps are as follows:

   a. Mature the financial instrument at the instrument rate.

   b. Discount the mature value at the rate of return required by the buyer.

2. Cash is only possible now. Hence, the focal date is the present.

3. Proceeds is the present value of a bank-discounted future value. Example: Find the proceeds for a \$2000, 91-day note sold on an 8% bank discount basis. The \$2000 is located at the 91-day mark and you are to solve for $P = S(1-dt)$.

4. If nothing is said, a rate is simple interest.

5. **a.** Find $I = S - P$. **b.** Calculate $i = I/Pt$.

6. **a.** Find $D = S - P$. **b.** Calculate $d = D/St$.

Odd Exercise Calculations

7. $S = P(1 + it)$

$S = 1000(1 + 0.06 * 2) = 1120 = \text{maturity}$

$P = S(1 - dt)$

$P = 1120(1 - 0.08 * 2) + 2000(1 - 0.08 * 3)$

$P = 940.80 + 1520 = \$2460.80 = \text{discounted value}$

0		2 y	3 y
1000	6% si →	1120	2000
|←	8% bd	|←	|

9.

3/3	4/5	5/15	6/1	10/2
62 d	95 d	135 d	152 d	275 d

5000 —— 90 d @8%si ——→ 5100

P_1 ← 17d@8%bd —— |

4000 —— 180d@6%bd ——→ 4120

P_2 ← 140d@8%bd —— |

Mature

$S_1 = 5000\left(1 + 0.08 * 90/360\right) = 5100$

$S_2 = 4000\left(1 + 0.06 * 180/360\right) = 4120$

Discount

$P_1 = 5100(1 - 0.08 * 17/360) = 5080.73$

$P_2 = 4120\left(1 - 0.08 * 140/360\right) = 3991.82$

Total proceeds = $9072.55

11.

9/25/05	7/25/06	9/25/06

1000 —— 10%si ——→ 1100

1083.50 ← 9%bd —— |

Mature

$S = 1000(1 + 0.10 * 1) = \$1100$

Discount

$P = 1100\left(1 - 0.09 * 2/12\right) = \$1083.50$

13.

3/1/06	4/1/06	12/1/06	1/1/07
1071.00 ← 10% bd	1080		
3066.38 ←	←	3315	
1833.33 ←	←	←	2000

Mature (time line not shown)

$S_1 = 1000(1 + 0.08 * 1) = 1080$

$S_2 = 3000\left(1 + 0.07 * 3/2\right) = 3315$

$S_3 = 2000$

Discount

$P_1 = 1080\left(1 - 0.10 * 1/12\right) = \$1071.00$

$P_2 = 3315\left(1 - 0.10 * 9/12\right) = \$3066.38$

$P_3 = 2000\left(1 - 0.10 * 10/12\right) = \$1833.33$

Total proceeds = $5970.71

15.

3/15/05		5/10/05		
8400	$\xrightarrow{56\text{d}}$	$\xrightarrow{9\%\text{si}}$	$\xrightarrow{37\text{d}}$	8595.30
		8502.54	$\xleftarrow{10.5\%\text{bd}}$	$\leftarrow\vert$

Mature $S = 8400\left(1 + 0.09 * 93/360\right) = \$8595.30$

Discount $P = 8595.30\left(1 - 0.105 * 37/360\right) = \$8502.54$

17.

10/2/04		12/19/04		1/21/05
23,743.15	$\xleftarrow{78\text{d}}$	24,242.44		
14,641.41	$\longleftarrow$	$\xleftarrow{111\text{d}}$	$\longleftarrow$	15,083.22

Mature (time line not shown) | Discount

$S_1 = 23,600\left(1 + 0.07 * \frac{140}{360}\right) = 24,242.44$ $\quad P_1 = S_1\left(1 - 0.095 * \frac{78}{360}\right) = \$23,743.45$

$S_2 = 14,500\left(1 + 0.08 * \frac{181}{360}\right) = 15,083.22$ $\quad P_2 = S_2\left(1 - 0.095 * \frac{111}{360}\right) = \$14,641.41$

Total proceeds = $38,384.86

19.

1/10/05		11/10/05		1/10/06
23,743.15	$\xleftarrow{10\text{m}}$	40,000		
21,660	$\longleftarrow$	$\xleftarrow{1\text{y}}$	$\longleftarrow$	22,800
57,988	$\longleftarrow$	$\xleftarrow{1\text{y}}$	$\longleftarrow$	61,040

Mature (time line not shown) | Discount

$S_1 = 20,000(1 + 0.07 * 2) = 22,800$ $\quad P_1 = 22,800(1 - 0.05 * 1) = \$21,660$

$S_2 = 54,500\left(1 + 0.08 * 18/12\right) = 61,040$ $\quad P_2 = 61,040(1 - 0.05 * 1) = \$57,988$

$S_3 = 40,000$ $\quad P_3 = 40,000(1 - 0.05 * 10/12) = 38,333.33$

Total proceeds = $117,981.33

Section 2.4 Solutions

Concept and Short Answer Exercises

1. The federal government
2. By bidding at less than the face value of the T-bill
3. 0.963 * 1,000,000 = $963,000
4. $1,000,000 – $963,000 = $37,000

Odd Exercise Calculations

5. $I = D = 19{,}000$

0		182d
481k	$\xleftrightarrow{\text{i or d}}$	500k

$$i = \frac{I}{Pt} \qquad d = \frac{D}{St}$$

$$i = \frac{19k}{481k * 182/360} = 7.81\% \qquad d = \frac{19k}{500k * 182/360} = 7.52\%$$

7. $P = \dfrac{S}{1+it}$

5/3/04		8/5/04		306d
= 124d		= 218d		
481,000				500,000
$\vert\leftarrow$	$\xleftarrow{\text{i\% si}}$	492,772.67	$\xleftarrow{\text{6\% si}}$	$\leftarrow\vert$

$$P = \frac{500{,}000}{1 + 0.06 * 88/360}$$

$\underline{P = \$492{,}772.67}$

$I = 11{,}772.67$ ($\xleftarrow{\text{i\% si}}$ part)

$$\text{Hence } i = \frac{I}{Pt} = \frac{11{,}772.67}{481{,}000 * 94/360} = 9.37\%$$

9. $I = D = 66{,}600$

0		91d
933.4k	$\xleftrightarrow{\text{i or bd}}$	1000k

$$i = \frac{I}{Pt} \qquad d = \frac{D}{St}$$

$$i = \frac{66.6k}{933.4k * 91/360} = 28.23\% \qquad d = \frac{66.6k}{1000k * 91/360} = 26.35\%$$

11. $P = S(1 - dt)$

12/10		2/10		3/1
= 0		= 2m		= 9
933.4k		$\xleftarrow{\text{9\% bd}}$	$\longleftarrow$	100
$\vert\leftarrow$	$\xleftarrow{\text{d\% bd}}$	990.3k	$\xleftarrow{\text{12\% bd}}$	$\leftarrow\vert$

$$P = 1000k(1 - 0.12 * 29/360)$$

$\underline{P = \$990{,}333.33}$

$D = 56{,}933.33$ (the $\xleftarrow{\text{d\% bd}}$ part)

$$d = \frac{D}{St} = \frac{56{,}933.33}{990{,}333.33 * 2/12} = 34.49\%$$

13. $I = D = 9000$

0		91d
491,000	$\xleftrightarrow{\text{i or bd}}$	500,000

$$i = \frac{I}{Pt} \qquad d = \frac{D}{St}$$

$$i = \frac{9000}{491{,}000 * 91/360} = 7.25\% \qquad d = \frac{9000}{500{,}000 * 91/360} = 7.12\%$$

15. $I = 5500$

9/15/04		11/6/04
259d		311d
491,000	$\xrightarrow{\text{i}}$	496,500

$$i = \frac{I}{Pt} = \frac{5500}{491{,}000 * 52/360} = 7.75\%$$

17. $I = D = 9000$

$$i = \frac{I}{Pt} = \frac{9000}{491{,}000 * 39/360} = 16.92\% \rightarrow d = 16.62\%$$

$$\begin{array}{lcr} 11/6 & \xrightarrow{39\text{d}} & \\ \hline 491\text{k} & \xleftarrow{\text{dbd}} & 500\text{k} \end{array}$$

19. $$P = \frac{S}{1+it} = \frac{1{,}000{,}000}{1+0.078 * 181/360}$$

$$\begin{array}{lcr} 0 & & 181\text{d} \\ \hline P & \xleftarrow{7.8\%\text{si}} & 1000\text{k} \end{array}$$

$$P = 962{,}263.24 \rightarrow \text{Bid} = \frac{962{,}263.24}{1{,}000{,}000} = 96.226\%$$

Section 2.5 Solutions

Concept and Short Answer Exercises

1. Orange County in California did just that. Hence, care should be taken when buying any bond.
2. The interest is often tax exempt, making the government bond worth more than just the value of the stated rate.
3. The face value is a FV while the PV is calculated by P = S(1 – dt).
4. Since you are an unknown, the banker's acceptance makes your money "good" by backing it with the bank's reputation.

Odd Exercise Calculations

5.

$$\begin{array}{lcccr} 8/1/05 & \xrightarrow{153\text{ d}} & 1/1/06 & \xrightarrow{47\text{ d}} & 2/17/06 \\ \hline P_1 & \longleftarrow & \xleftarrow{6\%\text{ bd}} & \longleftarrow & 250{,}000 \\ & & P_2 & \xleftarrow{7\%\text{ bd}} & | \end{array}$$

$$P_1 = S(1-dt) = 250{,}000(1-0.06*200/360) = \$241{,}666.67$$

$$P_2 = S(1-dt) = 250{,}000(1-0.07*47/360) = \$247{,}715.28$$

$$D = 247{,}715.28 - 241{,}666.67 = 6048.61 \rightarrow d = \frac{D}{st} = \frac{6048.61}{247{,}715.28*153/360} = 5.75$$

7.

$$\begin{array}{lcccr} 7/14/04 & \xrightarrow{45\text{d}} & 8/28/04 & \xrightarrow{15\text{ d}} & 9/12/04 \\ \hline P_1 & \longleftarrow & \xleftarrow{6.5\%\text{ bd}} & \longleftarrow & 2{,}000{,}000 \\ & & P_2 & \xleftarrow{7.75\%\text{ bd}} & | \end{array}$$

$$P_1 = S(1-dt) = 2{,}000{,}000(1-0.065*60/366) = \$1{,}978{,}688.53$$

$$P_2 = S(1-dt) = 2{,}000{,}000(1-0.0775*15/366) = \$1{,}993{,}647.54$$

$$I = 1{,}993{,}647.54 - 1{,}978{,}688.53 = 14{,}959.01 \rightarrow i = \frac{I}{Pt} = \frac{14{,}959.01}{1{,}978{,}688.53*45/366} = 6.15\%$$

$$D = 2{,}000{,}000 - 1{,}993.647.54 = 6352.46 \rightarrow d = \frac{D}{St} = \frac{6352.46}{2{,}000{,}000*15/366} = 7.75\%$$

9.

$$\begin{array}{ccccc} 6/1/03 & \xrightarrow{10\text{m}} & 4/1/04 & \xrightarrow{2\text{m}} & 6/1/04 \\ \hline 10{,}000 & \longrightarrow & \xrightarrow{8\%\text{ si}} & \longrightarrow & 10{,}800 \\ & & P & \xleftarrow{8\%\text{ bd}} & | \end{array}$$

$$S = P(1+it) = 10{,}000(1+0.08*1) = 10{,}800$$

$$P = S(1-dt) = 10{,}800(1-0.08*\tfrac{2}{12}) = \$10{,}656$$

$$D = 10{,}656 - 10{,}000 = 656 \rightarrow d = \frac{D}{St} = \frac{656}{10{,}656*\tfrac{10}{12}} = 7.39\%$$

11.

$$\begin{array}{ccccc} 5/22 & \xrightarrow{82\text{d}} & 8/12 & \xrightarrow{100\text{d}} & | \\ \hline 50{,}000 & \longrightarrow & \xrightarrow{6\%\text{ si}} & \longrightarrow & 51{,}516.67 \\ & & P & \xleftarrow{8\%\text{ bd}} & | \end{array}$$

$$S = P(1+it) = 50{,}000(1+0.06*\tfrac{182}{360}) = 51{,}516.67$$

$$P = S(1-dt) = 51{,}516.67(1-0.08*\tfrac{100}{360}) = 50{,}371.86$$

$$I = 50{,}371.86 - 50{,}000 = 371.86 \rightarrow r = \frac{I}{Pt} = \frac{371.86}{50{,}000*\tfrac{82}{360}} = 3.27\%$$

Section 2.6 Solutions

Concept and Short Answer Exercises

1. Simple interest is based on the present value with the interest added to the present value at the end of the term. Simple discount is based on the future value with the interest deducted from the future value at the beginning of the term.

2. $A(t) = \int_0^t 3s + 4\, ds = 3s^2/2 + 4s \big|_0^t = 3t^2/2 + 4t$

3. $A(t) = t^3/2 + 2t + 2 \rightarrow A(0) = 2$

   But $A(t) = A(0)a(t) = 2a(t) \rightarrow a(t) = \dfrac{A(t)}{2} = \dfrac{t^3/2 + 2t + 2}{2} = t^3/4 + t + 1$

4. **a.** $i_n = \dfrac{i}{1+i(n-1)} = \dfrac{0.08}{1+0.08(5-1)} = 6.06\%$

   b. $d_n = \dfrac{d}{1-d(n-1)} = \dfrac{0.08}{1-0.08(5-1)} = 11.76\%$

5. $d = \dfrac{i}{1+it} = \dfrac{0.065}{1+0.065(1.5)} = 5.92\%$

6. $i = \dfrac{d}{1-dt} = \dfrac{0.0725}{1-0.0725(27/12)} = 8.66\%$

Odd Exercise Calculations

7. **a.** $d_n = \dfrac{A(n)-A(n-1)}{A(n)} = \dfrac{[1+i(n)]-[1+i(n-1)]}{1+i(n)} = \dfrac{i}{1+in}$

$\therefore d_4 = 0.08/(1+0.08(4)) = 6.06\%$

b. $d_n = \dfrac{d}{1-d(n-1)} \rightarrow d_4 = \dfrac{0.08}{1-0.08(4-1)} = 11.76\%$

9. $i_n = \dfrac{i}{1+i(n-1)} = \rightarrow \dfrac{0.06}{1+0.06(n-1)} < .05$

$\therefore 0.06 < [.94+0.06n][0.05] \rightarrow n > 4.33 \rightarrow n = 5$

11. $720 = 580(1+it) \rightarrow it = 7/29$

$S = 5500(1+(1.015i)(2t)) = 5500(1+2.03it) = 5500(1+2.03*7/29) = \$8195$

13. $i = \dfrac{I}{Pt} = \dfrac{1}{t} * \dfrac{I}{P} = \dfrac{1}{T/360} * \dfrac{100-B}{B} = \dfrac{360(100-B)}{T*B}$

where T = time in days and B = bid/ $100.

Review Test for Bank Discount Solutions

1. **a.** $P = \dfrac{S}{1+it} = \dfrac{1000}{1+.08*94/360} = \$979.54$

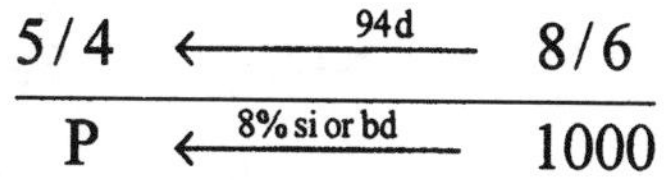

5/4	← 94d	8/6
P	← 8% si or bd	1000

b. $P = S(1-dt) = 1000\left(1-.08*{}^{94}\!/_{360}\right) = \$979.11$

2. **a.** US Rule

Step 1: $2000(1+0.08*3/12) = 2040$

less $400 = 1640$

Step 2: $1640(1+0.08*9/12) = 1738.40$

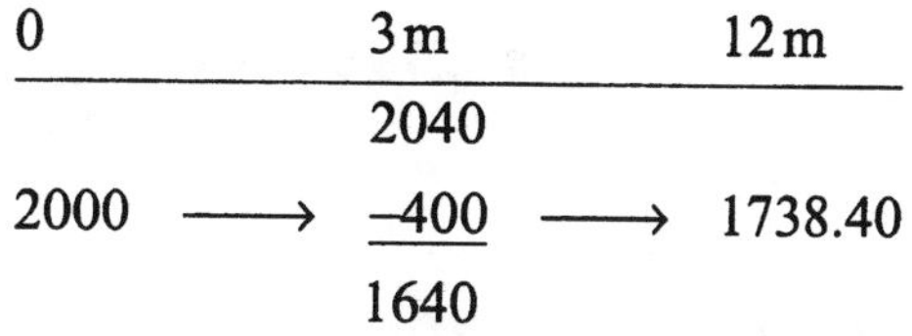

0		3m		12m
		2040		
2000	⟶	−400	⟶	1738.40
		1640		

b. Mechant's Rule

$x = 2000*(1+0.08*1) -$

$400(1+0.08*9/12) = \$1736$

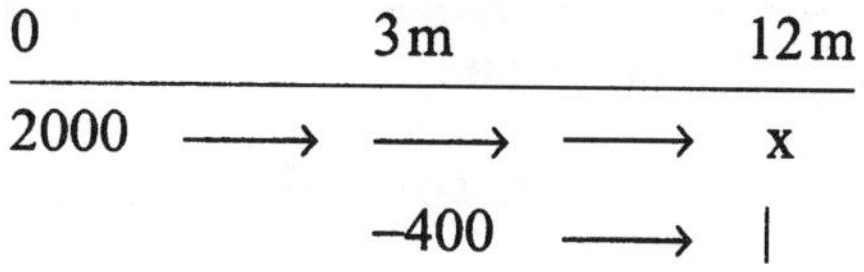

0		3m		12m
2000	⟶	⟶	⟶	x
		−400	⟶	|

3. Scheme 1: Cash → P = $2500

Scheme 2: Credit → $P = S(1-dt) = 3000(1-0.10*2) = \$2400$

Hence credit is better by $100.

4. $I = 58{,}000$

$i = \dfrac{I}{Pt} = \dfrac{58k}{942k*91/360} = 24.36\%$

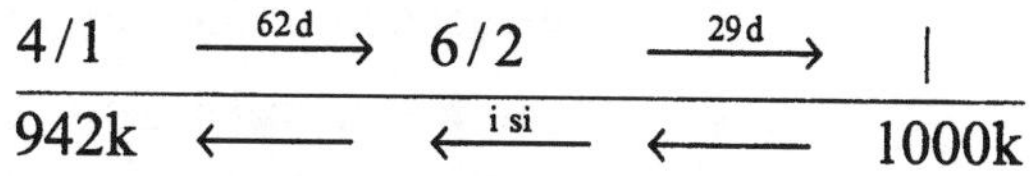

4/1	62d ⟶	6/2	29d ⟶	|
942k	⟵	⟵ i si	⟵	1000k

5. $P = \frac{S}{1+it} = \frac{1000k}{1+0.08*29/360}$

4/1	$\xrightarrow{62d}$	6/2	$\xrightarrow{29d}$	|
942k	$\longleftarrow$	$993k^{+}$	$\longleftarrow$	1000k

$P = 993{,}596.82$

$D = 993{,}596.82 - 942k = 51{,}596.82 \rightarrow d = \frac{D}{St} = \frac{51{,}596.82}{993{,}596.82*62/360} = 30.15\%$

6. $I = \$150$

$i = \frac{I}{Pt} = \frac{150}{2850*50/360} = 37.89\%$

10d		60d
2850	$\xrightarrow{1si}$	3000

7. Scheme 1: Remove money from MM.

$I = 3000*0.08*1/2 = \$120$

0	4m	6m
5000	−2000	

Scheme 2: Leave money in MM and avoid the penalty, but take out a loan.

$I = 5000*0.08*1/2 - 2000*0.12*2/12$

$I = \$200 \text{ gained} - \$40 \text{ lossed} = \$160$

Scheme 2 is better by $40.

8. $t = \frac{I}{Pi} = \frac{0.6}{1*0.08} = 7y + 6m$ $\quad t = \frac{D}{Sd} = \frac{0.6}{1.6*0.08} = 4.6875y = 4y + 251d$

9. $NPV@i = -5000 + \frac{2000}{1+.5*i} + \frac{4000}{1+1*i}$

0	6m	12m
−5000	2000	4000

$NPV@20\% = 151.52$

$NPV@30\% = -183.95$

$|\longleftarrow \downarrow \longrightarrow|$

Hence $IRR \doteq 20\% + \frac{151.52-0}{151.52-(-183.95)}(30\% - 20\%) = 24.52$

Chapter 3 Compound interest

Section 3.1 Solutions

Concept and Short Answer Exercises

1. At the compounding period the interest for the previous period is added (posted) to the account. Then for the next period, interest is paid on the principal + the accrued interest.
2. Only at the end of the term
3. At every compounding period
4. If interest accrues from the previous periods, then the amount for the next (one) period can be found by using the simple interest formula $S = P(1 + it)$ with $t = 1$, or by using the compound interest formula $S = P(1 + i)^n$ for $n = 1$.
5. $S = P(1 + it)$ is a linear (straight line) equation of S as a function of t.

6. $S = P(1 + i)^n$ is an exponential equation with a base of $(1 + i)$ and an exponent of n.

7. n = 7/1/10 – 7/1/05 = 0 m + 0 d + 5 y = 5 y

8. n = 7/1/10 – 4/1/05 = 3 m + 0 d + 5 y = 1 q + 20 q = 21 q

9. n = 1/1/10 – 7/1/05 = 13/1/09 – 7/1/05 = 6 m + 4 y = 6 m + 48 m = 54 m

10. n = 2/2/12 – 8/2/06 = 14/2/11 – 8/2/06 = 6 m + 5 y = 1 h + 10 h = 11 h

11. n = 5.5 – 0 = 5.5 y = 6 m + 60 m = 66 m

12. n = 2/2/08 – 8/2/06 = 14/2/07 – 8/2/06 = 6 m + 1 y = 2 q + 4 q = 6 q

13. 8% compounded semiannually = 8%(2)

14. 5% compounded yearly = 5%(1)

15. Use CI for the maximum number of full quarters = 3 y + 3m = 12 q + 1 q = 13 q and SI for the rest, here 2 months.

16. Use CI for the maximum number of full half years = 3 y = 6 h and SI for the rest, here 5 months.

Odd Exercise Calculations

17. **a.** $S = P(1+it)$

$S_1 = 1000(1+0.08*1) = 1080$

$S_2 = 1080(1+0.08*1) = 1166.40$

$S_3 = 1166.40(1+0.08*1) = 1259.71$

0	1	2	3
1000	1080	1166.40	1259.71

|——————————→|

b. $S = P(1+i)^n = 1000(1+8\%)^3 = 1259.71$

c. Compound interest accrues interest at each compounding period.

Hence, one gets interest on the principal + the accrued interest.

d. Exponential growth because of the $(1+i)^n$ term.

19. **a.** $S = P(1+i)^n = 2000(1+8\%/4)^8 = 2343.32$

b. $S = P(1+i)^n = 2000(1+8\%/12)^{24} = 2345.78$

c. $S = P(1+i)^n = 2000(1+8\%/360)^{720} = 2346.98$

0		2 y
2000	@8%(?) →	S

21. $S = P(1+i)^n = 6000(1+8\%/2)^5 = 7299.92$

$I = 7299.92 - 6000 = \$1299.92$

0		5h
6000	@ 8%(2) →	S

23. $n = 8/2/10 - 2/2/05 = 6m + 5y = 1h + 10h = 11h$

$S = P(1+i)^n$

$= 10{,}000(1+9\%/2)^{11} = \$16{,}228.53$

2/2/05		8/2/10
10,000	@ 9%(2) →	S

25. $S = P(1+i)^n$

$= 250(1+5\%/1)^{18} = \$601.65$

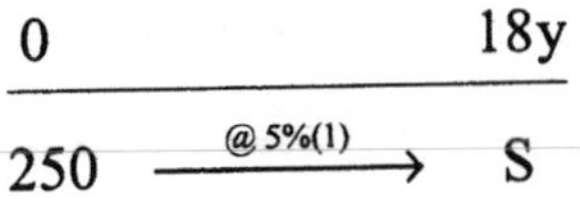

0 → 18y; 250 @ 5%(1) → S

27. $S = P(1+i)^n$

$= 100{,}000(1+4\%/1)^{14}$

$= \$173{,}167.64$

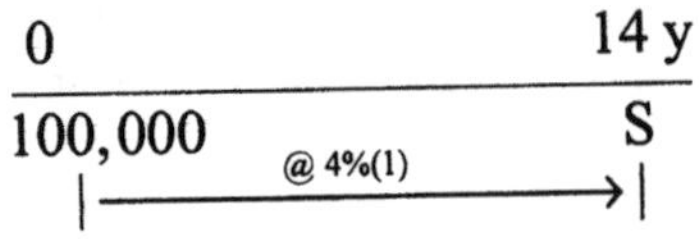

0 → 14 y; 100,000 @ 4%(1) → S

29. Date arithmetic: $1/1/11 - 10/1/11 = 6y + 3m = 25q$

$S = P(1+i)^n$

$= 5000(1+8\%/4)^{25}$

$= \$8203.03$

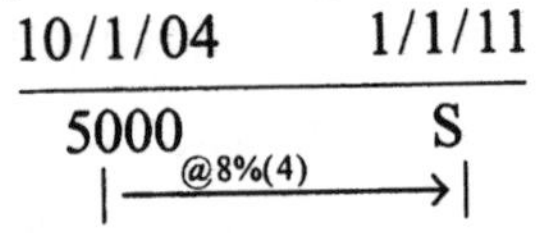

10/1/04 → 1/1/11; 5000 @8%(4) → S

31. Date arithmetic: $11/1/08 - 2/1/02 = 6\ y + 9\ m = 81m$

$S = P(1+i)^n$

$= 382.50(1+4\%/12)^{81}$

$= \$500.84$ Less \$500 is \$0.84

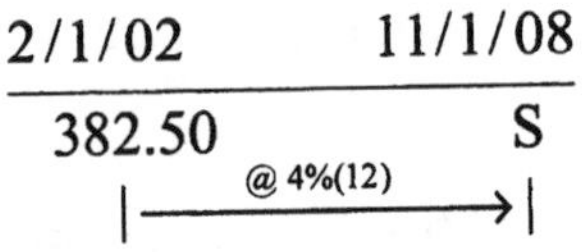

2/1/02 → 11/1/08; 382.50 @ 4%(12) → S

33. $n = 3/1/05 - 9/1/05 = 15/1/04 - 9/1/05 = 6m + 1y = 1h + 2h = 3h$

$S = P(1+i)^n$

$= 5000(1+6\%/2)^3 = \$5463.64$

Less \$3000 is \$2463.64 as the OB.

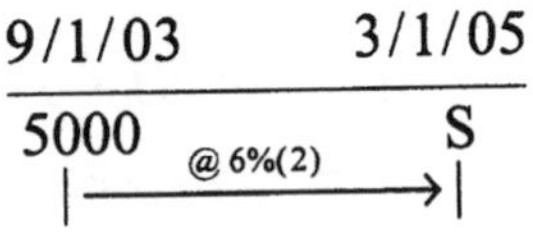

9/1/03 → 3/1/05; 5000 @ 6%(2) → S

35. Date arithmetic: $n = 11/1/08 - 2/1/02 = 9m + 6y = 6*12 + 9 = 81m$

Compound Interest Portion:

$S = P(1+i)^n$

$= 382.50(1+4\%/12)^{81}$

$= 500.84$

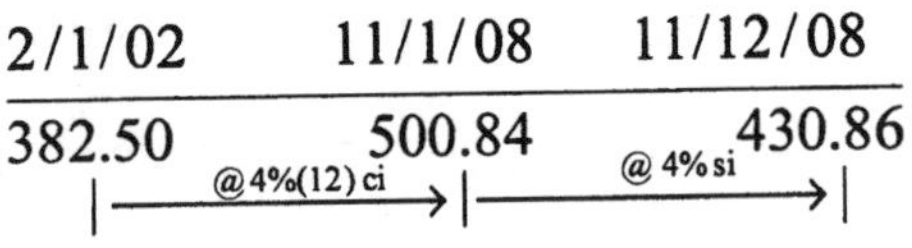

2/1/02 → 11/1/08 → 11/12/08; 382.50 @4%(12) ci → 500.84 @ 4% si → 430.86

Simple Interest Portion:

$S = P(1+it) = 500.84(1+0.04*11/360) = \$501.45$

Less the \$500 payment is O.B. of \$1.45

37. Date arithmetic: $9/1/04 - 9/1/03 = 1y = 2h$

Compound Interest Portion:

$S = P(1+i)^n$

$= 5000(1+6\%/2)^2 = 5304.50$

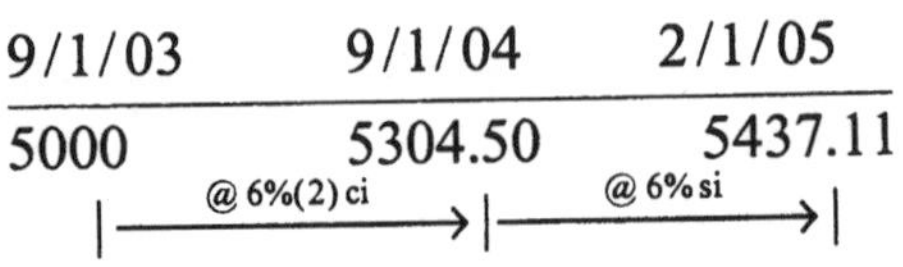

9/1/03 → 9/1/04 → 2/1/05; 5000 @ 6%(2) ci → 5304.50 @ 6% si → 5437.11

Simple Interest Portion:

$S = P(1+it) = 5304.50(1+0.06*5/12) = \$5437.11$ less $\$3000 \rightarrow OB = \$2437.11$

Section 3.2 Solutions

Concept and Short Answer Exercises

1. $P = S/(1+i)^n = S(1+i)^{-n}$
2. Backward
3. n is always entered as a positive whether you are solving for PV or for FV.
4. **a.** The PV of a FV of \$5000 over 20 years will be substantially < \$5000. Hence, \$1072.74 is reasonable.

   b. The answer must decrease — yet it increased. Absurd.

   c. It is the double negative. Excel and most financial calculators have the negative programmed in. Hence, if the user also provides a negative n, the program undoes it and moves the money forward, here 20 years.
5. 4 y + 6 m = 8 h + 1 h = 9 h
6. 4 y + 6 m = 16q + 2 q = 18 q

Odd Exercise Calculations

7. $P = S(1+i)^{-n}$

   $= 2000(1+9\%/2)^{-4} = \$1677.12$

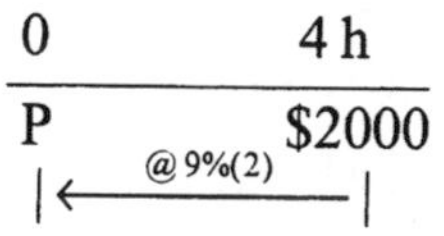

   Timeline: 0 — 4 h; P ← @ 9%(2) — \$2000

9. $P = S(1+i)^{-n}$

   $= 4068.65(1+7\%/4)^{-9} = \$3480.49$

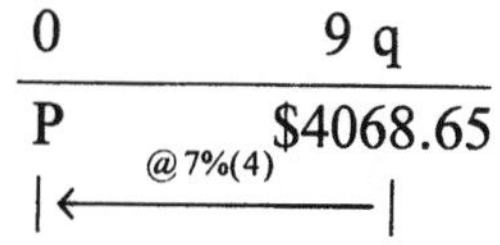

   Timeline: 0 — 9 q; P ← @ 7%(4) — \$4068.65

11. $x = 5000(1+7\%/2)^{1} + 2000(1+8\%/12)^{-22}$

    $= 5175 + 1728 = \$6903$

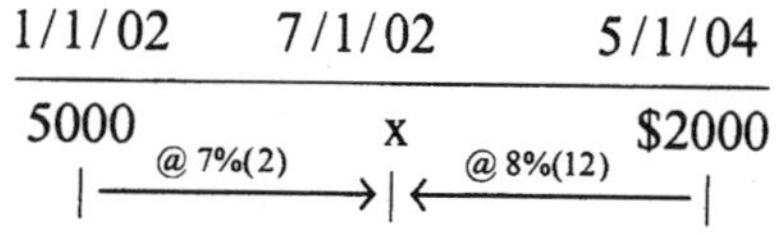

    Timeline: 1/1/02 — 7/1/02 — 5/1/04; 5000 → @ 7%(2) → x ← @ 8%(12) ← \$2000

13. $P = S(1+i)^{-n}$

    $= 6000(1+8\%/2)^{-6} = \$4741.89$

    Comp. disc. = 6000 − 4741.89 = \$1258.11

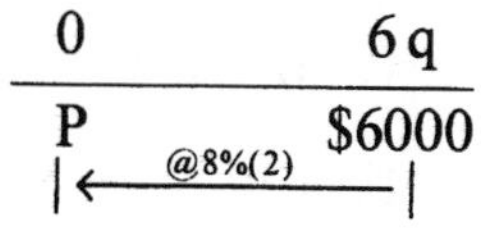

    Timeline: 0 — 6q; P ← @8%(2) — \$6000

15. $P = S(1+i)^{-n}$

    $= 25{,}000(1+9\%/4)^{-40} = \$10{,}266.14$

    Comp. disc. = 25,000 − 10,266.14 = \$14,733.86

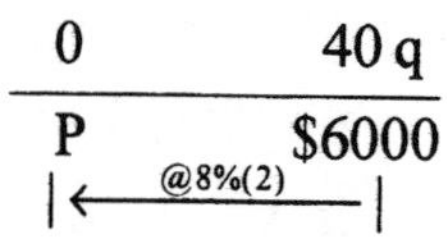

    Timeline: 0 — 40 q; P ← @8%(2) — \$6000

17. C.I. portion: $P_1 = S(1+i)^{-n}$

    $= 6000(1+8\%/2)^{-6} = \$4741.89$

    S.I. portion: $P_2 = S/(1+it)$

    $= \dfrac{4741.89}{1+.08*2/12} = \$4679.50$

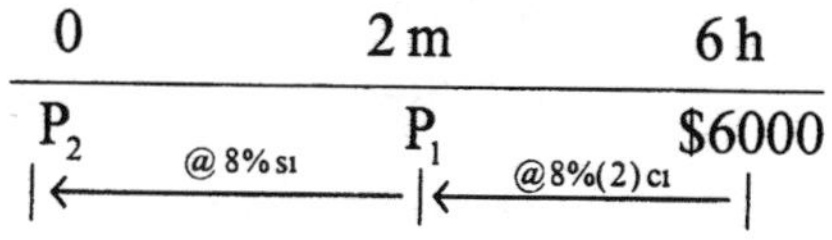

    Timeline: 0 — 2 m — 6 h; P_2 ← @ 8% SI — P_1 ← @8%(2) CI — \$6000

    The discount = 6000 − 4679.50 = \$1320.50

19. C.I. portion : $P = S(1+i)^{-n}$

$= 6000(1+8\%/2)^{-19/3} = \$4680.30$

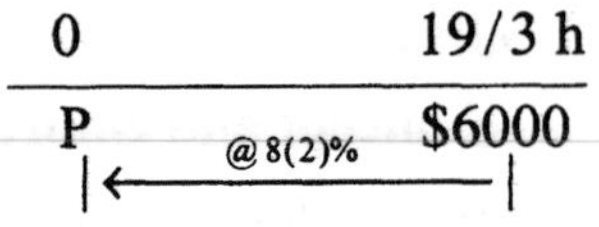

0		19/3 h
P	@ 8(2)%	\$6000
|←		|

21. $\$1(1+8\%/2)^{2/12} - 1 = i = 0.655819692\%/m$

C.I. portion : $P = S(1+i)^{-n}$

$= 6000(1+.655819692\%)^{-38} = \$4680.30$

The two answers are exactly the same.

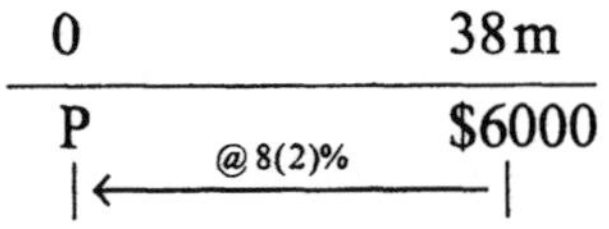

0		38m
P	@ 8(2)%	\$6000
|←		|

Section 3.3 Solutions

Concept and Short Answer Exercises

1. Compound interest is based on the present value with interest accruing on the interest + the principal from the previous period. Compound discount is based on the future value with the discount computed on the proceeds from the previous period.
2. $d_5 = i/(1+i)$
3. $i_7 = d/(1-d)$
4. $d = i/(1+i) = 0.065/1.065 = 6.1\%$
5. $i = d/(1-d) = .0875/(1-.0875) = 9.59\%$
6. **a.** $d = i/(1+i) \rightarrow 1/d - 1/i = (1+i)/i - 1/i = i/i = 1$

   b. $i(2-d) = 2i - id = 2i - (i-d) = i + d = i + i/(1+i) = (i + i^2 + i)/(1+i)$

   $= (2i + i^2)/(1+i) = i(2+i)/(1+i) = d(2+i)$

   c. $d^3/(1-d)^2 = d * (d/(1-d)) * (d/(1-d)) = d * i * i = di^2$
7. $(1+i)^n$ moves one dollar forward n periods giving some amount.

   $(1-d)^n = (1+i)^{-n}$ moves that amount back to one dollar.

9. $x = 1000(1+i)^k + 1000(1+i)^{-k}$

$x = 1000[(1+i)^k + (1+i)^{-k}]$

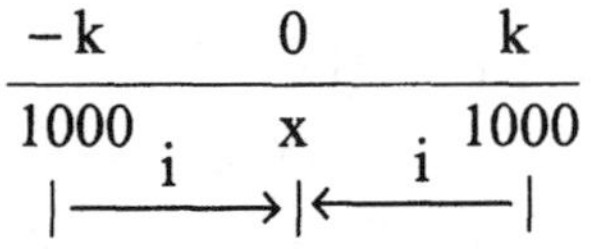

Is $x \geq 2000$?

Only if $(1+i)^k + (1+i)^{-k} \geq 2$

Multiply by $(1+i)^k$ and solve for 0 yields

$(1+i)^{2k} - 2(1+i)^k + 1 \geq 0 \Leftrightarrow [(1+i)^k - 1]^2 \geq 0$

−k		0		k
1000	i	x	i	1000
|——	→	|	←	——|

11. $x(1-d)^{-11} - x(1-d)^{-10} = 2x(1-d)^{-4} - 2x(1-d)^{-3}$

$1 - (1-d)^1 = 2(1-d)^7 - 2(1-d)^8 \rightarrow d = 9.43\%$ using solver.

13. $A(1) - A(0) = I_1,\ A(2) - A(1) = I_2, \ldots,$ and $A(k) - A(k-1) = I_k$

Added left sides = added right sides

$\therefore A(1) - A(0) + A(2) - A(1) + \ldots + A(k) - A(k-1) = I_1 + I_2 + \ldots + I_k$

$\therefore A(k) - A(0) = I_1 + I_2 + \ldots + I_k$

15. $P_1 = S(1-d)^n = 10000(1 - 7\%/4)^{12} = 8090.785$

$P_2 = P_1(1 - dt) = 8090.785(1 - 0.07/12) = \$8043.59$

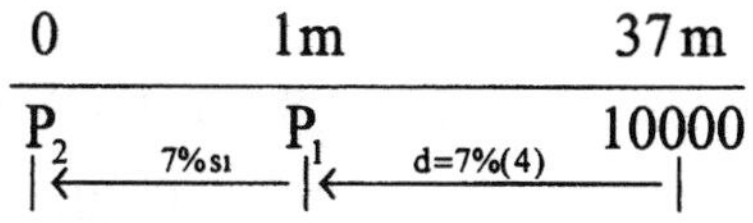

0	1m	37m
P_2	P_1	10000
← 7%SI	← d=7%(4)	

17. **a.** $1000(1.02)^3 = \$1061.21$ is better than $1000(1.03)^2 = \$1060.90$

b. $1000(1.02)^4 = \$1082.43$ is worse than $1000(1.03)^3 = \$1092.73$

Section 3.4 Solutions

Concept and Short Answer Exercises

1. Effective rate is the simple interest rate that yields the same amount as the compound rate for one year.
2. I = .085. Hence i = I/Pt = .085/1 * 1 = .085 = 8.5% is the effective rate.
3. I = .07632. Hence i = I/Pt = .07632/1 * 1 = .07632 = 7.632% is the effective rate.
4. $S = 1(1+i)^m$ is the FV of \$1 for 1 year. We must subtract 1 to get the effective rate. Hence, $r = (1+i)^m - 1$ is the effective rate.
5. Since both rates give the same monies for 1 year and since CI is nothing but repeated SI, the answers will be same for any equivalent rate and time period.
6. n = 10 years.

Odd Exercise Calculations

7. **a.** $(1 + 8\%/2)^2 = 1.0816 \to 8.16\%$

b. $(1 + 8\%/4)^4 = 1.082432 \to 8.24\%$

c. $(1 + 8\%/12)^{12} = 1.0829995 \to 8.30\%$

d. $(1 + 8\%/360)^{360} = 1.083277 \to 8.33\%$

9. **a.** $(1 + 12\%/2)^2 = 1.1236 \to 12.36\%$

b. $(1 + 12\%/4)^4 = 1.125509 \to 12.55\%$

c. $(1 + 12\%/12)^{12} = 1.126825 \to 12.68\%$

d. $(1 + 12\%/360)^{360} = 1.127474 \to 12.75\%$

11. $(1 + 7\%/4)^4 = 1.07186 \to 7.19\%$ Hence, 7.20% is higher.

13. Find the equivalent yearly interest rate of each:

$(1+12.3\%/4)^4 = 1.1288 \rightarrow 12.88\%$

$(1+12\%/12)^{12} = 1.126825 \rightarrow 12.68\%$

$\therefore 12.3\%(4)$ is higher.

15. $S = P(1+i)^n$

$= 10{,}000(1+8\%/4)^{12} = \$12{,}682.42$

$= 10{,}000(1+8\%/2)^6 = \$12{,}653.19$

Difference is \$29.23

0 — 3 y; 10,000 @8%(?) → S

17. $S = P(1+i)^n$

$= 5000(1+9\%/4)^8 = \$5974.16$

$= 5000(1+9.1\%/2)^4 = \$5974.01$

9%(2) is better by \$0.15

0 — 2 y; 5000 @9.?%(?) → S

19. Using the same logic as before, the rate for one 6 month period is 4.2%. Since CI is nothing but repeated SI, the equivalent rate is 4.2%/h or 8.4%(2).

21. $\$1(1+8\%/12)^{12/2} - 1 = 1.040672 - 1 = 0.040672 = 4.067\%/h = 8.13\%(2)$

23. $\$1(1+9\%/2)^{2/12} - 1 = 1.0073631 - 1 = 0.007363 = .7363\%/m = 8.84\%(12)$

25. From the theorem $\dfrac{d(m)}{m}\left[1+\dfrac{i(m)}{m}\right] = \dfrac{i(m)}{m}$.

Let i be the yearly effective rate for i(m)/m.

Hence $1+i = \left[1+\dfrac{i(m)}{m}\right]^m \rightarrow \left[1+\dfrac{i(m)}{m}\right] = (1+i)^{1/m}$

Thus $\dfrac{d(m)}{m}(1+i)^{1/m} = \dfrac{i(m)}{m}$. Multiply by m to find the result.

This relationship means that the nominal compound interest and discount rates have a ratio, $i(m)/d(m) = 1+$ rate per period.

27. $S = P(1+i)^n \rightarrow 1055 = 1000(1+i)^1 \rightarrow i = 5.5\%/\text{quarter} \rightarrow i(4) = 22.00\%(4)$

$[1+i(4)/4]^4 = [1-d(12)/12]^{-12} \rightarrow 1.055^4 = [1-d(12)/12]^{-12}$

Hence $d(12) = 12[1-1.055^{-4/12}] = 21.23\%(12)$

Section 3.5 Solutions

Concept and Short Answer Exercises

1. The rates would be equal.
2. \$1.36857
3. One must be negative and one positive.
4. –2. Please note the negative.
5. Use PV as 1000 and FV as –3320 with n as 20 and compute i.
   Use this i and this PV, a new n, say 30, to predict the 2010 population.
6. Growth models are always iffy because they assume the same rate of growth over the entire model. To push a model based on 20 years worth of data another 50 years in the future is called indiscriminant extrapolation of the data. The only way the model has a chance of being correct is for the average growth over the next 50 years to nearly equal the average growth over the last 20 years.

Odd Exercise Calculations

7. $S = P(1+i)^n$

   $500 = 200(1+i)^{48}$

   $i = 1.93\%/m \rightarrow i(12) = i * 12 = 23.13\%(12)$

0		48 m
200	@ i(12) →	500

9. $S = P(1+i)^n$

   $2 = 1(1+i)^{10}$

   $i = 7.18\%/h \rightarrow i(2) = i * 2 = 14.35\%(2)$

0		10 h
1	@ i(2) →	2

11. $S = P(1+i)^n$

    $1.60 = 1(1+i)^8$

    $i = 6.05\%/q \rightarrow i(4) = i * 4 = 24.20\%(4)$

0		8 q
1	@ i(4) →	1.60

13. a. $S = P(1+i)^n$

    $3400 = 100(1+i)^{100}$

    $i = 3.59\%/y = i(1)$

1900 = 0		2000 = 100	2010 = 110
100	@ i(1) →	3400	S

    b. $S = P(1+i)^n = 100(1+3.59\%/1)^{110} = 4838$ people

15. a. $S = P(1+i)^n$

    $35,000 = 20,000(1+i)^{10}$

    $i = 5.76\%/y = i(1)$

1990 = 0		2000 = 10	2010 = 20
20,000	@ i(1) →	35,000	S

    b. $S = P(1+i)^n = 20,000(1+5.76\%/1)^{20} = \$61,250.00$

17. **a.** $S = P(1+i)^n$

$1.35 = 1.85(1+i)^2$

$i = -14.58\%$ per year (drop) $= i(1)$

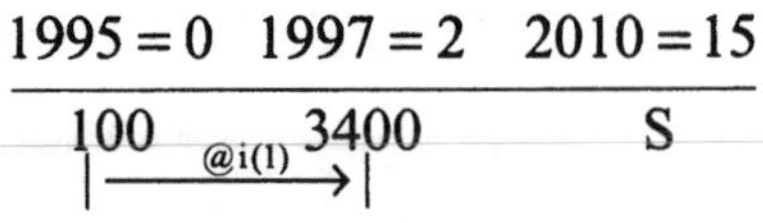

1995 = 0	1997 = 2	2010 = 15
100 —@i(1)→	3400	S

b. $S = P(1+i)^n = 1.85(1+(-14.58\%)/1)^{15} = 17$ cents a gallon.

Great price but unrealistic pattern to extrapolate.

19. **a.** $S = P(1+i)^n$

$24 = 12(1+i)^{14}$

$i = 5.07566\%/\text{y}$ gain $= i(1)$

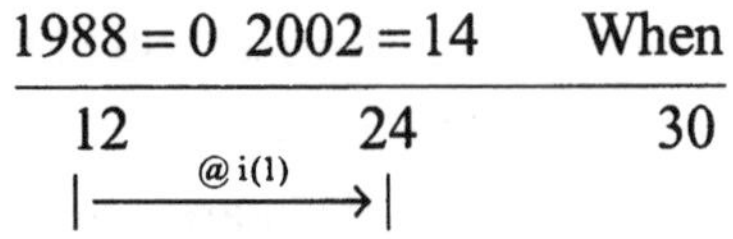

1988 = 0	2002 = 14	When
12 —@i(1)→	24	30

b. $S = P(1+i)^n$

$30 = 12(1+5.07566\%/1)^n \rightarrow n = 18.5\text{y}$

Hence we should reach 30 million in sales halfway through 2006.

21. Let d = compound discount rate per period.

Hence $P = S(1-d)^n \rightarrow d = 1-(P/S)^{1/n}$

To double in 7 years $\rightarrow d = 1-(.5)^{1/7} = 9.43\%(1)$

23. $500(1-d)^{-8} + 400(1-d)^{-4} + 800 = 2000$

$d = 4.4557\%/\text{half-year} \rightarrow d(2) = 8.91\%(2)$

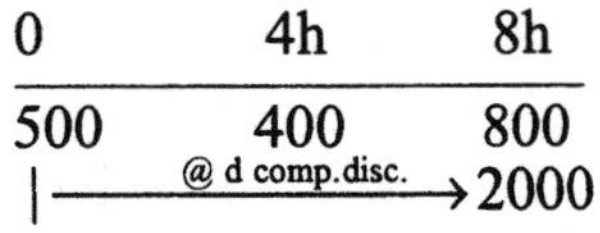

0	4h	8h
500	400	800
—@ d comp.disc.→		2000

Section 3.6 Solutions

Concept and Short Answer Exercises

1. 19 h

2. 20 h

3. **a.** Using CI move the 1000 forward for 19 full half-years to get $2918.96.

b. Rest of the problem is computing time in a SI problem.

$I = 3000 - 2918.96 = 81.04$

$t = I/Pr = 81.04/(2918.96 \times 0.116) = 0.2393 * 360$ day year $= 86.2$ days

4. 0.48 of a 180-day half-year = 86.4 days.

5. 40 q

6. 40 q

7. **a.** Find $S = 300(1+11.2\%/4)^{39} = 880.75$, the FV of 300 for the full periods.

b. Find $I = 900 - 880.75 = 19.25$.

c. $t = I/Pr = 19.25/(880.75 * 0.112) = 0.1951$ of a 360-day year = 70.25 days

8. 39.78 →0 .78 of a 90-day quarter = 70.2 days

9. 8.2 months

10. $1.75 = 3500/2000

Odd Exercise Calculations

11. $S = P(1+i)^n$

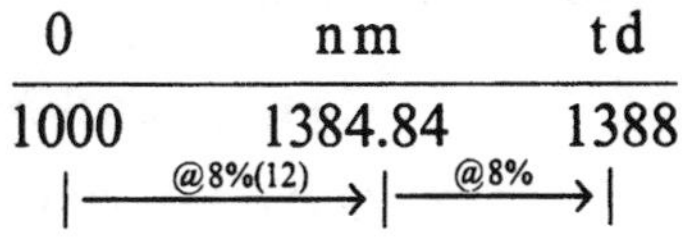

$1388 = 1000(1+8\%/12)^n \rightarrow n = 49.34\,m$

0 nm td
1000 1384.84 1388
|—@8%(12)→|—@8%→|

a. Rounded = 49 m **b.** Up = 50 m

c. 49 full m at ci and rest at d at si.

$S(@CI) = 1000(1+8\%/12)^{49} = 1384.84$

$I = 1388 - 1384.84 = 3.16 \rightarrow t = \frac{I}{Pi} = \frac{3.16}{1384.84 * 0.08} = 0.02852 \text{ of } 360 = 11d$

13. $S = P(1+i)^n \rightarrow 3 = 1(1+12\%/2)^n \rightarrow n = 18.85h$

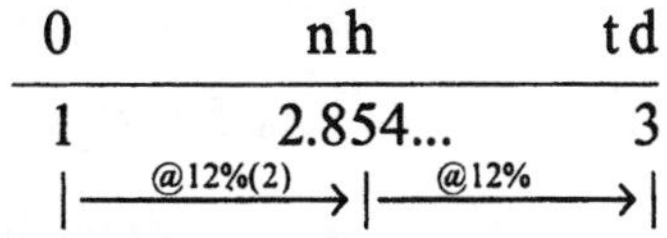

0 nh td
1 2.854... 3
|—@12%(2)→|—@12%→|

a. Rounded = 19 h **b.** Upped = 19 h

c. 18 full semiannual at ci and rest at days at si.

$S(@CI) = 1(1+12\%/12)^{18} = 2.854339$

$I = 3 - 2.854339 = .0145661 \rightarrow t = \frac{I}{Pi} = \frac{.0145661}{2.854339 * 0.12} = 0.42526 * 360 = 153$

15. $S = P(1+i)^n \rightarrow 20k = 12k(1+7\%/4)^n \rightarrow n = 29.4d$

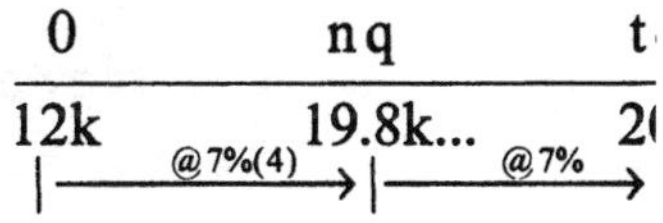

0 nq t
12k 19.8k... 2
|—@7%(4)→|—@7%→

a. Rounded = 29 q **b.** Round up = 30 q

c. 29 full q at ci and rest at d at si.

$S(@CI) = 12k(1+7\%/4)^{29} = 19{,}846.29$

$I = 20k - 19{,}846.29 = 153.71 \rightarrow t = \frac{I}{Pi} = \frac{153.71}{19{,}846.29 * 0.07} \text{ of } 360 = 40d$

17. $S = P(1+i)^n \rightarrow 250k = 100k(1+8\%/2)^n \rightarrow n = 23.36h$

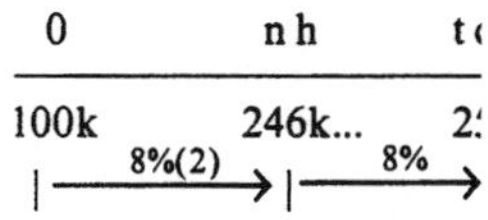

0 nh t
100k 246k... 2
|—8%(2)→|—8%→

a. Rounded = 23 h = 11 y & 6 m added to 6/1/02 = 12/1/13

b. Rounded up = 24 h = 12 y added to 6/1/02 = 6/1/14

c. 23 full q at ci and rest at d at si.

$S(@CI) = 100k(1+8\%/2)^{23} = 246{,}471.55$

$I = 250k - 246{,}471.55 = 3528.45 \rightarrow t = \frac{I}{Pr} = \frac{3528.45}{246{,}471.55 * 0.08} \text{ of } 360 = 65d$

$\therefore$ 65 days after 12/1/13 = 2/4/14

19. Let d = compound discount rate per period.

Hence $P = S(1-d)^n \rightarrow P/S = (1-d)^n \rightarrow n = \frac{\ln(P/S)}{\ln(1-d)}$

To double at $d(4) = 8\%(4) \rightarrow n = \frac{\ln(P/S)}{\ln(1-d)} = \frac{\ln(1/2)}{\ln(1-.02)} = 34.3q \rightarrow 35$ q.

Section 3.7 Solutions

Concept and Short Answer Exercises

1. Irrelevant. The focal date is irrelevant in that you will get the same answer no matter where the FD is placed.
2. Negative, positive. If two numbers are entered, most financial calculators and Excel require them to have opposite signs.
3. Beforehand. Now.
4. NPV @ 15% $= -1000 + 500(1+i)^{-1} + 600(1+i)^{-2} + 400(1+i)^{-3} = \$151.48$

   IRR $= 24.22\%(1)$

Odd Exercise Calculations

5. a. Moving 10k and 20k to time 0 y

   $X_a = 10k(1+8\%/4)^{-12} + 20k(1+8\%/4)^{-20}$

   $= 7884.93 + 13459.43 = \$21,344.36$

   b. Moving 10k and 20k to time 4 y

   $X_b = 10k(1+2\%)^4 + 20k(1+2\%)^{-4} = 10,824.32 + 18.476.91 = 29,301.23$

   c. Moving 10k and 20k to time 8 y

   $X_c = 10k(1+2\%)^{20} + 20k(1+2\%)^{12} = 14,859.47 + 25,364.84 = \$40,224.31$

0	3y	4y	5y	8y
X_a	10k	X_b	20k	X_c

7. $x = 500(1+7\%/4)^4$

   $-200(1+7\%/4)^3 - 300(1+7\%/4)^1$

   $= 539.93 - 210.68 - 305.25 = 19.99$ payoff

7/1/02	10/1/02	4/1/03	7/1/03
500	−200	−300	x

@ 7%(4) →

9. $x = 12k(1+16.9\%/12)^4 - 2k(1+16.9\%/12)^3$

   $-2k(1+16.9\%/12)^2 - 2k(1+16.9\%/12)^1$

   $= \$6519.82$

0m	1m	2m	3m	4m
12k	−2k	−2k	−2k	x

@ 16.9%(12) →

11. $x(1+7\%/2)^2 + x = 7000(1+7\%/2)^{22}$

    $1.071225x + x = 14,920.58$

    $x = \$7203.75$

10y	20y	21y
7000	x	x

@ 7%(2) →

13. $x(1+6\%/12)^{48} + x(1+6\%/12)^{12} + x =$

    $150,000(1+6\%/12)^{132}$

    $\therefore 3.3321669x = 289,741.97 \rightarrow x = \$86,953.02$

0y	7y	10y	11y
150,000	x	x	x

@6%(12) →

15. Mature: $S = 2000(1 + 8/2)^6 = 2530.64$

Discount: $P = 2530.64(1 + 6\%/4)^{-4} = 2384.33$

Original holder owned it for 2 years

$2348.33 = 2000(1+i)^2 \rightarrow i = 9.186\%(1)$

0y	8q	12q
2000	—@ 8%(2)→	2530.64
	2384.33 ←@ 6%(4)—	|

17. Mature: $S = 4000$ (noninterest)

Discount: $P = 4000(1 + 7\%/1)^{-1} = \$3738.32$

0y	1y	2y
4000	—noninterest→	4000
	3738.32 ←@ 7%(1)—	|

19. $NPV@i(2) = -10{,}000 + 8000(1 + i/2)^{-2}$

$+5000(1 + i/2)^{-4}$

$NPV@20\%(2) = 26.64$ (Used a financial calc.)

$NPV@25\%(2) = -557.54$

$IRR = 20.23\%(2)$

0	2h	4h
−10k	8k	5k
|←@ i(2)—		|

21. $NPV@i(1) = -500 + 400(1 + i/1)^{-1}$

$+300(1 + i/1)^{-2}$

$NPV@20\%(1) = 41.67$

$NPV@30\%(1) = -14.79$

$IRR = 27.17\%(1)$

0	1y	2y
−500	400	300
|←@ i(1)—		|

23. $20{,}000 = 12{,}000v^{-6/6} + 15{,}000v^{-15/6}$

Where $v = (1+i)$

$\therefore v = 1.1829 \rightarrow i = .1829 \rightarrow i(2) = 36.39\%(2)$

0	6m	15m
−20000	12000	15000
|←@ i(2)—		|

Section 3.8 Solutions

Concept and Short Answer Exercises

1. It means that money is compounded continuously.
2. $8\%(\infty)$ because the interest is accrued more often.
3. a. $S = Pe^{\delta t} = 1000e^{0.08*4} = \$1377.13$

   b. $S = P(1+i)^n = 1000(1 + 8\%/1000)^{4000} = 1377.11$

   c. $S = P(1+i)^n = 1000(1 + 8\%/10{,}000)^{40{,}000} = 1377.13$

   d. As $n \rightarrow \infty$, $P(1 + \delta/n)^n \rightarrow Pe^{\delta t}$ Hence $i(\infty) = \delta$

0		4y
1000	—8%(∞)→	1377.13

4. b. $1000 * 10 = 10{,}000$ periods

   c. $10{,}000 * 10 = 100{,}000$ periods

Odd Exercise Calculations

5. $S = Pe^{\delta t} = 200{,}000e^{0.065*182/365}$

$= \$206{,}588.38$

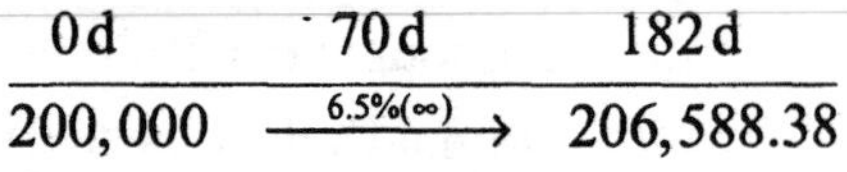

0d · 70d · 182d

200,000 —6.5%(∞)→ 206,588.38

7. $S = Pe^{\delta t} \rightarrow 206{,}588.38 = Pe^{0.07*112/365}$

$\rightarrow P = \$202{,}198.29$

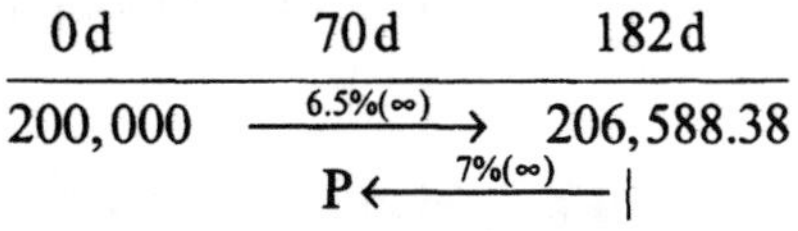

0d · 70d · 182d

200,000 —6.5%(∞)→ 206,588.38

P ←7%(∞)— |

9. $I = 202{,}198.29 - 200{,}000 = 2198.29 \rightarrow i = \frac{I}{Pt} = \frac{2198.29}{200{,}000 * 70/360} = 5.73\%$

11. $S = Pe^{\delta t} = 5000e^{0.0675*15/12}$

$= \$5{,}440.18$

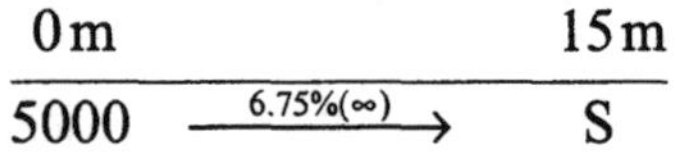

0m · 15m

5000 —6.75%(∞)→ S

13. $65{,}000e^{0.075*13} = x\,e^{0.075*7} + x\,e^{0.075*4} + x$

$172{,}325.87 = 1.69045x + 1.34985x + 1x$

$172{,}325.87 = (4.0403..)x \rightarrow x = \$42{,}651.56$

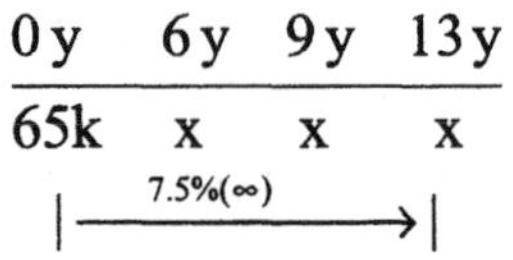

0y · 6y · 9y · 13y

65k · x · x · x

|—7.5%(∞)→|

15. **a.** $S = P(1+i)^n \rightarrow 67{,}850 = 26{,}500(1+i)^{25q}$

$\rightarrow i(4) = 4 * i = 15.33\%(4)$

b. $S = Pe^{\delta t}$

$67{,}850 = 26{,}500e^{\delta*75/12} \rightarrow \delta = 15.04\% = i(\infty)$

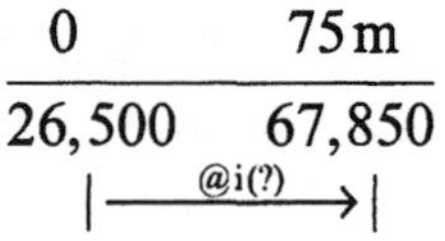

0 · 75m

26,500 · 67,850

|—@i(?)→|

17. $i(1) = 1e^{0.09*1} - 1 = 9.42\%(1)$

19. $i(1) = 1e^{0.09*1/2} - 1 = 4.6027\%/h = 9.21\%(2)$

Section 3.9 Solutions

Concept and Short Answer Exercises

1. Force of interest is the instantaneous change per unit value of the investment. Hence it measures the instantaneous relative change of one's investment and can be used as a financial speedometer to indicate how well the investment is matching the investment strategy.
2. In compound interest, the force of interest stays constant over time while for simple interest the force of interest decreases over time. Hence, CI is more reasonable.

3. **a.** $A(t) = Pe^{0.08t}$

$A'(t) = 0.08Pe^{0.08t}$

$\delta = \frac{0.08Pe^{0.08t}}{Pe^{0.08t}}$

$\delta = 0.08$

In three years

$\delta = 0.08$

In ten years

$\delta = 0.08$

b. $A(t) = P(1+0.08t)$

$A'(t) = 0.08P$

$\delta = \frac{0.08P}{P(1+0.08t)}$

$\delta = \frac{0.08}{(1+0.08t)}$

$\delta = \frac{0.08}{(1+0.08*3)} = 6.45\%$

$\delta = \frac{0.08}{(1+0.08*10)} = 4.44\%$

c. $A(t) = P/(1-0.08t)$

$A'(t) = 0.08P/(1-0.08t)$

$\delta = \frac{0.08P/(1-0.08t)^2}{P/(1-0.08t)}$

$\delta = \frac{0.08}{(1-0.08t)}$

$\delta = \frac{0.08}{(1-0.08*3)} = 10.53$'

$\delta = \frac{0.08}{(1-0.08*10)} = 40\%$

4. **a.** $\delta = \ln(1 + i) = \ln(1 + 8\%) = 0.07696 = 7.696\%$
   b. $7.696\%(\infty) \approx 8\%(1)$ because the FV of \$1 for 1 period is \$1.08 for both.
   c. The force of interest is the continuous compounded rate that will give the same amount of money as the original rate over the interval *t*.

5. **a.** $S = Pe^{\delta t} = P(1+i)^n$ for one year $\rightarrow e^{\delta} = (1+i) \rightarrow \delta = \ln(1+i)$

   $\therefore \delta = \ln(1+0.09) = 8.62\%$

   b. $S = Pe^{\delta t} = P(1-d)^{-n}$ for one year $\rightarrow e^{\delta} = (1-i)^{-1} \rightarrow \delta = -\ln(1-d)$

   $\therefore \delta = -\ln(1-0.09) = 9.43\%$

   c. $S = Pe^{\delta t} = P(1+i(m)/m)^{n*m}$ for one year $\rightarrow e^{\delta} = (1+i(m)/m)^m$

   $\therefore \delta = m*\ln(1+i(m)/m) = 2*\ln(1+0.09/2) = 8.80\%.$

   d. $S = Pe^{\delta t} = P(1-d(m)/m)^{-n*m}$ for one year $\rightarrow e^{\delta} = (1-d(m)/m)^{-m}$

   $\therefore \delta = -m*\ln(1-d(m)/m) = -12*\ln(1-0.09/12) = 9.03\%.$

Odd Exercise Calculations

7. **a.** $A(t) = P^{1/(1-kt)} \rightarrow A(0) = P^1 = 1000 \rightarrow P = 1000 \rightarrow A(t) = 1000^{1/(1-kt)}$

   b. $A(t) = 1000^{1/(1+kt)} \rightarrow A(1) = 1000^{1/(1-k1)} = 1050 \rightarrow \frac{1}{1-k}\ln(1000) = \ln(1050)$

   $\therefore k = 1 - \frac{\ln(1000)}{\ln(1050)} = 0.00701$ to 3 significant digits $\rightarrow A(t) = 1000^{1/(1-0.00701t)}$

   c. $A(t) = 1000^{1/(1-0.00701t)} \rightarrow A(3) = 1000^{1/(1-0.00701*3)} = \$1159.97 = \text{FV in 3 yrs.}$

   $A(t) = 1000^{1/(1-0.00701t)} \rightarrow A(4) = 1000^{1/(1-0.00701*4)} = \$1220.53 = \text{FV in 4 yrs.}$

   d. Year 4 average $= A(4) - A(3) = \$1220.53 - \$1159.97 = \$60.56$

e. $A'(t) = 1000^{1/(1-0.00701t)}\left(\frac{0.00701 * \ln(1000)}{(1-0.00701t)^2}\right) \rightarrow A'(4) = \$62.56$

f. $\delta_4 = \frac{A'(4)}{A(4)} = \frac{\$62.56}{\$1220.53} = 5.13\%$

g. The force of the interest will increase over time because the $\frac{A'(t)}{A(t)} = \frac{0.00701 * \ln(1000)}{(1-0.00701t)^2}$ is increasing as a function of t

h. It is not the same because of g.

i. The Excel table — note slight differences because of k.

A(0) = 1000
A(1) = 1050
k = 0.007013562

$$A(t) = P^{\frac{1}{1-kt}}$$

t	A(t)	A(t) – A(t–1)	i_t	A'(t)	δ_t
0	$ 1,000.00			$ 48.45	4.845%
1	$ 1,050.00	$ 50.00	5.000%	$ 51.59	4.913%
2	$ 1,103.27	$ 53.27	5.073%	$ 54.98	4.984%
3	$ 1,160.06	$ 56.79	5.147%	$ 58.64	5.055%
4	$ 1,220.65	$ 60.60	5.224%	$ 62.60	5.129%
5	$ 1,285.37	$ 64.71	5.302%	$ 66.88	5.203%
6	$ 1,354.53	$ 69.17	5.381%	$ 71.52	5.280%
7	$ 1,428.53	$ 73.99	5.463%	$ 76.54	5.358%
8	$ 1,507.76	$ 79.23	5.546%	$ 81.99	5.438%
9	$ 1,592.67	$ 84.91	5.631%	$ 87.91	5.520%
10	$ 1,683.75	$ 91.08	5.719%	$ 94.34	5.603%

9. $\lim_{m\to\infty} i(m) = \lim_{m\to\infty}\{m[e^{\delta/m} - 1]\} = \lim_{m\to\infty}\left\{\frac{e^{\delta/m} - 1}{1/m}\right\} = \frac{0}{0}$

Using L'Hôpital's rule $= \lim_{m\to\infty}\left\{\frac{e^{\delta/m}(-\delta/m^2)}{-1/m^2}\right\} = \delta$

11. $\lim_{m\to\infty} d(m) = \lim_{m\to\infty}\{m[1 - e^{-\delta/m}]\} = \lim_{m\to\infty}\left\{\frac{1-e^{-\delta/m}}{1/m}\right\} = \frac{0}{0}$

Using L'Hôpital's rule $= \lim_{m\to\infty}\left\{\frac{-e^{\delta/m}(--\delta/m^2)}{-1/m^2}\right\} = \delta$

13. $\delta = \frac{i}{1+it} = \frac{0.06}{1+(0.06)270/360} = 5.74\%$ for the simple interest, which is greater than

$\delta = \frac{d}{1-dt} = \frac{0.055}{1-(0.055)270/360} = 5.71\%$ for the bank discount.

15. i is the effective rate for i(m). Hence $i > i(m) > \delta$ because the effective rate has to exceed i(m) and i(m) is a decreasing function of m and $\delta = \frac{i}{1+i}$ for one year.

17. $\delta_t = 0.08/(1-2t) = a'(t)/a(t) = d(\ln(a(t))/dt \rightarrow \ln(a(t)) = \int 0.08/(1-2t)\,dt + c$

$\ln(a(t) = \frac{0.08\ln(1-2t)}{-2} + c = \ln(1-2t)^{-0.04} + c$

Hence $a(t) = k(1-2t)^{-0.04}$ where k is evaluated from an inital condition, a(0).

19. $\delta_t = \ln(1+i)$ for compound interest independent of t.

$i = (1+8\%/2)^2 - 1 \rightarrow \delta = \ln((1+8\%/2)^2) = 7.84414(\infty)$

$S = Pe^{\delta t} = 2500e^{0.0784414*4} = \$3421.42$

21. $\delta_t = \frac{i}{1+it} = \frac{d}{1-dt}$ at $t = 3 \rightarrow \frac{i}{1+i3} = \frac{d}{1-d3}$

$i - 3id = d + 3id \rightarrow i = d + 6id \rightarrow d = i/(1+6i)$

Hence d is equivalent to i after 6 years.

Hence S_1=100(1+3i) for the simple interest.

And $S_2 = \frac{100}{1\text{-}3d} = \frac{100}{1\text{-}3i/(1+6i)} = \frac{100(1+6i)}{1+3i}$

But $\frac{100(1+6i)}{1+3i} < 100(1+3i)$, because if you cross multiply you get

$(1+6i) < (1+3i)^2 = 1 + 6i + 9i^2$.

Chapter 3—Review Test for Compound Interest Solutions

1. **a.** $CI: P = 5000\left(1+8\%/4\right)^{-3} = \$4711.61$

$SI: P = \frac{4711.61}{1+0.08 * 1/12} = \$4680.41$

5/1/03	6/1/03	3/1/04
4608.41	4711.61	5000

|← 8%si →|← 8%(4)ci →|

b. $CI: S = P\left(1+8\%/4\right)^{3} = 5306.04$

3/1/04		12/1/04
5000	8%(4)ci →	5306.04

2. **a.** $1\left(1+9.2\%/12\right)^{12} - 1 = 9.60\%$

b. $1e^{0.092*1} - 1 = 9.64\%$

3. $S = P(1+i)^n\ 500\left(1+8\%/1\right)^{13} = \$1359.81$

$CI = 1359.81 - 500 = 859.81$

8y		21y
500	8%(1) →	S

4. $3000 = 2000(1+i)^6$

$i = 6.99\%/h \rightarrow i(2) = 13.98\%(2)$

0		6h
2000	j%(2) →	3000

5. $60 = 40(1+i)^5$

$i = i(1) = 8.45\%(1)$

$S = 40\left(1+8.45\%/1\right)^{13} = \$114,788$

2000 = 0y	2005 = 5y	2013 = 13y
40,000	60,000	S
|— 8.45%(1) →|		

6. $10,000 = 6000\left(1+4.2\%/4\right)^n$

$n = 48.91q$

5/1/04	nq	td
6000	S_1	10,000
|— 4.2%(4) ci →|	|— 4.2% si →|	

a. Rounded $= 49q = 12y$ and $3m = 8/1/16$

b. Rounded up is the same as 6a.

c. Use ci for 48q (12 y) and si for the rest.

$$S_1 = 6000\left(1+\frac{4.2\%}{4}\right)^{48} = 9905.91$$

$$I = 94.09 \rightarrow t = \frac{I}{Pi} = \frac{94.09}{9905.91 * 0.042} \text{ of } 360 = 81.4d = 82d$$

$5/1/04 + 12y + 82d = 7/22/16$

7.

0m	9m	18m	24m
4/1/05	1/1/06	10/1/06	4/1/07
2000	5000	−6000	x = payoff
|— 10%(12) →|			

$$x = 2000\left(1+10\%/12\right)^{24} + 5000\left(1+10\%/12\right)^{15} - 6000\left(1+10\%/12\right)^{6}$$

$x = 2440.78 + 5662.81 - 6306.32 = \$1797.27$

8. 6 yr old is 12 yrs from being 18

8 yr old is 10 yrs from being 18.

$x(1+8\%/2)^4 + x = 200,000\left(1+8\%/2\right)^{24}$

0y	10y	12y
0h	20h	24h
200,000	x	x
|— 8%(2) →|		

$(1.169\ldots)x + 1x = (2.169\ldots)x = 512,660.83 \quad \therefore x = \$236,264.63$

9. $NPV@i\%(2) = -10,000 + 7000(1+i)^{-2} + 6000(1+i)^{-4}$

$NPV@15\%(2) = \$550.13$

$IRR = 19.09\%(2)$

0	2h	4h
−10,000	7000	6000
|← j%(2) —|		

10. $NPV@i\%(12) = -2.5 + 1.1(1+i)^{-8} + 1.9(1+i)^{-15}$
$NPV@15\%(12) = .072925325m = \$72,925.33$
$NPV@18\%(12) = -.00379990449m = -\$3799.90$
$IRR = 17.84\%(12)$

0	8m	15m
−2.5	1.1	1.9
|←	j%(2)	|

Chapter 4 Ordinary Annuities

Section 4.1 Solutions

Concept and Short Answer Exercises

1. All four are yes.
2. Both give the same answer since the PV date for an ordinary annuity is one period before the first payment date.
3. $n = 12/1/05 - 11/1/00 = 1m + 5y = 1m + 60m = 61m$
4. $n = 12/1/05 - 6/1/00 = 6m + 5y = 1h + 10h = 11h$
5. $n = 11/1/20 - 4/1/04 = 7m + 16y = 7m + 192m = 199m$
6. $n = 11/1/20 - 11/1/03 = 17y = 34h$
7. $n = 21y - 11y = 10y$
8. $n = 65y - 24.75y = 40.25y = 160q + 1q = 161q$
9. $n = 12/1/05 - 9/1/00 = 3m + 5y = 1q + 20q = 21q$
10. $n = 12/1/05 - 12/1/99 = 6y$
11. $n = 11/1/20 - 2/1/04 = 9m + 16y = 3q + 64q = 67q$
12. $n = 21y - 11.75y = 9.25y = 36q + 1q = 37q$
13. $n = 65y - 24.5y = 40.5y = 80h + 1h = 81h$
14. $S_5 = 100(1+8\%)^4 + \cdots + 100(1+10\%)^1 + 100$
$S_n = Rs_{\overline{n}|i} \rightarrow S_5 = 100s_{\overline{5}|8\%/1}$

0	1	2	..	5
	100	100	..	100
|		8%(1)		→|

15. a. There are 5 even deposits of \$100.
b. Each payment is moved to the 5th period.
c. All the FVs are added.

0	1	2	..	5
	100	100	..	100
|		8%(1)		→|

16. a. There are 12 even payments of \$100.
b. Each payment is moved to the 12th period.
c. All the FVs are added.

0	1	2	..	12
	100	100	..	100
|←		8%(1)		|

Odd Exercise Calculations

17. **a.** $S_3 = 100(1+10\%)^2 + 100(1+10\%)^1 + 100$
$= 121 + 110 + 100 = \$331.00$
b. $S_n = Rs_{\overline{n}|i} = 100s_{\overline{3}|10\%/1} = \$331.0$

0	1	2	3
	100	100	100

|— 10%(1) →|

19. $S_n = Rs_{\overline{n}|i} = 500s_{\overline{20}|8\%/2} = \$14{,}889.04$

0	1	2	..	20h
	500	500	..	500

|— 8%(2) →|

21. $S_n = Rs_{\overline{n}|i} = 25s_{\overline{52}|6.5\%/4} = \$2018.80$

0	1	2	..	52q
	25	25	..	25

|— 6.5%(4) →|

23. $S_n = Rs_{\overline{n}|i} = 100s_{\overline{14}|7\%/1} = \$2255.05$

Note that $23 - 9 = 14$ y

9	10	11	..	23y
	100	100	..	100

|— 7%(1) →|

25. $S_n = Rs_{\overline{n}|i} = 2000s_{\overline{36}|12\%/1} = \$968{,}926.23$

29	30	31	..	65
	2k	2k	..	2k

|— 12%(1) →|

27.

0	1	..	20	21	..	40	41	..	60
	2000	..	2000	2500	..	2500	2000+R	..	2000+R

|— 7%(12) → 180,000

$$180{,}000 = 2000s_{\overline{20}|7\%/12}(1+7\%/12)^{40} + 2500s_{\overline{20}|7\%/12}(1+7\%/12)^{20} + (2000+R)s_{\overline{20}|7\%/12}$$

$$180{,}000 = 53{,}375.556 + 59{,}392.546 + 42296.2098 + R(21.1481049)$$

$$\therefore R = \frac{180{,}000 - [53{,}375.556 + 59{,}392.546 + 42296.2098]}{21.1481049} = \$1179.10$$

Section 4.2 Solutions

Concept and Short Answer Exercises

1. $0.8 \times 100{,}000 = \$80{,}000$
2. $120,000
3. $18,000
4. $50,000

Odd Exercise Calculations

5. $A_n = Ra_{\overline{n}|i} = 500a_{\overline{240}|9\%/12} = \$55{,}572.48$

0	1	2	..	240m
	500	500	..	500

$A_n \xleftarrow{9\%(12)} |$

7. $\$55{,}572.48 + \$15{,}000 = \$70{,}572.48$

Cash price = present value of payments + down payment.

9. $A_n = Ra_{\overline{n}|i} = 800a_{\overline{360}|9\%/12} = \$99{,}425.49$

$+15{,}000 \text{ down} = \$114{,}425.49$

Hence \$5574.51 short.

0	1	2	..	360m
	800	800	..	800

$A_n \xleftarrow{9\%(12)} |$

11. Scheme 1: Credit. Hence PV =

$A_n = Ra_{\overline{n}|i} = 852.49a_{\overline{12}|8\%/12} = \$9800.04$

Scheme 2: Cash. Hence PV = \$10,000

Credit is better by \$199.96.

0	1	2	..	12 m
	852.49	852.49	..	852.49

$A_n \xleftarrow{8\%(12)} |$

13. Scheme 1: Credit. Hence PV =

$A_n = Ra_{\overline{n}|i} = 20.56a_{\overline{24}|9\%/12} = \$450.04$

Scheme 2: Cash. Hence PV = \$400

Cash is better by \$50.04.

0	1	2	..	24m
	20.56	20.56	..	20.56

$A_n \xleftarrow{9\%(12)} |$

15. $A_n = Ra_{\overline{n}|i} = 660a_{\overline{180}|7.5\%/12} = \$71{,}196.46$

$+12{,}000 \text{ down} = \$83{,}196.46$

0	1	2	..	180m
	660	660	..	660

$A_n \xleftarrow{7.5\%(12)} |$

17. Scheme 2: Credit. Hence PV =

$A_n = Ra_{\overline{n}|i} = \$92a_{\overline{12}|8\%/12} = \$1057.61$

Scheme 1: Cash. Hence PV = \$1000

Cash is better by \$57.61·

0	1	2	..	12m
	92	92	..	92

$A_n \xleftarrow{8\%(12)} |$

19. **a.** $A_n = Ra_{\overline{n}|i} = 700a_{\overline{240}|6.2\%/12} = \$96{,}151.62$

b. $+30{,}000 \text{ down} = \$126{,}151.62$

c. $A_n = Ra_{\overline{n}|i} = 700a_{\overline{60}|6.2\%/12} = \$36{,}034.30$

0	1	2	..	240m
	700	700	..	700

$A_n \xleftarrow{6.2\%(12)} |$

21. **a.** $A_n = Ra_{\overline{n}|i} = 500a_{\overline{180}|7.3\%/12} = \$54{,}604.01$

b. $+50{,}000 \text{ down} = \$104{,}604.01$

c. $A_n = Ra_{\overline{n}|i} = 500a_{\overline{72}|7.3\%/12} = \$29{,}080.88$

0	1	2	..	180m
	500	500	..	500

$A_n \xleftarrow{7.3\%(12)} |$

23. **a.** $A_n = Ra_{\overline{n}|i} = 900a_{\overline{36}|2.8\%/12} = \$31,041.81$

b. $+6000$ other $= \$37,041.81$

c. $A_n = Ra_{\overline{n}|i} = 900s_{\overline{24}|8\%/12} = \$19,899.50$

(discounting 24 \$900 payments at 8%)

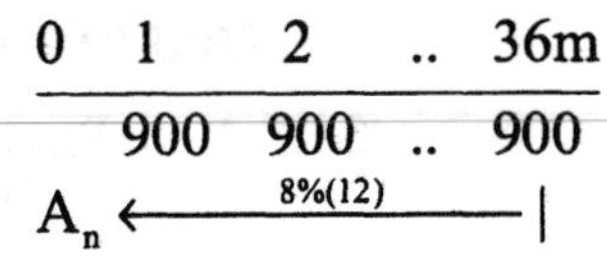

0 1 2 .. 36m
900 900 .. 900
$A_n \leftarrow$ 8%(12) |

25. Justin's Interest $= 7500(1+6\%/4)^{24} - 7500 =$ \$3221.27

Demi's Interest per quarter $= 7500 * 0.06/4 = 112.50$ for 24 quarters $=$ \$2700.00

Carlo's pmts : $7500 = Ra_{\overline{24}|6/4} \rightarrow R = \$374.43$ for 24

$= 8986.34$ less $7500 =$ \$1486.34

Total of all interest paid -- \$7407.61

27. $A_n = Ra_{\overline{n}|i} = R(1+i)^{-1} + R(1+i)^{-2} + ... + R(1+i)^{-m}$

$= R(1+i)^{-1}(1-(1+i)^{-n})/(1-(1+i)^{-1})$

$= R(1-(1+i)^{-n})/(1+i-1)$

Hence $A_n = Ra_{\overline{n}|i} = R\left[\frac{1-(1+i)^{-n}}{i}\right]$

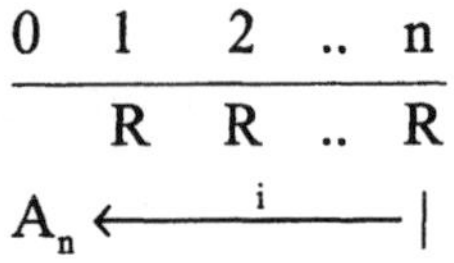

0 1 2 .. n
R R .. R
$A_n \leftarrow$ i |

Section 4.3 Solutions

Concept and Short Answer Exercises

1. \$671.43 or –\$671.43
2. \$459.73 or –\$459.73
3. **a.** The interest is charged against you in a loan and is paid to you in a savings account.
   b. Loans mean no waiting for the item, while savings account means you must wait until the money is saved.
   c. Loans, including credit cards, mean that you are indebted to someone else. Hence your future financial security could be at risk. If you fail on a loan payment, the item financed is at risk as is your credit rating. Savings mean that you are financially secure in that none of the loan risks are present. Hence all loans should be entered into advisedly.
4. I = Pit = \$20,000 * 0.15 * 1=\$3000. If the interest is not paid, the loan will get bigger and bigger (balloon).
5. I_1 = Pit = \$80,000 * 0.06 * 1/12 = \$400

   I_2 = Pit = \$36,000 * 0.09 * 1/12 = \$270

   ΣI = \$670 to cover just the interest. If they cannot meet this minimum of requirements, their mortgage will balloon.

6. **a.** To keep each payment low, bargain for a low interest rate.
   b. To keep each payment low, pay as much down as possible.
   c. To keep total payments low, shorten the term. To keep each payment low, lengthen the term.
   d. To keep total payments low, pay more often. If you pay every two weeks instead of every month, the total of all payments decreases.
   e. To keep payments low, bargain for a lower price.
   f. Taxes and insurance are often called escrow and typically are added to your monthly payments. Hence buying a home in a lower tax region will lower your payments. In any case, the taxes on a home loan for an actual dwelling are often tax deductible, which effectively lowers the payments.

Odd Exercise Calculations

7. $S_n = Rs_{\overline{n}|i}$

   $10{,}000 = Rs_{\overline{60}|4\%/12}$

   $R = 150.831 \to R = \$150.84$

0	1	2	..	60m
	R	R	..	R

   $| \xrightarrow{4\%(12)} 10k$

9. $A_n = Ra_{\overline{n}|i}$

   $30{,}000 = Ra_{\overline{20}|10\%/2}$

   $R = 2407.277 \to \$2407.28$

0	1	2	..	20h
	R	R	..	R

   $30k \xleftarrow{10\%(2)} |$

11. $A_n = Ra_{\overline{n}|i}$

   $30{,}000 = Ra_{\overline{20}|8\%/2}$

   $R = 2207.452 \to \$2207.46$

0	1	2	..	20h
	R	R	..	R

   $30k \xleftarrow{8\%(2)} |$

   Savings / payment = \$199.82 for 20 payments = \$3,996.40 total savings.

13. $A_n = Ra_{\overline{n}|i}$

   $600 = Ra_{\overline{12}|1.4\%/12}$

   $R = 50.379 \to \$50.38$

0	1	2	..	12m
	R	R	..	R

   $600 \xleftarrow{1.4\%(12)} |$

15. $S_n = Rs_{\overline{n}|i}$

   $12{,}500 = Rs_{\overline{36}|4\%/12}$

   $R = 327.383 \to R = \$327.39$

0	1	2	..	36m
	R	R	..	R

   $| \xrightarrow{4\%(12)} 12{,}500$

17. $S_n = Rs_{\overline{n}|i}$

   $S_n = 327.39s_{\overline{24}|4\%/12}$

   $S_n = \$8166.05$

0	1	2	..	24m
	327.39	327.39	..	327.39

   $| \xrightarrow{4\%(12)} S_n$

19.

0	1 ..	12	13 ..	24	25	..	36
	R ..	R	2R ..	2R	3R ..		3R

10,000 ← ——————————————— X

$$10{,}000 = Ra_{\overline{12}|6\%/12} + 2Ra_{\overline{12}|6\%/12}(1+6\%/12)^{-12} + 3Ra_{\overline{12}|6\%/12}(1+6\%/12)^{-24}$$

$$\therefore R = \frac{10{,}000}{a_{\overline{12}|6\%/12}[1+2(1+6\%/12)^{-12}+3(1+6\%/12)^{-24}]} = \$1803.31$$

21. $a_{\overline{n}|i} = \dfrac{1-(1+i)^{-n}}{i}$ and $s_{\overline{n}|i} = \dfrac{(1+i)^{n}-1}{i}$

$$\therefore \frac{1}{a_{\overline{n}|i}} - \frac{1}{s_{\overline{n}|i}} = \frac{i}{1-(1+i)^{-n}} - \frac{i}{(1+i)^{n}-1} = \frac{i}{1-(1+i)^{-n}} \times \frac{(1+i)^{n}}{(1+i)^{n}} - \frac{i}{(1+i)^{n}-1}$$

$$= \frac{i(1+i)^{n}-i}{(1+i)^{n}-1} = i\frac{(1+i)^{n}-1}{(1+i)^{n}-1} = i$$

Section 4.4 Solutions

Concept and Short Answer Questions

1. The final payment is always needed for a loan because you are paying interest. However, in a savings situation you are getting paid interest. Hence the interest on the previous balance may be enough to carry you over the top without a final deposit. But then again, the interest on the previous balance may not be enough and a final deposit may be needed.

2. In a savings account you are accruing interest. Hence, theoretically any positive periodic payment will accumulate to any desired balance given enough time. How long would it take yearly deposits of $1 to accumulate to $1,000,000? Answer: practically an infinite amount of time.

3. With PV = $1000, Pmt = –$5, I = 7%/1, FV = 0 → an error in calculating n. Why? Because the interest for one period = I = Prt = $1000.07 × 1 = $70 is the minimum payment.

4. With PV = $1000, Pmt = positive $5, I = 7%/1, FV = 0 → n is negative which is mathematically correct but practical foolishness. n is never negative in Excel as well as most financial calculators.

Odd Exercise Calculations

5. $S_n = Rs_{\overline{n}|i}$

$5000 = 100s_{\overline{n}|6\%/4}$

$n = 37.586\text{ quarters}$

0	1	2	..	nq's	n+1
	100	100	..	100	x

|—— 6%(4) ——→ 5000

a. Rounded $\rightarrow n = 38q$ **b.** Round up $\rightarrow n = 38q$

c. 37 full $100 deposits and a 39th partial of x

$$x = 5000 - 100s_{\overline{37}|6\%/4}\left(1+6\%/4\right)^1 = 5000 - 4898.5108\left(1+6\%/4\right)^1$$

$x = 5000 - 4971.99 = \$28.01$ final deposit

7. $A_n = Ra_{\overline{n}|i}$

$5020.40 = 200a_{\overline{n}|12.3\%/12}$

$n = 29.16\text{ m}$

0	1	2	..	nm's	n+1
	200	200	..	200	x

5020.40 ←—— 12.3%(12) ——|

a. Rounded $\rightarrow n = 29\text{ m}$ **b.** Round up $\rightarrow n = 30\text{ m}$

c. 29 full and a 30th partial of x

$$x = \left\{5020.40\left(1+12.3\%/12\right)^{29} - 200s_{\overline{29}|12.3\%/12}\right\}\left(1+12.3\%/12\right)$$

$$x = 33.534\left(1+12.3\%/12\right) = \$33.88$$

9. $S_n = Rs_{\overline{n}|i}$

$10{,}000 = 25s_{\overline{n}|5.1\%/12}$

$n = 234.2\text{ m}$

0	1	2	..	nm's	n+1
	25	25	..	25	x

|—— 5.1%(12) ——→ 10,000

a. Rounded $\rightarrow n = 234\text{ m}$ **b.** Round up $\rightarrow n = 235\text{ m}$

c. 234 full $25 deposits and a 235th partial of x

$$x = 10{,}000 - 25s_{\overline{234}|5.1\%/12}\left(1+5.1\%/12\right)^1 = 10{,}000 - 9986.361\left(1+5.1\%/12\right)^1$$

$x = 10{,}000 - 10{,}028.80 = -\$28.80$ too much. Hence, no final deposit.

11. $S_n = Rs_{\overline{n}|i} =$

$10{,}000 = Rs_{\overline{96}|5.1\%/12}$

$R = 84.575 \rightarrow \$84.58$

0	1	2	..	96m
	R	R	..	R

|—— 5.1%(12) ——→ 10,000

Hence we would advise $100/month just to make sure.

13. $A_n = Ra_{\overline{n}|i}$

0	1	2	..	nm's	n+1
	2500	2500	..	2500	x

$150{,}000 \leftarrow$ 12.3%(12) |

$150{,}000 = 2500a_{\overline{n}|8.5\%/12}$

$n = 78.40\text{ m}$

a. Rounded $\rightarrow n = 78\text{ m}$ **b.** Round up $\rightarrow n = 79\text{ m}$

c. 79 full and a 79th partial of x

$$x = \left\{150{,}000\left(1+{}^{8.5\%}\!/_{12}\right)^{78} - 2500s_{\overline{78}|8.5\%/12}\right\}\left(1+{}^{8.5\%}\!/_{12}\right)$$

$$x = 998.4032\left(1+{}^{8.5\%}\!/_{12}\right) = \$1005.48$$

15. $A_n = Ra_{\overline{n}|i}$

0	1	2	..	nmth	n+1
	700	700	..	700	x

$68{,}540 \leftarrow$ 7.75%(12 |

$68{,}540 = 700a_{\overline{n}|7.75\%/12}$

$n = 155.4\text{ m}$

a. Rounded $\rightarrow n = 155\text{ m}$ **b.** Round up $\rightarrow n = 156\text{ m}$

c. 155 full and a 156th partial of x

$$x = \left\{68{,}540\left(1+{}^{7.75\%}\!/_{12}\right)^{155} - 700s_{\overline{155}|7.75\%/12}\right\}\left(1+{}^{7.75\%}\!/_{12}\right)$$

$$x = 307.0058\left(1+{}^{7.75\%}\!/_{12}\right) = \$308.99$$

17. $A_n = Ra_{\overline{n}|i}$

0	1	2	..	nm's	n+1
	2500	2500	..	2500	x

$200{,}000 \leftarrow$ 12%(12) |

$200{,}000 = 2500a_{\overline{n}|12\%/12}$

$n = 161.74$ months

a. Rounded $\rightarrow n = 162\text{ m}$ **b.** Round up $\rightarrow n = 162\text{ m}$

c. 161 full and a 162nd partial of x

$$x = \left\{200{,}000\left(1+{}^{12\%}\!/_{12}\right)^{161} - 2500s_{\overline{161}|12\%/12}\right\}\left(1+{}^{12\%}\!/_{12}\right)$$

$$x = 1851.769\left(1+{}^{12\%}\!/_{12}\right) = \$1870.29$$

19. $S_n = Rs_{\overline{n}|i}$

0	1	2	..	nh's	n+1
	150	150	..	150	x

| 5%(2) $\rightarrow 3600$

$3600 = 150s_{\overline{n}|5\%/2}$

$n = 19.03$ half years

a. Rounded $\rightarrow$ n=19 h **b.** Round up $\rightarrow n = 20$ h

c. 19 full \$150 deposits and a 20th partial of x

$$x = 3600 - 150s_{\overline{19}|5\%/12}\left(1+{}^{5\%}\!/_{2}\right)^{1} = 3600 - 3591.9011\left(1+{}^{5\%}\!/_{2}\right)^{1}$$

$x = 3600 - 3681.70 = -\$81.70$ too much. Hence, no final deposit.

21. $A_n = Ra_{\overline{n}|i}$

$2{,}500{,}000 = 192000a_{\overline{n}|6.5\%/1}$

$n = 29.74\text{ y}$

0	1	2	..	ny's	n+1
	192k	192k	..	192k	x

2500k ← 6.5%(1) —— |

a. Rounded → n = 30 y **b.** Roundup → n = 30 y

c. 29 full and a 30th partial of x

$$x = \left\{2{,}500{,}000\left(1+6.5\%/1\right)^{29} - 192{,}000s_{\overline{29}|6.5\%/1}\right\}\left(1+6.5\%/1\right)$$

$$x = 135{,}156.3481\left(1+6.5\%/1\right) = \$143{,}941.51$$

23. $56{,}000 = Ra_{\overline{9}|6\%/12}(1+6\%/12) + Ra_{\overline{9}|6\%/12}(1+6\%/12)^{-11}$

$+Ra_{\overline{9}|6\%/12}(1+6\%/12)^{-23} + Ra_{\overline{9}|6\%/12}(1+6\%/12)^{-35}$

$56{,}000 = R[8.8222 + 8.31 + 7.827 + 7.373] \rightarrow R = \$1731.93/\text{month}$

25. $A_n = Ra_{\overline{n}|i}$

$x = (x/24)a_{\overline{n}|8\%/12} \rightarrow 24 = a_{\overline{n}|8\%/12}$

$n = 26.24\text{ months}$

0	1	2	..	ny's	n+1
	x/24	x/24	..	x/24	y

x ← 8%(12) —— |

26 full and a 27th partial of y

$$y = \left\{x\left(1+8\%/12\right)^{26} - (x/24)s_{\overline{26}|8\%/12}\right\}\left(1+8\%/12\right)$$

$$y = x(.0100289) \rightarrow y = x/100$$

Section 4.5 Solutions

Concept and Short Answer Exercises

1. Rate = i is being solved for. PV = 1000, FV = 0, PMT = –100, Term = n = 12
2. 12
3. Rate = i is being solved for. PV = 0, FV = 1000, PMT = –200, Term = n = 4
4. 2

Odd Exercise Calculations

5. $S_n = Rs_{\overline{n}|i}$

$3000 = 100s_{\overline{24}|i}$

$i = 1.885\%/m \rightarrow i(12) = 22.62\%(12)$

0	1	2	..	24m
	100	100	..	100

| —— i%(12) → 3000

7. $A_n = Ra_{\overline{n}|i}$

$2000 = 100a_{\overline{24}|i}$

$i = 1.51308\%/m \rightarrow i(12) = 18.16\%(12)$

0	1	2	..	24m
	100	100	..	100

2000 ← i(12) —— |

9. $A_n = Ra_{\overline{n}|i}$

$10{,}000 = 6000a_{\overline{2}|i}$

$i = 13.066\%/h \rightarrow i(2) = 26.13\%(2)$

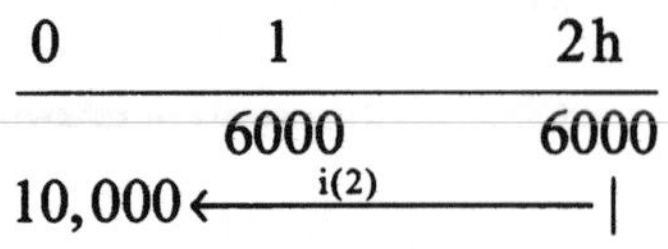

0	1	2h
	6000	6000
10,000 ←	i(2)	|

11. $S_n = Rs_{\overline{n}|i}$

$12{,}000 = 1300s_{\overline{8}|i}$

$i = 4.05\%/q \rightarrow i(4) = 16.20\%(4)$

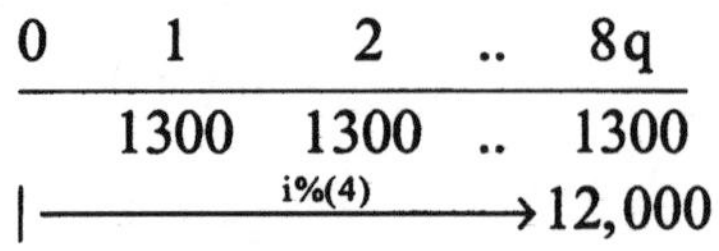

0	1	2	..	8q
	1300	1300	..	1300
|		i%(4)		→ 12,000

13. $A_n = Ra_{\overline{n}|i}$

$1055.20 = 50a_{\overline{24}|i}$

$i = 1.05537\%/\text{month}$

$i * 12 = i(12) = 12.66\%\%(12)$. Hence the 10% loan would be better.

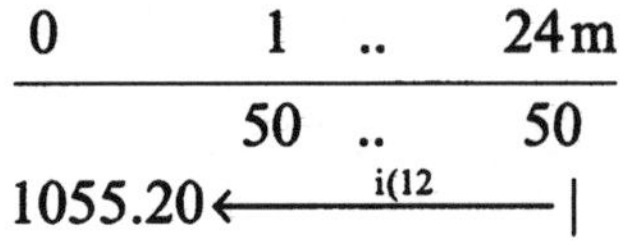

0	1	..	24m
	50	..	50
1055.20 ←	i(12		|

15. $A_n = Ra_{\overline{n}|i}$

$20{,}000 = 6000a_{\overline{4}|i}$

$i = 7.71\%/y \rightarrow i(1) = 7.71\%(1)$

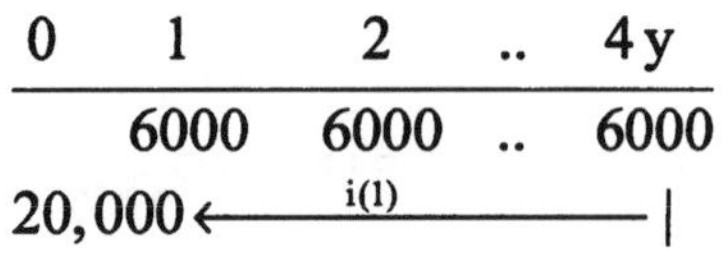

0	1	2	..	4y
	6000	6000	..	6000
20,000 ←		i(1)		|

17. $S_n = Rs_{\overline{n}|i} + P(1+i)^n$

$30{,}000 = 350s_{\overline{60}|i} + 5000(1 + 3.4\%/4)^{20}$

$i = .45420509\%/m \rightarrow i(12) = 5.45\%(12)$

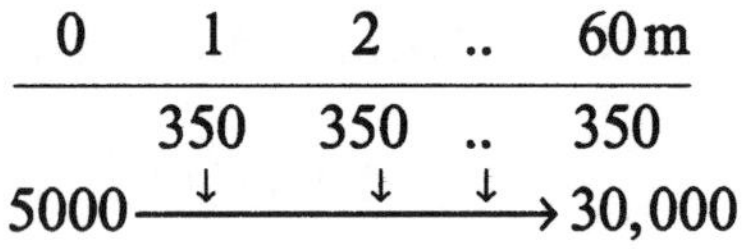

0	1	2	..	60m
	350	350	..	350
5000	↓	↓	↓	→ 30,000

19. $S_n = Rs_{\overline{n}|i}$

$15{,}000 = 800s_{\overline{18}|i}$

$i = .477799\%/m \rightarrow i(12) = 5.73\%(12)$

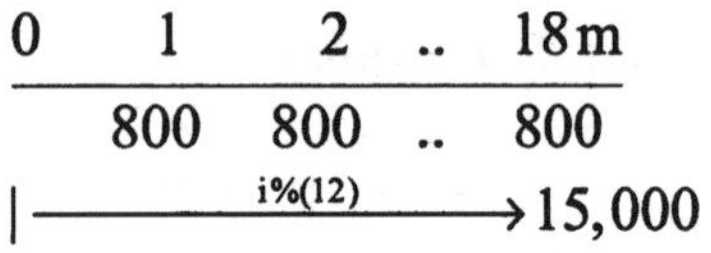

0	1	2	..	18m
	800	800	..	800
|		i%(12)		→ 15,000

21. $28{,}000 = 2000s_{\overline{5}|i}(1+i)^3 + 3000s_{\overline{3}|i}$

Using TI83 solver yields

$i(m) = 12.03\%(1)$

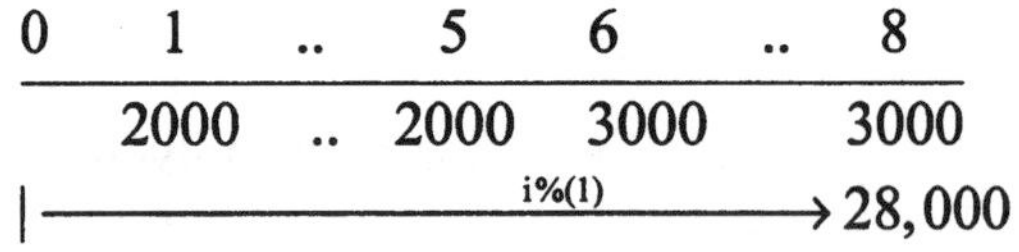

0	1	..	5	6	..	8
	2000	..	2000	3000		3000
|				i%(1)		→ 28,000

Section 4.6 Solutions

Concept and Short Answer Exercises

1. The deception is that when cash costs less than credit, the difference between the credit and the cash price is actually interest.
2. For add-on loans, the interest is charged on the original loan for the entire time, even though the loan principal decreases over time.
3. For discount loans, the interest is charged on the original loan for the entire time, though the loan principal actually decreases over time.

4. Under the Rule of 78s all of the interest is paid early and a portion is rebated if you pay off the loan early. In this example, paying off the loan with 12 of 36 months left means that 12/36th of the interest should be returned. With the Rule of 78s, (12 * 13)/(36 * 37)th (which is approximately 1/9th) of the interest will be returned.

Odd Exercise Calculations

5. $A_n = Ra_{\overline{n}|i}$

$1000 = 100a_{\overline{12}|i}$

$i = 2.9228\%/m \rightarrow i(12) = 35.07\%(12)$

Time line: 0, 1, 2, .., 12m; payments 100, 100, .., 100; 1000 ← i(12)

7. $A_n = Ra_{\overline{n}|i}$

$2800 = 150a_{\overline{24}|i}$

$i = 2.1165\%/m \rightarrow i(12) = 25.40\%(12)$

Time line: 0, 1, 2, .., 24m; payments 150, 150, .., 150; 2800 ← i(12)

9. Add-on amount $= 3000(1 + .08 * 2) = 3480$

Divided into 24 even monthly payments $= \$145/\text{month}$

$A_n = Ra_{\overline{n}|i}$

$3000 = 145a_{\overline{24}|i}$

$i = 1.223\%/m \rightarrow i(12) = 14.68\%(12)$

Time line: 0, 1, 2, .., 24m; payments 145, 145, .., 145; 3000 ← @i(12)

11. Total interest $= 24 * 145 - 3000 = \$480$

$$\text{Ratio} = \frac{1+2+..+6}{1+2+..+24} = \frac{6*7}{24*25} = 0.07 \text{ of interest}, \$480 = \$33.60$$

13. Add-on amount $= 9000(1 + 0.04 * 3) = 10,080$

Divided into 36 even monthly payments $= \$280/\text{month}$

$A_n = Ra_{\overline{n}|i}$

$9000 = 280a_{\overline{36}|i}$

$i = 0.62588\%/m \rightarrow i(12) = 7.51\%(12)$

Time line: 0, 1, 2, .., 36m; payments 280, 280, .., 280; 9000 ← @i(12)

15. Total interest $= 10,080 - 9000 = \$1080$

$$\text{Ratio} = \frac{1+2+..+12}{1+2+..+36} = \frac{12*13}{36*37} \text{ of interest}, \$1080 = \$126.49$$

17. Discount-add-on amount $= 3000/(1 - 0.08 * 2) = 3571.43$

Divided into 24 even monthly payments $= \$148.81/\text{month}$

$A_n = Ra_{\overline{n}|i}$

$3000 = 148.81a_{\overline{24}|i}$

$i = 1.444547\%/m \rightarrow i(12) = 17.33\%(12)$

Time line: 0, 1, 2, .., 24m; payments 148.81, 148.81, .., 148.81; 3000 ← @i(12)

19. Total interest = 3571.43 − 3000 = \$571.43

$$\text{Ratio} = \frac{1+2+..+6}{1+2+..+24} = \frac{6*7}{24*25} \text{ of interest}, \$571.43 = \$40$$

21. Discount-add-on amount = 9000/(1 − 0.04 * 3) = 10,227.27

Divided into 36 even monthly payments = \$284.09/month

$A_n = Ra_{\overline{n}|i}$

$9000 = 284.09a_{\overline{36}|i}$

$i = .70797\%/m \rightarrow i(12) = 8.50\%(12)$

0	1	2	..	36m
	284.09	284.09	..	284.09
9000 ←	@i(12)			|

23. Total interest = 10,227.27 − 9000 = \$1,227.27

$$\text{Ratio} = \frac{1+2+..+12}{1+2+..+36} = \frac{12*13}{36*37} \text{ of interest}, \$1227.27 = \$143.73$$

Chapter 4 Review Test for Annuity Solutions

1. $S_n = Rs_{\overline{n}|i} = 150s_{\overline{16}|7\%/1} = \$4183.21$

Note that 23 − 7 = 16y

7	8	9	..	23y
	150	150	..	150
|	7%(1)			→|

2. $A_n = Ra_{\overline{n}|i} = 2500a_{\overline{240}|6.5\%/12} = \$335,312.51$

0	1	2	..	240m
	2500	2500	..	2500
A_n ←	6.5%(12)			|

3. \$335,312.51 + \$20,000 = \$355,312.51

Cash price = present value of payments + down payment

4. Scheme 1: Credit. Hence PV =

$A_n = Ra_{\overline{n}|i} = 852.49a_{\overline{12}|8\%/12} = \$9800.04$

Scheme 1: Cash. Hence PV = \$10,000

Credit is better by \$199.96.

0	1	2	..	12m
	852.49	852.49	..	852.49
A_n ←	8%(12)			|

5. **a.** $A_n = Ra_{\overline{n}|i} = 900a_{\overline{36}|2.8\%/12} = \$31,041.81$

b. + 6000 other = \$37,041.81

c. $A_n = Ra_{\overline{n}|i} = 900a_{\overline{24}|8\%/12} = \$19,899.49$

0	1	2	..	36m
	900	900	..	900
A_n ←	2.8%(12) or 8%(12)			|

6. $A_n = Ra_{\overline{n}|i}$

$600 = Ra_{\overline{12}|1.4\%/2}$

$R = 50.379 \rightarrow \$50.38$

0	1	2	..	12m
	R	R	..	R
600 ←	1.4%(2)			|

7. $S_n = Rs_{\overline{n}|i}$

$10{,}000 = 25s_{\overline{n}|5.1\%/12}$

$n = 234.2$ months

0	1	2	..	n	n+1
	25	25	..	25	x

|—5.1%(12)→ 10,000

a. Rounded $\rightarrow n = 234$ m   **b.** Round up $\rightarrow n = 235$ m

c. 234 full \$25 deposits and a 235th partial of x

$$x = 10{,}000 - 25s_{\overline{234}|5.1\%/12}\left(1+5.1\%/12\right)^1 = 10{,}000 - 9986.361\left(1+5.1\%/12\right)^1$$

$x = 10{,}000 - 10{,}028.80 = -\$28.80$ too much. Hence no final deposit.

8. $A_n = Ra_{\overline{n}|i}$

$150{,}000 = 2500a_{\overline{n}|8.5\%/12} \rightarrow n = 78.40$ m

0	1	2	..	n	n+1
	2500	2500	..	2500	x

150,000 ←8.5%(12)—|

a. Rounded $n = 78$ m

b. Upped $n = 79$ m

c. 78 full and a 79th partial of x

$$x = \left\{150{,}000\left(1+8.5\%/12\right)^{78} - 2500s_{\overline{78}|8.5\%/12}\right\}\left(1+8.5\%/12\right)$$

$x = 998.4032\left(1+8.5\%/12\right) = \$1005.48$

9. $S_n = Rs_{\overline{n}|i}$

$12{,}000 = 1300s_{\overline{8}|i}$

$i = 4.05\%/q \rightarrow i(4) = 16.20\%(4)$

0	1	2	..	8q
	1300	1300	..	1300

|—i%(4)→ 12,000

10. Add-on amount $= 9000(1+0.04*3) = 10{,}080$

Divided into 36 even monthly payments $= \$280/\text{month}$

$A_n = Ra_{\overline{n}|i}$

$9000 = 280a_{\overline{36}|i}$

$i = 0.62588\%/m \rightarrow i(12) = 7.51\%(12)$

0	1	2	..	36m
	280	280	..	280

9000 ←@i(12)—|

11. Total interest $= 10{,}080 - 9000 = \$1080$

$$\text{Ratio} = \frac{1+2+..+12}{1+2+..+36} = \frac{12*13}{36*37} \text{ of the interest, } \$1080 = \$126.49$$

12. Discount amount $= 12{,}600/(1-.0725*30/12) = \$15{,}389.31$

Divided into 30 even monthly payments $= \$512.98/\text{month}$

$A_n = Ra_{\overline{n}|i}$

$12{,}600 = 512.98a_{\overline{30}|i}$

$i = 1.342...\%/m \rightarrow i(12) = 16.10\%(12)$

0	1	2	..	30m
	512.98	512.98	..	512.98

12,600 ←@i(12)—|

Chapter 5 Other Annuities Certain

Section 5.1 Solutions

Odd Concept and Short Answer Exercises

1. b, ordinary annuity, $A_n = R\,a_{\overline{n}|\,i}$
3. a, deferred annuity, $A_n(\text{def}) = R\,a_{\overline{n}|\,i}(1+i)^{-m}$
5. c, annuity due, $A_n(\text{due}) = R\,a_{\overline{n}|\,i}(1+i)$
7. d, ordinary annuity, $S_n = R\,s_{\overline{n}|\,i}$
9. e, annuity due, $S_n(\text{due}) = R\,s_{\overline{n}|\,i}(1+i)$
11. f, forborne annuity, $S_n(\text{for}) = R\,s_{\overline{n}|\,i}(1+i)^p$
13. f, forborne annuity, $S_n(\text{for}) = R\,s_{\overline{n}|\,i}(1+i)^p$
15. c, annuity due, $A_n(\text{due}) = R\,a_{\overline{n}|\,i}(1+i)$
17. b, ordinary annuity, $A_n = R\,a_{\overline{n}|\,i}$
19. d, ordinary annuity, $S_n = R\,s_{\overline{n}|\,i}$
21. a, deferred annuity, $A_n(\text{def}) = R\,a_{\overline{n}|\,i}(1+i)^{-m}$
23. e, annuity due, $S_n(\text{due}) = R\,s_{\overline{n}|\,i}(1+i)$

Section 5.2 Solutions

Concept and Short Answer Exercises

1. The present value "bundle" is located at the first payment or the future value "bundle" is located one period after the final payment; or wording of the questions includes phases like *payments begin immediately*, or *deposits are at the beginning of the period.*
2. Payments at the beginning of each period, or payments start immediately, or payments in advance, or annuity due.
3. 1st equation: $S_n(\text{due}) = Rs_{\overline{n}|i}(1+i)$

   2nd equation: $S_n(\text{due}) = Rs_{\overline{n+1}|i} - R$

0	1	2	..	n	n+1
	R	R	..	R	(R)
	↓	↓	..	↓	→ $S_n(\text{due})$

   Note both have their focal date at the (n+1)th period. The 1st equation sums the n payments and places the bundle at the nth peri That bundle is now moved forward one period. The 2nd equation places a "ghost" payment (R) at the (n+1)th period. Hence $Rs_{\overline{n+1}|i}$ sums up the n payments and the ghost payment and places the bundle at (n+1) and then subtract the last ghost payn

4. 1st equation: $A_n(\text{due}) = Ra_{\overline{n}|i}(1+i)$

2nd equation: $A_n(\text{due}) = Ra_{\overline{n-1}|i} + R$

0	1	2	..	n	(n+1)
	R	R	..	R	

$A_n(\text{due}) \leftarrow$ ... |

The 1st equation sums the n payments and places the bundle at the 0th period. That bundle is now moved forward one period. The 2nd equation removes the 1st payment. Hence $Ra_{\overline{n-1}|i}$ sums up the n − 1 payments (payments 2, 3, ... , n) and places the bundle at 1 and then adds the first payment back in.

5. Immediately

6. Each payment earns interest from the beginning of each period in contrast to an ordinary annuity that earns from the end of each period.

Odd Exercise Calculations

7. $S_n(\text{due}) = Rs_{\overline{n}|i}(1+i)$

$= 100s_{\overline{28}|4\%/12}(1+4\%/12)$

$= \$2939.48$

1/3/02	2/3	3/3	..	5/3	6/3/03
0m	1m	2m	..	28m	
100	100	..	100		

| ... $\rightarrow S_n(\text{due})$

9. $A_n(\text{due}) = Ra_{\overline{n}|i}(1+i)$

$= 100a_{\overline{28}|4\%/12}(1+4\%/12)$

$= 2669.063(1+4\%/12) = \$2677.96$

1/3/02	2/3	3/3	..	5/3/04
0m	1m	2m	..	28m
	100	100	..	100

$A_n(\text{due}) \leftarrow$ ... |

11. $A_n(\text{due}) = Ra_{\overline{n}|i}(1+i)$

$= 2000a_{\overline{28}|8\%/4}(1+8\%/4)$

$= \$43,413.80$ on 4/1/03

1/1/03	4/1	7/1	..	1/1/10
0q	1q	2q	..	28q
	2k	2k	..	2k

$A_n(\text{due}) \leftarrow$ ... |

13. $S_n(\text{due}) = Rs_{\overline{n}|i}(1+i)$

$= 2000s_{\overline{28}|8\%/4}(1+8\%/4)$

$= \$75,584.47$ on 4/1/10

1/1	4/1	7/1	..	1/1/10	4/1/10
0q	1q	2q	..	28q	
2k	2k	..	2k		

| ... $\rightarrow S_n(\text{due})$

15. **a.** 200k back 1 $= 200k\left(1+9\%/4\right)^{-1} = 195,599.022$

b. $A_n = Ra_{\overline{n}|i}$

$195k = Ra_{\overline{40}|9\%/4} \rightarrow R = \$7467.46$

0	1	2	..	40q
	R	R	..	R

$195k \leftarrow$ ... |

17. **a.** $200\text{k back } 1 = 200\text{k}\left(1+{}^{9\%}\!/_{4}\right)^{-1}$

$= 195{,}599.022$

0	1	2	..	nq	n+1
	10k	10k	..	10k	x
195k	↓	↓	..	↓	→|

b. $A_n = Ra_{\overline{n}|i}$

$195\text{k} = 10\text{k}a_{\overline{n}|9\%/4} \rightarrow n = 26.066 \rightarrow 26 \text{ full and a partial } 27\text{th} = x$

c. $x = \left[195{,}599.022\left(1+{}^{9\%}\!/_{4}\right)^{26} - 10{,}000 s_{\overline{26}|9\%/4}\right]\left(1+{}^{9\%}\!/_{4}\right)^{1}$

$x = 656.1019\left(1+{}^{9\%}\!/_{4}\right)^{1} = \$670.86$

19. **a.** $20\text{k back } 1 = 20\text{k}\left(1+{}^{5\%}\!/_{12}\right)^{-1}$

$= 19{,}917.01245 = 19\text{k}$

0	1	2	..	60m	61m
	R	R	..	R	
|	↓	↓	→	19k	← 20k

b. $S_n = Rs_{\overline{n}|i}$

$19\text{k} = Ra_{\overline{60}|5\%/12} \rightarrow R = \$292.87$ round up to \$293

21. **a.** $20\text{k back } 1 = 20\text{k}\left(1+{}^{5\%}\!/_{12}\right)^{-1}$

$= 19{,}917.01245 = 19\text{k}$

0	1	2	..	n	n+1
	500	500	..	500	500 x
|	↓	↓	↓	→	19k ← 20k

b. $S_n = Rs_{\overline{n}|i}$

$19\text{k} = 500 s_{\overline{n}|5\%/12} \rightarrow n = 36.93 \rightarrow 36\text{m full and a partial } 37\text{th} = x$

c. $x = 19{,}917.01 - 500 s_{\overline{36}|5\%/12}\left(1+\dfrac{5\%}{12}\right)^{1} = 19{,}917.01 - 19{,}457.40 = \$459.61$

23. **a.** $\ddot{a}_{\overline{n}|i} = \left[\dfrac{1-(1+i)^{-n}}{i}\right](1+i) = \left[1-(1+i)^{-n}\right](1+i)/i = \dfrac{1-(1+i)^{-n}}{i/(1+i)} = \dfrac{1-v^n}{d}$

b. $\ddot{a}_{\overline{n}|i} = \left[\dfrac{1-(1+i)^{-n}}{i}\right](1+i) = \left[\dfrac{(1+i)-(1+i)^{-n+1}}{i}\right] = \left[\dfrac{1-(1+i)^{-(n-1)}}{i}\right] + \dfrac{i}{i} = \ddot{a}_{\overline{n-1}|i} + 1$

c. $\ddot{a}_{\overline{n}|i} = 1 + v + v^2 + \cdots + v^{n-1} = 1 + v + v^2 + \cdots + v^{n-1} + v^n - v^n = 1 + a_{\overline{n}|i} - v^n$

25. $\dfrac{a_{\overline{2n}|i}}{a_{\overline{2}|i}} = \dfrac{1-v^{2n}}{1-v^2} = \dfrac{\left[1-v^2\right]\left[1+v^2+(v^2)^2+\cdots+(v^2)^{n-1}\right]}{1-v^2} = \ddot{a}_{\overline{n}|j}$, where $j = (1+i)^2 - 1$

27. $\ddot{s}_{\overline{5}|i} + \ddot{a}_{\overline{5}|i} = v^{-1} + v^{-2} + \cdots + v^{-5} + 1 + v^1 + v^2 + \cdots + v^4$, where $v = (1+i)^{-1}$

$= v^{-5}\left[v^{-6} + v^{-7} + \cdots + v^{-10} + v^{-5} + v^{-4} + v^{-3} + \cdots + v^{-1}\right]$

$= (1+i)^5 a_{\overline{10}|i}$

29. $x = R\ddot{a}_{\overline{n}|i} = R\left[1-(1-d)^n\right]/d$

$= 65[1-(1-9\%/12)^{12}]/(9\%/12)$

$= \$748.62$

0	1	2	..	12
	65	65	..	65

$x \xleftarrow{d(m)=9\%(12)} |$

Section 5.3 Solutions

Concept and Short Answer Exercises

1. Step 1 — Calculate the bundle of money for an ordinary annuity.
   Step 2 — Move that bundle using CI to its required location.
2. Step 1 — Move the bundle of money to an ordinary position.
   Step 2 — Calculate the payment using the ordinary annuity.
3. Step 1 — Move the bundle of money to the ordinary position.
   Step 2 — Calculate n using the ordinary annuity formula from Chapter 4.
   Step 3 — Calculate the final payment using the technique from Chapter 4.
4. $I = 24 * 100 - 2000 = \$400.$
5. $I = \$3000 - 24 * 100 = \$600$
6. **a.** 15 **d.** 28
   b. 20 **e.** 29
   c. 21 **f.** 36

Odd Exercise Calculations

7.

3/4/02	3/4/05	3/4/06	3/4/05	..	3/4/20
		2000	2000	..	2000

$A_n(\text{def}) \xleftarrow{m=3y} A_n \xleftarrow{n=15y} |$

$A_n(\text{def}) = Ra_{\overline{n}|i}(1+i)^{-m} = 2000a_{\overline{15}|9\%}(1+9\%)^{-3}$

$A_n(\text{def}) = 16{,}121.376(1+9\%)^{-3} = \$12{,}448.66$

9.

	0	1	2	..	36
0	24				
		200	200	..	200

$A_n(\text{def}) \xleftarrow{m=24m} A_n \xleftarrow{n=36m} |$

$A_n(\text{def}) = Ra_{\overline{n}|i}(1+i)^{-m} = 200a_{\overline{36}|9\%/12}(1+9\%/12)^{-24}$

$A_n(\text{def}) = 6289.36(1+9\%/12)^{-24} = \$5256.85$

11. $\text{Interest} = 36 * 200 - 5256.85 = \$1943.15$

13.

10	16	17	18	..	20
		R	R	..	R
10k $\xrightarrow{6y}$	15k⁺ ←	↓	↓ n=4		|

a. $10,000 \text{ forward } 6\text{ y} = 10,000(1+8\%)^6 = 15,868.743 = 15k^+$

b. $A_n = Ra_{\overline{n}|i} \rightarrow 15k^+ = Ra_{\overline{4}|8\%} \rightarrow R = \$4791.11$ rounded up.

15.

	0	1	2	..	n	n+1
0	6					
10	16	17	18			
		3k	3k	..	3k	x = final partial
10k $\xrightarrow{6y}$	15k⁺ ←	↓	↓	↓	↓	|

a. $10,000 \text{ forward } 6\text{ y} = 10000(1+8\%)^6 = 15,868.743 = 15k^+$

b. $15k^+ = 3ka_{\overline{n}|8\%} \rightarrow n = 7.149y \rightarrow 7 \text{ full and a partial 8th of } x$

$$x = \left[15k^+(1+8\%)^7 - 3000s_{\overline{7}|8\%}\right](1+8\%) = \$462.06$$

17.

6/1/04	7/1/04	8/1/04	..	7/1/44	..	7/1/50
	R	R	..	R	..	
| ←	↓	↓	..	1.4 mil ←		2 mil

$n = 7/1/44 - 6/1/04 = 1\text{m} + 40\text{ y} = 1\text{m} + 480\text{m} = 481\text{m}$

$p = 7/1/50 - 7/1/44 = 6\text{y} = 72\text{m}$

Step 1: $2,000,000 \text{ back } 72\text{m} = 2,000,000(1+5.5\%/12)^{-72} = \$1,438.931.94$

Step 2: $S_n = Rs_{\overline{n}|i} \Leftrightarrow 1.4 \text{ mil} = Rs_{\overline{481}|5.5\%/12} \Rightarrow R = \$822.24$

19. Total interest = bundle saved – total of the deposits

Total interest = $\$2,000,000 - 481 * 822.24 = \$1,604,502.56$

21. $$a_{\overline{n+m}|i} = \frac{1-v^{n+m}}{i} = \frac{1-v^n+v^n-v^{n+m}}{i} = \frac{1-v^n+v^n(1-v^m)}{i}$$

$$= \frac{1-v^n}{i} + v^n\frac{1-v^m}{i} = a_{\overline{n}|i} + v^n a_{\overline{m}|i}$$

23. $A_n(\text{Def}) = Ra_{\overline{n}|i}(1+i)^{-m} \rightarrow 175,000 = 200,00a_{\overline{20}|i}(1+i)^{-9}$

By TI Solver i(m) = 4.5%(1) (See Section 9.2 and App. B.5 for details on Solver.)

For \$40,000/year, i(m) = 8.74%(1)

Section 5.4 Solutions

Concept and Short Answer Exercises

1. The bundled ordinary FV gathers interest during the forborne period.
2. Start your retirement program early so that the exponential growth of compound interest will work for you.

Odd Exercise Calculations

3. $S_n(\text{for}) = Rs_{\overline{n}|i}(1+i)^p$

$S_n(\text{for}) = 100s_{\overline{240}|8\%/12}(1+8\%/12)^{60}$

$S_n(\text{for}) = 58{,}902.041..(1+8\%/12)^{60}$

$S_n(\text{for}) = \$87{,}754.95$

0 1 2 .. 240 .. 300m
100 100 .. 100
↓ ↓ ↓ ↓ → $S_n(\text{for})$

5. $800\text{k back } 30 = 800{,}000(1+6\%/12)^{-30}$

$= 688{,}823.748$

$688{,}823.748 = Rs_{\overline{180}|6\%/12}$

$R = \$2368.57$

0 1 2 .. 180 .. 210m
R R .. R
↓ ↓ ↓ → 688k⁺ ← 800k

7. $S_n(\text{for}) = Rs_{\overline{n}|i}(1+i)^p$

$S_n(\text{for}) = 100s_{\overline{480}|4\%/12}(1+4\%/12)^{120}$

$S_n(\text{for}) = \$176{,}210.66$ for Marci

$S_n(\text{for}) = 400s_{\overline{120}|4\%/12}(1+4\%/12)^{120} = \$87{,}809.92$ for Glenda

0 1 2 .. 480 .. +120
100 100 .. 100
↓ ↓ ↓ ↓ → $S_n(\text{for})$

Each has invested $48,000 but Marci has over twice as much as Glenda. The reason is that Marci started earlier and her money had time to work for her.

9. $S_n(\text{for}) = Rs_{\overline{n}|i}(1+i)^p$

$S_n(\text{for}) = 25s_{\overline{240}|4\%/12}(1+4\%/12)^{24}$

$S_n(\text{for}) = 9169.365(1+4\%/12)^{24} = \$9931.73$

0 1 2 .. 240 .. 264
25 25 .. 25
↓ ↓ ↓ ↓ → $S_n(\text{for})$

11. $S_n(\text{for}) = Rs_{\overline{n}|i}(1+i)^p$

$S_n(\text{for}) = 2000s_{\overline{41}|9\%}(1+9\%)^5$

$S_n(\text{for}) = 738{,}583.73(1+9\%)^5$

$S_n(\text{for}) = \$1{,}136{,}402.62$

24 25 26 .. 65 .. 70
2k 2k .. 2k
↓ ↓ ↓ → 182k⁺ → 400k

13. $S_n(\text{for}) = Rs_{\overline{n}|i}(1+i)^p$

$S_n(\text{for}) = 150s_{\overline{483}|8\%/12}(1+8\%/12)^{93}$

$S_n(\text{for}) = 534{,}647.18(1+8\%/12)^{93}$

$S_n(\text{for}) = \$991{,}827.82$

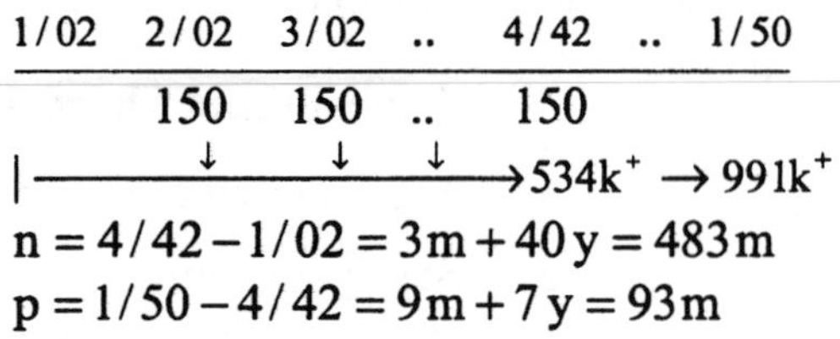

1/02	2/02	3/02	..	4/42	..	1/50
150	150	..	150			
↓	↓	↓	→534k⁺	→ 991k⁺		

$n = 4/42 - 1/02 = 3m + 40y = 483m$

$p = 1/50 - 4/42 = 9m + 7y = 93m$

15. $400\text{k back } 20 = 400{,}000(1+8\%/2)^{-20}$

$= 182{,}554.78$

$182{,}554.78 = Rs_{\overline{51}|8\%/2}$

$R = \$1{,}142.59$ rounded up

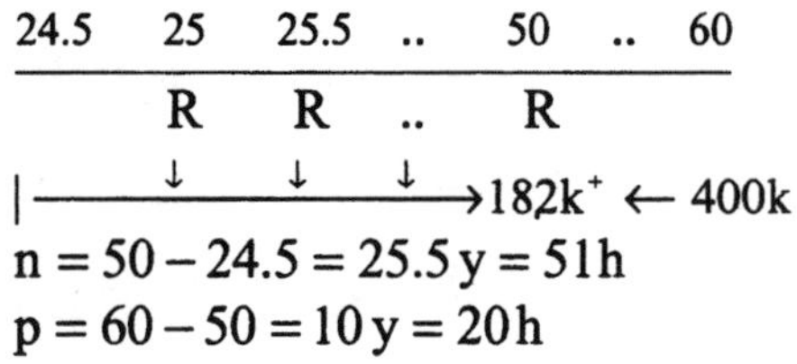

24.5	25	25.5	..	50	..	60
	R	R	..	R		
	↓	↓	↓	→182k⁺	← 400k	

$n = 50 - 24.5 = 25.5y = 51h$

$p = 60 - 50 = 10y = 20h$

17. Total $I = 991{,}828.82 - 483\times 150 = \$919{,}377.82$

19. Total $I = 400{,}000 - 51\times 1142.59 = \$341{,}727.91$

21. $$s_{\overline{n+m}|i} = \frac{v^{-n-m}-1}{i} = \frac{v^{-n-m}-v^{-n}+v^{-n}-1}{i} = \frac{v^{-n}-1+v^{-n}(v^{-m}-1)}{i}$$
$$= \frac{v^{-n}-1}{i} + v^{-n}\frac{v^{-m}-1}{i} = s_{\overline{n}|i} + v^{-n}s_{\overline{m}|i}$$

Section 5.5 Solutions

Concept and Short Answer Exercises

1. You can distribute the interest forever if you do not touch the principal.
2. The yearly grant for 20 years would be higher because you are giving away the interest and the principal.
3. 1/1/07
4. 12/1/07

Odd Exercise Calculations

5. $R = A_\infty i \rightarrow A_\infty = R/i$

$A_\infty = 400/(0.046/12)$

$A_\infty = \$104{,}347.83$

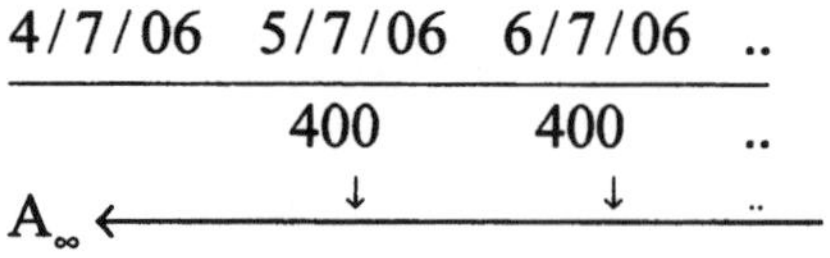

4/7/06	5/7/06	6/7/06	..
	400	400	..
A_∞ ←	↓	↓	..

7. $R = A_\infty i$

$R = 200{,}000 * 0.06/2$

$R = \$6000$

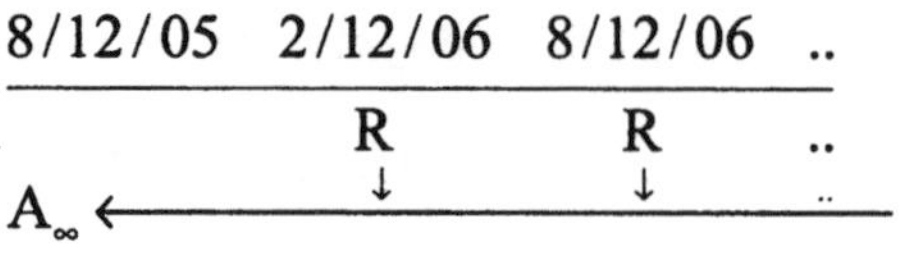

8/12/05	2/12/06	8/12/06	..
	R	R	..
A_∞ ←	↓	↓	..

9. $R = A_\infty i \rightarrow A_\infty = R/i$

$A_\infty = 2000/0.1 = \$20{,}000$

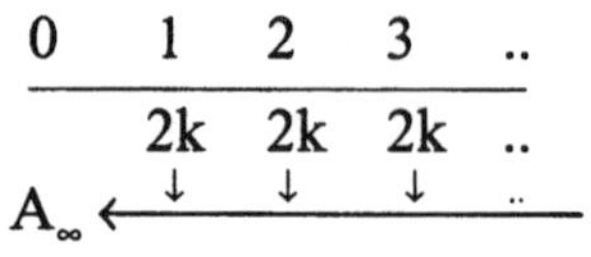

0	1	2	3	..
	2k	2k	2k	..
A_∞ ←	↓	↓	↓	..

11. As in Exercise 9, $A_\infty = \$20,000$.
Move that forward $1 = 20,000(1+10\%/1)^1 = \$22,000$

13. $R = A_\infty i \rightarrow i = R/A_\infty$
$i = 1000/100,000 = 1\%/\text{month}$
$i(12) = 12\%\,(12)$

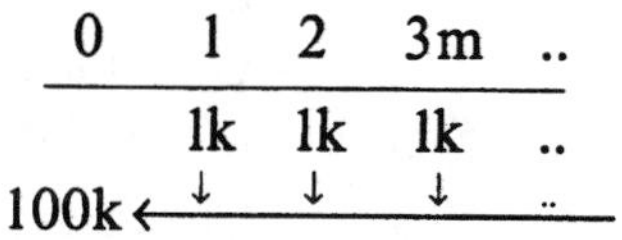

0 1 2 3m ..
1k 1k 1k ..
100k ←

15. $R = A_\infty i$ but $A_\infty = 100,000(1+i)^{11}$
$\therefore 1000 = 100,000(1+i)^{11} i$
$i \cong 0.905\%/m \rightarrow i(12) \cong 10.86\%\,(12)$

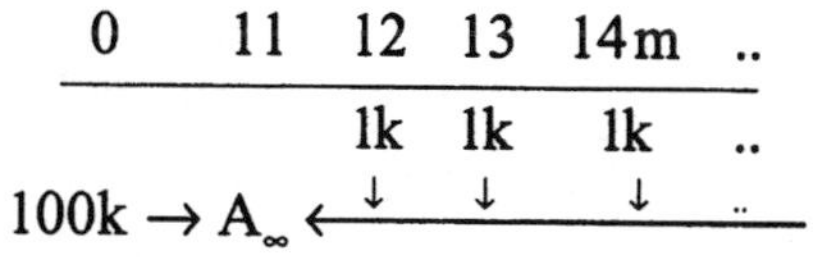

0 11 12 13 14m ..
1k 1k 1k ..
$100k \rightarrow A_\infty$ ←

17. $R = A_\infty i \rightarrow A_\infty = R/i = 10,000/0.05 = \$200,000$ policy.

19. $A_\infty = 1,000,000$ forward 3 h
$A_\infty = 1,000,000(1+7\%/2)^3$
$A_\infty = 1,108,717.875$

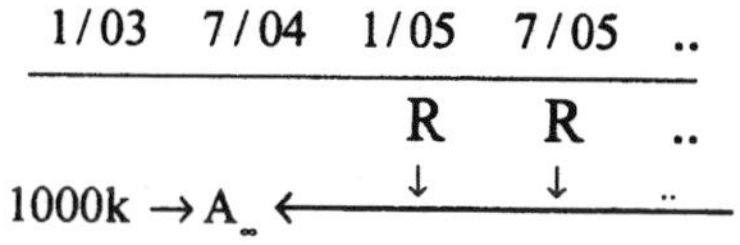

1/03 7/04 1/05 7/05 ..
R R ..
$1000k \rightarrow A_\infty$ ←

a. $1,108,717.875 = Ra_{\overline{21}|7\%/2} \rightarrow R = \$75,433.38$

b. $R = A_\infty i = 1,108,717,875 * 0.035 = \$38,805.13$

21. To be equivalent, the resultant perpetuity endowed by \$3.4 must give the same yearly stipends. Hence $3.4i = 2\times0.08+0.4\times0.06+1\times0.04$

$$\rightarrow i = \frac{2\times0.08+0.4\times0.06+1\times0.04}{3.4} = 6.59\%$$

23. $R = A_\infty i \rightarrow \text{funding} = R/i$ if perpetuity starts next period.

If delayed n periods funding $= \frac{R}{i}(1+i)^{-n}$.

$$\text{The difference} = \frac{R}{i} - \frac{R}{i}(1+i)^{-n} = R\left(\frac{1-(1+i)^{-n}}{i}\right) = Ra_{\overline{n}|i} = A_n.$$

Section 5.6 Solutions

Concept and Short Answer Exercises

1. $\{\$1.00(1+8\%/4)^{4/12} - 1\}*100 = .662271\%/m = 7.947\%(12)$
2. $\{\$1.00(1+9\%/12)^{12/2} - 1\}*100 = 4.58522\%/h = 9.1704\%(2)$
3. $\{\$1.00(1+6.8\%/1)^{1/4} - 1\}*100 = 1.6582\%/q = 6.633\%(4)$
4. $\{\$1.00(1+5.2\%/4)^{4/2} - 1\}*100 = 2.6169\%/h = 5.2338\%(2)$

5. Step1— Check the interest compounding period with the payment period. If they differ, then change the interest compounding period to match the payment period.
   Step 2—Calculate and ordinary annuity bundle.
   Step 3— Move the ordinary annuity bundle to the correct position.
6. Step 1— Check the interest compounding period with the payment period. If they differ, then change the interest compounding period to match the payment period.
   Step 2—Move the bundle to an ordinary annuity position.
   Step 3—Calculate R using the ordinary annuity formula.
7. Step 1— Check the interest compounding period with the payment period. If they differ, then change the interest compounding period to match the payment period.
   Step 2—Move the bundle to an ordinary annuity position.
   Step 3—Calculate n and final payment using the ordinary annuity formula.
8. **a.** Yes. All annuities have regular payments at regular intervals.
   b. No. If they are not equal, change the interest compounding period to match the payment period.
   c. No. Could be deferred or due.
   d. No. Could be forborne or due.

Odd Exercise Calculations

9. **a.** $9\%(2) \rightarrow ?(12)$

   $$\text{Hence } i = [1(1+9\%/2)^{2/12} - 1]\times 100\% = 0.7363..\%/m = 8.8357..\%(12)$$

   b. $A_n(\text{def}) = Ra_{\overline{n}|i}(1+i)^{-m}$

   $$A_n(\text{def}) = 200a_{\overline{36}|i}(1+i)^{-24}$$

   $$A_n(\text{def}) = \$6304.505(1+i)^{-24} = \$5286.71$$

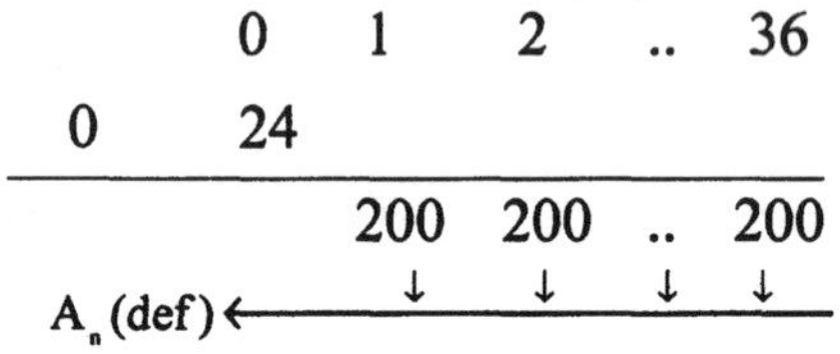

11. **a.** $9\%(12) \rightarrow ?(4)$

   $$\text{Hence } i = [1(1+9\%/12)^{12/4} - 1]\times 100\% = 2.2669..\%/q = 9.067..\%(4)$$

   b. 200k back 1 =

   $$200{,}000(1+i)^{-1} = 195{,}566.6656$$

   $$195k^{+} = 10ka_{\overline{n}|i} \rightarrow n = 26.13$$

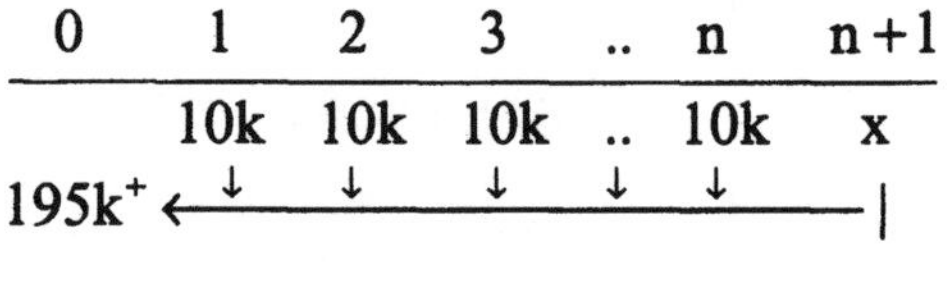

   Hence 26 full and a partial 27th of x

   $$x = (195{,}566.6656(1+i)^{26} - 10{,}000s_{\overline{26}|i})(1+i) = 1308.948(1+i) = \$1338.62$$

13. **a.** $7\%(12) \rightarrow ?(2) \rightarrow i=[1(1+\frac{7\%}{12})^{6}-1]\times 100\% = 3.551..\%/h = 7.10..\%(2)$

b. 1,000,000 forward 3 periods =

$1{,}000{,}000(1+i)^{3} = 1{,}110{,}371.824$

$1{,}110{,}371.824 = Ra_{\overline{21}|i} \rightarrow R = \$75{,}912.44$

Timeline: 0 1 2 .. 21 / 0 3; R R .. R; 1000k → 1110k ← ↓ ↓ ↓ ↓

c. $R = A_{\infty} i = 1{,}110{,}371.824 \times i(\text{as a decimal}) = \$39{,}434.19$

15. **a.** $5\%(1) \rightarrow ?(12) \rightarrow i=[1(1+5\%)^{1/12}-1]\times 100\% = 0.407..\%/m = 4.889..\%(2)$

b. 20,000 back 1 period =

$20{,}000(1+i)^{-1} = 19{,}918.848$

$19{,}918.848 = Rs_{\overline{60}|i} \rightarrow R = \$294$

Timeline: 0 1 2 .. 60 61; R R .. R; | ↓ ↓ ↓ → 19k⁺ ← 20k

17. **a.** $5\%(1) \rightarrow ?(12) \rightarrow i=[1(1.05)^{1/12}-1] = 0.407..\%/m = 4.889..\%(12)$

b. 20,000 back 1 =

$20{,}000(1+i)^{-1} = 19{,}918.848$

c. $19{,}918.848 = 500s_{\overline{n}|i} \rightarrow n = 36.99$

Timeline: 0 1 2 .. n n+1; 500 500 .. 500 x; | ↓ ↓ ↓ ↓ → 19k⁺ ← 20k

Hence 36 full deposits and (maybe) a 37th partial of x

$x = 19{,}918.848 - 500s_{\overline{36}|i}(1+i) = 19{,}918.848 - 19{,}423.46 = \$495.39$

19. $i = \$1e^{\delta/p} - 1$ is the equivalent per period rate to $\delta(\infty)$

$$S_n = Rs_{\overline{n}|i} = R\frac{(1+i)^n - 1}{i} = R\frac{(1+e^{\delta/p}-1)^n - 1}{e^{\delta/p}-1} = R\frac{e^{\delta n/p}-1}{e^{\delta/p}-1}$$

21. $$A_n = R\frac{1-e^{-\delta n/p}}{e^{\delta/p}-1} \rightarrow 50{,}000 = R\frac{1-e^{-.045*30*12/12}}{e^{.045/12}-1} \rightarrow R = \$65.49$$

Section 5.7 Solutions

Concept and Short Answer Exercises

1. \$1 in $1/p$ of a year earns $\$1e^{\delta/p}$. Hence $i = e^{\delta/p} - 1$.

2. $i(4)/4 = e^{\delta/p} - 1 = e^{0.08/4} - 1 = 0.0202013 \rightarrow i(4) = 8.08\%(4)$

3. $i(12)/12 = e^{\delta/p} - 1 = e^{0.0532/12} - 1 = 0.004443 \rightarrow i(12) = 5.33\%(12)$

4. $S_n = Rs_{\overline{n}|i} = R\frac{(1+i)^n - 1}{i} = R\frac{e^{\delta n/p}-1}{e^{\delta/p}-1}$ using the result of Exercise 1: $i = e^{\delta/p} - 1$.

5. $A_n = Ra_{\overline{n}|i} = R\frac{1-(1+i)^{-1}}{i} = R\frac{1-e^{-\delta n/p}}{e^{\delta/p}-1}$ using the result of Exercise 1: $i = e^{\delta/p} - 1$.

7. $$S_n = R\frac{e^{\delta n/p}-1}{e^{\delta/p}-1} = 90\frac{e^{0.0525*7*4/4}-1}{e^{0.0525/4}-1} = \$3025.45$$

9. $S_n = R\left(\dfrac{e^{\delta n/p}-1}{e^{\delta/p}-1}\right) \to 22{,}000 = 2000\left(\dfrac{e^{\delta 10/2}-1}{e^{\delta/2}-1}\right) \to \delta = 4.16\% = i(\infty)$

or $S_n = Rs_{\overline{n}|i} \to 22{,}000 = 2000s_{\overline{10}|i} \to i = 2.1001695\%$ per half year.

But $i = e^{\delta/p}-1 \to \delta = p\times\ln(1+i) = 2*\ln(1.021001695) = 4.16\%$

11.

1/05	4/05	7/05	..	10/08	..	1/10
0	1	2		15q		
				0	..	5q
	R	R		R		20,000
	↓	↓	↓	→|←		|

Date arithmetic: ann. $n = 10/1/08 - 1/1/05 = 9m + 3y = 15q$

for. $p = 1/1/10 - 10/1/08 = 3m + 1y = 5q$

First Way

Move 20,000 backward 5q : $P = Se^{-\delta t} = 20{,}000e^{-0.08\times5/4} = 18{,}096.75$

Solve for R : $S_n = R\dfrac{e^{\delta n/p}-1}{e^{\delta/p}-1} \to 18{,}096.75 = R\dfrac{e^{0.08\times15/4}-1}{e^{0.08/4}-1} \to R = \$1044.94$

Second Way is to calculate the quarterly $i = e^{0.08/4}-1 = 2.020134$

Move 20,000 backwards 5q : $P = S(1+i)^n = 20{,}000(1+i)^{-5} = 18{,}096.75$

Solve for R : $S_n = Rs_{\overline{n}|i} \to 18{,}096.75 = Rs_{\overline{15}|i} \to R = \$1044.94$

Review Test for Other Annuities Certain Solutions

1.

4/99	5/99	6/99		8/03		4/05	10/05	4/06		4/10
0	1	2		52m		0	1	2		10h
			..	0	..	20m			..	
	100	100	..	100			R	R	..	R
|	↓	↓	↓	→5790⁺	→	6290⁺ ←	↓	↓	↓	|

In Annuity:

Dates: $8/1/03 - 4/1/99 = 4y + 4m = 52m$

Rates: $5\%\,(4) \to ?(12)\ \therefore i = [1(1+5\%/4)^{4/12} - 1]*100\% = 0.4149..\%/m$

Dollars: $S_n = 100s_{\overline{52}|i} = \$5790.2787$

Sitting Period:

Dates: $4/1/05 - 8/1/03 = 1y + 8m = 20m$

Rates: $5\%(4) \rightarrow ?(12) \therefore i = [1(1+5\%/4)^{4/12} - 1] * 100\% = 0.4149..\%/m$

Dollars: $S = 5790.2787(1+i)^{20} = \$6290.227445$

Out Annuity:

Dates: $4/1/10 - 4/1/05 = 5y = 10h$

Rates: $5\%(4) \rightarrow ?(2) \therefore i = [1(1+5\%/4)^{4/2} - 1] * 100\% = 2.5156..\%/h$

Dollars: $6290.227445 = Ra_{\overline{10}|i} \rightarrow R = \$719.29$

Out Perpetuity:

Dollars: $R = A_\infty i = 6290.227445 * 0.02516... = \$158.24$

3.

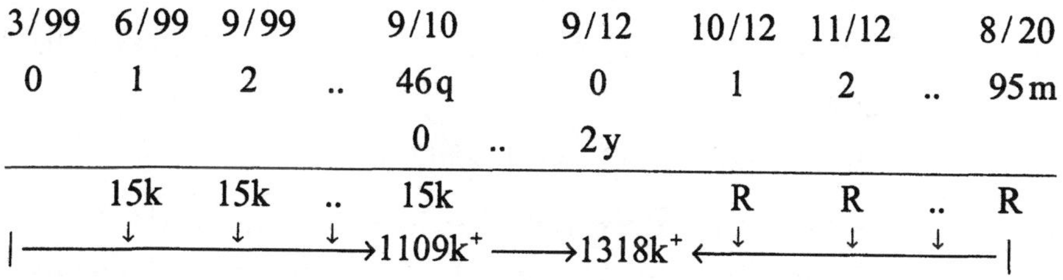

3/99	6/99	9/99		9/10		9/12	10/12	11/12		8/20
0	1	2	..	46q		0	1	2	..	95m
				0	..	2y				
	15k	15k	..	15k			R	R	..	R
	↓	↓	↓	→1109k⁺	→	1318k⁺ ←	↓	↓	↓	

In Annuity:

Dates: $9/1/10 - 3/1/99 = 11y + 6m = 46q$

Rates: $8\%(2) \rightarrow ?(4) \therefore i = [1(1+8\%/2)^{2/4} - 1] * 100\% = 1.98..\%/q$

Dollars: $S_n = 15{,}000 s_{\overline{46}|i} = \$1{,}109{,}414.313 = 1109k^+$ on the graph

Sitting Period :

Dates: $9/1/12 - 9/1/10 = 2y$

Rates: 9% (1) is just fine

Dollars: $S = 1{,}109{,}414.313(1+9\%/1)^2 = \$1{,}318{,}095.145 = 1318k^+$ (diagram)

Out Annuity:

Dates: $8/1/20 - 9/1/12 = 7y + 11m = 95m$

Rates: $9\%(1) \rightarrow ?(12) \therefore i = [1(1+9\%/1)^{1/12} - 1] * 100\% = 0.7207..\%/m$

Dollars: $1{,}318{,}095.145 = Ra_{\overline{95}|i} \rightarrow R = \$19{,}210.55$

Out Perpetuity:

Dollars: $R = A_\infty i = 1{,}318{,}095.145 * 0.007207... = \$9{,}499.94$

5.

8/66	9/66	10/66		11/99		11/42	11/43	11/44		11/3043
0	1	2	..	399		0	1	2	..	1001y
				0	..	43y				
	1k	1k	..	1k			R	R	..	R
	↓	↓	↓	→1539k⁺	→	29,665⁺ ←	↓	↓	↓	|

In Annuity:

Dates: $11/99-8/66=33y+3m=399m$

Rates: $7\%(2)\rightarrow ?(12)\ \therefore i=[1(1+7\%/2)^{2/12}-1]\times 100\%=0.5750039..\%/m$

Dollars: $S_n=1000s_{\overline{399}|i}=\$1{,}539{,}502.626=\$1539k^{+}$ on the graph

Sitting Period:

Dates: $11/1/42-11/1/42=43y=86h$

Rates: 7% (2) is just fine

Dollars: $S=1{,}539{,}502.626(1+7\%/2)^{86}=\$29{,}665{,}420.74=29{,}665k^{+}$ (diagram

Out Annuity:

Dates: $11/1/3043-11/1/2042=1001$

Rates: $10\%(4)\rightarrow ?(1)\ \therefore i=[1(1+10\%/4)^{4/1}-1]*100\%=10.381..\%/y$

Dollars: $29{,}665{,}420.74=Ra_{\overline{1001}|i}\rightarrow R=\$3{,}079{,}653.08$

Out Perpetuity:

Dollars: $R=A_{\infty}i=29{,}665{,}420.74*0.10381...=\$3{,}079{,}653.08$

Chapter 6 Debt Retirement Methods

Section 6.1 Solutions

Concept and Short Answer Exercises

1. Amount financed = 20,000 − 3000 = $17,000.
2. Upping payments keeps the last one from being a larger payment.
3. a. $x=\left\{A_n(1+i)^n-Rs_{\overline{n}|i}\right\}(1+i)$

   b. $x=A_n(1+i)^{n+1}-Rs_{\overline{n}|i}(1+i)$

   c. $x=A_n(1+i)^{n+1}-Rs_{\overline{n+1}|i}+R$

	0	1	2	..	n	n+1
		R	R	..	R	x
A_n	→	↓	↓	↓	↓	→|

4. Total interest = 24 * 1000 − 20,000 = $4000

5. $OB_n = A_n(1+i)^n - Rs_{\overline{n}|i}$

$OB_{14} = 10{,}000(1+8\%/12)^{14} - 300s_{\overline{14}|8\%/12}$

$OB_{14} = \$6587.93$

0	1	2	..	14
	300	300	..	300
10,000	↓	↓	↓	→ |

6. Establish the loan in your financial calculator.
PV=10,000, FV=0, i=8%/12, n= anything 14 or larger, PMT=–300
Put 14 in for the line and hit the amortization button. Sometimes it takes several toggles through this button to get the outstanding balance.

7. a. Yes — The authors use OB_n for this concept.

b. Yes — If you are aware that you have already paid the nth payment. The total amount you will pay on that day is $R + OB_n$.

c. Yes — This is the amount left immediately after the nth payment.

d. Yes — If you are aware that you have already paid the nth payment. The total amount you will pay on that day is $R + OB_n$

8. An amortization schedule tells the state of the loan after each payment. Included is the number (date) of the payment, the payment, how much of the payment goes to interest, how much goes against the principal, and the outstanding balance immediately after making that payment.

9. Establish the loan (see Exercise 6). Enter 14 for the line. Hit the amortization button. You will get something like the following: to principal = $254.38, to loan = $45.62, OB=$6,587.93. Please note that some calculators sum the *to interest* and the *to principal* amounts from the beginning of the loan.

10.

Principal	$ 10,000
Rate	8% per year
Term	24 months
Payments	$452.28 per month

Date	Beg. Bal.	Payment	To Int.	To Prin.	Outs. Bal.
8/1/04					$ 10,000.00
9/1/04	$ 10,000.00	$ 452.28	$ 66.67	$ 385.61	$ 9,614.39
10/1/04	$ 9,614.39	$ 452.28	$ 64.10	$ 388.18	$ 9,226.20
11/1/04	$ 9,226.20	$ 452.28	$ 61.51	$ 390.77	$ 8,835.43
12/1/04	$ 8,835.43	$ 452.28	$ 58.90	$ 393.38	$ 8,442.05
1/1/05	$ 8,442.05	$ 452.28	$ 56.28	$ 396.00	$ 8,046.05
2/1/05	$ 8,046.05	$ 452.28	$ 53.64	$ 398.64	$ 7,647.41
3/1/05	$ 7,647.41	$ 452.28	$ 50.98	$ 401.30	$ 7,246.12
4/1/05	$ 7,246.12	$ 452.28	$ 48.31	$ 403.97	$ 6,842.14
5/1/05	$ 6,842.14	$ 452.28	$ 45.61	$ 406.67	$ 6,435.48
6/1/05	$ 6,435.48	$ 452.28	$ 42.90	$ 409.38	$ 6,026.10
7/1/05	$ 6,026.10	$ 452.28	$ 40.17	$ 412.11	$ 5,614.00
8/1/05	$ 5,614.00	$ 452.28	$ 37.43	$ 414.85	$ 5,199.14
9/1/05	$ 5,199.14	$ 452.28	$ 34.66	$ 417.62	$ 4,781.52

10/1/05	$ 4,781.52	$ 452.28	$ 31.88	$ 420.40	$ 4,361.12
11/1/05	$ 4,361.12	$ 452.28	$ 29.07	$ 423.21	$ 3,937.91
12/1/05	$ 3,937.91	$ 452.28	$ 26.25	$ 426.03	$ 3,511.89
1/1/06	$ 3,511.89	$ 452.28	$ 23.41	$ 428.87	$ 3,083.02
2/1/06	$ 3,083.02	$ 452.28	$ 20.55	$ 431.73	$ 2,651.29
3/1/06	$ 2,651.29	$ 452.28	$ 17.68	$ 434.60	$ 2,216.69
4/1/06	$ 2,216.69	$ 452.28	$ 14.78	$ 437.50	$ 1,779.19
5/1/06	$ 1,779.19	$ 452.28	$ 11.86	$ 440.42	$ 1,338.77
6/1/06	$ 1,338.77	$ 452.28	$ 8.93	$ 443.35	$ 895.41
7/1/06	$ 895.41	$ 452.28	$ 5.97	$ 446.31	$ 449.10
8/1/06	$ 449.10	$ 452.10	$ 2.99	$ 449.11	$ (0.00)

Odd Exercise Calculations

11. **a.** $A_n = Ra_{\overline{n}|i}$

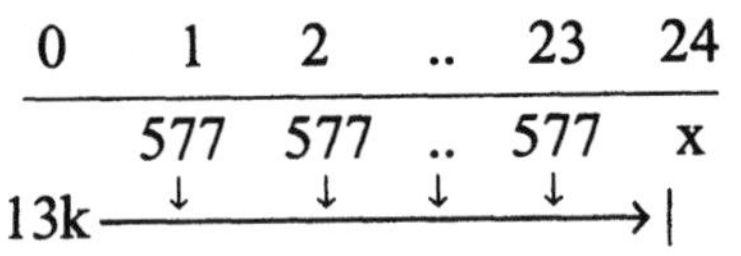

$13{,}000 = Ra_{\overline{24}|6\%/12}$

$R = \$577$

0 1 2 .. 23 24
577 577 .. 577 x
13k → |

b. $OB_{24} = \text{Excess} = 13{,}000(1+6\%/12)^{24} - 577s_{\overline{24}|6\%/12}$

$OB_{24} = \$21.16 \rightarrow x = \$577 - 21.16 = \$555.84$

c. Total interest = total payments − loan

Total interest $= (23 * 577 + 555.84) - 13{,}000 = \$826.84$

d. For line 1: $OB_0 = \$13{,}000$

To int $= OB_0 * r * t = \$13{,}000 * 0.06 * 1/12 = \$65.00$

To loan = Payment − To Int $= \$577 - \$65.00 = \$512$

$OB_1 = OB_0 -$ To loan $= \$13{,}000 - \$512 = \$12{,}488$

For line 2: $OB_1 = \$12{,}488$

To int $= OB_1 * i * t = \$12{,}488 * 0.06 * 1/12 = \$62.44$

To loan = Payment − To Int $= \$577 - 62.44 = \$514.56$

$OB_2 = OB_1 -$ To loan $= \$12{,}488 - \$514.56 = \$11{,}973.44$

e. For line 12: $OB_{11} = 13{,}000(1+6\%/12)^{11} - 577s_{\overline{11}|6\%/12} = \$7225.07$

To int $= OB_0 * i * t = \$7225.07 * 0.06 * 1/12 = \$36.13$

To loan = Payment − To Int $= \$577 - \$36.13 = \$540.87$

$OB_1 = OB_0 -$ To loan $= \$7225.07 - \$540.87 = \$6684.20$ (rounding error)

13. $65{,}000 * (1 - .15) = \$55{,}250 =$ Loan

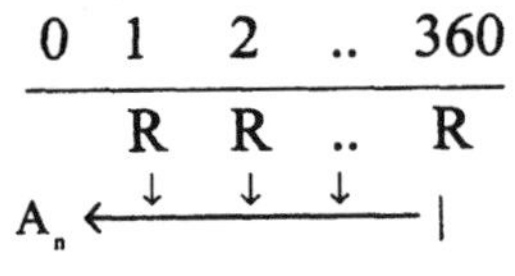

$A_n = Ra_{\overline{n}|i} \rightarrow \$55{,}250 = Ra_{\overline{360}|9\%/12} \rightarrow R = \$444.56$

If $8.5\%(12) \rightarrow R = \$424.83$

Savings/month $= \$444.56 - \$424.83 = \$19.73$ for 360 m $= \$7102.80$

0 1 2 .. 360
R R .. R
A_n ← |

15. $38,500 - 8900 = \$29,600 = \text{Amount financed}$

$A_n = Ra_{\overline{n}|i} \rightarrow \$29,600 = Ra_{\overline{48}|9.5\%/12}$

$\rightarrow R = \$743.65$

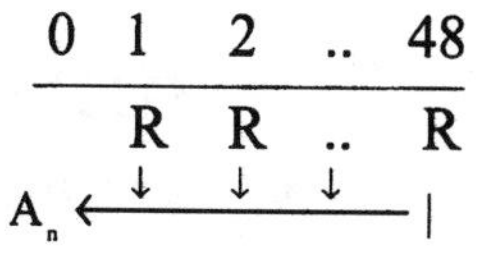

0 1 2 .. 48
R R .. R
$A_n \leftarrow$

17. $A_n = Ra_{\overline{n}|i} \rightarrow L = Ra_{\overline{6}|6\%}$

$OB_2 = 3523.36 = L(1+6\%)^2 - Rs_{\overline{2}|6\%}$

$\rightarrow 3523.36 = Ra_{\overline{6}|6\%}(1+6\%)^2 - Rs_{\overline{2}|6\%}$

$\rightarrow R = 3523.36/[a_{\overline{6}|6\%}(1+6\%)^2 - s_{\overline{2}|6\%}] = \$1016.81 \rightarrow L = \$5000$

$OB_0 = 5000 \rightarrow I_1 = 5000 * 0.06 * 1 = 300 \rightarrow P_1 = \$1016.81 - 300 = \$716.81$

$OB_5 = 959.26 \rightarrow I_6 = 959.26 * 0.06 = 57.56 \rightarrow P_6 = \$1016.81 - 57.56 = \$959.26$

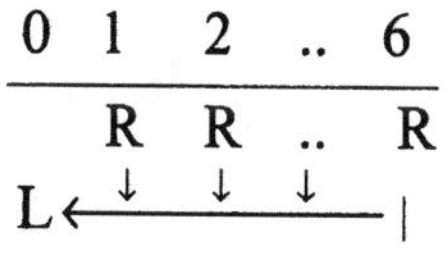

0 1 2 .. 6
R R .. R
$L \leftarrow$

19. $i = d/(1-d) = 0.07/12/(1-0.07/12) = 0.586756\%/m$

$A_n = Ra_{\overline{n}|i} \rightarrow 9400 = Ra_{\overline{36}|i}$

$\rightarrow R = \$290.43$

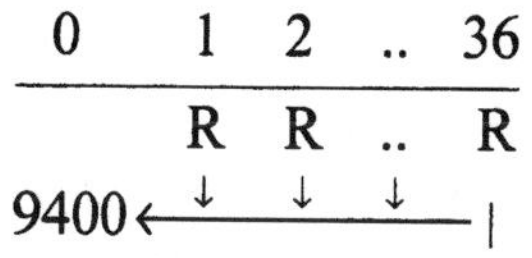

0 1 2 .. 36
R R .. R
$9400 \leftarrow$

Section 6.2 Solutions

Concept and Short Answer Exercises

1. Sometimes the interest rate on home loans drops below what the lending institution would like or needs to get, so points are added to the loan for the privilege of getting a loan at the lower rate. Some say that points are paid to buy a lower interest rate. Example: A $100,000 loan with 4 points. $100,000/(1 – 0.04) = $104,166.67. Hence the buyer and/or the seller will pay $4166.67 to the lending institution to secure the loan. Be sure to shop for your home loan. Points and rates differ widely and the best deal should be secured.
2. $\$80,000/(1-0.03) = \$82,474.23$
3. $225,000/(1-0.02) = \$229,591.84$
4. $A_n = Ra_{\overline{n}|i} \rightarrow \$20,000 = 1000a_{\overline{24}|i} \rightarrow i = 1.513\%/m \rightarrow 18.16\%(12)$
5. $A_n = Ra_{\overline{n}|i} \rightarrow \$100,000 = 733.76a_{\overline{360}|i} \rightarrow i = 0.66666\%/m \rightarrow 8.00\%(12)$
6. $A_n = Ra_{\overline{n}|i} \rightarrow \$30,000 = 625.67a_{\overline{60}|i} \rightarrow i = 0.7666856\%/m \rightarrow 9.20\%(12)$
7. **a.** See which APR is lower.
   b. See which monthly payment is lower.
8. **a.** Still see which APR is less.
   b. If you shorten the term, the payment will go up even if the rate is unchanged. Hence comparison of the monthly payment is not viable if the term changes.

Odd Exercise Calculations

9. **a.** \$200,000 less the 10% down payment = \$180,000 = Amt financed

$$\text{Amt with points financed} = \frac{\text{Amt financed}}{1-\text{the points}} = \frac{180{,}000}{1-0.032} = \$185{,}950.41$$

b. $A_n = Ra_{\overline{n}|i} \rightarrow 185{,}950.41 = Ra_{\overline{240}|9\%/12}$

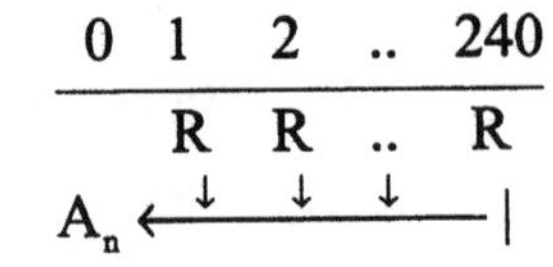

$R = 1673.044$ rounded up $= \$1673.05$

0	1	2	..	240
	R	R	..	R

$A_n \leftarrow$ (↓ ↓ ↓)

c. Actually used amt financed = \$180,000

$A_n = Ra_{\overline{n}|i} \rightarrow \$180{,}000 = \$1673.05a_{\overline{240}|i} \rightarrow i = 0.7882\%/m \rightarrow 9.46\%(12)$

11. **a.** \$100,000 less the 20% down payment = \$80,000 = Amt financed

$$\text{Amt with points financed} = \frac{\text{Amt financed}}{1-\text{the points}} = \frac{\$80{,}000}{1-0.02} = \$81{,}632.65$$

b. $A_n = Ra_{\overline{n}|i} \rightarrow \$81{,}632.65 = Ra_{\overline{180}|10.3\%/12}$

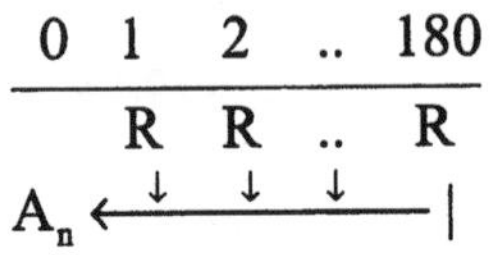

$R = 892.271$ rounded up $= \$892.28$

0	1	2	..	180
	R	R	..	R

$A_n \leftarrow$ (↓ ↓ ↓)

c. Actually used amt financed = \$80,000

$A_n = Ra_{\overline{n}|i} \rightarrow 80{,}000 = 892.28a_{\overline{180}|i} \rightarrow i = 0.8883\%/m \rightarrow 10.66\%(12)$

13. **a.** $A_n = Ra_{\overline{n}|i} \rightarrow \$100{,}000 = Ra_{\overline{240}|6\%/12}$

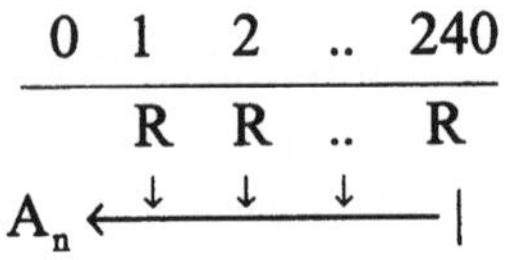

$R = \$716.44$

b. $A_n = Ra_{\overline{n}|i} \rightarrow \dfrac{\$100{,}000}{1-0.02} = Ra_{\overline{240}|5.8\%/12}$

$R = \$719.33$

0	1	2	..	240
	R	R	..	R

$A_n \leftarrow$ (↓ ↓ ↓)

6%(12) without points is cheaper than 5.8%(12) with 2 points.
The loan principal is irrelevant since what is cheaper for \$100,000 would also be cheaper for any other principal. Hence use \$1 for PV.

15. **a.** $A_n = Ra_{\overline{n}|i} \rightarrow \dfrac{\$200{,}000}{1-0.02} = Ra_{\overline{300}|8\%/12}$

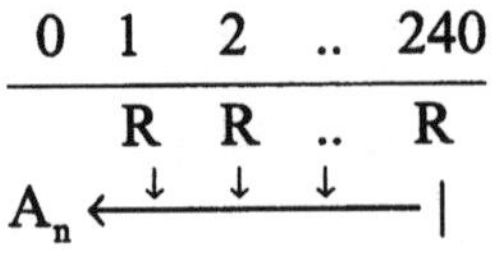

$R = \$1575.14$

b. $A_n = Ra_{\overline{n}|i} \rightarrow \dfrac{\$200{,}000}{1-0.04} = Ra_{\overline{300}|7.9\%/12}$

$R = \$1594.18$

0	1	2	..	240
	R	R	..	R

$A_n \leftarrow$ (↓ ↓ ↓)

8%(12) with 2 points is cheaper than 7.9%(12) with 4 points.
The loan principal is irrelevant since what's cheaper for \$100,000 would also be cheaper for any other principal. Hence use \$1 for PV.

17. Equivalent means that the two loans would have the same payments.

$$\text{Original loan}=\frac{40000}{1-0.0175}=Ra_{\overline{180}|8\%/12}\rightarrow R=389.07$$

$$\text{New loan}=\frac{40000}{1-r}=389.07a_{\overline{180}|7.5\%/12}\rightarrow r=4.695\text{ pts}$$

19. Payments will be in two parts. First part pays off the loan and the second part pays off the points.

Part 1: $A_n=R_1a_{\overline{n}|i}\rightarrow 60000=R_1a_{\overline{180}|6.5\%/12}\rightarrow R_1=\$522.67$

Part 2: $\frac{60000}{1-.0175}-60000=R_2a_{\overline{180}|5\%/12}\rightarrow R_2=\$8.45$

$\text{Total payments}=\$531.12$

Hence to calculate the APR: $60000=531.12a_{\overline{180}|i}\rightarrow i(12)=6.755\%(12)$

Section 6.3 Solutions

Concept and Short Answer Exercises

1. To principal $=\$280.39$, to interest $=\$219.61$, balance $=\$43{,}642.01$

2. $OB_{23}=50{,}000(1+6\%/12)^{23}-500s_{\overline{23}|6\%/12}$
   To interest $=OB_{23}*0.06/12$
   To principal $=500-$ To interest
   $OB_{24}=OB_{23}-$ To principal

3. To principal $=\$77.62$, to interest $=\$22.38$, balance $=\$2906.07$

4. $OB_{29}=5000(1+9\%/12)^{29}-100s_{\overline{29}|9\%/12}$
   To interest $=OB_{29}*0.09/12$
   To principal $=100-$ To interest
   $OB_{30}=OB_{29}-$ To principal

Odd Exercise Calculations

5. a. $A_n=Ra_{\overline{n}|i}\rightarrow 55{,}600=Ra_{\overline{180}|7.5\%/12}$

   $R=515.4188\nearrow\$515.42$

0	1	2	..	180
	R	R	..	R
$A_n\leftarrow$	↓	↓	↓	|

   b. $OB_n=PV(1+i)^n-Rs_{\overline{n}|i}$

   $OB_{72}=55{,}600(1+7.5\%/12)^{72}-515.42s_{\overline{72}|7.5\%/12}=\$40{,}390.01$

7. a. \$115,800 less the 20% down payment = \$92,640 = Amt financed

$$\text{Amt with points financed} = \frac{\text{Amt financed}}{1-\text{the points}} = \frac{\$92,640}{1-0.0125} = \$93,812.66$$

b. $A_n = Ra_{\overline{n}|i} \rightarrow \$93,812.66 = Ra_{\overline{360}|8.8\%/12}$

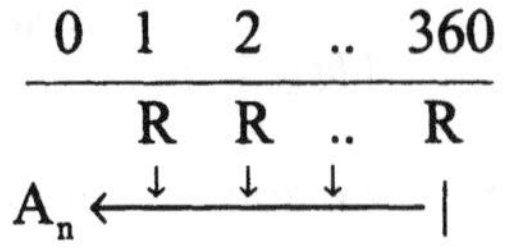

$R = 741.377 \nearrow \$741.38$

0 1 2 .. 360; R R .. R; $A_n \leftarrow$

c. $OB_n = PV(1+i)^n - Rs_{\overline{n}|i}$

$OB_{200} = \$93,812.66(1+8.8\%/12)^{200} - \$741.38s_{\overline{200}|8.8\%/12} = \$69,688.75$

9. a. $A_n = Ra_{\overline{n}|i} \rightarrow \$75,000 = Ra_{\overline{180}|6.75\%/12}$

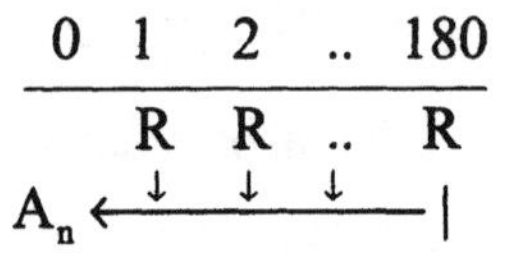

$R = \$663.69$

0 1 2 .. 180; R R .. R; $A_n \leftarrow$

b. $OB_n = PV(1+i)^n - Rs_{\overline{n}|i}$

$OB_{55} = \$75,000(1+6.75\%/12)^{55} - \$663.69s_{\overline{55}|6.75\%/12} = \$59,463.97$

To int $= \$59,463.97 * 0.0675 * 1/12 = \$334.48$

To loan $= 663.69 - 334.48 = \$329.21$

$OB_{56} = OB_{55} - \text{To loan} = \$59,463.97 - \$329.21 = \$59,134.77$

11. Prove $OB_k = A_n(1+i)^k - Rs_{\overline{k}|i} = Ra_{\overline{n-k}|i}$

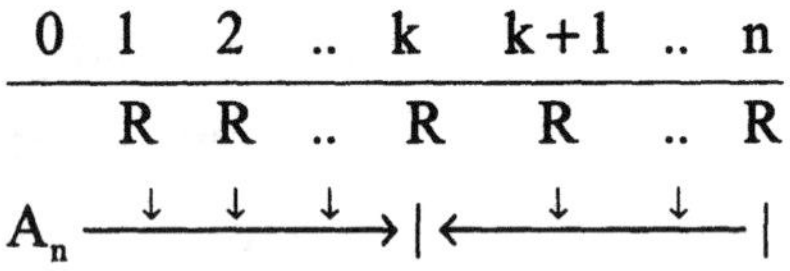

$A_n(1+i)^k - Rs_{\overline{k}|i} = Ra_{\overline{n}|i}(1+i)^k - Rs_{\overline{k}|i}$

$= R\frac{1-v^n}{i}v^{-k} - R\frac{v^{-k}-1}{i} = R\frac{1-v^{n-k}}{i} = Ra_{\overline{n-k}|i}$

0 1 2 .. k k+1 .. n; R R .. R R .. R; $A_n \rightarrow | \leftarrow$

13. $OB_{k-1} = a_{\overline{n}|i}(1+i)^{k-1} - s_{\overline{k-1}|i}$

$\rightarrow I_k = i \times OB_{k-1} = (1-v^n)v^{-k+1} - [v^{-k+1} - 1] = 1 - v^{n-k+1}$

$\rightarrow P_k = 1 - I_k = v^{n-k+1}$

Section 6.4 Solutions

Concept and Short Answer Questions

1. When you save a substantial amount by refinancing. The general rule of thumb is that the loan rate must drop by one percent or more to make it worthwhile. However, closing costs may eat the savings. Hence, a calculation of the savings is always a good step.
2. Be sure to consider other costs of refinancing, such as lawyer fees, bank fees, and points. These are called closing costs and can affect whether refinancing is worthwhile. If refinancing saves \$50,000 over the next 20 years but costs an additional \$10,000 in closing costs immediately, the decision is made difficult.

3. Variable rate loans are loans whose rates vary with the financial dynamics such as the prime rate. Usually the initial rate will be lower than the current fixed rate, but the rates can increase in high interest times. At such times the fixed rate with its slightly higher initial rate might be better. If a variable rate loan is chosen, it might be a good idea to have as part of your mortgage the provision that a change to a fixed rate will result in only small closing costs. Math deals with patterns. If a variable rate loan has no pattern, then the loan is handled payment by payment in a program like Excel, since each line of the amortization table could have a different rate and/or payment.

4. **a.** Refinance term can be any length. If the current term is kept then the refinance term = old term – refinance date.
   b. Refinance balance = OB of the old loan at the refinance date.
   c. Refinance payment = payment on the refinance balance for the refinance term at the refinance rate.

5. **a.** Savings $= \$100/\text{month for } 20 * 12 \text{ months} = \$24{,}000$
   b. Savings $= \$1000 * 240 - \$900 * 180 = \$78{,}000$

6. **a.** Savings $= \$300/\text{month for } 15 * 12 \text{ months} = \$54{,}000$
   b. Savings $= \$1500 * 15 * 12 - \$1200 * 10 * 12 = \$126{,}000$

Odd Exercise Calculations

7. Loan with points $= \$185{,}950.41$, 9%(12), $R = \$1673.05$, term = 240

   a. $OB_n = PV(1+i)^n - Rs_{\overline{n}|i} = \text{Refinanced amount}$

   $OB_{60} = \$185{,}950.41(1+9\%/12)^{60} - \$1673.05s_{\overline{60}|9\%/12} = \$164{,}950.68$

   b. Refinacing on this OB, 7%(12), term $= 240 - 60 = 180\text{m}$ left.

   $A_n = Ra_{\overline{n}|i} \rightarrow \$164{,}950.68 = Ra_{\overline{180}|7\%/12} \rightarrow R = \$1482.63 = \text{new pmt.}$

   c. Savings/month $= \$1673.05 - \$1482.63$ for 180 months $= \$34{,}275.60$

9. Loan with points $= \$81{,}632.65$, 10.3%(12), $R = \$892.28$, term $= 180\text{m}$

   a. $OB_n = PV(1+i)^n - Rs_{\overline{n}|i} = \text{Refinanced amount}$

   $OB_{84} = \$81{,}632.65(1+10.3\%/12)^{84} - \$892.28s_{\overline{84}|10.3\%/12} = \$58{,}190.41$

   with 3 points $= \$59{,}990.12$

   b. Refinacing on this value, 7.1%(12), term $= 180 - 84 = 96\text{m}$ left

   $A_n = Ra_{\overline{n}|i} \rightarrow \$59{,}990.12 = Ra_{\overline{96}|7.1\%/12} \rightarrow R = \$820.88 = \text{new pmt.}$

   c. Savings/month $= \$892.28 - \$820.88$ for 96 months $= \$6854.40$

   d. 120th line of the loan = 36th line of the new loan

   $OB_{35} = \$41{,}929.97$

   To int $= \$41{,}929.97 * 0.071/12 = \$248.09$

   To loan $= \$820.88 - \$248.09 = \$572.79$

   $OB_{36} = \$41{,}929.97 - \$572.79 = \$41{,}357.18$

11. Suppose we have 15 years of payments and that in each year we make 9 consecu payments and then miss the other 3. Hence at the beginning of each year we have the 9 payments are worth $Ra_{\overline{9}|9\%/12}$. Hence

$$50k = Ra_{\overline{9}|9\%/12} + Ra_{\overline{9}|9\%/12}(1+i)^{-12} + Ra_{\overline{9}|9\%/12}(1+i)^{-24} + \cdots + Ra_{\overline{9}|9\%/12}(1+i)^{-12\times 14}$$

$$50k = Ra_{\overline{9}|9\%/12}(1+(1+i)^{-12} + (1+i)^{-24} + \cdots + (1+i)^{-12\times 14})$$

$$50k = Ra_{\overline{9}|9\%/12}a_{\overline{15}|j}(1+j) \text{ where } j = (1+9\%/12)^{12} - 1. \rightarrow R = \$668.74$$

Section 6.5 Solutions

Concept and Short Answer Exercises

1. $S = P(1+i)^n = 200{,}000(1+3\%)^{10} = \$268{,}783.28$
2. Equity = appreciated value − what is still owed.
   Equity = \$268,783.28 − \$150,000 = \$118,783.28
3. $S = P(1+i)^n = 20{,}000(1-15\%)^3 = \$12{,}282.50$
4. Equity = appreciated value less what is still owed.
   Equity = \$12,282.50 − \$6000 = \$6282.50
5. Establish the loan in your calculator: PV = 50,000, PMT = −500, i = 6%/12, n = say 80, FV = 0. If you have an ACC button, do 25 P1/P2 button, 36 P1/P2 button. Hit the ACC button: answer is total to principal = \$3476.04 and total to interest = \$2523.96
6. Total to principal = $OB_{36} - OB_{24}$
   Total to interest = 12 * payment − Total to principal

Odd Exercise Calculations

7. **a.** $150{,}000(1-10\%) = 135{,}000$ = Loan without points

   $$\text{Loan with points} = \frac{135{,}000}{1-0.02} = \$137{,}755.10$$

   b. $A_n = Ra_{\overline{n}|i} \rightarrow \$137{,}755.10 = Ra_{\overline{240}|7.74\%/12}$

   $R = \$1130.05$

0	1	2	..	240
	R	R	..	R
A_n ←	↓	↓	↓	|

c. $A_n = Ra_{\overline{n}|i} \rightarrow 135{,}000 = \$1130.05a_{\overline{240}|i} \rightarrow i = 0.6675\%/m \leftrightarrow 8.01\%(12)$

d. 60th line of amortization table

$OB_n = PV(1+i)^n - Rs_{\overline{n}|i}$

$OB_{59} = \$137{,}755.10(1+7.74\%/12)^n - \$1130.05s_{\overline{59}|7.74\%/12} = \$120{,}480.97$

$\text{To int} = \$120{,}480.97 * 0.0774/12 = \$777.10$

$\text{To loan} = \$1130.05 - \$777.10 = \$352.95$

$OB_{60} = \$120{,}480.97 - \$352.95 = \$120{,}128.02$

e. Calculated in d.

f. 5th year interest = total of 12 pmts $-(OB_{60} - OB_{48})$

5th year interest $= 12 * 1130.50 - (124{,}217.25 - 120{,}128.02) = \$9471.37$

g.

Appreciated value at CI = $150{,}000(1+4\%/1)^5$	$= \$182{,}497.94$
Less what is still owed = OB_{60}	$= \$120{,}128.02$
Owner's equity	$= \$62{,}369.91$

h. OB_{60} = Amt refinanced = \$120,128.02

i. $A_n = Ra_{\overline{n}|i} \rightarrow \$120{,}128.02 = Ra_{\overline{180}|6.01\%/12} \rightarrow R = \$1{,}014.36$

j. Per month saved = 1130.05 − 1014.36 for 180 months = \$20,824.20

k. All savings is in interest. Hence = \$20,824.20 **l.** I would refinance.

m. For the original loan: Total of payments = 60 * 1130.05 = \$67,803.00

To principal $= OB_0 - OB_{60} = 137{,}755.10 - 120{,}128.02 = \$17{,}627.08$

To interest = difference of above = \$50,175.92

n. For the refinanced loan : (start n over at 0)

Total of payments = 180 * 1014.36 = \$182,584.80

To principal $= OB_0 - OB_{180} = 120{,}128.02 - 0 = \$120{,}128.02$

To interest = difference of above = \$62,456.78

o. 15th yr = 10th yr of new loan

Total of payments = 12 * 1014.36 = \$12,172.32

To principal $= OB_{108} - OB_{120} = 61{,}188.08 - 52{,}455.21 = \$8732.87$

To interest = difference of above = \$3439.45

p. 180th line = 120th line of new loan

$OB_{119} = 53{,}203.11$

$\text{To int} = 53{,}203.11 * 0.0601/12 = \$266.46$

To loan = Pmt − To int = \$747.90

$OB_{120} = OB_{119} - \text{To loan} = 53{,}203.11 - 747.90 = \$52{,}455.21$

Section 6.6 Solutions

Concept and Short Answer Questions

1. Interest = 1300 − 12 ∗ 100 = $100
2. Interest = 20,000 − 8 ∗ 2400 = $800
3. A sinking fund is a savings account in anticipation of future needs.
4. For each deposit date a sinking fund schedule gives the date of the deposit, the interest gained on previous balance, the deposit, and the current balance.
5. $S_n = Rs_{\overline{n}|i} = 200s_{\overline{20}|4\%/2} = \$4129.24$

0	1	2	..	20
	200	200	..	200
	↓	↓	↓	→ S_n

6. $S_n = Rs_{\overline{n}|i} = 20{,}000s_{\overline{5}|8\%} = \$117{,}332.02$

0	1	2	..	5
	20k	20k	..	20k
	↓	↓	↓	→ S_n

7. Sinking funds for roof repair, additions, car insurance, retirement funds, and property taxes.
8. Sinking funds for new buses, new buildings, major repairs, retirement funds, and band equipment.
9. Sinking funds for new end loaders, new trucks, building repair, retirement funds, and expansion.
10. Pay into an IRA for many years, let money sit, and take it out at age 72.5.

Odd Exercise Calculations

11. **a.** $12/1/04 - 12/1/00 = 4\text{y} = 8\text{h}$

$S_n = Rs_{\overline{n}|i} = 500s_{\overline{8}|6\%/2} = \$4446.17$

12/00	6/01	12/01	..	12/04
	500	500	..	500
	↓	↓	↓	→ S_n

b. Line 1: deposit at end $\rightarrow S_1 = 500$

Line 2: $I = S_1 * i * t = 500 * 0.06/2 = \$15$

$S_2 = S_1 + I + \text{Deposit} = 500 + 15 + 500 = \$1015.00$

Line 3:

$I = S_2 * r * t = 1015 * 0.06/2 = \$30.45$

$S_3 = S_2 + I + \text{Deposit} = 1015 + 30.45 + 500 = \$1545.45$ etc.

c. Line 4 without going through the first 3:

$S_3 = Rs_{\overline{n}|i} = 500s_{\overline{3}|6\%/2} = \$1545.45$

$I = S_3 * i * t = \$1545.45 * 0.06/2 = \$46.36$

$S_4 = S_3 + I + \text{Deposit} = \$1545.45 + \$46.36 + 500 = \$2019.81$

13. **a.** $S_n = Rs_{\overline{n}|i} \rightarrow 7000 = Rs_{\overline{36}|3.8\%/12} \rightarrow R = \$183.88$

0	1	2	..	36
	R	R	..	R

$\vdash \downarrow \downarrow \downarrow \rightarrow S_n$

b. $S_{36} = 183.88s_{\overline{36}|3.8\%/12} = \$7000.04 \rightarrow 0.04$ too high.

Hence final $R = \$183.88 - 0.04 = \$183.84$

c. Line 20 without going through the first 19:

$S_{19} = Rs_{\overline{n}|i} = \$183.88s_{\overline{19}|3.8\%/12} = \$3595.10$

$I = S_{19} * r * t = \$3595.10 * .038/12 = \$11.38$

$S_{20} = S_{19} + I + \text{Deposit} = \$3595.10 + \$11.38 + \$183.88 = \$3790.36$

15. **a.** $6.5\%(2) \rightarrow ?(12)\ \therefore i = [1(1+6.5\%/2)^{2/12} - 1) * 100 = 0.534474\%/m$

b. $\text{Coupon} = 2{,}000{,}000 * .00534474 = \$10{,}689.48/m$

c. $S_n = Rs_{\overline{n}|i} \rightarrow 2{,}000{,}000 = Rs_{\overline{120}|5.75\%/12} \rightarrow R = \$12{,}370.51$

d. Total cost per month $= \$12{,}370.51 + \$10{,}689.48 = \$23{,}059.99$

17. **a.** $\text{Coupon} = 650{,}000 * 0.075/4 = \$12{,}187.50/q$

b. $S_n = Rs_{\overline{n}|i} \rightarrow 650{,}000 = Rs_{\overline{8}|6.8\%/4} \rightarrow R = \$76{,}537.83/q$

c. Total cost per quarter $= \$12{,}187.50 + \$76{,}537.83 = \$88{,}725.33$

19. $FV = 1(1+i)^{2n-2} + 1(1+i)^{2n-4} + \cdots 1(1+i)^2 + 1$

$= (1+j)^{n-1} + (1+j)^{n-2} + \cdots + 1 = s_{\overline{n}|j}$, where $j = (1+i)^2 - 1$

Let $v = (1+i)^{-1}$ and $w = (1+j)^{-1} = v^2$

Hence $s_{\overline{n}|j} = \dfrac{w^{-n} - 1}{j} = \dfrac{v^{-2n} - 1}{v^{-2} - 1} = \dfrac{[v^{-2n} - 1]/i}{[v^{-2} - 1]/i} = \dfrac{s_{\overline{2n}|i}}{s_{\overline{2}|i}}$

21. Each year for n years, let the teacher make p consecutive monthly payments and miss the $12 - p$ "summer" payments. Finding the FV at the end of the "summer":

$FV = [Rs_{\overline{p}|i}(1+i)^{12\times(n-1)} + Rs_{\overline{p}|i}(1+i)^{12\times(n-2)} + \cdots + Rs_{\overline{p}|i}](1+i)^{12-p}$

$FV = Rs_{\overline{p}|i}[(1+i)^{12\times(n-1)} + (1+i)^{12\times(n-2)} + \cdots + 1](1+i)^{12-p}$

$\therefore FV = Rs_{\overline{p}|i}s_{\overline{n}|j}(1+i)^{12-p}$ with $j = (1+i)^{12} - 1$

Section 6.7 Solutions

Concept and Short Answer Exercises

1. It means that the interest on the loan is paid every period. Hence the principal is still owed at the end. A sinking fund is established to cover the loan.

2. Reason 1 is the savings account rate is higher than the loan rate. Hence you are making more interest than you are paying. You might keep your money in your savings account as long as you can.

Reason 2 is the need for cash flow. Even if you must have the interest payment, the sinking fund deposit can be delayed and the cash used elsewhere. Of course, the delayed deposits will catch you in the end.

3. Interest $= 1000 * 0.12/12 = \$10$

4. $S_n = Rs_{\overline{n}|i} \rightarrow 1000 = Rs_{\overline{12}|7\%/12} \rightarrow R = \$80.70$

5. Total $= \$10 + \$80.70 = \$90.70$

0 1 2 12
R R R
S_n

6. Interest $= 20{,}000 * 0.08/2 = \$800$

7. $S_n = Rs_{\overline{n}|i} \rightarrow 20{,}000 = Rs_{\overline{2}|9\%/2} \rightarrow R = \$9779.96$

8. Total $= \$800 + \$9779.96 = \$10{,}579.96$

0 1 2
R R
S_n

9. The SF is paying less than the loan is charging. Hence the SF to cover the loan will cost you more than the original amortized 10%(4) loan.

10. The SF is paying more than the loan is charging. Hence the SF to cover the loan will cost you less than the original amortized 8%(2) loan.

Odd Exercise Calculations

11. a. $A_n = Ra_{\overline{n}|i} \rightarrow 2000 = Ra_{\overline{6}|10\%/12} \rightarrow R = \$343.13$

b. Interest $= 2000 * 0.10/12 = \$16.67$

$S_n = Rs_{\overline{n}|i} \rightarrow 2000 = Rs_{\overline{6}|5\%/12} \rightarrow R = \$329.88$

total $= \$16.67 + \$329.88 = \$346.55$

0 1 2 .. 6
R R .. R
A_n
S_n

c. A loan is better than the sinking fund because the savings rate < the loan rate. We might do the sinking fund to cover the loan to increase cash flow for the first five months since we have to pay only \$16.67 interest. But we're merely putting off the inevitable since all \$2000 is due that last month.

d. The SF to cover a loan table

Saving	\$ 2000.00	Loan rate	10%
Rate	5% / year		
Comp.	12 / year		
Rate	0.4167% / period		
Term	6 Periods		
Deposit	\$329.88		

Period	SF Beg. Bal.	SF Int.	SF Pmt.	SF End	Loan Int.	Tot Pmt.
1			\$ 329.88	\$ 329.88	\$ 16.67	\$ 346.55
2	\$ 329.88	\$ 1.37	\$ 329.88	\$ 661.13	\$ 16.67	\$ 346.55
3	\$ 661.13	\$ 2.75	\$ 329.88	\$ 993.77	\$ 16.67	\$ 346.55
4	\$ 993.77	\$ 4.14	\$ 329.88	\$ 1,327.79	\$ 16.67	\$ 346.55
5	\$ 1,327.79	\$ 5.53	\$ 329.88	\$ 1,663.20	\$ 16.67	\$ 346.55
6	\$ 1,663.20	\$ 6.93	\$ 329.87	\$ 2,000.00	\$ 16.67	\$ 346.53
Totals		\$ 20.73			\$ 100.00	

13. **a.** Amortization (a loan):

$A_n = Ra_{\overline{n|}i} \rightarrow 8000 = Ra_{\overline{36|}6\%/12} \rightarrow R = \$243.38$

Sinking fund to cover the loan:

Interest $= 8000 * 0.06/12 = \$40.00$

$S_n = Rs_{\overline{n|}i} \rightarrow 8000 = Rs_{\overline{36|}8\%/12} \rightarrow R = \$197.36$

Total $= 40 + 197.36 = \$237.36$

Sinking fund is better because the savings rate exceeds the loan rate.

b. Sinking fund schedule is as before. Add the loan interest.

$S_{24} = \$197.36 s_{\overline{24|}8\%/12} = \$5118.17$

SF interest $= \$5118.17 * 0.08/12 = \$34.12$

$S_{25} = S_{24} + \text{SF interest} + \text{deposit} = \$5118.17 + 34.12 + 197.36 = \$5349.65$

Loan interest $= \$8000 * .06/12 = \$40$

Total Pay $= \$197.36 + 40 = \$237.36$

15. **a.** $S_n = Rs_{\overline{n|}i} \rightarrow 20{,}000{,}000 = Rs_{\overline{40|}7\%/2} \rightarrow R = \$236{,}545.65$

b. Interest $= 20{,}000{,}000 * 0.0675/2 = \$675{,}000$

Hence total $= 236{,}545.65 + 675{,}000 = \$911{,}545.65$

c. Total deposit to sinking fund $= 40 * 236{,}545.65 = \$9{,}461{,}826$

Rest of \$20,000,000 was interest $= \$10{,}538{,}174$

d. $40 * \$675{,}000 = \$27{,}000{,}000$

17. As a loan, $A_n = R_1 a_{\overline{n|}i} \rightarrow 40{,}000 = R_1 a_{\overline{15|}7.5\%} \rightarrow R_1 = \$4531.49$

As a sinking fund, \$4531.49 = sum of the sinking fund rent, R_2, $+40{,}000 * 0.07$,

where $40{,}000 = R_2 s_{\overline{15|}i} \rightarrow R_2 = \dfrac{40{,}000}{s_{\overline{15|}i}}$.

Hence $\$4531.49 = \dfrac{40{,}000}{s_{\overline{15|}i}} + 40{,}000 * 0.07 \rightarrow 40{,}000 = 1731.49 s_{\overline{15|}i} \rightarrow i = 5.90\%$

Review Test for Debt Retirement Methods Solutions.

1. Gary's decision problem:

a. Taxes $= 0.05 * 50{,}000 = \$2500$

DP $= 3000$

Financed $= \$50{,}000 + \$2500 - \$3000 = \$49{,}500$

b. $A_n = Ra_{\overline{n}|i} \rightarrow 49{,}500 = Ra_{\overline{60}|4\%(12)}$

$R = 911.62$

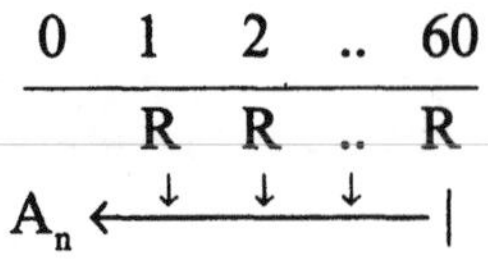

0	1	2	..	60
	R	R	..	R

$A_n \leftarrow$ ↓ ↓ ↓ |

c. $OB_9 = \$42{,}690.13$

$\text{To int} = \$42{,}690.13 * 0.04/12 = \$142.30$

$\text{To loan} = 911.62 - 142.30 = \$769.32$

$OB_{10} = \$42{,}690.13 - \$769.32 = \$41{,}920.81$

d. Total interest 2nd year = $\sum$ interests for lines 13 to 24 OR

Total interest 2nd year $= 12 * \text{Pmt} - (OB_{12} - OB_{24})$

$= 12 * 911.62 - (40{,}374.46 - 30{,}877.14) = \$1442.12$

e.

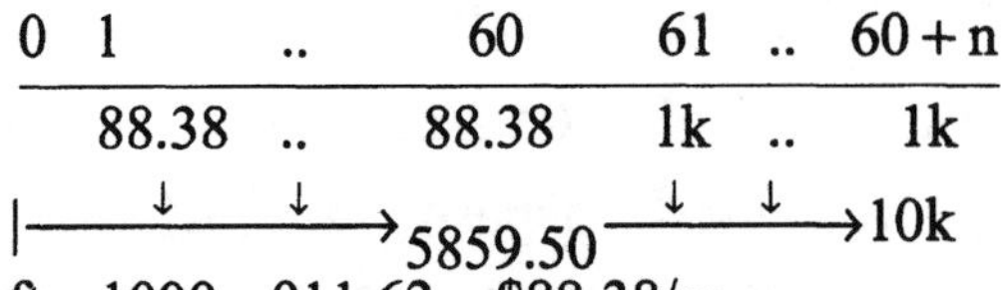

0	1	..	60	61	..	60+n
	88.38	..	88.38	1k	..	1k

| ↓ ↓ → 5859.50 ↓ ↓ → 10k

Have left = 1000 − 911.62 = \$88.38/m

$S_n = Rs_{\overline{n}|i} = \$88.38 s_{\overline{60}|4\%(12)} = 5859.50$

Now we need to accumulate 10,000

Hence $10{,}000 = 5859.50(1 + 4\%/12)^n + 1000 s_{\overline{n}|4\%(12)} \rightarrow n = 4.04$ months

Hence 4 full \$1000 and a partial 5th = \$8.75
Therefore, 5 years and 5 months to accumulate the DP if we buy the new car.

f. $S_n = Rs_{\overline{n}|i} \rightarrow 10{,}000 = 1000 s_{\overline{n}|4\%/12} \rightarrow n = 9.853$

Hence 9 full and a partial of \$601.75

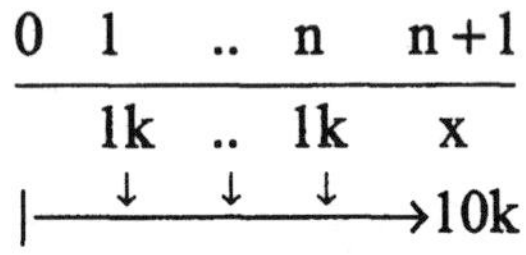

0	1	..	n	n+1
	1k	..	1k	x

| ↓ ↓ ↓ → 10k

g. Probably will choose between home and car.

h. Old loan: pmt = 911.62 for 60 months = \$54,697.20

New loan: $A_n = Ra_{\overline{n}|i} \rightarrow 49{,}500 = Ra_{\overline{130}|4\%/26}$

$\rightarrow R = 420.41$ every two weeks

0	1	2	..	130
	R	R	..	R

$A_n \leftarrow$ ↓ ↓ ↓ |

for 130 periods = \$54,653.30

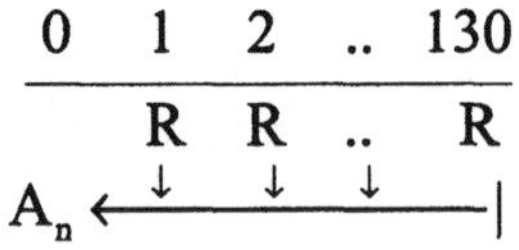

Savings = \$43.90 for doing nothing but paying when you get paid.

i. Take the extra expense or savings and divide it into the number of payments.

2. a. $S_n = Rs_{\overline{n}|i} \rightarrow 20{,}000 = Rs_{\overline{60}|8\%/12} \rightarrow R = \$272.20$

b. $S_{24} = \$7059.01$

c. $I = \$7059.01 * 0.08/12 = \$47.06$

Total = \$7059.01 + 47.06 + 272.20 = \$7378.27

3. a. $A_n = Ra_{\overline{n}|i} \rightarrow 20{,}000.00 = Ra_{\overline{60}|8\%/12} \rightarrow R = \$405.53$

b. $I = Prt = 20{,}000 * 0.08/12 = \$133.33$

$S_n = Rs_{\overline{n}|i} \rightarrow 20{,}000 = Rs_{\overline{60}|5\%/12} \rightarrow R = \$294.10$

$\text{Total} = \$133.33 + \$294.10 = \$427.43$

4. a. $A_n = Ra_{\overline{n}|i} \rightarrow \dfrac{.80 * 50{,}000}{1-.05} = Ra_{\overline{60}|10\%/12} \rightarrow R = \$894.62$

$A_n = Ra_{\overline{n}|i} \rightarrow 40{,}000 = Ra_{\overline{60}|i} \rightarrow i = 1.0199\%/m \rightarrow APR = 12.24\%(12)$

b. $OB_9 = \$37{,}045.24$

$\text{To } I = Prt = 37{,}045.24 * 0.10/12 = \$308.71$

$\text{To } P = \$894.62 - \$308.71 = \$585.91$

$OB_{10} = \$37{,}045.24 - \$585.91 = \$36{,}459.33$

c. $\sum I = 12 * 894.62 - (35{,}272.83 - 27{,}724.94) = \$3187.56$

d. $\text{Appreciated value} = 50{,}000(1+8\%/1)^2 = \$58{,}320$

$OB_{24} = \$27{,}724.94 \rightarrow \text{Equity} = \text{difference} = \$30{,}595.06$

e. $i = \$1.00(1+8\%/4)^{4/12} - 1 = 0.66227..\%/m$

$OB_{24} = \$27{,}724.94 \rightarrow A_n = Ra_{\overline{n}|i} \rightarrow \$27{,}724.94 = Ra_{\overline{36}|i} \rightarrow R = \$868.13$

$\text{Savings} = (\$894.62 - \$868.13) * 36 = \$953.64$

$\text{Total interest} = 36 * \$868.13 - \$27{,}724.94 = \$3527.51$

Chapter 7 Investment in Stocks and Bonds

Section 7.1 Solutions

Concept and Short Answer Exercises

1. The coupon is the periodic interest paid to the holder of the bond.
2. If the bid is at less than par—less than 100%—then a profit is made.
3. If a bond is called at, say, 103, then the bond will make an extra 3%.
4. Since bonds are not as liquid as some other financial instruments, you must wait until a maturity date to cash it in. However, any financial instrument can be bought or sold on a secondary market.
5. \$942, \$1000, discount, \$58
6. \$5183.50, \$5000, premium, \$183.50
7. Call provision allows the bond issuing group to "call" the bond early by giving a bonus to the holder.
8. \$4052, \$4128

Odd Exercise Calculations

9. **a.** Coupon = Fr = 1000 * 0.08 / 2 = \$40

$V_n = S(1+i)^{-n} + Fra_{\overline{n}|i}$

$V_8 = 1000(1+10\%/2)^{-8} + 40a_{\overline{8}|10\%/2}$

$V_8 = \$935.37$

0 1 2 .. 8
40 40 .. 40
1000
$V_8 \leftarrow$

b. Discount of \$1000 − \$935.37 = \$64.63

c. $V_n = S(1+i)^{-n} + Fra_{\overline{n}|i}$

$V_4 = 1030(1+10\%/2)^{-4} + 40a_{\overline{4}|10\%/2}$

$V_4 = \$989.22$

0 1 2 3 4
40 40 40 40
1030
$V_4 \leftarrow$

11. **a.** Coupon = Fr = 500 * 0.09 / 2 = \$22.50

$V_n = S(1+i)^{-n} + Fra_{\overline{n}|i}$

$V_{33} = 500(1+8\%/2)^{-33} + 22.50a_{\overline{33}|8\%/2}$

$V_{33} = \$545.37$

0 1 2 .. 33
22.50 22.50 .. 22.50
500
$V_{33} \leftarrow$

b. Premium of \$545.37 − \$500 = \$45.37

c. $V_n = S(1+i)^{-n} + Fra_{\overline{n}|i}$

$V_{13} = 525(1+8\%/2)^{-13} + 22.50a_{\overline{13}|8\%/2}$

$V_{13} = \$539.98$

0 1 2 .. 13
22.50 22.50 .. 22.50
525
$V_{13} \leftarrow$

13. **a.** Premium because the yield bid rate < coupon rate

b. Discount because the yield bid rate > coupon rate

c. Par (face value) because the yield bid rate = coupon rate

15. **a.** Coupon = Fr = 1000 * 0.10 / 2 = \$50

$V_n = S(1+i)^{-n} + Fra_{\overline{n}|i}$

$V_{20} = 1000(1+8\%/2)^{-20} + 50a_{\overline{20}|8\%/2}$

$V_{20} = \$1135.90$ = Bought

0 1 2 .. 20
50 50 .. 50
1000
$V_{20} \leftarrow$

b. $V_n = S(1+i)^{-n} + Fra_{\overline{n}|i}$

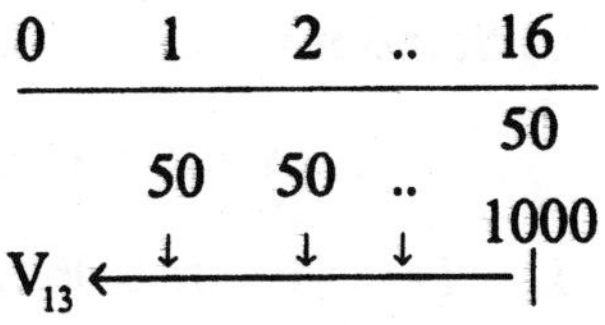

$V_{16} = 1000(1+9\%/2)^{-16} + 50a_{\overline{16}|9\%/2}$

$V_{16} = 1056.17 = \text{Price}$

0	1	2	..	16
				50
	50	50	..	1000
V_{13} ←	↓	↓	↓	|

c. $V_n = S(1+i)^{-n} + Fra_{\overline{n}|i}$

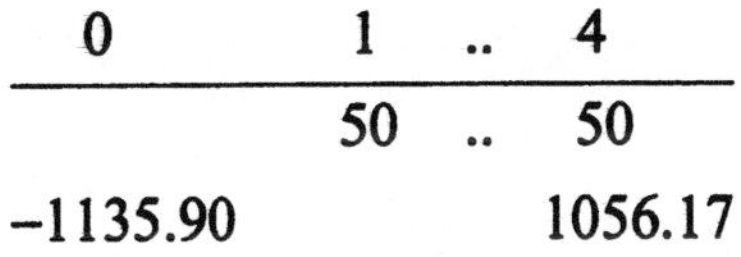

$-1135.90 = 1056.17(1+i)^{-4} + 50a_{\overline{4}|i}$

$i = 2.7169\%/h \rightarrow i(2) = 5.43\%(2)$

0	1	..	4
	50	..	50
−1135.90			1056.17

17. **a.** $\text{Coupon} = Fr = 5000 * 0.092/2 = \$230$

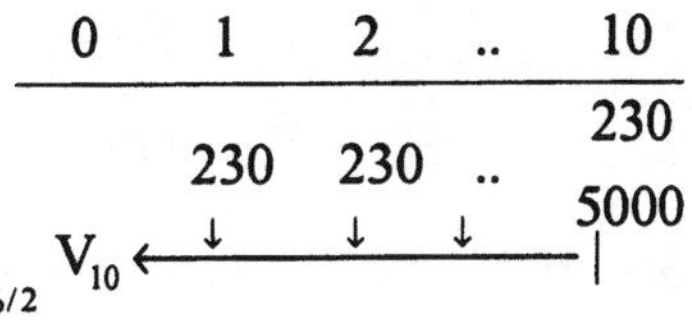

$V_n = S(1+i)^{-n} + Fra_{\overline{n}|i}$

$V_{10} = 5000(1+10.6\%/2)^{-10} + 230a_{\overline{10}|10.6\%/2}$

$V_{10} = \$4733.63 = \text{Bought}$

0	1	2	..	10
				230
	230	230	..	5000
V_{10} ←	↓	↓	↓	|

b. $V_n = S(1+i)^{-n} + Fra_{\overline{n}|i}$

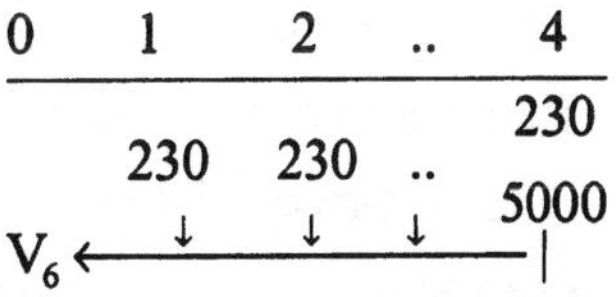

$V_4 = 5000(1+7.8\%/2)^{-4} + 230a_{\overline{4}|7.8\%/2}$

$V_4 = 5127.35 = \text{Price}$

0	1	2	..	4
				230
	230	230	..	5000
V_6 ←	↓	↓	↓	|

c. $V_n = S(1+i)^{-n} + Fra_{\overline{n}|i}$

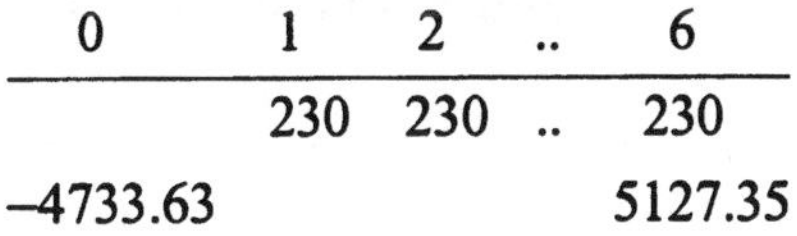

$-4733.63 = 5127.35(1+i)^{-6} + 230a_{\overline{6}|i}$

$i = 6.05\%/h \rightarrow 12.10\%(2)$

0	1	2	..	6
	230	230	..	230
−4733.63				5127.35

19. $\text{Coupon} = Fr = 1000 * 0.06/2 = \$30$

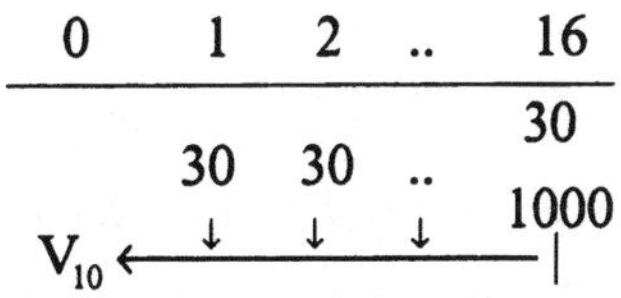

$V_n = S(1+i)^{-n} + Fra_{\overline{n}|i}$

$V_{16}(i) = 1000(1+i)^{-16} + 30a_{\overline{16}|i}$

0	1	2	..	16
				30
	30	30	..	1000
V_{10} ←	↓	↓	↓	|

$V_{16}(3\%) = 1000 \text{ while } V_{16}(4\%) = 833.47 \rightarrow \%\text{change} = -11.65\%$

21. $V_n = F + [Fr - Fi]a_{\overline{n}|i} \rightarrow [V_n - F] = [Fr - Fi]a_{\overline{n}|i}$

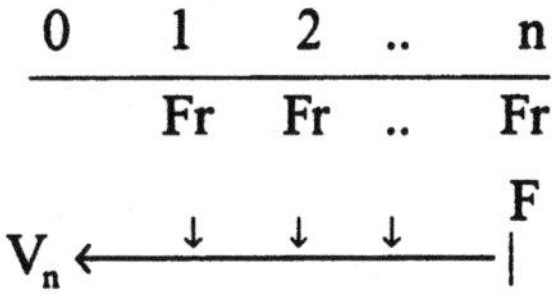

Hence use $[V_n - F]$ as A_n and $[Fr - Fi]$ as R

and solve $A_n = Ra_{\overline{n}|i}$ for n

0	1	2	..	n
	Fr	Fr	..	Fr
				F
V_n ←	↓	↓	↓	|

23. $V_n = F + [Fr - Fi]a_{\overline{n}|i} \rightarrow V_{2n} = F + [Fr - Fi]a_{\overline{2n}|i}$

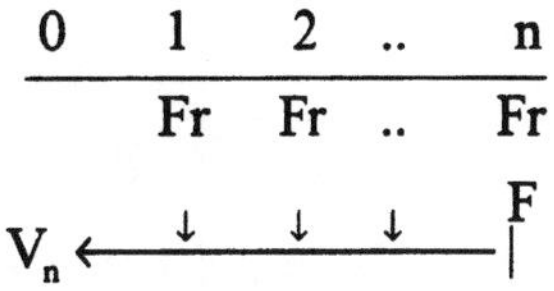

$\rightarrow V_{2n} - V_n = [Fr - Fi][a_{\overline{2n}|i} - a_{\overline{n}|i}]$

$$\rightarrow V_{2n} - V_n = [Fr - Fi]\left[\frac{1-(1+i)^{2n}}{i} - \frac{1-(1+i)^{n}}{i}\right]$$

$$\rightarrow V_{2n} - V_n = \frac{[Fr - Fi]}{i}(1+i)^n[1-(1+i)^n]$$

0	1	2	..	n
	Fr	Fr	..	Fr
				F
V_n ←	↓	↓	↓	|

but the equation $x(1+x)$ has a max of 1/4 at $x = 1/2$ $\rightarrow V_{2n} - V_n \le \dfrac{[Fr - Fi]}{4i}$

Section 7.2 Solutions

Concept and Short Answer Exercises

1. $Fr = \$1000 * 0.06/2 = \$30 = \text{coupon}$

0h	1	2	..	30
	\$30	\$30	..	\$30
\$827.08				\$1000
V_{30} ←	↓	↓	↓	|

2. V_{30} is located one period before the first coupon date.

3. Since we move backward, V_{20} is right of V_{21}.

4. $V_n = S(1+i)^{-n} + Fra_{\overline{n}|i} = 10{,}000(1+9\%/2)^{-20} + 400a_{\overline{20}|9\%/2} = 9349.60$

5. $V_n = S(1+i)^{-n} + Fra_{\overline{n}|i} = 10{,}000(1+9\%/2)^{-21} + 400a_{\overline{21}|9\%/2} = 9329.76$

6. $1000 + (1/6) * 120 = \$1020$

7. $2000 - (5/6) * 300 = \$1750$

8. Quoted price = 9329.76 + (2/6) * 19.84 = \$9336.37

9. Purchase price = 9329.76 (1+0.09 * 2/12) = \$9469.71

10. Quoted price = 9469.71 – 2/6* 400 = \$9336.37

Odd Exercise Calculations

11.

0h	(4m)	1h	..	9h
		40	..	40
				1000
V_9 ←	Pur.Dt.	↓	↓	|

$V_n = S(1+i)^{-n} + Fra_{\overline{n}|i} = 1000(1+10\%/2)^{-9} + 40a_{\overline{9}|10\%/2} = \$928.92$

$V_{pur} = \$928.92(1+0.10*4/12) = \$959.89$

Interpolated coupon $= 40*4/6 = 26.67$

$V_{net} = V_{pur} - \text{above} = \$959.89 - 26.67 = \$933.22$

13.

4/1/04		10/1/04	..	10/1/20
0h	5/1/04	1h		33h
		22.50	..	22.50
				500
V_{33} ←	Pur.Dt.	↓	↓	|

$n = 10/1/20 - 4/1/04 = 6m + 16y = 33h$

$V_n = S(1+i)^{-n} + Fra_{\overline{n}|i} = 500(1+8\%/2)^{-33} + 22.50a_{\overline{33}|8\%/2} = \$545.37$

$V_{pur} = \$545.37(1+0.08*1/12) = \$549.00$

Interpolated coupon $= 22.50*1/6 = 3.75$

$V_{net} = V_{pur} - \text{above} = \$549.00 - 3.75 = \$545.25$

15.

0h	(2m)	1h	..	10h
		250	..	250
				5000

$V_9 \leftarrow$ ↓(pur.dt.) ↓ ↓

$V_n = S(1+i)^{-n} + Fra_{\overline{n}|i} = 5000(1+12\%/2)^{-10} + 250a_{\overline{10}|12\%/2} = \$4631.9956$

$V_{pur} = \$4631.9956(1+0.12*2/12) = \$4724.64$

Interpolated coupon $= 250*2/6 = 83.33$

$V_{net} = V_{pur} - \text{above} = \$4724.64 - 83.33 = \$4641.31$

17.

6/1/03		12/1/03		6/1/10
0h	11/12/03	1h	..	14h
		400	..	400
				10,000

$V_{33} \leftarrow$ Pur.Dt. ↓ ↓

Convert $i = [1(1+10\%/4)^{4/2} - 1]*100 = 5.0625\%/h$

$n = 6/1/10 - 6/1/03 = 7y = 14h$

$V_n = S(1+i)^{-n} + Fra_{\overline{n}|i} = 10{,}000(1+i)^{-14} + 400a_{\overline{14}|i} = \$8952.46$

$t = 11/12/03 - 6/1/03 = 164\,d$

$V_{pur} = \$8952.46(1+i*164/180) = 9365.39$

Interpolated coupon $= \dfrac{164}{180}*400 = 364.44$

$V_{net} = V_{pur} - \text{above} = \$9365.39 - 364.44 = \$9000.95$

19.

3/1/04		9/1/04		3/1/12
0h	7/15/04	1h	..	16h
		32.50	..	32.50
				1000

$V_{16} \leftarrow$ Pur.Dt. ↓ ↓

a. $n = 3/1/08 - 3/1/04 = 8h$

$V_n = S(1+i)^{-n} + Fra_{\overline{n}|i} = 1030(1+4.5\%)^{-8} + 32.50a_{\overline{8}|4.5\%} = \$938.65$

$t = 7/15/04 - 3/1/04 = 136\,d$

$V_{pur} = \$938.65(1+0.09*136/360) = \$970.56$

b. $n = 3/1/12 - 3/1/04 = 16h$

$V_n = S(1+i)^{-n} + Fra_{\overline{n}|i} = 1000(1+4.5\%)^{-16} + 32.50a_{\overline{16}|4.5\%} = \$859.57$

$V_{pur} = \$859.57(1+0.09*136/360) = \$888.80$

Section 7.3 Solutions

Concept and Short Answer Questions

1. $45 is the coupon and is placed on each half-year. Hence one has a per period return of $45 from the coupon.
2. $180 was lost on the premium bid, which, if averaged out over 17 periods gives a $10.59 loss per period.
3. $Fr + (S - V_{quote}) / n$ is the per-period return.
4. $(S + V_{quote}) / 2$, because the bond is worth the bid at the beginning and the face value at the end.
5. If you make $5 on $100 in a half-year, then you are making 5%/half-year on hyour money. The BSF does the same thing.
6. The YTM is a yearly rate and would be twice the half-year rate.
7. Current yield = yearly return from the coupon over the bid cost.
8. Adjusted current yield = yearly return from coupon and the bid divided by the bid cost of the bond.
9. Adjusted current yield = yearly return from coupon and the bid divided by the average worth of the bond.
10. $V_n = S(1+i)^{-n} + Fra_{\overline{n}|i} = S(1+i)^{-n} + Fr\left[\frac{1-(1+i)^{-n}}{i}\right]$

$$\therefore V_n \doteq S(1-ni) + Fr\left[\frac{1-(1-ni)}{i}\right] = S(1-ni) + Frn$$

$$\therefore Sni \doteq S + Frn - V_n$$

$$\therefore i \doteq \frac{Fr - (V_n - S)/n}{S}$$ Note that n was divided into each numerator term.

The above would be the BSF if the denominator, S, were replaced by the average worth of the bond, $(V_n + S)/2$.

Odd Exercise Calculations

11. a. $\text{coupon} = Fr = 2000 * 0.08/2 = \$80$

$\text{cost} - \text{bid} = 2000 - 1920 = \$80$ spread out over 10 $= \$8$

$\text{average price} = (1920 + 2000)/2 = \$1960$

$$i = \frac{Fr + \text{avg gain or loss}}{\text{avg price}} = \frac{\$80 + \$8}{\$1960} = 4.4897\%/h$$

$BSF = i(2) = 8.98\%(2)$

b. current yield $= \dfrac{\text{Total coupons for the year}}{\text{bid}} = \dfrac{2*80}{1920} = 8.33\%$

c. adjusted yield $= \dfrac{(\text{Total coupons} + \text{gain because of bid})\,\text{per year}}{\text{bid}}$

adjusted yield $= \dfrac{2*80+2*8}{1920} = 9.17\%$

d. actual yield (this is actually the easiest and most accurate with the modern calc.)

$V_n = S(1+i)^{-n} + Fra_{\overline{n}|i} \to 1920 = 2000(1+i)^{-10} + 80a_{\overline{10}|i}$

$i = 4.505\% \to 9.01\%(2)$

13. **a.** coupon $= Fr = 500*0.07/2 = \$17.50$

$S = 500*1.02 = \$510.00$ on 10/1/12

$n = 10/1/12 - 4/1/05 = 6m + 7y = 15h$

cost − bid $= 510 - 530 = -\$20$ spread out over $15 = -\$1.33$

average price $= (510+530)/2 = \$520$

$i = \dfrac{Fr + \text{avg gain or loss}}{\text{avg price}} = \dfrac{\$17.50 - \$1.33}{\$520} = 3.1096\%/h$

$BSF = i(2) = 6.22\%(2)$

b. current yield $= \dfrac{\text{Total coupons for the year}}{\text{bid}} = \dfrac{2*17.50}{530} = 6.60\%$

c. adjusted yield $= \dfrac{(\text{Total coupons} + \text{gain because of bid})\,\text{per year}}{\text{bid}}$

adjusted yield $= \dfrac{2*17.50 + 2*(-1.33)}{530} = 6.10\%$

d. actual yield (this is actually the easiest and most accurate with the modern calc.)

$V_n = S(1+i)^{-n} + Fra_{\overline{n}|i} \to -530 = 510(1+i)^{-15} + 17.50a_{\overline{15}|i}$

$i = 3.10\% \to 6.20\%(2)$

15. $V_n = S(1+i)^{-n} + Fra_{\overline{n}|i} \to -950 = 1000(1+i)^{-24} + 40a_{\overline{24}|i}$

$i = 4.3394\% \to 8.68\%(2)$

17. See Section 7.1 Calculation Exercises number15.

19. See Section 7.1 Calculation Exercises number17.

21. $V_n = F + F[r-i]a_{\overline{n}|i} \to 1210 = 1000 + 1000(0.02)a_{\overline{16}|i} \to i = 3.033\% \to 6.07\%(2)$

23. $n = 6/15/16 - 9/1/06 = 9m + 14d + 9y = 1.5h + 14/180h + 18h = 19.261h$

$V_n = S(1+i)^{-n} + Fra_{\overline{n}|i} \to 800 = 1000(1+i)^{19.261} + 32.50a_{\overline{19.261}|i}$

$\to i = 4.8558\% \to i(2) = 9.71\%$

25. Bid * current yield rate = yearly coupon.

$\rightarrow$ Bid * 0.0732 = 60 $\rightarrow$ bid = \$819.67

$V_n = S(1+i)^{-n} + Fra_{\overline{n}|i} \rightarrow -819.67 = 1000(1+i)^{16} + 30a_{\overline{16}|i}$

$\rightarrow i = 4.62\% \rightarrow 9.24\%(2)$

Section 7.4 Solutions

Concept and Short Answer Exercises

1. In the short run the growth rate fluctuates widely. Further, yearly dividends may change from year to year. Hence we will use an average growth rate and an average dividend to analyze stocks over the long haul.
2. $V = D/k$ is the same as the perpetuity formula $A_\infty = R/i$ if you note that when the stock is held over a long period all of the value comes from the periodic dividend and the rate of return you are making.
3. The dividend for as many periods as the stock is held = D× (# periods held).
4. You can do long-term analysis, but short-term examination is very difficult.

Odd Exercise Calculations

5. $V = \dfrac{D(1+g)}{k-g} \rightarrow 45 = \dfrac{2.15(1+0.055)}{k-0.055} \rightarrow 45k - 2.475 = 2.26825$

$\therefore 45k = 4.74325 \rightarrow k = 10.54\%$

7. $V = \dfrac{D}{k} = \dfrac{10.50}{0.12} = \$87.50$

9. **a.** Actual dividends = 2.45 * 0.45/share = \$1.10/share

$V = \dfrac{D(1+g)}{k-g} = \dfrac{1.10(1+0.045)}{0.105-0.045} = \$19.16$

b. $E(r) = D/P + g = 1.10/22.00 + 0.045 = 9.5\%$

11. $V_n = S(1+i)^{-n} + Ra_{\overline{n}|i}$

$V_8 = 100(1+12\%)^{-8} + 4.85a_{\overline{8}|12\%}$

$V_8 = \$64.48$

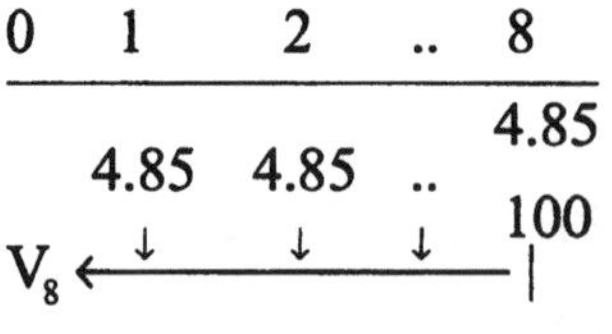

0	1	2	..	8
	4.85	4.85	..	4.85
				100
V_8 ←	↓	↓	↓	|

13. $V_n = S(1+i)^{-n} + Ra_{\overline{n}|i}$

$-60 = 100(1+i)^{-8} + 4.85a_{\overline{8}|i}$

$i = 13.26\%$

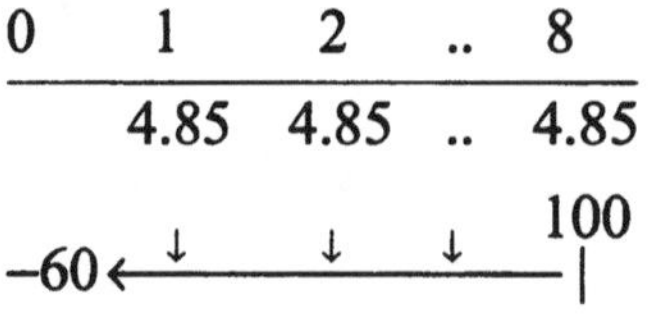

0	1	2	..	8
	4.85	4.85	..	4.85
				100
−60 ←	↓	↓	↓	|

15. $D = Pk$ (similar to $R = A_\infty i$) $\rightarrow k = D/P = 8/50 = 16\%$

17. $V = \frac{D(1+g)}{k-g} \rightarrow V = \frac{3.05*0.8*(1+-.07)}{0.15-0.07} \rightarrow \$32.64$

19. $E(r) = D/P + g = 4.05/62 + 0.065 = 13.03\%$ at least

21. $D = Pk$ (similar to $R = A_{\infty}i) = 76*0.095 = \$7.22$

23. $44.75 = 1.10(1+i)^{-1} + 1.35(1+i)^{-2} + 1.55(1+i)^{-3} + (1.70 + 54.75)(1+i)^{-4}$

Use the IRR scheme with -44.75 at 0, 1.10 at 1, 1.35 at 2, etc.

IRR = 8.09%

25. $78.30 = 2.20(1.15)^{-1} + 2.20(1.15)^{-2} + 2.20(1.15)^{-3} + (3.10 + \text{Price})(1.15)^{-4}$

$\rightarrow$ Price in 4 years=\$125.06

I also solved using the bond formula $V_n = S(1+i)^{-n} + Fra_{\overline{n}|i}$ with

$-78.30 = S(1+15\%)^{-4} + 2.20a_{\overline{4}|15\%} \rightarrow S = 125.96$

Hence $2.20 + 125.96 = 3.10 + \text{Price} \rightarrow \text{Price} = \$125.06$

Review Test for Investing in Stocks and Bonds Solutions

1. Coupon = $Fr = 1000*0.07/2 = \$35$

4/04	4/08	10/18
V_n	1030	1000

a. $V_n = S(1+i)^{-n} + Fra_{\overline{n}|i}$

$V_n = 1030(1+9.5\%/2)^{-8} + 35a_{\overline{8}|9.5\%/2}$

$V_n = \$939.08$

b. $V_n = 100(1+9.5\%/2)^{-29} + 35a_{\overline{29}|9.5\%/2}$

$V_n = \$813.16$

2. Coupon = $Fr = 5000*0.00/2 = \$0$

0	78m
V_n	5000

$V_n = S(1+i)^{-n} + Fra_{\overline{n}|i}$

$V_n = 5000(1+8\%/2)^{-13} + \$0a_{\overline{13}|8\%/2}$

$V_n = \$3002.87$

3.

3/30/05	8/15/05	9/30/05	3/30/06	3/30/20
V_{30} ←	Pur.dt.	300	300 ...	300+10000

7.5%si →

$7\%(4) \approx ?(2) \rightarrow i = \left(1[1+7\%/4]^{4/2} - 1\right)*100 = 3.530624..\%/h$

$V_n = S(1+i)^{-n} + Fra_{\overline{n}|i} = 10{,}000(1+i)^{-30} + 300a_{\overline{30}|i} = \$9027.81$

$V_{quote} = \$9027.81(1 + 0.075*138/360) = \$9287.36$

$V_{pur} = 9287.36 - 138/180*300 = \$9057.36$

4. 6/05/05   12/05/05   6/05/06   12/5/12

840 ← 27.50   27.50 ...   27.50+1000

$V_n = S(1+i)^{-n} + Fra_{\overline{n}|i} \rightarrow -840 = 1000(1+i)^{-15} + 27.50a_{\overline{15}|i} \rightarrow i = 4.210\%/h$

Hence YTM = 8.42%(2)

$\text{Adjusted current yield} = \dfrac{2(27.50 + (1000 - 840)/15)}{840} = 9.09\%$

5. 4/8/04   8/8/04   2/8/05 ⋯ 8/8/22

1185 ← 40   40 ...   40+1000

$V_n = S(1+i)^{-n} + Fra_{\overline{n}|i} \rightarrow -1185 = 1000(1+i)^{-36.\bar{6}} + 40a_{\overline{36.\bar{6}}|i} \rightarrow i = 3.143\%/h$

Hence YTM = 6.29%(2)

6. $V = D/r = 8.20/0.09 = \$91.11$

7. $V = \dfrac{D(1+g)}{k-g} \rightarrow \dfrac{0.65 * 2.38(1+0.05)}{0.10-0.05} = \$32.49$

$E(r) = \dfrac{D}{P} + g = \dfrac{0.65 * 2.38}{34.50} + 0.05 = 9.48\%$

8. 0   1   2   10

V_n ← 6.25   6.25 ...   6.25+100

$V_n = S(1+i)^{-n} + Da_{\overline{n}|i} = 100(1+12\%)^{-10} + 6.25a_{\overline{10}|12\%} = \$67.51$

9. $-70.50 = 100(1+i)^{-10} + 6.25a_{\overline{10}|i} \rightarrow i = 11.328\%/h \rightarrow 22.66\%(2)$

Index

C

D

E

PART 2

Taken from:

Understanding Finance: Money, Capital, and Investments

by Karen D. Halpern

CHAPTER

2 KEY FINANCIAL CONCEPTS

LEARNING OBJECTIVES

1. Describe the concept of time value of money.
2. Distinguish between simple interest and compound interest.
3. Distinguish between present value and future value.
4. Calculate the future value (or maturity value) of an investment using compound interest.
5. Calculate present value of a future lump sum value.
6. Describe the benefit of setting up a sinking fund.
7. Calculate sinking fund principal payments.
8. Understand the difference between an annuity due and an ordinary annuity.
9. Compute the present value of an annuity.
10. Calculate the future value of a stream of payments (an annuity).
11. Describe the various forms of investment risk.
12. Distinguish between diversifiable and systematic risk.

A bird in the hand is worth two in the bush.
A penny saved is a penny earned.
90 days, same as cash.

What do all these sayings have in common? Each recognizes that there is a value in having money in the present rather than in the future. Except for rare historical periods of deflation, the money that one has in one's pocket today purchases more than the identical amount of money would next year or, more significantly, 5 years from now. **Time value of money** captures two related concepts: money that we have now, in the present, can be invested, which should result in having more in the future. The investment we make can either be in the form of investing in productive assets such as equipment or it can be placed in an interest-bearing investment such as a savings account. In either case, the amount of money we have now should be used to yield more in the future.

THE TIME VALUE OF MONEY

Several economic factors influence the value of our money, both in the present and in the future. For example, inflation, the increase in the cost of goods and services in an economy, shrinks the buying power of today's dollars. When the cost of energy to heat your home increases, it leaves less money for the purchase of other items. If this inflation continues over time, and your earnings do not increase, you will have suffered a loss of purchasing power. However, if your income increases at a rate faster than inflation, your real purchasing power will have increased.

Finance managers are interested in mentally moving money between the present and the future. Money that the firm has today should not be left idle or it will lose real value. It should be put to work earning interest or creating income for the firm. Companies also need to plan for future investment in new technology or equipment. Although the actual cash outlay may come at some point in the future, finance managers need to prepare for the expenditure, which requires decision making in the present.

We usually describe changes in the value of money in percentage terms. The local newspaper may report that the inflation rate is expected to be 2.45% this year. The cost of energy has increased at an annual rate of 30% this year. The average wage increase in 2001 for skilled workers in Smith County was 3.25%. Notice that each of the descriptions contains a percentage (a rate) and a time period.

One way of looking at the time value of money is to ask "What is this investment worth to me today? How else could I employ the same funds and have the same return?" The time value of money depends on its alternate uses. For example, Cole Property Management has a small apartment complex near the local university. The building is smaller than the other units they own, and the firm has decided that it is not cost effective for them to manage that size property. They have received two purchase offers: the Applegate Company has offered $1,300,000, payable immediately. Cole received a purchase offer of $1,500,000 from Gilbert Properties, but the terms of the purchase are staggered: $500,000 in 6 months, a second payment of $500,000 at the end of the year, and the final $500,000 in 18 months. If Cole wants the higher price, they will not receive the final payment for a year and a half. Is this a good deal? The answer depends on what Cole could do with the $1,300,000 that Applegate is offering. Among the considerations are the amount of interest Cole could earn on the money, the rate of inflation, and whether they could reinvest the proceeds in an apartment complex that more closely matches their preferred properties. Later in the chapter, we will determine which purchase offer Cole should accept.

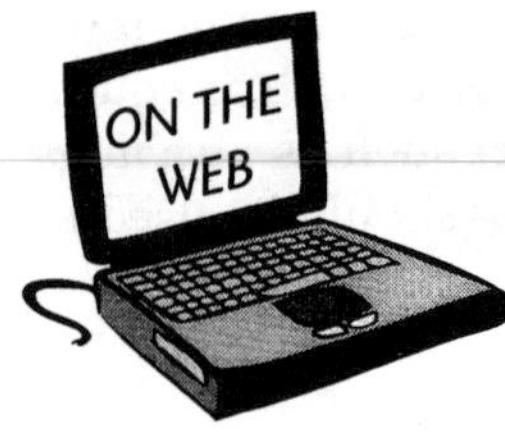

The Bureau of Labor Statistics (www.bls.gov/) uses census data to calculate the effect of inflation. The **consumer price index (CPI)** describes the change in price of a market basket of consumer goods. Eight major groups of expenditures are measured:

Food and beverages
Housing
Apparel
Transportation
Medical care
Recreation, which also includes durable goods such as televisions
Education and communication
Other goods and services such as tobacco, haircuts, and other personal services

Also included in the measurement are user fees for things such as water and sewage charges, sales tax, and automobile registration fees.

The consumer price index is important in part because it is used as an overall economic indicator. It can be used as the benchmark when setting up an escalator clause in a contract. For example, a union might negotiate a labor contract that increases wages in line with the increase in the CPI.

Because the CPI measures an average market basket, it does not necessarily reflect the inflation experienced by a single consumer. Still, it is interesting to use the CPI to move prices from "old" advertisements into the present and examine the effect of inflation. You can find the inflation calculator at the Bureau of Labor Statistics Web page.

FUTURE VALUE

Future value describes the amount of money one could expect to have (or owe) in the future when today's value of the money is known. The future value includes total amount of principal along with the accumulated interest earned. The future value can also be referred to as the maturity value.

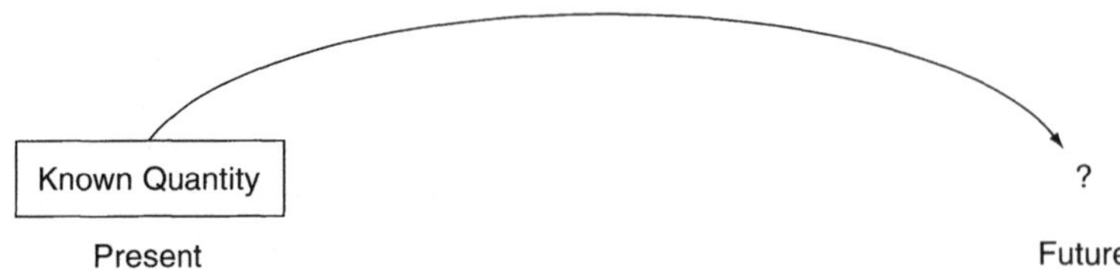

The future value is the value of today's principal and all of the interest it earns over the course of the investment.

Stop and Think

Teachers have agreed to a 3-year contract that will give them a 3% raise each year of the contract. The average teacher's pay is $34,725 per year. What will be the new average at the end of the 3-year contract?

When Andrew was 3 years old, his grandparents opened a $500 savings account that earns 6% compounded daily. How much will it be worth in 15 years when Andrew goes to college?

In both cases, we know that the amounts will have increased over time, but what will they actually be worth? We'll see the answers at the end of this section.

Most of us are familiar with the concept of interest: money that is paid by a borrower as a fee for having the current use of money and earned by the lender for assuming the risk of that loan. **Simple interest** is expressed as an annual percentage even if the period of the loan is not exactly a year. The formula for simple interest calculation is

$$I = PRT$$

where

I = Interest earned
P = Principal (the amount borrowed/loaned)
R = Rate of interest (expressed as an annual percentage rate)
T = Time of the loan (expressed as some component of a year)

If Sally borrowed $500 at 8% for 1 year, the simple interest would be

$$I = PRT$$
$$I = \$500 \times 8\% \times 1$$
$$I = \$40$$

The maturity value of the investment, the amount that Sally has to repay on the due date, would be $540, which represents the original amount borrowed (P) as well as the interest owed (I). The **maturity value** is merely another name for the future value of an investment.

$$MV = P + I$$
$$MV = \$500 + \$40$$
$$MV = \$540$$

If Sally required the money for only 6 months, the formula would be

$$I = PRT$$
$$I = \$500 \times 8\% \times \tfrac{6}{12}$$

The time component has changed to 6/12 or 6 months of a 12-month year. The simple interest payment on the loan would be only $20, or half the amount in the first example. In this case, the maturity value is $520(MV = P + I).

Loans can be taken for longer than a single year. Sally is in college and does not expect to be able to repay the $500 for 3 years. Using simple interest, the maturity value, or future value, of her loan is:

$$I = PRT$$
$$I = \$500 \times 8\% \times 3$$
$$I = \$120$$
$$MV = \$500 + \$120$$
$$MV = \$620$$

Simple interest calculations can be performed quickly on any basic calculator. Unfortunately, simple interest loans are not common in the business world. In most cases, lenders charge compound interest. In **compound interest,** interest is posted to the account or charged to the loan at regular intervals. This requires some adjustments to the formula we have been using.

Let's say the same borrower required a $500 loan, however the lender charged 8% interest compounded quarterly. The time period of the loan remains one year, however during that year the interest will be calculated and posted to the account quarterly, four times during the year. Let's see what effect that would have on Sally.

After the first quarter, the lender would need to calculate interest.

$$I = PRT$$

where

P = $500
R = 8%
T = $\frac{1}{4}$ of the year

$$I = \$500 \times 8\% \times \tfrac{1}{4}$$
$$I = \$10$$

That interest is added to the principal, which means that at the end of the second quarter, P has increased. The interest charge for the second quarter is

$$I = PRT$$

where

P = $510
R = 8%
T = $\frac{1}{4}$

$$I = \$510 \times 8\% \times \tfrac{1}{4}$$
$$I = \$10.20$$

In the second quarter of the loan, the interest has increased \$.20. We can calculate the quarterly interest charges and the total amount owed for the balance of the loan by following the pattern we have already established.

Third installment:

$$I = PRT$$

where

$P = \$520.20$
$R = 8\%$
$T = \frac{1}{4}$

$$I = \$520.20 \times 8\% \times \tfrac{1}{4}$$
$$I = \$10.40 \text{ (rounded)}$$

Fourth installment:

$$I = PRT$$

where

$P = \$530.60$
$R = 8\%$
$T = \frac{1}{4}$

$$I = \$530.60 \times 8\% \times \tfrac{1}{4}$$
$$I = \$10.61 \text{ (rounded)}$$

When the final interest charge is added to the loan, the borrower will repay \$541.21. The maturity value (MV) is the original principal (P) plus the four quarterly interest charges (I). The price to the borrower of the compound interest is \$1.21 over the course of the year. While that may seem small, think about the difference if the loan had been \$5,000 or \$500,000. The effects of compounding become far more costly.

The method we have used to calculate compound interest is both tedious and imprecise. By the third period, we were forced to round even though we had used a whole interest rate that could easily be divided into its periodic equivalent. Imagine if we had used 8.27% compounded daily. The loan would have required 365 separate calculations, which is not a good use of time and would have inevitably resulted in significant rounding errors.

There are many tools available that will provide exact interest calculations. For simplicity's sake, we will rely on tables that can be found in Appendix A. There are two that will give us the future value of an investment: compound interest chart (A-1) and daily compound interest chart (A-2). Notice that both of the charts give the maturity value of the investment—both the original principal and the earned interest are included in the factor.

Toolbox

> Even using the charts in Appendix A can be tedious. Many software programs include basic financial formulas including future value and present value. Some of the programs, such as Excel, are designed for widespread use, while others are developed on a proprietary basis for specific clients such as a bank or auto dealer's lending subsidiary. If your job requires that you perform frequent future value calculations, you should invest in an appropriate software package and learn its idiosyncrasies. Each of them has its own syntax and assumptions embedded within the program, but once you are familiar with the format, calculations become far simpler and quicker.

Compound Interest Chart

The compound interest chart allows a single calculation to be performed for an investment with any number of compounding periods (subject to the limitations of the chart). The values in the table provide the maturity value (P + I) of the investment. Thus, the effect of the four calculations we made above can be re-created in a single transaction. But to do so, we will need to adjust our original formula slightly.

$$MV = P + I$$
$$I = PRT$$

where

P = \$500
R = 8%
T = 1 year
Compounded quarterly

Now look at the chart in Appendix A-1. The left-hand column reads "n*". The asterisk explains that n is the number of compounding periods. To calculate n, you must multiply the time period of the loan (T) by the number of compounding periods per year. In this example $n = 1$ year $\times$ 4 quarters = 4. However, if we do not also adjust the interest rate to its periodic equivalent, we will be quadrupling the interest owed. The lender may appreciate that, however the borrower most certainly will not. The interest rate (R) must be divided into quarterly units of 2%, expressed as i.

The new format would be expressed as

$$MV = P \times TV(n,i)$$

where

P = \$500
$i = 8\% \div 4$ quarters = 2%
$n = 1$ year $\times$ 4 quarters = 4

Follow down the far left column until you find the correct value for *n*. Read across the top row until you find the value for *i*. At the intersection of the two is a factor (or table value: TV), which when multiplied by the principal will give you the maturity value of the investment. The table value bundles together the interest and rate components of the simple interest formula. Rather than multiply the principal by two numbers, the compound interest table allows you to use one factor that includes both the interest rate and time.

$$\text{MV} = \$500 \times 1.08243$$
$$\text{MV} = \$541.22 \text{ (rounded)}$$

The use of the chart simplified the process of calculating compound interest and, except for the effect of rounding in both problems, produced the same result. The compound interest chart can be used to estimate the future value of an investment with periodic interest payments. However, the compound interest chart does not allow you to reduce interest to a daily rate. For that reason, there is a second compound interest chart in Appendix A.

Daily Compound Interest Chart

The daily compound interest chart is simple to use. The left-hand column indicates the length of the loan in terms from days to years. The top row provides the annual interest rate. At the intersection of the row and column, you will find a number, the factor (or table value), which when multiplied by the principal will give you the maturity value of the loan. This chart does not require you to adjust the time (T) component to reflect the compounding period, therefore, you will not adjust the annual interest rate.

Let's say our $500 loan now carries 8% interest compounded daily.

$$\text{MV} = \text{P} \times \text{TV (T,R)}$$

where

P = $500
R = 8%
T = 1 year
Compounded daily

$$\text{MV} = \$500 \times 1.08328$$
$$\text{MV} = \$541.64$$

Since each chart gives us the maturity value of the investment, we can compare the effect of compounding on the interest charged to the borrower.

Simple interest:	$540.00
Compounded quarterly:	$541.22
Compounded daily:	$541.64

Stop and Think

Teachers have agreed to a 3-year contract that will give them a 3% raise each year of the contract. The average teacher's pay is $34,725 per year. What will be the new average at the end of the 3-year contract?

Note: Because the teachers get a raise at the end of each school year, the compounding period will be annual (once per year).

$$MV = P \times TV(n,i)$$

where

P = $34,725
$i = 3\% \div 1$ period = 3%
$n = 3$ years × 1 period = 3
Compounded annually

$$MV = \$34{,}725 \times 1.09273$$
$$MV = \$37{,}945.05$$

When Andrew was 3 years old, his grandparents opened a $500 savings account that earns 6% compounded daily. How much will it be worth in 15 years when Andrew goes to college?

$$MV = P \times TV\,(R,T)$$

where

P = $500
R = 6%
T = 15 years
Compounded daily

$$MV = \$500 \times 2.45942$$
$$MV = \$1{,}229.71$$

As the frequency of compounding increases, so does the interest owed on the loan. Let's return to the questions at the beginning of this section.

In the preceding problems, we knew what the interest rate was: the teachers' contract was a legal document and we assumed that the savings account would always earn 6%. Sometimes firms have to estimate what they will earn on an investment. For example, property situated on the banks of the Puget Sound, with a view of Mount Rainier to the east, the Olympic Mountains on the north, and spectacular sunsets over the water, will increase in value over time because that type of parcel is a scarce commodity. To estimate the future value, the developer could estimate the yearly increase in value of comparable properties. The interest rate, or in this case growth rate, would reflect the uniqueness of the investment and the near impossibility of duplicating it. However, there is no guarantee that the past rate of growth will continue into the future just as there is no guarantee that interest rates will remain constant over time. Future value calculations make assumptions about continuity that may or may not remain accurate throughout the life of the investment.

Future value computations are often used to calculate the effect that inflation will have on a firm's future investments. We assume that the future value of an investment will be higher than its present cost. That is not always an accurate perception.

Just For Fun

My grandfather was an amateur painter. When he framed a picture, he often used newspaper between the drawing and the backing of the frame. When I reframed an old picture, I found an advertisement dated Sunday, January 31, 1960.

The style of the 40-year-old gas range and oven looks odd to me. The cooking surface has four burners and a backsplash that looks like the one on my washing machine. The "king-size superoven" looks tiny to me. It takes up about a quarter of the space at the top left-hand side immediately below the burners. The ad boasts that this range, with its separate pullout broiler, is so advanced that even the oven and broiler light without matches!

Budget-conscious homemakers were urged to rush to the store and buy the range, which was on sale for $169.88.

There have undoubtedly been improvements in energy efficiency and product design but not the same type of radical technological advances in stoves and ovens, as we have seen in other products such as typewriters, word processors, and computers. Because of that, we can more easily compare prices between 1960 and 2001 ovens.

What would the budget-conscious homemaker expect to pay for a gas range if we applied the consumer price index? Using the Bureau of Labor Statistics CPI calculator (www.bls.gov/) and bringing the price to its 2001 equivalent, I would have to pay $1,081.71 for a gas range. However, a quick phone call to the local home improvement store resulted in a quote of $399 for a comparable product. How can this be?

The CPI estimates the change in price for a "market basket" of consumer goods. It does not take into account the effect of technological innovation, lower manufacturing costs due to increased worker productivity, a change in price for basic commodities, and other factors of production that might relate to a single item such as an oven or washing machine. The disparity that we see between the expected price and the actual 2001 price represents the value gained through innovation. In real terms, the price of the oven fell compared with prices in general.

(continued)

(continued)

When using time value of money calculations, whether you are using the consumer price index or trying to estimate the amount your firm needs to save for a future investment, it is important to consider more than just inflation. The price of money, the lost opportunity of not having cash in hand, may be offset by the improvements to be gained through investment in technology or innovation.

Think about the changes in automobiles in the past 40+ years. The same newspaper had an advertisement for a brand new 1960 Mercury, 2-door Monterey Sedan, factory equipped for only $2,495.00. The CPI inflation calculator tells me that the car should sell for $14,961.57 in 2001 dollars. Just for fun, try to find an example of a 1960s car and then go to a local auto dealer. See what sort of technology you could buy today for slightly less than $15,000 and compare it to that 1960s car, if you can find one!

PRESENT VALUE

In some cases, we know how much we will need in the future to buy an item. In essence, we know the maturity value. If we put the money away today in an interest-bearing savings account, the interest earned will help defray the cost of the item we plan to purchase. We know the interest rate we will earn and the length of time we can leave the money in the investment account. What we do not know is the **present value,** or the principal component. How much do we need today in order to purchase the item in the future?

In order to move that future desired amount (the maturity value) into present-day dollars, we turn to the present value chart (A-3).

This chart looks very much like the compound interest chart. It, too, has a column labeled *n*, which corresponds to the number of compounding periods, and an interest rate (*i*), which is the periodic interest rate. An inspection of the table values shows that unlike the compound chart, the table values are all less than 1.0. This makes sense since we are solving for the present value of an investment, the principal component only, and we

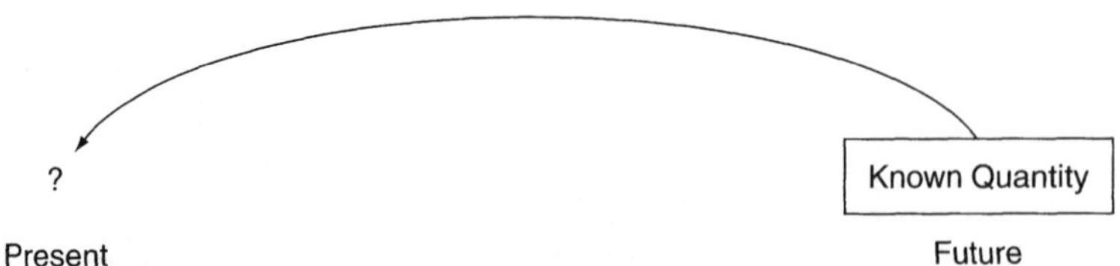

When the firm knows the future value (maturity value) that it requires, it can calculate the present value, or principal, that must be invested at a certain rate of return in order to reach the desired maturity value.

The factors in the present value table are in decimal form. If you converted them to percents, they would express the percent of the maturity value that must be invested today. The complement (100% − the table value) is the percent of the final investment that is earned interest.

know the future value, which is the principal as well as the interest earned. You would not want to invest more money in a savings account than you received in the future, would you?

$$PV = MV \times TV(n,i)$$

where

PV = The present dollar amount that needs to be invested (in other words, the principal)
MV = The maturity value that we desire
i = The annual interest rate ÷ the number of compounding periods
n = The number of years × the number of compounding periods

Notice again that the table value combines the interest rate and the time period into one factor.

Sam's parents estimate that in 5 years from now they will need $5,000 to pay the first year of tuition at the state college Sam is interested in attending. How much must they invest today in a 5-year certificate of deposit that offers 6% compounded monthly?

$$PV = MV \times TV(n,i)$$

where

MV = $5000
i = 6% ÷ 12 months = 0.5%
n = 5 years × 12 months = 60

$$PV = MV \times TV(n,i)$$
$$PV = \$5{,}000 \times 0.74137$$
$$PV = \$3{,}706.85$$

Remember that the difference between the $3,706.85 that Sam's parents invested and the $5,000 that they estimate they will need is the value of the interest they have earned during the 5 years ($1,293.15). For purposes of this chapter, we are going to disregard any taxes that might be owed on interest income. In future chapters, we will look at the tax implications of investment income.

Both the compound interest and present value tables assume that there is a single transaction. A specific amount is deposited in an investment account and

Stop and Think

How do we know for sure that an investment will return a set amount of income or interest?

We have assumed that interest rates will remain constant over a relatively long period of time. In the example of the teachers' pay, the contract called for a specific rate of increase in each of 3 years, so we can use that figure with assurance. The other examples imply that the interest rate earned at the time of the investment will continue throughout its entire life. Unfortunately, there is no guarantee that the interest rate on savings accounts will remain constant in perpetuity. If the firm is valuing an investment such as a piece of property that will be held for future sale, the annual rate of return is even more difficult to assess.

The best strategy for choosing a discount rate (or an expected rate of return) is to use historical averages, if they exist, and adjust for current economic conditions that may influence those averages. An astute financial manager should construct several possible values for a single investment (conservative, realistic, and optimistic), which would allow for a range of possible future values. The discount rate used to determine each value should be stated, along with the assumptions that influenced the choice of rate.

earns interest until the maturity value is reached or a loan is negotiated to be due in full at some future date. In these instances we know the current value and are seeking the future (or compound) value. Perhaps we know the amount of a future expenditure and want to invest now (the present value) so that the money is available when needed. In both cases a lump sum is deposited. Interest may be posted as periodic payments, but the investment itself is not periodic.

INVESTING OVER TIME

As the amount of money required by the firm increases, the firm's ability to make lump sum investments diminishes. The firm begins to utilize a variety of payment plans, each of which takes advantage of interest earned but spreads payments over the length of the investment.

Lucinda wants to buy the gymnastics studio that she has managed for the past several years. She knows that the owners are contemplating retirement 5 years from now and are interested in selling the business. If she starts now, she hopes to save enough money for a sizeable down payment on the business. Lucinda has estimated that she will need $50,000 five years from now. The calculations we have performed thus far assume that Lucinda can invest a lump sum today at some agreed-upon interest rate. Assume that Lucinda can earn 6% compounded quarterly.

$$PV = MV \times TV(n,i)$$

where

MV = \$50,000
$i = 6\% \div 4 = 1\frac{1}{2}\%$
$n = 5$ years $\times$ 4 quarters = 20

PV = \$50,000 $\times$ 0.7424704
PV = \$37,123.52

Although her investment will earn interest of \$12,876.48, in order to have the \$50,000 down payment in 5 years time, Lucinda would already have to have amassed more than \$37,000. That may not be practical. She needs to begin investing now, in smaller increments, in order to meet her goal.

SINKING FUND

A firm can set up a savings account, called a **sinking fund,** into which it makes periodic payments and earns interest. After the payments have been made and interest posted, the firm will have reached the desired maturity value of that investment. If the firm is setting up a sinking fund (savings account) for some future use, it needs to calculate the present value of the payments that will result in attaining the desired maturity value. The funds that are immediately deposited will earn interest throughout the life of the investment, while later deposits will earn interest from the time that they are added to the fund.

Once again, the sinking fund chart resembles the charts we have seen earlier. There is a column labeled n, which corresponds to a number of compounding periods, and a row at the top that gives the periodic interest rate (i). The intersection of the two columns provides a table value that is multiplied times the desired maturity value. Note that the table values are very small, even smaller than the values in the present value table. The sinking fund chart (A-4) assumes that the deposits are made at the same interval that interest is compounded. In the real world, that may not be accurate: a firm may be able to add to the savings vehicle at any time with interest credited on specific dates. However, for the sake of simplicity, we will allow the previous assumption to stand.

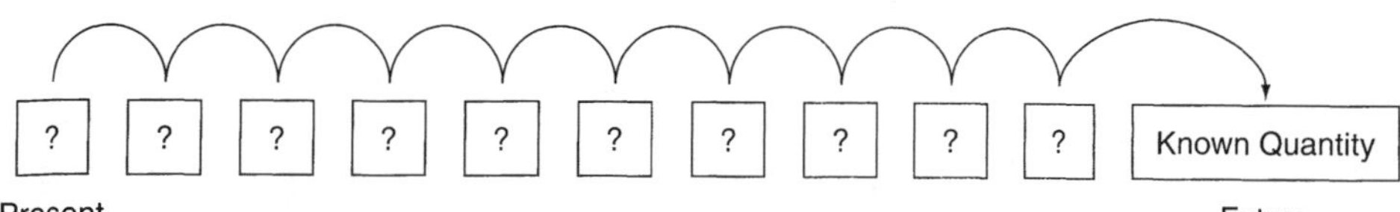

In some cases the firm has a desired maturity value in mind, however, the single sum is not readily available. A sinking fund, or savings account, allows the firm to save in increments and earn interest to attain its longer-term goal.

> *If the present value factor represents the percent of maturity value that must be invested at the beginning of the savings period, the sinking fund factor represents the percentage of maturity value that must be deposited* each time *the investor adds to the sinking fund. Since there are multiple periodic payments, each one will be a smaller proportion of the maturity value than a lump sum deposit.*

When we solve an equation using the sinking fund chart, we know the final maturity value that we desire. What is unknown are the principal payments that need to be made in order to attain that maturity value.

Lucinda needs to have \$50,000 in 5 years. Her bank offers the 6% compounded quarterly rate for lump sum deposits or quarterly deposits. Lucinda calculates her quarterly payments:

$$\text{SF} = \text{MV} \times \text{TV}(n,i)$$

where

$$\text{MV} = \$50,000$$
$$i = 6\% \div 4 \text{ quarters} = 1\tfrac{1}{2}\%$$
$$n = 5 \text{ years} \times 4 \text{ quarters} = 20$$

$$\text{SF} = \text{MV} \times \text{TV}(n,i)$$
$$\text{SF} = \$50,000 \times 0.0432457$$
$$\text{SF} = \$2,162.29 \text{ (rounded)}$$

Each payment will earn interest, just as the lump sum investment earned interest, but the timing of the investment allows Lucinda to make smaller and perhaps more affordable payments.

Stop and Think

> How much total interest will Lucinda earn on her sinking fund payments? If Lucinda makes 20 payments of \$2162.29 each, her total principal investment will be
>
> $$\$2,162.29 \times 20 = \$43,245.80$$
>
> By definition, the sinking fund account will be worth \$50,000, which means that Lucinda has earned
>
> $$\$50,000 - \$43,245.80 = \$6,754.20 \text{ in interest.}$$
>
> The interest earned on the sinking fund is less than she would have earned had she invested a lump sum, however, the sinking fund allows her to spread payments over time and may cause less disruption to her cash flow.

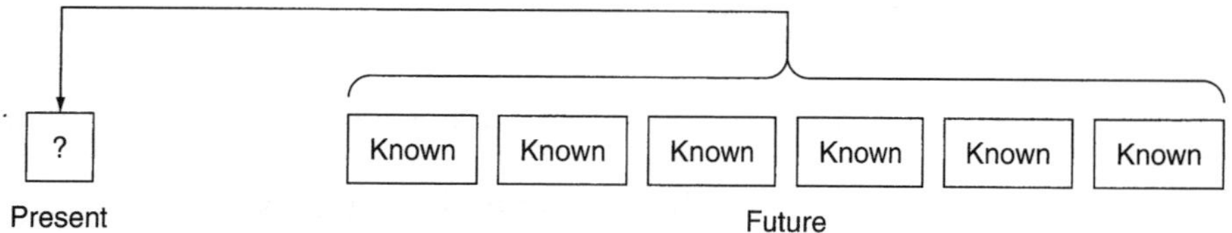

What sum would have to be invested today in order to yield a stated stream of future payments? That is the present value of an annuity.

ANNUITIES

The root word of annuity is *anno,* which means year. **Annuities** are a series of payments, usually of equal amounts and in specific intervals, which earn interest. The investment interval does not have to be a year; it can be monthly, quarterly, or even biweekly. It is possible to use the compound value and future value charts we have already looked at to determine a future value of a stream of payments, but the value of each payment would have to be calculated individually, which requires more work than necessary. Instead, we use annuity charts that are also found in Appendix A.

The value of annuities is influenced by whether the payments are made at the beginning or end of a compounding period. The principal in an annuity due is invested at the beginning of the compounding period and begins earning interest at that time. The first payment of an annuity that compounds monthly will have accumulated 12 interest payments by the end of the first year. By contrast, an ordinary annuity allows payments to be made at the end of a compounding period. The first payment does not earn interest until the second compounding period because there was no principal invested until the conclusion of the compounding period. After 1 year, the first monthly payment will have received 11 additions of interest.

PRESENT VALUE OF AN ANNUITY

Many states have lotteries in order to fund state services. Most lotteries promise to pay the jackpot in 20 or 25 annual installments. The lottery commission needs to determine what portion of ticket revenue needs to be invested now to fund the future payments of lottery winnings and what portion can be used for other purposes. The commission knows the value of each payment that will be made; it needs to determine the present value of that stream of expenditures.

Let's assume that the jackpot was $1,000,000 and there will be 25 annual payments made at the beginning of the year. Each payment will be $40,000 ($1,000,000 ÷ 25). We know the value of each payment that will be made; we need to determine the amount of money invested today that will allow us to make those guaranteed payments. We will use the chart for the present value of an annuity due (A-5).

$$\text{PV(a)} = \text{A} \times \text{TV}(n,i)$$

where

PV(a) = the present lump sum value that needs to be invested (in other words, the principal)
A = the value of each annuity payment
i = the periodic interest rate
n = the number of compounding periods

Assume that the lottery commission can invest funds at 5% compounded annually.

$$PV(a) = A \times TV(n,i)$$

where

A = \$40,000
n = 25 years × 1 payment per year
i = 5% × 1 payment per year

$$PV(a) = \$40{,}000 \times 14.7986$$
$$PV(a) = \$591{,}944$$

For a present investment of \$591,944, the lottery commission can guarantee that it will have sufficient capital to fund 25 yearly payments of \$40,000 each. Whatever revenue it earned in excess of the present value of the annuity can be directed to some other use.

Another use for the present value of an annuity chart is to determine the present value of income that a firm will receive over a period of time. Remember the apartment complex that Cole Property Management wanted to sell? Gilbert Properties would like to acquire the building and has offered to pay the entire asking price, however, they wish to stagger the payments over 18 months, making three payments of \$500,000 each at the end of 6-month intervals. Cole has another offer for cash to be paid immediately, however, the second buyer is only offering \$1,300,000 for the apartment building. In order to compare the two offers, Cole Property Management needs to have a present value for the stream of payments that Gilbert Properties is offering. Cole assumes that it could earn 6% compounded semiannually if it had the cash in hand. Gilbert's payments will be made at the end of the period, thus it is an ordinary annuity and we will use the present value of an ordinary annuity chart (A-6).

$$PV(a) = A \times TV(n, i)$$

where

A = \$500,000
i = 6% ÷ 2 = 3%
n = 18 months ÷ 6-month compounding period = 3

$$PV(a) = \$500{,}000 \times 2.8266$$
$$PV(a) = \$1{,}413{,}300$$

The equation tells us that if Cole received $1,413,300 today, it would be the same as receiving the semiannual payments from Gilbert. The cash offer Cole received was only $1,300,000, which is less than the present value of the stream of payments; therefore Cole should accept Gilbert's offer.

The present value of Gilbert's offer would change, however, if Cole could find an alternative investment that paid more than the 6% assumed in the previous example. Suppose that Cole could invest today and earn 12% compounded semiannually.

$$\text{PV(a)} = \$500{,}000 \times 2.6730$$
$$\text{PV(a)} = \$1{,}336{,}500$$

Gilbert's offer is still better than the cash offered by the Applegate Company, however, the difference between the two is less. If Applegate can be convinced to increase their offer to $1,340,000, Cole Property Management should take the cash.

Another Way of Saying It. . .

Another term for the present value of an annuity is **discounted cash flow.** The value of the cash inflows has been discounted by the interest rate that could have been earned had the firm had the cash.

FUTURE VALUE OF AN ANNUITY

When we calculated sinking fund payments, we were looking for the principal payment, which when augmented with interest would yield a known future value. Sometimes the principal payment and rate of interest are known, however, the future value of that investment is not known.

Alexander and Adams is a partnership. In order to protect the firm from loss should one of the partners die, the partnership has purchased a life insurance policy. The partners could buy a term insurance policy; at the end of term the policy would expire and there would be no residual (cash) value. However, the partners would also like to set up a savings vehicle. The insurer has offered a universal policy that includes a guaranteed death benefit as well as a cash

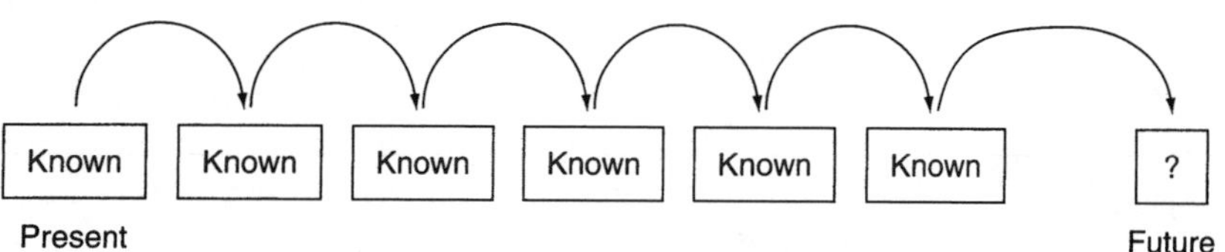

The maturity value of steady payments, each earning a stated rate of interest, is the future value of an annuity.

value component. Alexander and Adams's policy states that \$100 of each monthly premium is credited toward the cash value of the policy and will earn 4% compounded quarterly. Although they do not intend to cash out the policy, Alexander and Adams want to be able to calculate the cash value of the annuity. They know the value of each principal payment and the interest earned. Since payments are being made at the beginning of each month, it is an annuity due and Alexander and Adams will use the future value of an annuity due chart (A-7).

$$\text{FV(a)} = \text{A} \times \text{TV}(n, i)$$

where

FV(a) = the future value of a stream of known payments
A = the value of each payment
i = the periodic interest rate
n = the number of compounding periods

After 5 years, the cash value of Alexander and Adams's policy is

$$\text{FV(a)} = \text{A} \times \text{TV}(n,i)$$

where

A = \$100
$i = 4\% \div 4$ quarters $= 1\%$
$n = 5$ years $\times$ 4 quarters = 20

$$\text{FV(a)} = \$100 \times 22.2392$$
$$\text{FV(a)} = \$2{,}223.92$$

Alexander and Adams have made 20 payments that decreased the balance in their checkbook by a total of \$2,000, however, the cash value of the insurance policy is \$2,223.92. The difference is the value of the interest they have received.

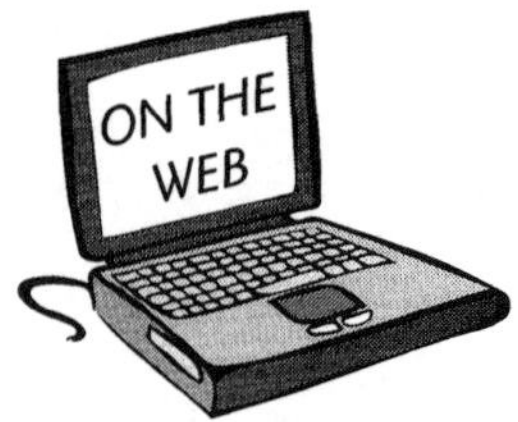

In calculating the present value of a stream of future earnings, we have been comparing the value of different investment options. There has been no assumption that the stream of income would actually be converted into present-day cash. However, there are firms that are involved in what is called the "cash flow industry" that do buy future earnings streams.

(continued)

(continued)

In order to find some of these firms, I went to a search engine and asked it to find sites having to do with lottery payments. The list below includes the firms that I found after one quick search. Each of the firms promises to purchase a variety of income: lottery and casino winnings, owner-held real estate contracts, insurance settlements, and military pensions, among other things. The seller is encouraged to fill out an on-line form that describes the stream of payments, and each of these firms promises to respond with a purchase offer.

http://integrityfunding.net
http://structured-settlements.org
www.drw.com
www.discovery-funding.com
www.stanfordservices.com
www.eastbaymortgage.com
www.fredcoutts.com
www.rp-capital.com
www.annuity-mort-purchase.com

I have to confess that the Web addresses for the next two companies appealed to the marketer in me. The addresses are easy to remember and express very clearly what the business is about!

www.money-now.net
www.webuypayments.com

Since you would know the value of the periodic payments you were receiving and the firm's cash offer, you could calculate the discount rate that they had used to construct their purchase price by rearranging the terms in the present value of annuity formula.

$$\text{PV(a)} = \text{A} \times \text{TV}(n, i)$$

becomes

$$\frac{\text{PV(a)}}{\text{A}} = \text{TV}(n, i)$$

To find the discount rate using the charts in Appendix A, you would go to the row that described the number of payments remaining and follow that line across the chart until you found a value closest to PV(a)/A.

It would be interesting to know if the discount rate varies depending on the type of income stream, for example, lottery winnings versus personal injury insurance settlements.

RISK AND RETURN

Calculating the value of financial investments at any given point in time requires making assumptions about the economic conditions that will exist in the future. As a result, many of the decisions that are made are based on the best guess of the forecaster and may or may not turn out exactly as planned. We call this uncertainty **risk.** Risk is neither positive nor negative. The word

Book Report

Against the Gods: The Remarkable Story of Risk
By Peter L. Bernstein, New York: John Wiley and Sons, Inc., 1998.

The title of this fascinating book alludes to the fact that until the Renaissance, the gods were given credit or blame for any occurrence that could not be predicted with complete certainty. The sun rose in the east but what was the chance that it would rain on any given day? Many explanations were offered but until very recently (in historical terms), there was no framework to describe the range of chances that existed. Now the local weather report will predict what percent likelihood there is that it will rain. The higher the percentage, the more likely it is that current atmospheric conditions will result in rainfall. The prediction describes what is expected to happen today based on patterns that have been established over time. The ability to provide a glimpse of the future within some degree of certainty provided a significant perceptual shift.

Mr. Bernstein begins his book by reminding us that gambling has been present, in some form or another, for as long as we have recorded history. And yet, gamblers did not have a system for determining the likelihood of success for each wager. A good result was often attributed to Lady Luck or the Fates, while a run of bad luck might be blamed on the interference of a not-so-benign deity. Modern-day gamblers may still practice this logic, but they have far more sophisticated predictors at their disposal.

The book moves from gambling as exemplified by games of chance to the idea that one could predict a community's mortality rate given statistics collected over a length of time. Being able to predict life expectancy allowed the growth of the insurance industry. Without a system of risk management, pricing of policies would be based on whim, not science, and the chances of financial ruin would be high.

The book's later chapters describe some of the more complex risk management strategies that have been employed such as futures, options, and derivatives. This section becomes more complicated, but it is well worth the effort. Probability and statistics were never this intriguing when I was in school!

does not indicate that all of the decisions will adversely affect an investment. The "risk" in falling interest rates is that a borrower may be able to renegotiate a loan and receive a lower interest rate. For the borrower the "risk" has been positive. For the lender, who is receiving less interest income, the risk is perceived to be negative. Risk itself is a neutral concept.

Investors and business owners are compensated for taking risks by the rate of **return** that they receive on their investment. Treasury notes issued by the United States government are considered virtually risk-free, and their return is low compared to other investments. Lending money to a bankrupt company is very risky, and the return that the investor would require is commensurately high.

The compensation, or return, that investors require varies between investments because the level of risk varies. One type of risk can occur due to the effect of management decisions. For example, a firm might decide to increase its leverage by using a higher proportion of debt financing than equity. If sales revenue decreases, interest charges become a higher percentage of the firm's operating earnings and more sharply reduce its net income. Risk is also influenced by market conditions unrelated to the firm issuing the security. In a period of high inflation, bonds that have a lower coupon rate (interest rate) will be less valuable, regardless of the business strength of the issuing corporation. The interest rate, even in the absence of other information, has made the bond less desirable.

There are several specific types of risk that investors should consider when calculating the expected return of an asset.

Liquidity risk describes the possible inability to liquidate an asset at fair market value. U. S. savings bonds can be cashed in at any bank in town during normal banking hours. There is no liquidity risk. On the other hand, the owner of a restaurant may find it more difficult to sell the building and equipment. Although the land and equipment can be carried on a balance sheet at some fair market value, there is no guarantee that the owner will find a buyer who is interested in obtaining precisely that location and mix of equipment. Even if the potential purchaser wishes to open another restaurant at the same location, the type of food to be prepared may necessitate investment in different equipment, which reduces the value of the existing property below its theoretical market value. The longer it would take to sell the asset, the higher its liquidity risk.

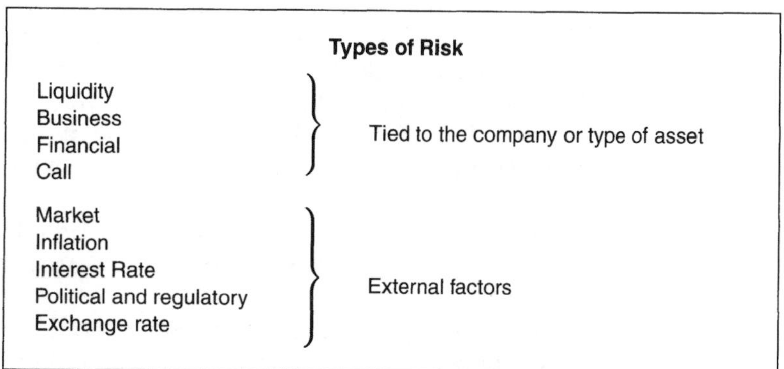

There are many types of financial risk, not all of which can be avoided by the prudent investor.

Business risk describes the type of uncertainty that is a result of the firm's operations. It can be as a result of industry changes or the decisions of an individual firm. For example, after years of growth, the personal computer market is slowing. The number of individuals who own personal computers has increased markedly over the years, so there are not as many new customers available. In addition, consumers do not perceive a need to upgrade their computers as frequently as a new model can be engineered. In order to stimulate sales, personal computer manufacturers are reducing prices, which in turn, lowers profit margins. Business risk can increase across an industry but at varying rates for participants within that industry, depending on how they adjust to market conditions. Business risk can also occur as a result of strategic decisions made by individual companies within a more stable industry. The decision not to extend store hours may cost a retailer revenue that then flows to a rival merchant. Business risk has increased as a result of the choice not to stay open later.

Financial risk is related to the amount of debt that a company issues. As the firm becomes more highly leveraged, its risk increases. Leverage describes the amount of debt a firm has in contrast to its equity, or the owners' investment in the firm. In a growing economy the risk due to leverage may not be as apparent, however, if sales revenue decreases, the proportion of interest expense to operating income will increase. In addition to interest, the firm may also be required to make periodic principal payments that decrease its working capital. The more highly leveraged the firm, the more risk there is that the firm may not be able to repay its debts.

Firms can assume debt by borrowing from a bank or by issuing bonds. Each bond issued has terms that the borrower must meet and these are spelled out in an indenture. We will discuss bonds and indentures in more detail in Chapter 13. Among the options available to the bond issuers is the right to call in the bonds under specified circumstances. A company would choose to call in their bonds if they could retire higher-priced debt and replace it with lower interest loans or bonds. **Call risk** is the risk to bondholders that the bond may be called by the issuer before maturity. In that case, the investor does not receive the interest payments that were expected. Although the principal has been repaid in full, the investor may not be able to realize as high a rate of return without increasing the risk of the substitute investment.

These first types of risk are closely tied to the type of asset or specific company that issued the securities. To some degree, these types of risk are known and can be managed. The investor can choose to purchase a callable bond, knowing the risk involved, and will demand a higher coupon rate to compensate for the call risk. Companies with higher financial risk will be required to offer higher coupon rates on their bonds to offset the risk the investor is taking. In each of these cases, the risk is considered diversifiable risk. The type of assets within an investment portfolio can be balanced, or diversified, to include both high- and low-risk holdings.

Other sources of risk result from broader-based economic or social changes that affect a wide variety of businesses and are considered systematic or undiversifiable risks.

Market risk is associated with overall market movements. For many years, it appeared that the stock market could only increase in value. However in 2001, the stock markets lost value across the board. Even if a corporation had sound business strategies and limited debt, the value of stock plummeted. Bond values were also affected by consumer confidence rather than just the underlying creditworthiness of the issuing firm. Some analysts claim to have the ability to predict market movements, however, there is no surefire formula that determines exactly how the market will behave.

The change in general market interest rates can affect the value of an investment. This is called **interest rate risk.** When interest rates rise, the value of existing bonds usually falls: a bond that had been issued at 6.5% will be worth less than a bond that now must be issued at 8% to meet prevailing interest rates. The higher the interest rate climbs, the less the older bond will be worth. Conversely, if interest rates fall, bonds that carry a higher rate of interest will increase in value. The gain or loss in value will not be realized unless the bond is sold, so a bondholder whose investment has theoretically fallen in value will not suffer a capital loss if the bond is held to maturity. There is a lost opportunity to have earned more on the investment. Interest rate risk affects stock prices as well. As interest rates rise, the company's cost of borrowing increases, leaving less profit for owners/shareholders and causing stock prices to fall. If interest rates fall, the price of stock tends to increase. Changes in interest rates also affect the value of fixed assets such as land and buildings. If interest rates rise, the business owner might be more reluctant to invest in new property as the total cost of the acquisition (land and interest charges) increases. In order to keep monthly expenses within a targeted range, the price of the property needs to decrease in order to absorb the effect of rising interest rates.

Inflation risk is commonly referred to as purchasing power risk. When market prices increase faster than the revenue that a firm receives or the interest that an investor earns, the real value of the investment has decreased. A bank that issues a fixed rate mortgage is subject to inflation risk if interest rates rise and it is required to pay more to depositors than it receives from mortgage income. This situation occurred in the 1980s and contributed to the savings and loan failures. A retired worker may calculate living expenses and invest in order to provide that level of income. If the cost of goods and services increases, the fixed income from investments will not keep pace with living expenses, and the retiree will have suffered from inflation risk.

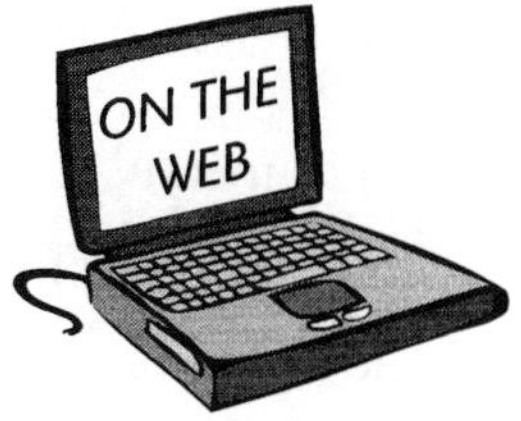

Between 1966 and 1979 interest rates fluctuated dramatically in part as a response to high levels of inflation. Because savings and loan associations were limited in the amount of interest they could pay on deposits and were also restricted from investing in anything other than home mortgage loans, the stage was set for a financial disaster.

The Federal Deposit Insurance Corporation (FDIC) provides an outline of the factors that led to the savings and loan crisis, including the effects of interest rate and inflation risks.

For more information go to www.fdic.gov/ and look at the tab called Bank Data. You'll find a section entitled Banking Industry, which provides analysis, statistics, and history.

Inflation risk is also tied to interest rate risk. During inflationary periods, the Federal Reserve often pushes interest rates higher as we will see in Chapter 4. Inflation causes the price of goods and services to rise, interest rates to rise, and stock prices (and profits) to fall. The rate of inflation has a strong enough effect on the economy that we often separate it from interest rate calculations and talk about interest rates, the inflation rate, and the real rate of interest, which is the market interest rate less the rate of inflation.

Governments and municipalities create regulations and impose taxes in order to provide for the public good. **Political and regulatory risk** describes the costs that result from those decisions. If the government wishes to stimulate the economy and lowers taxes in order to do so, the cost of operating a firm may decrease. If the government imposes a tariff on imported goods, the cost of goods sold increases, which could adversely affect the firm. Changes in capital gains taxes have been debated for many years in Congress as well as during presidential elections. A change in this law might affect investors' willingness to hold or sell certain types of securities and could increase the risk for issuers. A change in pollution control laws affects corporate expenses, which in turn affect the rate of return for shareholders.

Any firm that engages in international trade or any investor who invests in global securities incurs **exchange rate risk.** Currency values fluctuate in relationship to one another and converting income between currencies can result in a gain or loss. Procter & Gamble Corporation manufactures and sells consumer goods around the world. The revenue earned in Great Britain could be combined with revenue from Mexico to fund the expansion of a plant in Cincinnati, Ohio. A contractor in Ohio wants to be paid in dollars, so Procter & Gamble must convert its earnings into the currency desired by that specific vendor. In some cases it will be dollars, in others it may be the yen, the peso, or the euro. Each time the conversion is made, however, the company may receive a different ratio of dollars to yen or pesos to euros. The difference in exchange rates can have a significant impact on a multinational corporation such as Procter & Gamble. It can also affect a small company whose largest client is an

In the News

Pension funds that offer a defined monthly benefit often contain a clause that raises the monthly allowance in step with the increase in the consumer price index (CPI). Cost of living adjustments (COLAs) are meant to increase monetary payments in order to maintain purchasing power. For senior citizens, the CPI might not be an accurate gauge.

An article in *Business Week* explains that expenses for elderly have risen 3.5% since December 1982, compared with 3.3% for all consumers. The difference is largely due to the cost of health care, which has increased at a faster rate than other components of the CPI. For senior citizens, the general inflation rate may understate the increase in their cost of living.

Source: der Hovanesian, Mara. "Seniors, Beware of a Thief called Inflation." *Business Week,* July 30, 2001, p. 96.

Toolbox

Measuring risk is important, however, the calculations can be complex. What portion of investment risk is attributable to financial risk assumed by a firm and what part to interest rate risk? How much of a factor is inflation? Tax policy? How will all of these factors affect an investment in a specific stock or bond issue?

There are a few published tools that can assist an investor. No formula or designation can guarantee the level of risk that is being assumed, but there are some guides.

As we will see in Chapter 13, the coupon rate (or interest) that a bond carries is determined in part by the level of financial or business risk of the issuer. The higher the bond rating, the less risky the bond is. An investor who wishes to minimize business and financial risk can choose a bond with a rating of AAA through A, leaving the more risky bonds to other investors.

Although it is difficult to predict how the stock market will perform, it is possible to describe how a particular stock will do relative to the market. A beta coefficient is an index of risk that measures the stock's return relative to the market. If the stock has a beta of 1.0, it moves exactly with the market as a whole. If the market is down 10%, the stock will decline by 10%. A beta coefficient of less than 1.0 means that the stock is less susceptible to market fluctuations, whether the market goes up or down. A coefficient of 0.7, for example, means that if the market increases in value by 10%, the stock will increase by only 7%. That may not be desirable in an expanding market but in the case of a recession, the stock will lose less value relative to the market as a whole. A coefficient of 1.2 means that the stock will increase 12% when the market gains 10% and will lose 12% if the market decreases by 10%. Beta coefficients are published by Value Line, a company that sells investment reports. Firms that are interested in obtaining a report can subscribe to the Value Line service or contact the firm for specific reports. Many libraries have a copy of Value Line in their reference section.

overseas buyer. In both cases, exchange rate risk describes the fluctuations in earnings that can occur simply because of the variability of exchange rates.

TERMS TO KNOW

Time value of money
Consumer price index (CPI)
Future value
Maturity value
Simple interest
Compound interest
Present value
Sinking funds
Annuities
Discounted cash flow
Risk
Return
Liquidity risk
Business risk
Financial risk
Call risk
Market risk
Interest rate risk
Inflation risk
Political and regulatory risk
Exchange rate risk

TERM PAPERS AND PROJECTS

1. If you currently receive a stream of payments such as an annuity or military retirement income, contact some of the companies that purchase cash flows and see if you can figure out the discount rates they are using when they make the cash offer for your annuity.
2. Interview a business broker who buys notes from owners who have financed the sale of their house. Ask what criteria are used to value the note.
3. How does a financial manager for an insurance company, pension fund, or lottery commission determine what investments need to be made in order to make sure that organization can fund its liabilities?
4. Bethlehem Steel announced that it would file for bankruptcy protection in November 2001. It stated that one of the reasons for its financial difficulties was that the number of pensioners was five times the size of its current workforce and that funding future retirement benefits had become an unwieldy expense. What has happened to the company since then? Did it emerge from bankruptcy? If so, how did it handle its long-term pension obligations?
5. Can you afford to retire? See Supplement A.

REVIEW QUESTIONS

1. What do we mean by the future value of money?
2. Describe simple and compound interest. Give a short example of each.
3. What is maturity value?
4. What is present value?
5. Describe a sinking fund. What is its purpose? Give an example.
6. What is an annuity? Give an example of an annuity and why it might be preferable to a lump sum payment.
7. Name and describe the types of risk associated with investments.
8. Discuss how the finance manager can moderate the level of risk assumed by the firm.

PROBLEMS

1. Rebecca got an income tax refund of $650. If she invests the money in an account that pays 8% interest, compounded quarterly, how much will she have at the end of 10 years?
2. Ralph invests $1,500 in his credit union account, which pays 6.5% interest, compounded daily. What will be the value of Ralph's account in 5 years?
3. Nancy wants to go to Europe the summer after she graduates from college. She expects to graduate in 2 years and would like to have $7,500 for her trip. How much does she have to invest today in an account that yields 6% interest, compounded monthly, in order to have the amount she wants?
4. Brian and Kristin want to begin saving for a house. They estimate that they will need $35,000 for a down payment and plan to buy the house in

4 years. How much should they put away each month in an account that yields 6% interest per year?

5. Georgia has received a lump sum settlement as a result of an accident. She would like to invest a portion of the settlement so that it provides $25,000 of income for the next 25 years. If the investment company is willing to offer 5% interest, compounded annually, how much will Georgia pay for the annuity?
6. Ted's grandmother has been adding $500 per quarter to a college savings account. She began saving 15 years ago and the account has earned 4% interest per year, compounded quarterly. How much is the account worth today?

Supplement A:

CAN YOU AFFORD TO RETIRE?

Although retirement seems to be very far away, we will see that saving small amounts regularly is the key to having a good amount of money at retirement. But how much do you need to save? That is the point of this exercise.

Where to start:

1. Estimate the number of years you believe you have until retirement.
2. Estimate how many years you will live after you retire.

Now for the figuring:

Identify each investment account you have by type. Is it one that has a balance now but will not be added to on a regular basis? Then you will need to look at it as a "lump sum." Do you have a pension or an IRA that you add to on a regular basis with a predictable amount of money? That is two accounts: the lump sum value that is in the account now and the annuity that you will be adding in the future.

Think about this, though: Those items that will be investments in the future are only those items that you might sell and use the proceeds in order to support yourself. Thus, if you plan to pay off the mortgage and continue to live in the exact same house, the house is not an investment. If you have property that would be sold at some point and the proceeds disbursed over time, that *is* an investment. If you plan to stay in your current house until you retire, sell it at that point and move to a less expensive place, the difference between the current value of your larger house and the current value of a house that would meet your retirement needs can be considered an investment since a certain portion of the equity in the house would be freed up.

The same logic applies to checking accounts. Most of us keep a certain amount of money in our checking account to cover the monthly bills:

(continued)

(continued)

utilities, mortgage, and food. If you are using your checking account as a money management tool, the value for investment purposes is zero. A savings account can be either an investment or a cash management tool as well. For example, if you keep only a small amount in your savings account to meet unexpected bills, it would have no future investment value since it is assumed that you will always want that stable and secure backup. If, however, you are using your savings account as a long-term investment, include it in your calculations.

The most efficient way to define your assets is to list each one in a worksheet such as the following:

RETIREMENT WORKSHEET

Asset	*Definition*	*Current Value*	*Estimated Growth*	*Future Value*
House	Current and future residence			None
Land held for investment	Lump sum	$15,000		
Savings account	Current working funds or investment?			It depends on its definition
Checking account	Current working funds			None
Pension:				
Current value	Lump sum	$43,250		
Contributions	Annuity	$3,600/year		

You will need to calculate:

3. The lump sum future value of your current investments.

Calculate the future value at some interest rate that reflects the amount you believe you will earn on your investments. You can choose differing discount rates for each type of investment, such as a pension fund invested in stock or the piece of property in a rapidly growing area. Each asset needs to be valued.

You will also need to adjust for inflation. Rather than come up with an astronomical number that we cannot equate to current spending patterns, subtract what you believe will be the growth in the economy over the long-term horizon that you envision. For example, if I believe that stock market investments will grow at their historical rate of 10% per year, and I believe that inflation can be held to 3% per year, I will use an

(continued)

(continued)

adjusted rate of 7%. If I have invested in a certificate of deposit that earns 4.5%, the inflation-adjusted earnings are only 1.5%. Use the column labeled "Estimated Growth" to define the rate of increase you expect by asset.

Using the tables found in Appendix A, determine the future value for each asset. For example, the land held for investment may be appreciating at a rate of 12% per year because it is located in an area where demand for housing has increased. If inflation is assumed to be 3% per year, the after inflation rate of growth is 9%. Using the number of years until your retirement and the future value of a lump sum table, calculate the inflation-adjusted value of the property. This value should appear in your worksheet under the heading "Future Value." Note that the assets that are assumed to remain in use, such as your residence, have been assigned no value.

When you have valued each item separately, combine them to determine the estimated future value of your current investments.

Next:

4. Using an inflation-adjusted rate of return and the number of years you estimated that you will live *after* retirement, calculate the value of the annuity you would receive from that lump sum. Compare the value with your estimate, in today's dollars, of the income that would provide the lifestyle that you desire during retirement. Remember that if you have calculated no value for your house but have assumed that it will provide shelter, your future housing costs will be different from your current costs.

There may be a shortfall at this point. Now you will have to work backward:

5. How much more would you like to have when you retire (in current dollars)?
6. What is the present value of that investment at the end of your working life? Remember, you are working backward now.
7. That "present value" becomes a future value for this next question. How much do you need to start saving now to have that future value/present value on the day you retire, given the earning assumptions you have chosen?

One final thinking question: In your own words, explain what effect it would have on your decision making if you inherited money from Great-Aunt Matilda. What effect would an unanticipated lump sum bequest have on your financial planning?

CHAPTER

10 CAPITAL BUDGETING

LEARNING OBJECTIVES

1. Describe capital budgeting and why it is important to the firm.
2. Identify the types of assets that are covered by capital budgeting.
3. Calculate costs and cash inflows associated with the purchase of a long-term asset.
4. Differentiate between start-up costs and ongoing expenses related to a new investment.
5. Discuss the effect of depreciation on the decision to purchase an asset.
6. Distinguish between an operating lease and a capital lease.
7. Calculate the payback period for an asset.
8. Explain why risk occurs in capital budgeting decisions.
9. Calculate the value of an investment using the net present value method.
10. Use the profitability index to evaluate investments with different levels of required funding.
11. Calculate the value of an investment using the internal rate of return.

LONG-TERM DECISION MAKING

The history of American business is full of stories of entrepreneurs who began what are now multimillion-dollar businesses by packing their wares into a canvas bag and selling them door-to-door or building the next best invention in the basement or garage. These visionaries started on a shoestring, but as their companies grew a structure emerged—office buildings, factories, and equipment all had to be procured. The items could be purchased or leased, but the acquisition of these long-term assets was necessary for the expansion and continued success of the organization.

And so it is for other businesses. In Chapters 8 and 9 we looked at relatively short time horizons such as annual budgets and even 10-day cash payment periods. In this chapter we address capital budgeting, or planning for the future of our organization when the future revenue stream is uncertain.

Capital budgeting can be a very complex subject, one to which we could devote several chapters or even books. The focus here will be on analyzing the strategic implications of various investment alternatives and examining three tools we can use to evaluate the alternatives: payback period, net present value, and internal rate of return.

INVESTMENT IN THE FUTURE OF THE COMPANY

The crux of the long-term investment decision is that we are making choices in the present that will not realize their full return for several years. As a result, our analysis in this chapter will rely heavily on the time value of money concepts that were introduced in Chapter 2. In most cases, the cost of the equipment is known with some certainty but the returns will be best-guess estimates. This does not mean that companies should be paralyzed by uncertainty nor does it mean that they should leap into a new venture without doing any analysis whatsoever. It is simply a reminder that before the final decision is made, assumptions should be examined for decision biases, among them basing future sales growth only on recent trends, ignoring the effect of potential economic cycles, underestimating the effect of competition or government regulation, and continued consumer acceptance of our product.

Occasionally, the choice to make long-term investments are out of the firm's control. State and federal environmental regulations that call for companies to improve recovery of pollutants or clean up past waste sites may require that the firm invest in equipment specific to the task. Another example is replacement of an obsolete piece of machinery. At some point it becomes more expensive to repair or maintain equipment than to purchase new equipment. The decision is not whether to invest but which alternative is most efficient for the organization.

The types of assets we will consider will be primarily property such as land, buildings, and equipment, and either new technology or the replacement of existing machinery. For some companies, their most significant investment is the cost of research and development. The Pharmaceutical Research and Manufacturers of America, an industry trade group, estimates that it takes more than 14 years on average for a new medicine to go from lab to the marketplace and only 20% survive clinical trials and FDA scrutiny.[1] Once the drug makes it to the marketplace it has patent protection for 7 years, during which time the manufacturer hopes to recoup the investment in that drug as well as provide cash flow for further research and development. The length of the operating cycle and uncertainty of success make forecasting a challenge. The examples we will use are far more concrete.

All investments incur costs. The direct cost of a new truck can be calculated. Whether it is leased or purchased, there will be some form of payment (either monthly or in a lump sum) tied to the **acquisition** of the truck. However, we must not forget to factor in the change in **operating costs** that could accompany the acquisition such as increased insurance premiums or maintenance costs, the need for garage space, the additional license and property taxes,

[1]"A Health Cost Time Bomb?" *Business Week*, August 7, 2000, p. 153.

and other recurring expenses attributable to the purchase. If they are significant, these cash flows could affect whether the investment is profitable.

In addition to estimating costs, the finance manager needs to predict cash inflows, a task that can be difficult. The most obvious place to look is in the gross revenue figure. The addition of a second retail outlet should increase sales volume. Adding a second production line will increase goods available for sale and, if we have correctly forecast demand, result in increased revenue. Other investments add value by reducing cash outflows. If the firm maintains the same level of sales revenue but by investing in improved production processes can reduce waste by 10%, raw materials usage (a component of inventory) should decrease, increasing the value of net working capital. The firm might also choose to invest based on its future expectation of costs. The decision to automate should include an analysis of current and projected labor wage rates. If wage rates are rising, the savings from technological investment may increase over time, thus justifying investment.

Estimating the Cost of the Investment

The first step is to calculate the cost of the investment, including any financing assumptions. Because the final purchase decision may depend on the availability and attractiveness of financing, all possible options should be examined. For example, if our firm is interested in buying a piece of commercial property, the seller may offer us several payment options: a lower price for payment in full or a higher price in three installments spaced 6 months apart.

The list that follows lays out some questions that the firm should ask before it analyzes the purchase of a fixed asset. Some of the questions pertain more to equipment than property and the list is by no means exhaustive, but it will help to frame the assumptions that the firm is making.

The first set of costs are one-time or start-up costs. When we set up the analysis, they will be allocated to the first year (with the obvious exception of the payment plan described above and the second entry in the following list).

- Determine the underlying cash cost of the equipment. What would the firm be charged to obtain this piece of equipment if payment were made in cash today? The buyer is not literally going to walk into negotiations with sacks of money. However, the point of the question is to determine the lowest possible price that could be negotiated now. Often a vendor will offer better terms if the customer is willing to pay in full because it increases the vendor's working capital and lessens the exposure to risk of default.
- Are there other purchase options with implied financing such as payment in three installments or an initial down payment, monthly interest charges, and final balloon payment?
- What is the **disposal value** of any existing machinery? If the company is replacing an existing asset, it may retain residual value that could either be applied to the purchase of the new asset or be realized through sale to another company. Conversely, there may be an expense associated with disposal of the old asset, which creates a liability for the firm.
- What installation or start-up costs are associated with purchase of the asset? Are there transfer costs such as title search for property transactions or fees for registering change in vehicle ownership? Does the asset

require significant shipping and assembly fees, either provided by the vendor or as additional work performed by hourly workers?

- Will the purchase of the asset require additional supporting fixed assets? If we buy two new trucks, do they fit within the existing garage or will we be required to expand? What would be the timing of the expansion?
- Are there training costs involved? The cost of training includes any enrollment (or service fees) involved as well as travel expenses, per diem food costs, and time away from regular duties.

In addition to the start-up costs, we may incur ongoing costs. Remember that we are looking only at costs now, not the benefits that will result from the purchase.

- Working capital adjustments. If the fixed asset is a retail location or production line, how will it affect inventory, cash, and accounts receivable needs?
- If we are financing a machine or a piece of real property, what will be the current portion of the long-term debt and how will that affect current liabilities, thus working capital?
- Does the acquisition require greater investment in personnel? Will the number of employees increase? Will we require employees with higher skill levels? Are there recruitment or severance costs associated with redistribution of the workforce?
- Do operating expenses increase such as utility costs, insurance, maintenance, or permits?
- Are there tax implications? Local and state property taxes, including inventory tax, may increase.

Profit From the Investment

Calculating the cost of the investment was easy compared with determining the profit that will result. Again, we will use a list to prompt the type of questions the firm should ask in determining where cost savings and profits will occur.

- Are we projecting increased sales revenue? If so, is sales quantity increasing? How will the increase in quantity sold affect the price per item? Are we projecting price per unit increases? How will that affect demand? How long will this investment allow us to have a proprietary advantage? How soon will our competitors be able to duplicate this technology and would that affect prices? Will the sales revenue gained from this product or service line decrease sales or profits in another area of the company? What is the net gain?
- Are we projecting cost savings based on current expenditures? If so, are the relevant costs increasing at the rate of inflation or at some other rate? Do we need to adjust our savings assumptions?
- Are cost savings tied to raw material use? Do cost savings come from a change in raw materials or inventory mix?

- How soon will savings begin to appear? What is the learning curve of this machine or technology?
- Will there be savings in personnel? If so, what proportion is direct labor and what is salaried overhead?

In a very real sense, the opportunity to purchase machinery or invest in technology has returned us to the assumptions we made in break-even analysis. The distinction is that the financial analysis we are about to perform will take place over an extended time period, as opposed to the single-period analysis that we performed for break-even analysis.

THE VALUE OF DEPRECIATION

The subject of **depreciation** has been conspicuously absent from this text. All of the preceding balance sheets have given a fixed asset value with no corresponding offset for accumulated depreciation; the asset value has been assumed to be a net value. Because depreciation is a non-cash expense, it was not included in the cash budget. However, depreciation does affect the purchase decision for long-term assets because the ability to deduct depreciation expense reduces the firm's income tax liability. As a result, some mention of it will be included here. For simplicity, we will use the Modified Accelerated Cost Recovery System (MACRS) method of depreciation that is accepted by the Internal Revenue Service. Within its financial statements a firm may choose to utilize one of the other depreciation methods (straight-line, units of production, sum-of-the-years, or declining balance method), however what we are interested in are the tax implications of investment decisions so we will use only MACRS. For more a detailed discussion of the benefits of various forms of depreciation, the firm should defer to its accountants.

The MACRS method of depreciation is used for any asset placed into service after 1986. It assumes no salvage (residual) value for any asset and puts assets into one of nine recovery classes. The chart is reprinted in Appendix B and is available from the Internal Revenue Service. Depreciation is expressed as a percent of the depreciable value (which will be the same as the original cost). Because depreciation expense reduces profit by the full amount of the depreciation deduction, thus reducing taxable income, depreciation causes a net cash inflow to the organization in a sum equal to the depreciation expense times the firm's tax rate.

For example, Ben is considering buying a truck to use in his construction business. The truck will cost $35,000 and Ben has a marginal income rate of 30%. Using the MACRS depreciation schedule, the first year's depreciation is 20% of the cost of the truck or $7,000. Depreciation is subtracted from operating income. The noncash charge of $7,000 saves Ben $2,100 in taxes ($7,000 less income taxed at a 30% rate). The savings is real money, although the depreciation charge is not. Since MACRS depreciation rates vary by year, the annual tax savings will also vary. Depreciation does not cost the firm cash out of pocket, but it can add to the attractiveness of an investment.

Just because a machine has been depreciated to zero, as it would be under the MACRS method, does not mean that it has no productive value to the firm. Capital budgeting plans need to take into account the actual productivity of the equipment rather than the "useful life" ascribed to it by the IRS and depreciation methods.

Remember, too, that while the useful life for depreciation purposes may be 5 years, it does not mean that the equipment will last that long. Depending on the rate of technological innovation, capital assets may become obsolete much sooner than current depreciation tables recognize.

LEASING EQUIPMENT

Before we begin to analyze whether the asset will add value to the firm, we need to consider the option of leasing rather than purchasing the asset. There are two types of leases: capital lease and operating lease. A **capital lease** meets at least one of the following criteria:

1. The lease culminates with a bargain purchase price.
2. The title transfers to the lessee at the end of the lease.
3. The term of the lease is longer than 75% of the economic useful life (as measured by the MACRS recovery chart).
4. The present value of the minimum lease payments cannot exceed 90% of the purchase price.

Under FASB rules, capital leases are accounted for in the same way as an asset purchased with financing from the vendor. For that reason, we will treat capital leases as a form of financed purchase.

An **operating lease** does not satisfy any of the conditions set out above. It does not show up as an asset on the lessor's balance sheet; it is simply an operating expense on the income statement and fully deductible from earnings.

A capital lease meets at least one of these criteria:

1. The lease culminates with a bargain purchase price.
2. The lessee owns the item outright at the end of the lease.
3. The term of the lease is longer than 75% of the MACRS useful life.
4. The present value of the minimum lease payments exceeds 90% of the purchase price.

The qualities that define a capital lease. If an item meets one of these four criteria, it must be shown as a capital lease in the financial statements.

QUANTIFYING COSTS AND BENEFITS

Numbers need to be assigned to each of the costs and benefits that the firm has identified since they occur over a set period of years. The template used can be as simple or detailed as the firm needs. If in answering the list of questions in the earlier section the firm determined that the investment decision would be subject to subtle shifts in cost or income projections, it might want to create pro forma income statements showing revenue patterns, cost structure, and the net income attributable to this specific investment during a several-year period. Creating a pro forma statement for each investment opportunity takes concerted effort, and a firm may decide that rougher estimates will suffice.

The simplest format would show a single number representing net cash inflow (after yearly operating costs) for each year of the asset's expected life. For example, Ben is thinking of buying a new truck for $35,000 to use in his construction business. He has estimated the added revenue attributable to the truck (minus yearly operating expenses) for each of the 6 years he intends to keep the truck:

BEN'S TRUCK

	Net cash inflow
Year 1	$15,000
Year 2	12,500
Year 3	11,000
Year 4	10,000
Year 5	7,500
Year 6	4,000

The total net cash inflow is $60,000. How Ben arrived at those calculations is anyone's guess. Without some sort of spreadsheet, we can't examine the underlying assumptions. Although we do not have that level of detail, we will accept Ben's projections and use them to demonstrate the three evaluation methods that follow.

PAYBACK PERIOD

The payback method considers how many years it takes for the cash inflows to equal the original cost of the item. If the cash inflows are constant over time, the **payback period** is

$$\text{Payback} = \frac{\text{Cost}}{\text{Net cash inflows}}$$

If Ben had assumed that the added value was $10,000 per year for all 6 years, his payback period would be 3.5 years ($35,000/$10,000). In Ben's case, the truck will add decreasing value as the years go by, perhaps because Ben is assuming that maintenance and repair costs will increase. Since the added revenue stream is uneven, Ben will estimate the payback period. After the first year, it will have contributed $15,000 in increased revenue. The cumulative increase is $27,500 in year 2 and by the end of year 3, net inflow of $38,500 exceeds the purchase price. Sometime toward the end of year 3, the truck has paid for itself.

The payback method is simple to use, however, it does not take into account the time value of money. Using the payback method, the return on each of the following $10,000 investments would be equally valuable because the investment would have paid for itself at the end of the second year:

	A	*B*	*C*
Year 1	$5,000	$6,000	$2,000
Year 2	5,000	4,000	8,000
Year 3	5,000	2,000	2,000
Year 4	5,000		
Year 5	5,000		

Once the investment has paid for itself, the added value of later income is not considered. The payback method also does not allow us to adequately compare mutually exclusive investments that have dissimilar patterns of return. In the preceding example, the firm would not logically forgo the income produced by investment A in favor of either B or C. Clearly, a more sophisticated method is needed.

RISK AND CAPITAL BUDGETING

As soon as we project savings or expenses into the future, we are introducing an element of **risk.** Ben's estimates of the incremental cash benefit of the truck were "best guesses" based, most likely, on a gut feeling of what would happen. Every projection we make into the future includes the chance that we will "guess" wrong: that inflation will rise, that consumers will not accept a higher price or new variety for our product, that wage rates will escalate beyond our predictions, or that our cost of borrowing will change. The pharmaceutical industry knows that 80% of the products first created in the lab will not make it into the consumer's medicine cabinet. If they knew which would fail, they wouldn't pursue them and risk would be reduced. Since it can't be eliminated, the objective is to mitigate the risk and to set investment criteria that attempt to minimize loss while still encouraging innovation. Therefore, the cost of financing includes not just the cost of borrowing but an added risk premium.

When analyzing the future benefits of today's investments, companies often develop risk profiles based on the type of change represented. Replacing obsolete machinery with more productive, lower maintenance equipment carries a low risk. The chance for loss is minimized since we are not changing production techniques but in fact we are improving them. The change in our end product may be so slight that the only way our consumer would notice any change at all is because we were able to reduce our price by a penny or two. Risk has been reduced to almost nothing.

Automating a production line may carry slightly higher risk—the investment in equipment is fixed where labor can be variable. A machine cannot be laid off during a recession, so our cost structure has become less flexible at lower production levels. The risk of making the "wrong" decision has increased somewhat. However, as wages rise, the risk due to lack of flexibility may be offset by the higher wage rate. Managers will have to decide what risk premium, if any, they want to add to the cost of financing.

Investing in production equipment dedicated to an entirely new product line adds yet another form of risk; the risk that consumers will not accept the product or its pricing in quantities sufficient to generate a profit. In order for the firm to invest in new capital equipment, it will have to meet a higher hurdle rate such as the financing cost and a more significant risk premium. These three simple examples of the varying levels of risk that a company might face illustrate the fact that capital budgeting decisions need to be analyzed in the context of the firm's current operations and future strategic goals.

NET PRESENT VALUE

In Chapter 2 we introduced the time value of money. We said that money we have now can be invested, either in a savings account or in a business, and earn income for us in the future. Money we will not receive until the future is earning interest for someone else and is worth less (or perhaps nothing depending on the level of risk) to us in the present. The **net present value** (NPV) calculation brings a stream of future payments into the present and subtracts the current cost of the investment. If the present value of the stream of future earnings is greater than the cost of the investment, we should proceed with the investment. If our calculation results in a negative net present value, we would be better off investing elsewhere.

The key to net present value is choosing the discount value. There are two factors involved: the cost of borrowing money and the risk inherent in the investment. Unless we can finance all investments from internally generated funds, we will have to borrow money to finance our operations. The income we could receive from this potential investment comes at the cost of borrowed funds. If we assume that the income is risk-free, that is, there is no possibility of loss from the investment, we would use our cost of borrowing (or cost of capital). If, however, there is significant risk involved with this decision, we will want to set a higher discount rate. We should estimate the return we would expect for a similarly risky investment and add it to our risk-free cost of capital.

Once we have established a **discount rate**, we need to move the future earnings back toward the present. If the earnings are a steady stream, we can use a present value of an annuity calculation. In the case of Ben's truck, the earnings are unsteady so each year's revenue needs to be moved back as a lump sum. The present value is totaled and the current cost of the investment is subtracted. If the result is a positive number, the investment should be made. A negative number shows that the cash derived from the investment does not equal the cost of financing the investment.

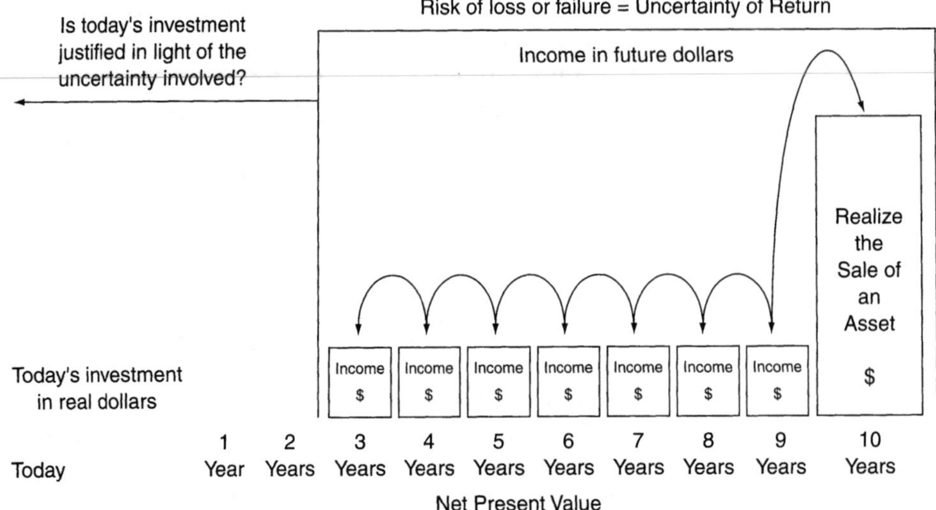

How do we assess the current value of an investment? The cost to us, in today's dollars, should be less than the present value of the income stream and any residual value, discounted to reflect the level of risk inherent in the investment.

Let's return to Ben's purchase of the truck. We will assume that the discount rate is 9% since that is the cost of the loan that Ben's bank will provide. We also assume that the cash benefit comes at the end of the year, so the cash flow for each year is discounted to the end of that year.

Ben's truck: Net present value

	Cash inflow	*Discount factor*	*Present value*
Year 1	$15,000	0.917431	$13,761
Year 2	12,500	0.841680	10,521
Year 3	11,000	0.772183	8,494
Year 4	10,000	0.708425	7,084
Year 5	7,500	0.649931	4,875
Year 6	4,000	0.596267	2,835
Total present value:			$47,120
Cost of the truck:			35,000
Net present value			$12,120

Moving the cash inflows to the present and subtracting the current price of the truck leaves us with a positive benefit of $12,120. Ben should buy the truck.

Often there are multiple alternatives that are mutually exclusive. Let's recall the opportunities we looked at in the payback section. We have $10,000 to invest and three choices, each of which would appear equal under the payback method. Which, if any, should we invest in?

Our first task is to determine the discount rate. We begin by assuming that each of these options carries the same level of risk, which the firm decides requires a 2% premium, and each can be financed at the firm's current cost of borrowing, which is 8%. The total discount rate is 10%.

OPTIONS

	PV factor	*Net cash inflow*					
		A		*B*		*C*	
		$	*PV*	*$*	*PV*	*$*	*PV*
Year 1	0.909091	$5,000	$4,545	$6,000	$5,455	$2,000	$1,818
Year 2	0.826446	$5,000	$4,132	$4,000	$3,306	$8,000	$6,612
Year 3	0.751315	$5,000	$3,757	$2,000	$1,503	$2,000	$1,503
Year 4	0.683013	$5,000	$3,415				
Year 5	0.620921	$5,000	$3,105				
Present value			$18,954		$10,264		$ 9,933
Cost			$10,000		$10,000		$10,000
NPV			$8,954		$264		−$67

Given the risk assumptions the firm has made, alternative A is the preferred investment because it returns the greatest value over time. Examine alternatives B and C. Each of them seems to return $12,000 in cash inflows but given the timing of the inflows, only B would be a viable option. The difference is due to the time value of money.

Some investments are made in stages. A firm may not have the borrowing capacity to complete an investment at one time, or it may be able to negotiate purchase terms that include staggered payments. In that case, several alternatives and multiple time lines may have to be factored. If the firm can calculate cash inflows that are tied to the various investment alternatives, both the cash inflows and the timing of the cash outflows will need to be discounted back to the present, and the investment with the higher net present value should be chosen.

PROFITABILITY INDEX

Another way of looking at the capital budgeting decision is to compare the present value of the cash inflows with the present value of the cost. The ratio is called a **profitability index (PI)** and is calculated

$$PI = \frac{\text{PV benefits}}{\text{PV costs}}$$

For the three investments above, the PIs are

A: 1.895

B: 1.023

C: 0.993

In the News

When sales of durable goods fall, manufacturers try to increase sales by offering incentives that can include lower financing costs, rebates, or reduced prices. Although this stimulates the sales of new products, it can drastically affect the value of used but still useful products.

When automakers offered 0% financing on new cars at the end of 2001, buyers chose to buy new cars rather than used cars. With no cost to the financing, the monthly payment for a new car was less than or equal to the payment on a used car. As a result, inventories of used cars increased.

Manufacturers also found that leased cars at the end of their contracts were selling for less than expected. When the manufacturer prices the lease, it does so with some idea of the residual value that the vehicle is expected to maintain. If the purchase price at the end of the lease is lower than expected, the net present value is adversely affected.

Source: "New-Car Deals Shake Up Market for Used Vehicles," *Wall Street Journal*, November 16, 2001.

This means that at the discount rate we chose, alternative A will yield $1.895 for every $1.00 invested. Both A and B return a profit, although B returns a much smaller one. Alternative C returns less than a dollar for every dollar invested, making it a poor choice. Note that the PI ratios will provide the same ranking that the NPV did.

One benefit to using a profitability index is to allow the firm to compare investments with different funding requirements. Look at the present value calculations for the following set of options, all discounted at 10%:

OPTIONS

		P		*Q*		*R*	
	PV factor	*$*	*PV*	*$*	*PV*	*$*	*PV*
Year 1	0.909091	$5,000	$4,545.45	$7,000	$6,363.64	$6,000	$5,454.55
Year 2	0.826446	5,000	4132.23	5,500	4,545.45	4,500	3,719.01
Year 3	0.751315	3,000	2,253.95	4,500	3,380.92	3,000	2,253.94
Year 4	0.683013	3,000	2,049.04	3,000	2,049.04	2,500	1,707.53
Year 5	0.620921	2,000	1,241.84	1,500	931.38	1,000	620.92
Present value			$14,222.51		$17,270.43		$13,755.95
Cost			10,000.00		12,500.00		9,750.00
NPV			$4,222.511		$4,770.428		$ 4,005.95

Looking at the present value of the cash flows, it appears that option Q is the best choice. It returns a net present value of $4,770, which is the largest return. However, the cost of the investments varies. If we analyze the investments from the standpoint of profitability, our choice would be different. Option Q, which had the highest net present value, also requires the largest investment. When the alternatives are compared based on cost and benefits, option P provides the highest profit per dollar invested. Even option R, which returns the least in terms of real dollars, is a more profitable choice than option Q.

	P	*Q*	*R*
Present value	$14,222.51	$17,270.43	$13,755.95
Cost	10,000.00	12,500.00	9,750.00
NPV	$4,222.511	$4,770.428	$4,005.952
Profitability Index	1.422251	1.381634	1.410867

As with all of the other analytical tools we have seen, the profitability index is only as valid as the assumptions the firm has made. However, it does provide a straightforward way of comparing unlike investment choices.

PRESENT VALUE OF A NON-INCOME-PRODUCING ASSET

Not every investment can be credited with a discrete set of cash inflows. We said earlier that changes in government regulations may require a firm to invest in pollution control equipment. Although the firm has no choice, the purchase will not result in revenue. Fixed assets such as a maintenance shop or warehouse are part of the cost of doing business and do not add value directly. In evaluating those investments, the finance manager should look for the lowest negative present value. Let's look at an example.

San Nicolas Manufacturing is located in a light industrial park. Demand for their products is growing steadily, and they expect to increase sales by 20% in each of the next 2 years. After that the increase in demand will not be as dramatic, however they believe the company will continue to grow. Their current manufacturing facility has enough space to allow them to double production, but they have just about reached the capacity for their warehouse. Two adjoining parcels have come on the market and the company needs to evaluate which would be the better choice. Both pieces of property are the same acreage and have all of the required improvements: sewer, utilities, easements, and roads.

The north parcel is vacant land that would cost $250,000. San Nicolas does not need the warehouse space for 2 years, at which time it believes it could build an appropriate facility for $125,000. They estimate that the warehouse would last for 15 years with no substantial alterations.

The south parcel already has a warehouse on it. The cost of the second parcel is $300,000. The warehouse is adequate and could be used as soon as the firm needs it, however, it is several years old and San Nicolas estimates that it would need to be refurbished in 7 years at a cost of $100,000. If San Nicolas uses an 8% discount factor, which alternative is the best? Since both of the alternatives require a cash outflow, they should choose the alternative that costs less in the present.

SAN NICOLAS WAREHOUSE

	North	*PV Factor*	*PV*
Today's cost	$250,000		$250,000
2 years	$125,000	0.857339	$107,167
			$357,167
	South		
Today's cost	$300,000		$300,000
7 years	$100,000	0.643506	$64,351
			$364,351

There is a very slight difference between the two alternatives. With the information we have been given, San Nicolas should buy the land and build the warehouse in 2 years because that decision represents the lower present cost. Of course, there are more questions San Nicolas could ask:

- If we buy the land, are we sure that we won't need a warehouse sooner than 2 years? Could we build before we ran out of space or would we have to lease elsewhere while we were building? What would that cost?
- If we buy the existing warehouse, can we rent it to another tenant, thus creating some cash inflow and reducing the current expense? How rapidly are construction costs escalating? Are we sure that years from now the warehouse can be refurbished for only $100,000?

The assets do not generate cash flows, so the uncertainty, or risk, of the investment centers around the costs inherent in the proposal. This type of investment is also one of the first that might be cut or scaled back in a recession.

INTERNAL RATE OF RETURN (IRR)

The **internal rate of return** describes the discount rate that will make the present value of the cash inflows exactly equal to the present value of the cash outflows. This particular rate of return is called an "internal" rate because it is specific to each investment and the cash it generates. In essence, the equation would be

$$\text{PV of cash outflows} = \text{Present value of cash inflows}$$

The present value of the cash outflows will be the present cost of the investment unless payments are being made in increments as we did in the San Nicolas warehouse. In that case, cash outflows need to be brought to the present.

In the net present value equation we chose the discount rate that we would use to bring the set of cash inflows to the present. In the internal rate of return, we assume that both present values are equal and solve for the discount rate that would make that true. If the cash inflows are a steady stream, we can solve the IRR with an annuity due table from Appendix A.

Let's assume that we have an investment that will cost \$15,000 and yield \$4,000 per year for 5 years.

$$\begin{aligned} \text{PV cash outflows} &= \text{PV inflows} \\ \$15{,}000 &= \$\,4{,}000\ (\text{PV of an annuity } X\%,\ 5\text{years}) \\ 3.75 &= \text{PV of an annuity } X\%,\ 5\text{years} \end{aligned}$$

We need to look at the present value of an annuity table in Appendix A and find the interest rate closest to 3.75 in the 5-year column. Unfortunately, there is not an exact match. We estimate that the internal rate of return for this investment is somewhere between 10.0% (3.79079) and 10.5% (3.74286). Is that estimate good enough? If we want an idea of the investment's value, this method will suffice. It won't work if we have uneven cash inflows. For that, we need to use a spreadsheet program like Excel or a financial calculator.

The internal rate of return allows us to determine if an investment will yield more than our cost of borrowing or the hurdle rate we have set for projects with similar risk profiles. The internal rate of return and the net present value method are similar in that they use the cash inflows generated by an investment and adjust for the time value of money. Where they differ is in the discount rate. The net present value method allows managers to set the discount rate and analyze whether the investment meets that goal. The internal rate of return method seeks the rate that the project would generate and then allows the manager to decide if the rate is acceptable. Either method provides a valid decision tool, but many managers prefer the net present value method. It is easier to understand and allows the firm to set a discount rate that equals the cost of capital and a risk premium. If the investment meets its target, it is accepted. If it has a negative net present value, it is rejected. The analysis is relatively simple to calculate and explain.

THE EFFECT OF CORPORATE STRATEGY ON INVESTMENT DECISIONS

Corporate strategy has an enormous impact on long-term investment decisions. Pfizer and Apotex are pharmaceutical companies. Because they manufacture products that will be ingested, they must maintain factories that meet the highest standards of cleanliness and safety. Their products must be produced to exact specifications and require significant investment in plant and equipment. But although both produce medicines, Pfizer has chosen to develop new, patented, and branded drugs while Apotex produces generic equivalents. Pfizer's strategy calls for sizeable investments in research and

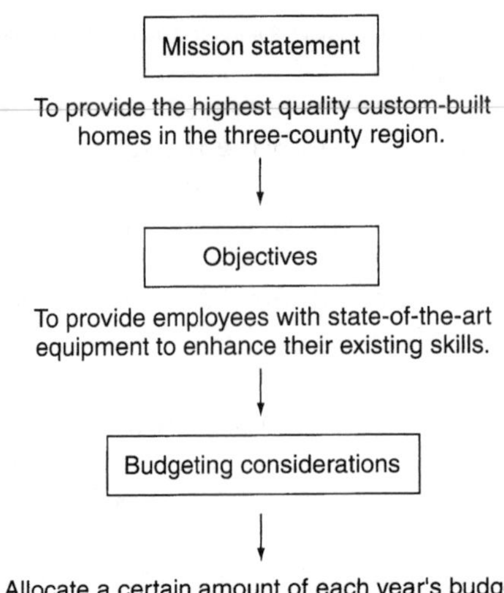

Mission statements often help define the types of investments that the firm will make.

development, which carries far greater risk than does Apotex's strategy. In both cases, equipment will be evaluated based on its ability to reduce manufacturing costs and increase productivity at a return that is greater than the cost of capital. However, given Pfizer's strategic direction a higher proportion of its investment dollars will be targeted to research. The cash inflows from its products have to support the risk that the company is taking.

There is no single framework that guarantees that the firm will always make a correct choice, however, the tools provided in this section will help take some of the guesswork out of long-term budgeting.

TERMS TO KNOW

Acquisition costs
Operating costs
Disposal value
Depreciation
Capital lease
Operating lease
Payback period
Risk
Net present value (NPV)
Discount rate
Profitability index (PI)
Internal rate of return (IRR)

TERM PAPERS AND PROJECTS

1. Determine the cost of financing a long-term investment. Include all the costs associated with lease or purchase including loan origination fees, penalties for early repayment, and any sort of loan insurance. How does this affect the total cost, the payback period, net present value, and profitability index?

2. Compare the cost of leasing a long-term asset versus buying it outright. Be sure to include maintenance costs or the value of a vendor-supplied maintenance agreement, the value of depreciation to the owner, and any residual value that might be realized if the asset were purchased. In the case of the asset you evaluated, does lease or purchase make more sense?
3. Investment in capital goods including significant investments in computers, automated factory systems, and telecommunications improvements fueled a good portion of the economic growth in the late 1990s. When the economy contracted in 2001, capital spending fell. What has happened to corporate investment spending since then? How has capital spending affected the economy? Did the Federal Reserve rate cuts in 2001 spur the type of corporate investment that the Fed intended?
4. Investigate the types of warehouse space that are available for sale or lease in your community. What is the vacancy rate for warehouse space? Is it in demand or have occupancy rates declined? Look at the availability of unimproved land. What costs would a company incur if they needed warehouse space? The choices would include buying an existing facility, leasing space, or buying property and building a warehouse.

REVIEW QUESTIONS

1. Describe three situations where a company might find itself in need of long-term investments.
2. Distinguish between start-up costs and ongoing costs. Give examples of each.
3. Businesses intend to make money, therefore they must profit from their investments. Give examples of profit-related questions that a firm must ask when considering a long-term investment.
4. What is depreciation? How does it affect an investment? What are the advantages of depreciating equipment?
5. Describe the difference between a capital lease and an operating lease.
6. What is a payback period? How is it used in decision making?
7. Name two types of risk a company takes when making long-term investments.
8. Why is it important for a company to estimate present value and profitability index in evaluating long-term investments?
9. Discuss the factors that would influence the discount rate that a firm chose to use for a specific investment.
10. What can be determined from the internal rate of return?

REVIEW PROBLEMS

1. What is the payback period for an investment that costs $54,000 and is expected to generate the following cash inflows?

Year	*Cash inflows*
1	$17,500
2	$15,000
3	$12,000
4	$10,500
5	$ 6,500

2. A company is considering three projects. The company's cost of capital is 12%. The cash flow estimates for each project are given below. The first year's value represents the costs associated with the project.

Year	*Project A*	*Project B*	*Project C*
1	($5,000)	($4,000)	($5,000)
2	$3,000	$1,000	$ 0
3	$2,000	$2,500	$4,000
4	$1,000	$3,000	$6,000

a. Calculate the payback period for each project.
b. Calculate the NPV for each project.
c. Calculate the PI for each project.
d. Estimate the IRR for each project.
e. If the projects are mutually exclusive, which one should the firm accept?
f. If the firm can fund two of them, which two should it fund?

CHAPTER

12 INVESTMENT OVERVIEW

LEARNING OBJECTIVES

1. Define who a lender might be.
2. Describe two ways to transfer funds to businesses.
3. Compare and contrast speculation and investment.
4. Describe the different types of investments available from a bank.
5. Discuss the services of an investment banker.
6. Describe the characteristics of equity.
7. Understand what commodities are and why one might invest in them.
8. Discuss hedging of currency as an investment strategy.

Throughout Part II we looked at individual companies and their need for financing to expand operations. One firm's need for cash provides another's investment opportunity, often with the help of a financial intermediary. Both individuals and companies invest excess cash in hopes of earning a positive rate of return within an acceptable range of risk. In Part III we will examine investment opportunities that result from the financing decisions of individual firms. This first chapter provides an overview of the types of investment vehicles that exist and their characteristics. Chapters 13 and 14 describe the types of bonds available and the mechanics of issuing, trading, and analyzing stock, respectively.

FINANCIAL INTERMEDIARIES

One of the main purposes of financial intermediaries is to transfer assets between lenders and borrowers. In this discussion, the term *lenders* is not synonymous with a bank or savings institution. **Lenders,** in this case, are those individuals or institutions that find themselves with an excess of cash. The process of transferring excess capital from one source to another results in a wide array of financial products that are created and administered by any number of financial intermediaries.

There are two basic methods for transferring funds to businesses. The first is a direct transfer from a lender to a borrower. This occurs when individuals invest in partnerships or buy securities (stocks or bonds) directly from the issuing company. Direct transfer can also be a privately funded mortgage contract or promissory note. Unless a single investor has enough excess cash to fund the needs of the borrower, this becomes a cumbersome process. The borrower needs to find enough investors with sufficient capital to fund the expansion. If the investment is in the form of a loan, the borrower would need to make payments to each of the lenders. The process becomes more complex as the amount of financing increases. For the investor, having a significant amount of capital invested in a single entity increases risk.

A second strategy for transferring funds is to pool the excess capital of many savers and transfer it to one or many borrowers. In this case, a financial intermediary is involved. For a fee the intermediary will ensure that the necessary funds are available, draw up terms and contracts, and arrange for the administration of the investment pool. The borrower has access to larger sums of money and individual lenders can diversify their risk.

SPECULATION VERSUS INVESTMENT

A **speculator** is someone who buys a security because of a belief that it will experience a significant increase in value during a very short time period, sometimes even in the space of hours. Speculators attempt to take advantage of pricing fluctuations that occur over short periods of time. The profit from speculation is not the long-term growth in value of the asset but capturing its short-term volatility.

An **investor** is someone who buys a security or puts money into a bank account, with the expectation that the value of the asset will increase over time and generate an appropriate rate of return. The time horizon can be as short as several months or as long as many years. There is less risk for an investor than a speculator because the expected time horizon is longer and the timing of the sale of the asset can be adjusted for short-term price fluctuations. If the buyer has researched the investment, it should be clear what the underlying risks are, what stream of income is likely to be produced over what time period, and what the risk-return relationship should be.

For most firms speculation is too risky. In Chapter 10, San Nicolas Manufacturing needed a warehouse to expand its operations. Until the firm had enough capital to make a purchase offer, the excess funds that it had accumulated might very well be invested in another asset such as a certificate of deposit or short-term corporate bond. But to speculate on the daily or hourly movements of stock prices or commodities might cost San Nicolas money they could ill afford to lose. With that in mind, we will be looking at investment opportunities rather than speculative ventures.

Read More About It

Warren Buffett is one of the richest men in America. He is the Chairman and CEO of Berkshire Hathaway, a holding company for his investments. Berkshire Hathaway owns property and casualty insurance companies, shoe companies, jewelry stores, and the candy company, Sees. The company also has large stakes in corporations including American Express, Gillette, Coca-Cola, and Wells Fargo.

Buffett's strategy is to buy companies that have fundamental strength because of tight operating controls, strong brand loyalty, dominant market share, or clear strategic vision. Whether or not it is a direct quote, his investment philosophy is that if you aren't going to hold a stock for 10 years, you shouldn't buy it for 10 minutes. He is the antithesis of a day trader!

As chairman of Berkshire Hathaway, Buffett writes the annual letter to the shareholders. Each year the letter is a gem, explaining the thinking that preceded that year's acquisitions and is full of humor, often self-deprecating. The letter truly is written to the shareholders who are invited to the annual meeting that is held every April in Omaha, Nebraska. The meeting is actually a shareholder's *weekend* where Buffett and his vice chairman and partner, Charlie Munger, meet with shareholders and answer questions from 9:30 until 3:30 in the afternoon, with a short break for lunch! There are opportunities for shareholders to buy from vendors representing various divisions of the company and a chance to play bridge (Buffett's passion), backgammon, or baseball.

Even if you are not a shareholder (shares trade at thousands of dollars per share), you can learn from Buffett and enjoy the benefit of his musings by viewing the most recent annual report at www.berkshirehathaway.com.

SAVINGS ACCOUNTS

We have looked at financial intermediaries earlier in this book when we examined financial institutions such as banks, credit unions, and savings and loans. We have also mentioned several different kinds of accounts that are available to borrowers. For investors, banks provide several basic types of vehicles. Some of the accounts are insured up to $100,000 by the FDIC, which means that there is no risk for those funds. Although they are safe, they do not offer high returns.

Checking accounts, also called demand deposits, allow firms to withdraw money on demand (hence the name) but do not pay interest. Most depositors pay for the checking account either through monthly fees or by maintaining a minimum monthly balance. The use of a checking account is essential for a business, however, from the standpoint of maximizing the return on excess cash, it is not a good *investment* choice.

Some financial institutions offer interest-bearing checking accounts, also known as negotiable order of withdrawal (NOW) accounts. **NOW accounts** pay interest but often require a higher monthly balance. Most NOW accounts offer relatively low interest, so the firm would need to determine whether the interest earned on the NOW account was sufficient to justify leaving the minimum balance invested. If the firm could obtain a NOW account for the same minimum balance that a non-interest-bearing checking account required, the firm would have a net gain. However, this is still not a place to invest large sums of excess capital.

A **savings account,** also called a time deposit, offers a slightly higher rate of interest but does not allow you to write checks. The rate of interest is guaranteed for a specified period of time. In order to withdraw the money, you must go to the bank and, technically, a bank can require a grace period before it releases the money to you. For that reason, the savings account is less liquid and has a slightly higher risk. Although savings accounts offered by an insured financial institution are guaranteed by the FDIC, there is a risk factor involved in the time that it may take for you to convert the deposit into cash.

Money market deposit accounts (MMDAs) are an alternative to savings accounts offered by many banks. The interest rate for a money market account is not guaranteed; it varies with the current market rate of interest. In general, money market rates are slightly higher than the rate earned on savings accounts. Some money market deposit accounts allow you to write a limited number of checks per month, but they are not substitutes for checking accounts since the number of checks allowed is few, often three per month.

MMDAs often carry a higher monthly minimum balance than a regular savings account. If the balance falls below the minimum, service fees are charged. Depending on the level of cash that a firm wishes to keep, a money market deposit account may not be flexible enough, given its relatively low rate of interest.

A **certificate of deposit (CD)** is a savings account that pays a higher fixed rate of return for keeping your funds on deposit for a set period of time, ranging from 30 days to several years. In general, higher rates of return are offered for certificates of longer duration and often require a higher minimum investment. If general market interest rates fall during the CD's term, you still receive the agreed-upon amount. There is a risk that interest rates will rise during the time that the money is invested, in which case the investor has missed an opportunity to earn more. Money in a CD can be withdrawn before the term elapses, however, the investor will incur a penalty for early withdrawal. Rates on certificates of deposit vary from one institution to another and also vary from region to region. If you invest in a distant financial institution, you should also consider any fees that are imposed for wire transfer of money.

One of the benefits of a certificate of deposit is that it allows a firm to invest excess cash for a short period of time with no risk of capital loss. For a small business with relatively little excess cash, CDs can provide an important cash management tool.

In addition to the accounts that are insured, some banks offer money market mutual funds, which are different from money market deposit accounts. **Money market mutual funds** pool money from many individuals and firms and invest in very large, creditworthy notes (debt financing) issued by the government or large corporations. Because they hold the assets of many individual investors, the funds are able to buy notes in large denominations, which tend to carry higher rates of return. Mutual funds are run by investment professionals and carry an investment management fee. The investor earns interest, minus an administrative fee, which is posted to the account on a regular basis. Money market mutual funds may be issued through a bank and allow you check writing privileges, but they are not insured by the bank nor the FDIC. Banks that offer money market mutual funds are required to notify the investor that the funds carry an investment risk, including the possibility of lost principal.

DEBT AND ITS CHARACTERISTICS

Checking accounts yield no interest and savings accounts yield very little. During some periods, the interest earned on savings accounts has not kept pace with inflation. Money invested lost purchasing power even though it was earning interest. Some investors prefer to own the debt of another institution. We discuss different types of debt instruments and their valuation in Chapter 13. Here we will discuss why an investor might choose to hold debt and some of the intermediaries involved.

When an investor buys a **debt instrument,** he or she is buying a stream of interest payments as well as the promise to repay in full the principal that was borrowed. Debt obligations can be short term, such as commercial paper, or long-term obligations such as mortgages. Most debt instruments have a face value, (the amount that is being borrowed), a stated interest rate, and a maturity date. If the investor holds the debt from issue date to maturity, he or she will know precisely what the income per period will be as well as how the principal is being repaid—either in periodic increments such as a mortgage or in a lump sum at the end such as a bond. If the investor does not sell the debt before its maturity date, the risk of the investment is twofold: the investor has missed an opportunity to invest at a higher rate and the issuer will default. The interest rate on debt instruments varies depending on the length of the loan and the quality of the borrower. In many cases, the original owner of the debt can sell the investment if he or she needs cash, however, this not only involves transaction costs but the risk that another investor might not readily be found.

If the borrower does enter bankruptcy, creditors have an earlier claim on the firm's assets than equity holders (or shareholders). Debt, whether it is short or long term, is listed closer to the top of a balance sheet, illustrating its greater liquidity.

There are many places where a company or individual can buy debt. U. S. treasury bills, or T-bills, are issued by the federal government with maturities ranging from 3 months to 12 months. T-bills do not pay interest directly; instead, they are sold at a discount and pay face value at the maturity date.

Debt

An obligation that the firm assumes in order to fund its operations.

Debt instruments can be as simple as accounts payable, a form of trade credit, or as complex as sophisticated bond issues.

Most debt instruments include a promise to pay interest along with the repayment of principal.

Debt and its characteristics.

Knowing the term of the note and its implied interest rate, the investor can calculate the initial dollar cost of the T-bill. They can be purchased directly from the Federal Reserve Bank branches, however, the minimum denomination is \$10,000, which effectively puts them out of reach of many small businesses.

Another debt instrument that is readily available but carries a smaller initial investment is a U.S. Series EE savings bond. The face value of Series EE bonds ranges from \$50 to \$10,000, but like T-bills, the bond is discounted so that it yields its face value at maturity. Savings bonds are very liquid. They can be redeemed at many banks before their maturity date for their current value, which would include any accrued interest.

Both of these forms of debt are issued by the U.S. government and are assumed to have no risk of default. An added benefit is that the income is exempt from state and local taxes.

Debt can be purchased directly from the issuer. Although we usually refer to it as accounts receivable, a retail jewelry store that finances its own sales is holding the debt of the issuer, in this case its customers. Manufactured home companies could set up finance subsidiaries and hold debt from customers. Collection agencies buy distressed debt at a discount and then attempt to turn it into cash. Private investors run advertisements in the classified section of the newspaper, offering to buy privately issued mortgages or promissory notes. However, most of the debt that companies buy is in the form of bonds issued by other companies or municipalities. They can buy directly from the corporation or through the intermediary of an investment banker.

INVESTMENT BANKERS

Unlike commercial banks, investment banks are not depository financial institutions. **Investment bankers** assist corporations in raising money by issuing securities, both bonds and stock. There are several steps in the process, which is supervised by the Securities and Exchange Commission.

First, the investment bank identifies a company that may want to sell securities and attempts to sell its services to that company. There are many investment bankers and they compete intensely for each bond or stock issue. Once an agreement is reached, the investment bank makes a detailed study of

The Many Roles of an Investment Banker

- Examine the creditworthiness of the client
- Determine the nature of financing: stock or bonds
- Determine an interest rate on bond issues
- Recommend an initial selling price
- Help find buyers for the securities
- Provide an estimate, or in some cases guarantee, of the net proceeds from the sale of the securities

These are among the many jobs of an investment banker. In light of some of the scandals of the last few years, the role of investment bankers is being reexamined.

the financial conditions of the client company. This report is called due diligence and is used to construct the company's offering.

Developing a new offering usually requires performing the following tasks:

- Determine whether the company should be issuing bonds, preferred stock, or common stock.
- If the company and its advisors decide on a bond issue, what is the prevailing interest rate for bonds of this quality?
- If the company is issuing stock, what is the initial public offering price? Will that yield the amount of capital that the firm needs?
- Select the features of the issue. Should the bond be callable or convertible? If the offerer is a municipality, will the bond be tax exempt? Will a certain number of bonds be retired each year or will the whole issue be redeemed at the maturity date?
- When will the issue be released? Whether it is a stock or bond issue, the timing of issue may be important. When does the client need the proceeds? Is there a competitive issue that will compete with this one and lower the proceeds?
- What fees will be charged for these services? Is the investment bank willing to underwrite the issue? Will they guarantee a threshold of capital for the issuer regardless of the volume of bonds or stock that is sold?

Once the type of offer has been determined, the investment banker draws up a prospectus. A **prospectus** clearly describes the issuer's finances and the risks associated with the offering. The material contained in the prospectus is strictly regulated by the Securities and Exchange Commission, if the securities are issued by a national company and expected to trade nationally. For a small company that does business in a limited area, the prospectus is usually supervised by the secretary of state. In every case, it is the responsibility of the issuer to fully disclose any facts that would materially affect the value of the investment.

Once the prospectus has been written, the investment banker attempts to find buyers for the securities. In some cases, major corporations such as insurance companies or large pension funds with significant sums of cash will buy large blocks of securities offerings. In other cases, the investment banker has to find a larger number of small investors. Sometimes the investment banker will underwrite the issues, which means to assume some of the risk of selling the securities. In an underwriting agreement, the investment bank agrees to purchase the securities at an agreed-upon price, called a *firm commitment price*. The issuing company has been assured of a certain level of funding and the investment banker is free to sell the issue at what is called the *offer price*. The difference between the firm commitment price and the offer price allows the investment bank to cover its costs. The issuing corporation has put the risk of not selling the securities onto the investment banker.

Bonds often have face value of $1,000 or $5,000, making them more affordable for a small investor. However, marketing costs are high enough that an investment bank is not likely to sell a single bond; they would prefer to sell large lots. Most small investors buy bonds from a local stockbroker, an investment firm, or from an on-line brokerage.

EQUITY AND ITS CHARACTERISTICS

When we talk about equity or equities, what springs to mind is the stock of publicly traded companies. But equity is any ownership portion of a company. Investing in a limited liability partnership is equity. Buying a membership in a grain co-op or even a local food co-op gives you equity rights.

In general, equity is the least liquid form of investment. If the equity is half of a partnership, it may be impossible to withdraw without disbanding the business. In a small corporation, there may be a limited market for shares. Equity holders have a residual claim on the assets of an organization; in case of bankruptcy or liquidation, they are the last to be reimbursed and have the highest risk of not being paid.

As owners, equity holders have the right to the profits of the organization. If all of the profits were paid out, however, the firm would not grow. For that reason, most balance sheets show several descriptions under the equity heading including retained earnings. Retained earnings are the profits that have been reinvested in the company. As such, they belong to the shareholders and are listed as part of the equity section. Retained earnings are not synonymous with cash, however. They may have been reinvested in the form of inventory or equipment or research and development.

There are many avenues by which a company can invest in equity. Some successful entrepreneurs provide seed capital to other small business start-ups. These individuals are often called angel investors. In return for an initial investment, the "angel" receives an ownership share of the company. The terms of the investment are negotiated between the two parties and are as individual as the parties who sign them.

Other forms of equity are the shares of public or privately held corporations. A privately held corporation does not sell stock to the public, however, it does have ownership shares. Many small biotechnology firms started as privately held corporations, funded initially by investment companies. Shares in the firm were assigned to the investment company as well as to the scientists who would provide the knowledge base for the firm. In order to reward employees for long hours and sometimes low pay, the companies issued stock. There was no outside market for the stock; it was hoped that these firms would be successful and would register with the Securities and Exchange Commission and go public.

Equity

Equity represents an ownership interest in an organization.

Equity is the least liquid form of investment.

The issuer is not obligated to repurchase equity.

In theory, equity holders have rights to the profits from the business. In practice, those profits are often reinvested and do not get distributed to shareholders.

In case of bankruptcy, equity holders are paid only after the creditors' claims are settled.

Equity and its characteristics.

Stop and Think

> What do you *do* with retained earnings? When I was in accounting classes, it used to frustrate me no end to see all of that lovely money sitting in retained earnings! If only I could take it and *do something* with it!
>
> Retained earnings and shareholders' equity describe money that is already, in a sense, spent. The liability and equity side of the balance sheet describes how the assets on the other side of the ledger have been funded (or financed). Sometimes there is debt associated with the assets, for example, the amount of inventory that is still not paid for because the accounts payable are not yet due. Or the office building that I bought that still has a mortgage lien against it. That form of financing is pretty clear.
>
> During the course of the business year, the proceeds from the firm are reinvested in inventory or hiring personnel or purchasing trucks, warehouses, or computer systems. If the funds have been invested with no corresponding debt, the increase in business has been funded by the owners and will show up as part of retained earnings. The earnings have been retained and used to further the growth of the firm. Those profits have already been put to work.
>
> At the end of the financial year, the accountant takes the net income figure (the amount of money earned by the firm, not paid out in dividends) and adds it to the retained earnings account. As a matter of fact, the money has already been added to the asset side of the balance sheet during the course of the year and the year-end entry merely squares the record.
>
> I have to admit that I still don't like that retained earnings account! I'm not an accountant. There's a reason I teach finance instead of accounting—I look at the retained earnings entry and see a black hole. Lots of money just sort of gets posted to the account at the end of the fiscal year and I haven't seen it.
>
> If only I could get my hands on that money. What I could do with it!

If and when they did, the stock would be valued by public markets and the original employees would be rewarded for the investment of their time and talent. A private investor who picked the "right" biotech company could have made money. There were, of course, high risks to this investment.

Many firms invest in equities through a stockbrokerage, whether with a personal stockbroker or through the use of electronic trading. We'll look at the mechanics of this in Chapter 14.

INVESTING AND SPECULATING IN OTHER ITEMS

Commodities are items such as corn, sugar, fuel oil, and metals like copper and zinc. Investors can buy a contract for the future delivery of a set amount of a certain quality of commodity through one of several commodities markets. The Chicago Board of Trade handles future contracts for agricultural products such as corn, wheat, and soybeans. The Coffee, Sugar, and Cocoa Exchange in New York City handles those items and others. Companies that use significant quantities of agricultural products invest in long-term commodities contracts in order to smooth the effect of fluctuating prices. Long before the coffee harvest is complete, companies that produce large quantities of ground coffee need to ensure that they will have the raw material they need at a predictable price. On any given day, a commodities trader might be able to get a contract for less than the long-term price that the company has locked in, however, the goal of the coffee roaster is not to always get the lowest price but to get the lowest consistent price for its raw materials inventory.

Some speculators brag about the money they have made trading commodities, and, indeed, the commodities market is an exciting spectacle. Traders wearing brightly colored coats wave frantically in order to attract the attention of whoever is buying or selling a contract that they want. Commodities trading is a specialized form of investment that would not be appropriate for a firm that needed a short-term working capital investment.

The New York Mercantile Exchange is the largest physical commodities trading center in the world. In the pits of the New York Merc, gold, copper, silver, gas, oil, sugar, cocoa, and other commodities are bought and sold. The New York Mercantile Exchange has a Web site (www.nymex.com) where they give information about trading commodities, buying a seat on the exchange, and visiting when you are in New York. You can also download educational publications including one titled "Why Do They Need to Yell and Make Funny Gestures?" That would be fun to read!

The Chicago Board of Trade (www.cbot.com) acts as the trading location for buyers and sellers of certain types of commodities. Many of the commodities traded at the Chicago Board of Trade are agricultural, which is logical when you think about where it is located—in the heart of the nation's farming regions. The Board of Trade provides a good introduction in their frequently asked questions section. One of the questions asked is: "How much of what is traded actually gets delivered?" The answer: typically 4% or less is actually delivered!

Like many of the contracts traded on the Board of Trade, trades made on the Chicago Mercantile Exchange (www.cme.com) are often not delivered. The Chicago Mercantile Exchange sells futures contracts, often called "derivatives" because their value derives from change in the value of the security that underlies the contract. For example, some of the futures contracts deal with foreign exchange products. Remember that we said that a firm engaged in foreign trade might want to **hedge** their exposure to foreign currency fluctuation by setting the value of a certain number of British pounds in terms of Korean won for delivery at a certain date. In that case, the firm would carry out the transfer of won for pounds. In other cases, traders will buy and sell future currency settlements if the price of the underlying currency fluctuates.

That's a complicated enough concept, however, what about buying "heating-degree days"? If you go to the Chicago Mercantile Exchange information page, they will explain that weather can destroy a company's

(Continued)

(Continued)

profits. We know that from experience. If a heat wave hits just as farmers need the rain to water new crops, the crops can be destroyed. A colder than expected winter will tax the production of power. California faced rolling power outages in the summer of 2001 when electrical generation capacity in the western region fell below demand. Prices soared and the two main power providers, Pacific Gas and Electric and Southern California Edison, were faced with huge power bills that they could not pass along to consumers. They would have liked to have put that risk off onto another party.

CME offers futures and options based on indices of heating and cooling degree-days in selected areas that experience significant weather-related risks. The derivatives allow firms to protect revenues in times of decreased demand or increased costs due to weather conditions. A full explanation of the weather futures and options can be found at the CME Web site under Weather Products.

To be honest, the idea of a degree-day strikes me as rather odd. I wonder if it is a "commodity" that will last for long or whether one of Chicago's famous gusts of wind will (figuratively) blow it off the Merc trading floor?

Real estate is a popular investment, both as undeveloped land and in the form of income-producing properties. A company might buy land with the expectation that it would be needed in the future. If the price of land were increasing at a higher rate than the cost of buying and holding the land, the company would be wise to buy the land. A company might also look at buying a warehouse or office building that could be leased until such time as the company needed the space if the revenue generated by the property met the company's discount rate. The warehouse or office building becomes a long-term asset whose present value can be calculated.

Real estate is also an attractive investment for a construction company. A residential builder might buy property in expectation that the growth of the market area would create future demand for homes. Having a parcel of land would allow the builder to create a housing development that could be built as a unified project. Working in one large tract would reduce the travel time for laborers and supervisors and create efficiencies. Buying property in advance of the region's population growth would be a logical long-term investment for this type of company.

In the News

Although our currency is not based on the gold standard, people still consider gold a valuable investment, especially when times are unsettled.

In November 2001, the World Gold Council ran an advertisement in the *Wall Street Journal.* The headline was "Be Prepared. Whatever the Forecast." The advertisement went on to say that gold was a "solid" investment alternative. (It *is* solid—when I was at the Federal Reserve

(Continued)

(Continued)

Bank of New York, our tour guide showed us dents in the concrete floor that were made when gold bars fell off the trolleys as they were being moved from one cage to the next!) The ad also states that gold helps stabilize an investment portfolio when "conventional" assets fluctuate.

There are several interesting facets to this advertisement. First, at the time that it ran, the country was in the first recession in a decade and was fighting a war against terrorism in Afghanistan. Consumer confidence had fallen to a very low level, and although the stock market had rebounded from its September lows, it was still volatile. For years, some of my students have told me that they would like to have a few gold coins hidden away somewhere, "just in case." I've always had my little bit of savings in the bank or an investment fund. It had never occurred to me to invest in gold, but it has always seemed safer and more secure to a certain group of my students than the mutual funds that we talk so easily about in class.

Second, the ad contrasts gold with "conventional" assets. What would conventional assets be? Historically speaking, it wasn't long ago that gold was a conventional asset for many people. Until recently, stocks and bonds were only for the wealthiest Americans. Mutual funds, which pool money and allow smaller investors to participate in the gains of the stock and bond markets, are relatively recent inventions. Land has always been an investment, but it is easier to sell precious metal than a small portion of a farm in eastern Oregon or central Nebraska.

Last, the ad says that you can sell gold coins and bars almost anywhere in the world. Gold can be exchanged for any form of currency, wherever you are. I could put gold coins in my suitcase and go!

For more information, the ad suggests that you contact the World Gold Council at www.gold.org.

Some investors prefer to buy commodities or items that they believe have intrinsic value. (Getty Images, Inc.)

TERMS TO KNOW

- Lender
- Speculator
- Investor
- Negotiable order of withdrawal (NOW) account
- Savings account
- Money market deposit account (MMDA)
- Certificate of deposit (CD)
- Money market mutual fund
- Debt instrument
- Investment banker
- Prospectus
- Commodities
- Hedging

CLASS PROJECT: BUILD YOUR OWN MUTUAL FUND

Each student should choose one company that is publicly traded. The mutual fund will arbitrarily purchase 100 shares of the companies' stock for the beginning balance of the portfolio.

During the duration of the class, students should research their own company just as a mutual fund analyst would do. Analysis should include financial statement examination and an assessment of the strategic position of the company. News about each firm should be shared with the class.

The instructor or the class can decide whether they are willing to buy and sell shares from the fund during the academic period. If they decide to trade, they will have to determine criteria such as

- Will the person who first chose the stock have the right to veto its sale?
- Does there have to be a majority consensus to sell or replace a stock?
- Does the portfolio need to be balanced between certain types of stock holdings or can it be a mixed portfolio?

Keep track of the market as a whole during the time period that you have the mutual find. Assess how well your picks did versus the market.

Note: There are several on-line services that will track closing prices for a stock portfolio. Some of them have limits on the number of stocks that can be held in the portfolio. If that is the case, an excel spreadsheet can be created and each student be held responsible for monitoring their own stock price.

TERM PAPERS

1. Write a book report. There is a book whose title fascinates me, but that I have not read. It is *How Wall Street Captured a Nation: J. P. Morgan, Teddy Roosevelt, and the Panama Canal* by Ovidio Diaz Espino. Knowing that Teddy Roosevelt did not particularly like J. P. Morgan makes this title all the more intriguing!
2. Warren Buffet takes long-term stakes in companies. Compare his views on the economy (as found in his letter to the shareholders of Berkshire Hathaway) with those of the chairman of the Federal Reserve System.
3. Work with an investment advisor to set up a savings and investment plan given your age, financial situation, and savings goals. Evaluate the

different investment options available to you and discuss the risks and potential rewards of several strategies.

4. Research the types of commodities that can be bought and sold on the different exchanges. Watch price fluctuations and determine what underlies the volatility. Determine which companies might be interested in hedging rather than speculating in these futures.

REVIEW QUESTIONS

1. Describe the two methods of transferring funds to businesses.
2. Differentiate between speculation and investing.
3. What is the difference between a NOW account and a checking account?
4. How are money market deposit accounts different from money market mutual fund accounts?
5. Why would a CD be an important cash management tool for small businesses?
6. What is a debt instrument? Give an example of a short-term debt instrument and a long-term debt instrument.
7. How do investment banks differ from commercial banks?
8. How does an investment bank operate?
9. What is meant by equity?
10. What are commodities? Why can they be risky as an investment?

CHAPTER

13

TYPES OF BONDS AND THEIR VALUATION

LEARNING OBJECTIVES

1. Describe what form of financing is represented by bonds.
2. Describe the information necessary on a bond and what it means.
3. Discuss the types of covenants that a bond might carry.
4. Explain the meaning of bond ratings.
5. Describe the types of risk associated with owning bonds.
6. Name the most common types of bonds.
7. Discuss the difference between a revenue bond and a general obligation bond.
8. Describe alternative ways of paying back a bond issue.
9. Calculate the price you should be willing to pay for a bond.
10. Discuss why bonds would trade at a discount or a premium.
11. Calculate the current yield for a bond.

In Chapter 12 we looked at investment philosophies and the general characteristics of differing types of investment vehicles. In this chapter we will look specifically at the types of bonds available and the method of valuing them.

WHAT ARE BONDS?

Bonds are a form of long-term debt. They are liabilities that carry a specified **principal value,** usually $1,000 or $5,000, and a maturity date by which the principal must be repaid. The principal is also referred to as **face value,** the value printed on the face of the bond, or **par value.** The bond's price is quoted as a percentage of its par value. For example, if the bond trades at 97½

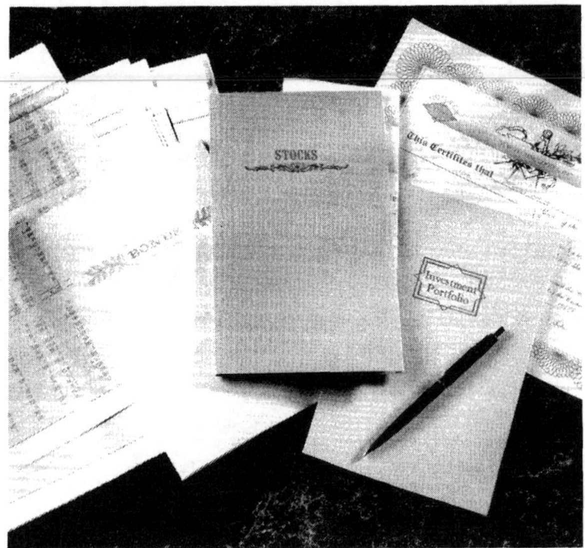

Stocks and bonds are types of securities. Bonds are specifically a form of debt which must be repaid. (Getty Images, Inc.)

it is worth 97.5% of the face value. For a $1,000 bond, that would be $975. For a $5,000 bond, the price would be $4,875. Quoting value in relationship to the par value allows buyers to see whether the bond is selling at a premium or a discount.

Bond owners receive interest that is stated on the face of the bond. Interest is also referred to as yield and is expressed in one of two ways: current yield or yield to **maturity,** both of which are explained later in the chapter. Many years ago, bonds were issued with coupons that the bondholder cut from the bond and redeemed for the interest. If the coupon was not cut and taken to the authorized agent, the interest went unpaid. Interest on bonds does not compound, so a delay in redeeming the coupon could be costly. Interest is expressed as simple annual interest and most often disbursed in semiannual payments. Today, many bondholders do not even take physical possession of the bond, let alone cut coupons, however, you will still hear the interest rate referred to as a "**coupon rate.**"

BOND TERMS AND CONDITIONS

Each debt instrument has terms that the debtor must meet. The terms, also called **covenants,** are stated in a legal document called an indenture and vary based on the financial condition of the borrower. One of the most common requirements is collateralization of the debt, that is, pledging tangible assets in order to secure the loan. For example, a mortgage is collateralized by the land or property that was purchased with the loan. If the borrower is unable to meet the terms of the loan, it is said to be in default and the lender can seize the property and sell it to recoup the principal, unpaid interest, and administrative costs incurred.

Covenants are designed to protect the bondholders from risk that the company could incur after the bonds are issued. Systemic risk cannot be averted but financial risk can be mitigated through use of restrictions on the future financial behavior of the company. Following are some examples of covenants that bondholders can request:

- Limits on dividend payments or stock buybacks if the cash outflow would reduce the firm's ability to make future principal and interest payments
- Limits on the issuance of additional debt
- The requirement to periodically retire portions of the debt
- A restriction on issuing lower-cost bonds to retire the current issue
- A description of the minimum financial ratios the firm must maintain

This list is by no means exhaustive but serves to illustrate the type of protection investors might seek.

The bond is said to be in default if the issuer does not make the required interest or principal payment, or if it violates one of the covenants spelled out in the indenture. If the issuer defaults, the indenture states what actions the investors can take.

While it is important to be aware of the terms of the bond issue and monitor the performance of the company, in practical terms it is difficult for the buyers to exercise that type of constant oversight. For that reason, a trustee is appointed for each publicly held bond. The trustee's job is to see that the terms of the indenture are met and to work with the company in cases where intervention is needed. Large banks often act as trustees for major corporate bond issues.

Chapter 2 examined the different types of risk that occur. Four types are of particular importance to this discussion: the risk of default, the risk that the price of the bond will decline, the risk that inflation will increase, and the risk that the company will call the bond before maturity.

Two rating services, Moody's and Standard & Poor's, have developed rating charts that describe the level of risk for each bond issue. High-quality debt, which has the lowest risk of default, receives a triple A rating (AAA), while the lowest-quality debt receives lower ratings. The two charts have slight variations in lettering but both serve the bond buyer by evaluating risk.

The rating of the bond issue has a significant impact on its original offering terms, as well as the subsequent resale value of the debt. Even companies that have very poor financial prospects can issue bonds, however, they will be required to meet stricter covenants and pay higher interest rates to compensate the buyers for the increased possibility of default. They may also find it more difficult to sell the initial offering since some investors will not purchase bonds that carry a low credit rating. The rating on a bond issue can change over the life of the bond if there are changes in the business or financial risk of the company. For example, the difference between an AA rating and an A rating is the possibility that future payments may be affected by adverse effects. Sales at an automotive company are susceptible to cyclical downturns in the economy. If consumer confidence falls, unemployment rises, and automobile sales decrease markedly, the credit rating of the company's bonds will be lowered even if the company has been making the required payments on time and in full. The ratings reflect not just current behavior but future expectations, especially for bonds that still have a long time until maturity.

Bond rating chart

S&P	Interpretation	Moody's	Interpretation
AAA	Highest rating	Aaa	Prime quality
AA	Very strong capacity to pay	Aa	High-grade
A	Strong capacity to pay; somewhat susceptible to changing business conditions	A	Upper-medium grade
BBB	More susceptible than A rated bonds	Baa	Medium grade
BB	Somewhat speculative	Ba	Somewhat speculative
B	Speculative	B	Speculative
CCC	Vulnerable to nonpayment	Caa	Poor standing; may be in default
CC	Highly vulnerable to nonpayment	Ca	Highly speculative; often in default
C	Bankruptcy petition filed or similar action taken	C	Lowest rated; extremely poor chance of ever attaining real investment standing
D	In default		

Standard and Poor's (S&P) and Moody's are agencies that rate the creditworthiness of firms. Although the ratings differ somewhat in appearance, the underlying rating criteria are strongly related.

In the News

AT&T issued $10.09 billion of bonds in November 2001, even though bond buyers were worried about the company's prospects. Bond rating agencies had downgraded the company in the weeks before the offering, worried about the debt load that the company already carried.

In order to successfully sell its bonds, the company had to offer enticing premiums. The 5-year bonds sold with an interest rate of 6.504%, which was 2.58% above the 5-year treasury bonds. Ten-year bonds sold for 7.35%, or 2.78% above the treasury bills. The 30-year AT&T bonds sold with a coupon rate of 8.096%, or 2.95% higher than the treasury bonds. Note that the premium continues to increase the further out the AT&T bonds are sold. The higher interest rate on the longer-term bonds demonstrates the risk inherent in lengthening the time until maturity. The interest rate also takes into account concerns that AT&T will not be able to service the debt.

Source: "AT&T sells $10.09 Billion of Corporate Bonds as Investors Line Up, Lured by Enticing Yields," *Wall Street Journal*, November 16, 2001, by Gregory Zuckerman and Richard A. Bravo.

Debt also carries the risk of price fluctuations if the holder sells the debt before maturity. The price of the bond can be affected by a reduction in the quality of the bond, but it is also subject to market conditions. Bonds carry a fixed interest rate. If market interest rates increase, the value of the bond will decrease since the investor can now get a similarly risky investment at a higher rate of return. The price of the bond on the secondary market will fall until it reaches a point that the interest earned on the capital invested matches the prevailing market interest rate. By contrast, when interest rates fall, as happened in early 2001 when the Federal Reserve attempted to stimulate the economy and stave off recession, the price of existing bonds will rise because investors cannot get the same rate of return as they did previously. The closer the bond is to maturity, the less its price will fluctuate because the bondholder will soon be receiving the principal, which must be repaid in full.

The third risk is that **inflation** will occur during the life of the bond and decrease the purchasing power of the interest earned and the principal repayment. If investors believe that inflation will be a factor during the life of the bond, they will add a premium for the length of the bond and their perception of the inflation risk.

Call risk occurs when a company reserves the right to repurchase bonds at specific intervals for a specific price. The company is attempting to manage its interest expenses by giving itself the option of retiring high interest bonds and replacing them with lower interest debt. The issuer benefits from the callable bond; the buyer incurs the risk. If the bond carries a call provision, it should also carry a higher rate of interest in order to offset call risk.

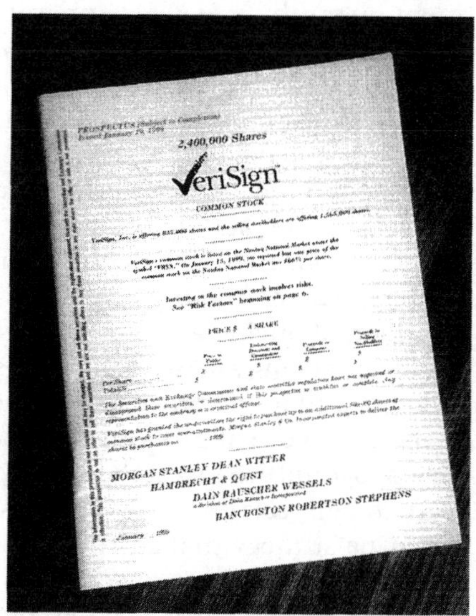

The prospectus outlines the rights and responsibilities of both borrower (the issuer of the bond) and the lender (the bond holder). (PhotoEdit)

COMMON TYPES OF BONDS

There are many types of corporate bonds and each has characteristics that differentiate it from the others. While each company's bonds are rated based on the underlying business and financial risk associated with the company, the type of bond also figures into the risk calculation.

Secured bonds are backed by company-owned property. Mortgages are perhaps the most familiar type of secured bond and are backed by real estate assets. Other forms of collateral depend on the nature of the business that is issuing them. An airline company would have bonds backed by its airplanes, a shipping company could collateralize its containers, manufacturers could issue bonds tied to equipment, and a retailer could pledge accounts receivable from its credit card operation. If the firm defaults on its bond, the bondholders, represented by the trustee, could seize the asset and sell it to settle the debt. They could also take possession of the asset and put it to use. In the case of a warehouse, the bondholders could accept the property and become the lessor. While collateralized bonds are the least risky, the bondholders do not want to take possession of the asset. The investors choose bonds because they want to earn the interest, not because they want to operate an airline or shipping company. In addition, if the bondholders were forced to sell the underlying asset, they might receive liquidation value rather than market value, and there is no guarantee that the sale would cover the company's indebtedness. Under a worst-case scenario, the collateralized bonds of a bankrupt firm will be the first ones paid. For that reason, they are the safest and carry the lowest interest rate of the bonds issued by the firm.

Debentures are unsecured long-term bonds of a corporation. Debentures are more risky than secured debt because, in the case of liquidation, debentures are paid after the secured bondholders have been satisfied. Firms with more than one set of debentures often describe the hierarchy of payment in the indenture that accompanies the bond issue. Bonds that are lower in the payment hierarchy are called subordinated debentures, and they increase in risk as their position on the balance sheet descends. Because of the increased risk, subordinated debentures require that the firm pay a higher rate of interest.

In spite of the higher interest rate, debentures may be preferred to secured debt because they do not encumber the underlying asset. Suppose that San Nicolas Manufacturing buys the property and warehouse that they were considering in Chapter 10, financing it with a mortgage bond. If San Nicolas sells the warehouse, their first responsibility is to settle with the mortgage bondholders, leaving them with less cash. If they have sold the property with the intention of buying a parcel that better suits their needs, they will need to reapply for financing and will run the risk that the new bond will carry a higher rate of interest than the previous one. Additionally, if there is a lag between the sale of the first piece of property and the purchase of the second, San Nicolas loses the opportunity to invest the entire proceeds in an interest-bearing account. The secured debt carries a lower interest rate but allows the firm less flexibility.

One strategy that a firm can use to lower the interest on its subordinated debentures is to add a convertibility feature. **Convertible bonds** are technically debt; that is, they have a stated maturity value and coupon rate, but they offer the investor the opportunity to convert the debt to equity at stated periods of time. For example, Green Manufacturing could offer a \$1,000, 10-year bond that was convertible into 20 shares of common stock during a 2 month window during the fifth year. The value of this bond would depend on the investors' assessment of Green Manufacturing's risk profile as well as expectations that the common stock value would increase. The convertible bond allows the bondholder two earning opportunities. If the common stock is worth $10 on the conversion date, the bondholder would keep the bond rather than exchange it since the conversion value is $200 (20 shares at $10 apiece). The company must continue to honor the bond, paying the periodic interest and retiring it at full face value upon maturity. However, if the stock value has increased to $75 per share, the bondholder would convert the $1,000 bond into $1,500 (20 shares at $75) of common stock. The principal would have increased by 50%, and the bondholder would also have received 5 years of interest at the stated interest rate.

The firm benefits from the conversion feature because convertible bonds carry a lower rate of interest than subordinated bonds without the conversion feature. The conversion rate is set above the price of common stock at the issuing date so that if the company has to redeem the bond for shares, it issues fewer than it would have on the origination date. The company's management hopes that the stock price appreciates enough that the bondholders do convert to stock. Bonds require that the company not only pay interest but also redeem the bond for cash upon maturity. If the stock price appreciates, a long-term liability is converted to equity. The bondholder receives cash value for the shares from a third-party investor, not the corporation. On the balance sheet, the value of the bond has moved from liability to equity, which reduces the debt-to-equity ratio. Once the firm has converted the bond, it has increased its ability to issue new debt and maintain a favorable amount of leverage.

MUNICIPAL BONDS

When voters approve a tax levy to fund local schools, a library, or airport improvements, they have authorized their local taxing authority to issue one of many types of municipal bonds. **Municipal bonds** are issued by states, counties, cities, and authorized public authorities such as school boards, highway commissions, and port districts. The funds appropriated by the citizens will be paid over a period of time as stated in the levy proposal, but it allows the agency to sell bonds immediately to fund the covered projects. Municipal bonds are able to offer a lower rate of interest than corporate bonds because the interest income is exempt from federal income taxes. In addition, if you buy a municipal bond issued by the city or state in which you live, it is exempt from city and state taxes as well. The purchase of municipal bonds is often promoted to individuals who pay high marginal tax rates, especially those in locations that have city, state, and federal income tax.

There are two types of municipal bonds: general obligation and revenue bonds. **General obligation bonds** are backed by the full faith and credit of the issuer. Because it is assumed that the municipality is able to raise taxes as needed, the bond is backed by tax revenue, often property taxes. **Revenue bonds** derive their funds from the income stream produced by the funded asset. For example, voters were asked to approve revenue bonds for a swimming pool in a neighboring community. The principal and interest payments would come from the receipts earned each summer minus the cost of operating the facility.

Now You Know

I've always wondered how the local school board sells its bonds. Who buys them? Through what selling agent? I know I pay taxes to fund the "bond issues," but who is getting that money?

The Olympian (Olympia, Washington) ran an advertisement on Sunday, November 11, 2001, sponsored by the City of Tacoma Finance Department. They were offering the opportunity to purchase tax-free minibonds with a $1,000 face value. Investors could purchase up to $10,000 and the proceeds would go to fund environmental services. The interest rate was not stated in the newspaper ad, although it did say that interest would be paid twice annually beginning on June 1, 2002.

While this may not be the most traditional way to sell bonds, you could have contacted the City of Tacoma Finance Department who would have sent you a prospectus detailing the costs, benefits, and risks of these municipal bonds. But the time for buying them was short: November 5–16, 2001.

Because the revenue bond has a stated interest rate and maturity date (as all bonds do), a revenue shortfall could cause the issuer to default.

Although municipal bonds are issued by a government entity, they are not risk-free. Unlike the federal government, local municipalities do not have the authority to print or issue money. If the tax or revenue receipts are not sufficient to repay the bond, it will default. Although defaults are uncommon, they do occur.

One of the difficulties with municipal bonds is the illiquid nature of the investment. Although there is an active secondary market for corporate bonds, for a small town or school district there may not be a large pool of investors.

INTEREST RATES AND MATURITY VALUES

All bonds carry a stated interest rate and a **maturity value.** A standard bond promises that in return for lending the face value, the bondholder will receive semiannual interest payments and a return of the principal at maturity. Zero-coupon bonds carry a stated interest rate but use it to discount the maturity value, thus determining the present value of the bond. Interest accrues to the bond during its life, and the full face value, which is paid at the maturity date, is the original loan plus the value of the accrued interest. Zero-coupon bonds are an attractive investment for people who want a specific amount of capital at a given point in time but do not need the periodic interest income. Zero-coupon bonds can be issued by corporations, municipalities, or the federal government. For the issuer, the initial cash inflow from a $1,000,000 zero-coupon bond issued at its discounted value is less than the same issue of interest-bearing bonds. The issuer would need to decide whether the working capital benefits of not having to pay periodic interest would be outweighed by the lower level of capital infusion into the firm. The buyer would have to decide if it were worth forgoing the cash interest payments in order to take advantage of lower out-of-pocket investment costs.

JUNK BONDS

Entire books have been written about junk bonds, also known as high-yield securities. "Junk" is the name given to bonds that are rated less than investment grade, which is below BBB or Baa. Early junk bonds were also called "fallen angels," which in some ways describes their fate. The bonds were originally issued by companies with sound financial situations and carried an investment grade rating. However, due to the financial or business misfortunes that had befallen the issuer, the bonds had become highly speculative or had technically defaulted. As the companies' fortunes declined, the market value of their bonds also decreased to the point that they traded significantly below face value. The market value was minimal, which made them worth about as much as junk, hence the name.

Because of their riskier profile, junk bonds must pay higher interest than safer bonds. The higher interest rate that the "fallen angels" earned was a result of the loss that original bondholders incurred when they sold the bond. If you had invested in a 10-year, 10%, $1,000 bond that was rated AA upon origination, continued to hold the bond when it fell to B, and were lucky enough to get all of your interest and principal at the end of 10 years, you would have received the promised 10% return on your original investment. If you were uncomfortable with the deteriorating financial picture and sold the bond, the subsequent investor would not have been willing to pay the $1,000 par value because the risk demanded a higher return. Since the semiannual interest payment was fixed at $50 (10% × 1,000 × ½), the second investor would bid down the price until it reached a level where the $50 semiannual interest payment equaled perhaps 13% or 14% of the newly determined market price. In the process, the seller lost part of his or her principal.

In the News

Just because a company has declared bankruptcy does not mean that its bondholders will go unpaid and its bonds become junk. Regal Cinemas, Inc., is the largest movie theater chain in America. On October 11, 2001, Regal filed bankruptcy, but it went into court with a reorganization plan that was backed by 95% of its creditors.

The reorganization was expected to take 3 months at the most. Between 20 and 25 older theaters would be closed, leaving the firm with more than 300 locations.

Creditors were in favor of the reorganization plan because they will receive full payment of their accounts. The only parties that will lose money are the leveraged buyout firms of Kohlberg Kravis Roberts & Co., and Hicks, Muse, Tate & Furst, Inc., who purchased the firm for $1 billion in a leveraged buyout. Under the reorganization they will emerge with nothing.

Source: The Olympian, Sunday, October 13, 2001, by Olympian Staff, News Services.

In the 1980s, a new type of junk bond emerged in response to the financing needs of leveraged buyout groups and hostile takeover participants. A prevalent strategy was to use massive amounts of debt in order to buy out the existing shareholders and obtain control of the corporation. The level of debt was so high in proportion to the equity that was created in the transaction that there was no possible rating for these bonds other than "speculative." Of course, each management group believed that it could quickly sell nonperforming assets to pay down debt, reduce operating expenses to generate increasing cash flows, and streamline formerly moribund organizations, turning them into dynamos that would attract a whole new infusion of equity capital with which to retire even more of the debt. Sometimes it worked. However, there were plenty of examples of LBOs and takeovers that ended in bankruptcy.

The structure of this new junk bond differed from the original "fallen angels" in that it had never been a high-quality issue. The interest rate on its face was designed to compensate investors for the risks inherent in the financing strategy.

Junk bonds have always been a speculative investment, whether they have lost credit standing or whether they were originally issued as high-yield securities. Investors who hold high-yield bonds have to assume that some will default. Each company that issues them doesn't plan to be the one that does.

In the News

The value of distressed debt that is available for sale rose dramatically between 1998 and the first quarter of 2001. Less than $150 billion of debt was available for sale in 1998. In the first quarter of 2001 alone, there was nearly $600 billion of defaulted and downgraded debt on the market.

Who would buy it? *Business Week* described three types of vultures: the Baron Vultures, Fast-Buck Vultures, and Last-Hope Vultures.

The Baron Vultures hope to pick up distressed debt and swap it for equity. These investors want the assets of the company that is in disarray in order to build a larger organization.

Fast-Buck Vultures buy troubled loans of debt-plagued companies at a sizeable discount. Most of the Fast-Buck Vultures want senior debt so that in any reorganization their claim will be the first paid. More senior debt also allows the investor to have a say in how the reorganization will progress. Although this group is called "Fast-Buck," there is an incredible commitment of time to negotiate the price that will eventually be paid on the defaulted bonds. Even with time and energy committed to the reorganization process, the strategy has risks and even senior bonds do default.

The Last-Hope Vultures are usually mutual funds or investment banks that originally purchased bonds at par and have seen them deteriorate to junk status. These "vultures" are not buying bonds; they already own them. Their strategy is to attempt to intervene in the bankrupt organization and enforce some sort of discipline on the company to stem future losses.

Source: "The Return of the Wall Street Vulture," *Business Week*, September 10, 2001, by Emily Thornton in New York, with Christopher Palmeri in Los Angeles and Mara De Hovanesian and Susan Rutledge in New York.

ISSUING BONDS

In Chapter 12 we talked in general about the services that an investment banker provides. When a company is issuing bonds, they will turn to an investment banker to facilitate the process. Investment bankers charge fees for the various services that they provide to companies during the financing process. The level of fees will depend on the complexity of the bond offering and the number of services the issuer requires. Fees and services provided are negotiable, so the company should check with different bankers before settling on one. As we look at issuing bonds in this section, we will ignore the investment banking fees and other transaction costs associated with the primary bond offering. From the practical standpoint, this perspective is unrealistic because the fees can be significant. However, since the fees and services are so variable even for the same company at different times, we will simply restate the fact that they exist and the firm should negotiate terms and conditions.

The firm should determine how much capital they would like to generate with the bond issue and the cost of borrowing. The bond issue can be tested for its effect on the balance sheet and income statement by creating pro forma financial statements and changing the interest rate and principal assumptions for the bond. The firm will also need to decide if it will retire a certain portion of the bond issue each year, or whether it plans to repay the entire principal at the maturity date. If the firm retires debt at a steady pace, it will lose the use of the money it has borrowed. However, if interest rates fall during the life of the bond, the firm can issue new debt at a lower rate. Retiring debt also releases the firm from the obligation to pay interest on the bonds that no longer exist. The firm has to weigh the costs of each of these choices.

Even if the firm plans to keep the principal for the duration of the bond's life, it will still have to plan for the eventual retirement of debt. Most firms would prefer to set up a disciplined savings plan in anticipation of the maturity date rather than having to use a substantial portion of cash in the maturity year. The firm can also take advantage of the effects of compound interest by setting up a sinking fund to which it makes regular contributions. However, the bond repayment assumptions will affect the amount of money invested in the sinking fund.

Green Manufacturing is planning to issue $100,000 of debentures with a coupon rate of 10% and maturity value of 10 years in order to expand its operations. Green plans to spend part of the issue's proceeds to buy new equipment, but does not want to secure the bond to the equipment because it feels that an unsecured issue gives more flexibility. Green's credit rating is good, so it has confidence that the bond will sell. Nan Green, the company's treasurer, has developed two alternatives for paying back the interest and principal.

The first option is to repay the entire amount of principal on the maturity date. The company would have use of the $100,000 for a full 10 years but would also have to pay interest to the bondholders for that time. Nan has proposed setting up a sinking fund to which the company would contribute every year in anticipation of the debt repayment. The future value of the sinking fund is predicated on needing $100,000 in 10 ten years. Nan estimates that the sinking fund could be invested to earn an 8% return.

The second option that Nan has looked at is a schedule that would call for the repayment of the bond in five equal installments of $20,000 beginning at the end of the second year. In this case, the interest owed would decrease based on the amount of the bond issue still outstanding. Nan has assumed that the sinking fund contributions should fund the 2-year, $20,000 debt repayment cycle with no additional use of company funds. At the end of each 2-year cycle, the beginning balance of the sinking fund would be zero, but it would be funded to meet a lower payout. The fund would still return 8%.

Even with the assumptions Nan has made, there are many questions about each of the alternatives. However, to start a discussion, Nan has developed the following spreadsheet that demonstrates the present value of each set of assumptions. The present value is calculated at 10% because Nan is assuming that that is the firm's cost of capital. Note that they can invest funds at less than the cost to borrow or use them. That is not an inconsistent assumption.

GREEN MANUFACTURING: BOND RETIREMENT CALCULATIONS

	Option 1: Retire all debt at the end of 10 years			*Option 2: Retire 20% of debt per year*		
Assumptions:						
Bond's coupon rate		10%			10%	
FV of sinking fund		$100,000			$20,000	
Earnings on sinking fund		8%			8%	
Firm's cost of capital		10%			10%	
	Outstanding principal	*Interest on debt*	*Sinking fund payment to retire debt*	*Outstanding principal*	*Interest on debt*	*Sinking fund payment to retire debt*
Year 1	$100,000	$10,000	$6,903	$100,000	$10,000	$9,615
Year 2	$100,000	$10,000	$6,903	$100,000	$10,000	$9,615
Year 3	$100,000	$10,000	$6,903	$80,000	$8,000	$9,615
Year 4	$100,000	$10,000	$6,903	$80,000	$8,000	$9,615
Year 5	$100,000	$10,000	$6,903	$60,000	$6,000	$9,615
Year 6	$100,000	$10,000	$6,903	$60,000	$6,000	$9,615
Year 7	$100,000	$10,000	$6,903	$40,000	$4,000	$9,615
Year 8	$100,000	$10,000	$6,903	$40,000	$4,000	$9,615
Year 9	$100,000	$10,000	$6,903	$20,000	$2,000	$9,615
Year 10	$100,000	$10,000	$6,903	$20,000	$2,000	$9,615
PV@8%		$61,446	$42,415		$41,479	$59,082
Total PV		$103,861			$100,562	

Note the effect of some of Nan's assumptions: Option 1 calls for repayment at the end of the life of the bond. Interest remains constant at $10,000 per year, reflecting the 10% coupon and full value of the principal outstanding. The present value of interest for this option is higher because the interest does not decrease over time. However, the sinking fund contribution is far lower, even though the future value of the sinking fund is five times that of Option 2. The sinking fund payment shows the value of compound interest. Payments made in the first 2 years will earn interest for 7 or 8 years. Using the rule of 72, the value of the first 2 years' payments will more than double during the life of the sinking fund. Option 2 depletes the fund every 2 years. The first 2 years' payments will not have to cover a lower payment but also will not have the chance to accrue a sizeable amount of interest earnings.

The difference between the present value of the two options is relatively small. In the absence of any other information, Nan should recommend that the firm follow the repayment plan outlined in Option 2 since it has the lowest present value. However, there are issues that have not yet been addressed by her analysis.

- Taxes. Interest payments to bondholders reduce taxable income and interest earned on the sinking increases taxable income. Nan will have to adjust the sinking fund payments to reflect the taxes paid on earnings. She will also be able to adjust the interest payments to reflect their true cost to the firm (the interest payments are an outflow, but the taxes not paid as a result of interest expense are considered a cash inflow).
- The use of the money. Green Manufacturing is borrowing money to expand its operations. Does it believe that the cash generated by the business expansion will be sufficient to meet working capital needs and allow it to repay the bond as quickly as Option 2 assumes?
- The overall financing of the firm. The bond that Green Manufacturing issues is not the only form of debt that it has on the balance sheet, and the costs and benefits of the different forms need to be seen in combination. If repaying the bond results in Green having to increase short-term borrowing, the interest cost of short-term loans might exceed the interest rate on the bond, making Option 2 more expensive overall.
- The risk profile of the company or industry. In order to obtain a more favorable coupon rate, Green might have to agree to retire the debt at regular intervals. Retiring the principal in stages reduces the risk of the overall issue. Nan's analysis might include a higher rate for Option 1, which in turn would affect its present value.
- The stability of future interest rates. Green is obligating itself to pay 10% for the next 10 years and has estimated that it can earn 8% on the sinking fund. If interest rates fall and Green has not locked in the 8% rate, it will have to increase sinking fund payments to offset the lower interest earnings. Of course, if interest rates rise, Green will earn more on the sinking fund investment. In addition, Green may be able to buy the bonds in the secondary market for less than face value, thus lowering its cash outflow.

Clearly, Green Manufacturing has many decisions relating to the issue of this bond that only they can answer. Present value analysis provides a starting point for evaluating the effect of other assumptions.

BUYING A BOND

If a bond carries the appropriate level of interest based on its risk, it should always sell at par value regardless of where in its life cycle the investor purchases it. While this may not seem intuitive, we will look at several time horizons in order to prove the statement. The key to the explanation returns us to the time value of money.

Green Manufacturing is issuing a 10-year, 10% debenture in $1,000 denominations. Because interest is paid on the face or par value of the bond, the investor can expect to receive $100 in interest per year. To simplify the calculations, we will assume that interest is paid once per year at the end of the year. We could assume that the interest was paid semiannually, in which case the investor would receive $50 per period (10% × $1,000/2). The result would remain the same. Assuming the investor purchased the bond on its issue date, here is the present value of all future cash flows from the bond:

	Interest	*PV @ 10%*	*PV*
Year 1	$ 100.00	0.909091	$ 90.91
Year 2	$ 100.00	0.826446	$ 82.64
Year 3	$ 100.00	0.751315	$ 75.13
Year 4	$ 100.00	0.683013	$ 68.30
Year 5	$ 100.00	0.620921	$ 62.09
Year 6	$ 100.00	0.564474	$ 56.45
Year 7	$ 100.00	0.513158	$ 51.32
Year 8	$ 100.00	0.466507	$ 46.65
Year 9	$ 100.00	0.424098	$ 42.41
Year 10	$ 100.00	0.385543	$ 38.55
Maturity value	$1,000.00	0.385543	$ 385.54
Present value of cash flows			$1,000.00

The present value of the principal repayment is less than $400. Remember that the purpose of present value analysis is to determine what you would be willing to pay today for money received in the future. If the investor had $385.54 today and could invest for 10 years at 10%, the principal would be worth $1,000. The difference between $385.54 and the $1,000 price the investor will pay for this bond is the value of the interest received over the course of 10 years.

The closer the bond comes to maturity, the more the investor would be willing to pay for the lump sum payment. Assume that the 10% coupon rate is still valid, given the risk. If the investor bought Green Manufacturing's bond after 6 years had passed, the present value of the $1,000 principal would be $683.01, much higher than it was when the bond was issued. If the investor put

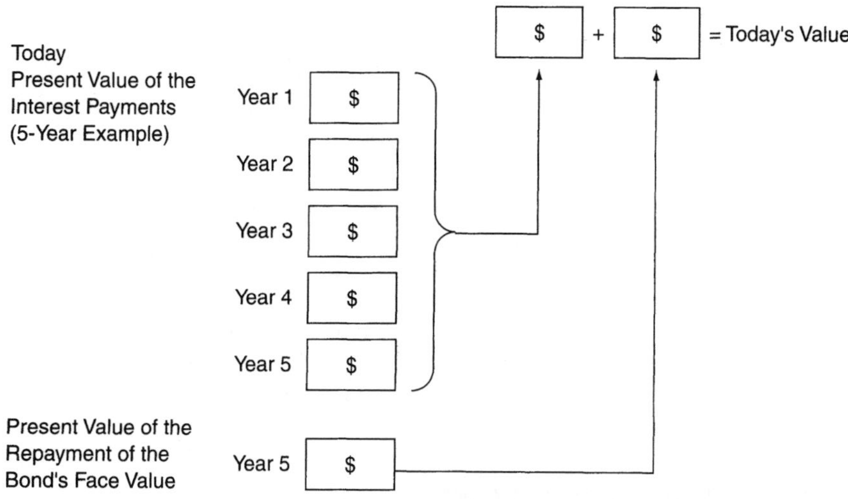

A bond is priced such that the present value of the interest earnings and the present value of the principal repayment accurately reflect the risk of the security and existing economic conditions.

that sum into a certificate of deposit that yielded 10%, he or she would have $1,000 at the end of 4 years, which is what the bond has remaining before repayment. There will be only 4 years' worth of interest payments, so the proportion of par value that is attributable to interest has decreased as the present value of the principal increases.

	Interest	*PV @ 10%*	*PV*
Year 7	$ 100.00	0.909091	$ 90.91
Year 8	$ 100.00	0.826446	$ 82.64
Year 9	$ 100.00	0.751315	$ 75.13
Year 10	$ 100.00	0.683013	$ 68.30
Maturity value	$1,000.00	0.683013	$ 683.01
Present value of cash flows			$1,000.00

Perhaps the clearest comparison of the time value of principal between a certificate of deposit and Green's bond can be seen if the investor chose to buy the bond in its last year. The cash the investor will receive at the end of the year is worth the same as a $909.09 investment in a 1-year certificate of deposit. The investor is paying $90.91 more for the bond because that represents the value of the interest that will be paid at the end of the tenth year. Using present value, you can see that the value of the bond will always be its par value if the coupon rate remains appropriate for the level of risk involved with the bond.

	Interest	*PV @ 10%*	*PV*
Year 10	$ 100.00	0.909091	$ 90.91
Maturity value	$1,000.00	0.909091	$ 909.09
Present value of cash flows			$1,000.00

Let's review that last statement: The bond will sell at par assuming the coupon rate remains appropriate for the level of risk. It contains a huge assumption. Even the interest on debt issued by the U. S. Treasury, which carries no risk of default, varies based on inflation fears, general economic conditions, and the government's monetary policy. Add to that the possibility of financial or business risk, and you can see that the value of corporate bonds does not stay constant at par.

BONDS AT A DISCOUNT

Six years have passed since Green Manufacturing issued its bond. The company has made every interest payment and the business continues to show steadily increasing profits. The bond rating has remained constant during the period, and there is no reason to believe that it won't continue to do so. However, the country has entered an inflationary period. Bonds with the same rating as Green's that are currently being issued carry a coupon rate of 12%. Clearly, an investment of $1,000 will now provide $120 annual interest instead of the $100 that Green's bonds pay, so they will not trade at par value. The bond's price in the secondary market is the present value of the cash flow using a 12% discount instead of the previous 10%.

	Interest	*PV @ 12%*	*PV*
Year 7	$ 100.00	0.892857	$ 89.29
Year 8	$ 100.00	0.797194	$ 79.72
Year 9	$ 100.00	0.71178	$ 71.18
Year 10	$ 100.00	0.635518	$ 63.55
Maturity value	$1,000.00	0.635518	$ 635.52
Present value of cash flows			$ 939.25

The current market price for this bond should be $939.25, which means that the holder of the bond has suffered a $60.75 capital loss. The bonds are now being sold at a discount. Green itself is not directly affected by the change in market value of this particular bond. The decrease in value is based on economic conditions outside Green's control, not the creditworthiness of the firm. It must still repay the full principal at the end of year 10, and the interest expense is $100 per bond outstanding. Green can benefit from the lower market value if it chooses to buy bonds on the secondary market and retire them since they are trading at less than maturity value. However, if Green were to need additional debt funding in the near future, it might incur the higher prevailing interest rates.

Debentures also trade at a discount if the company's financial condition deteriorates. Illusion Enterprises issued 10%, 10-year bonds with a par value of $1,000. Over the course of 6 years, Illusion lost market share as a result of quality control difficulties and incurred substantial costs due to lawsuits. Although the company believes it can recover, in order to compensate for the increased level of risk, investors are requiring a 24% rate of return. With 4 years remaining until maturity, Illusion's bonds currently trade at $663.30.

	Interest	*PV @ 24%*	*PV*
Year 7	$ 100.00	0.806	$ 80.60
Year 8	$ 100.00	0.650	$ 65.00
Year 9	$ 100.00	0.524	$ 52.40
Year 10	$ 100.00	0.423	$ 42.30
Principal	$1,000.00	0.423	$ 423.00
Present value of cash flows			$ 663.30

Notice how sharply the present value of the interest declines from year 7, the first year that the investor holds the bond, to year 8. Because of the uncertainty surrounding Illusion's future viability, investors do not feel that the future interest payment is worth much. Compare the value of the $100 to be paid by Illusion with the $100 interest to be paid by Green Manufacturing under the same purchase time frame. Because Green is a solid company, the present value of next year's interest is $79.72 compared with Illusion's $65.00. The present value of the principal payment alone is greater for Green than the entire value of Illusion's bond. Changes in business condition can have a drastic effect on the market value of debt.

BONDS AT A PREMIUM

A change in economic conditions could cause the value of existing bonds to rise. If interest rates decrease, the value of existing bonds will increase because investors cannot get as attractive a rate of return on newly issued debt. Instead of an inflationary cycle, let's assume that interest rates have fallen in the 6 years since Green issued its notes. The current market rate for bonds of the same quality is now 8.5%. In order to earn $100 per year interest, the investor would have to commit more current dollars. As a result, the value of Green's bonds will rise. Investors will bid up the price until it reaches equilibrium, where the interest earned (which is fixed by the coupon rate and the par value) matches the price the investor has paid.

Looking Back

The Confederate States of America began its existence with no currency. Its chief commodity was cotton, which it exported to England. Cotton accounted for a sizeable portion of the exports of the United States before the Southern states seceded. The Confederacy thought that the importance of its cotton sales to European buyers would bring diplomatic recognition and hard currency to the Southern states.

In order to fund the war with the Union, the Confederate States issued bonds. Each bond was printed with coupons attached and signed by hand. A coupon was cut off every 6 months and redeemed at the CSA Treasury.

One morning as I was window-shopping downtown, I saw a strange item in the window of a little antique store. It was a Confederate bond with some of the coupons still attached. The bond was authorized by an Act of Congress, C.S.A., on August 19, 1861. The face value of the bond is $500 and it carries 8% interest.

Although the bond was authorized in 1861, it was not entered until February 24, 1863, and signed on March 6.

What is curious to me is that there are not enough coupons left on the bond! If Robert E. Lee surrendered to the Union forces on April 14, 1863, it would seem to have been the end of the sovereignty of the Confederate States. However, all of the coupons prior to July 1873 are gone. Where did the 10 years' worth of coupons go? Did the Confederacy have enough money to pay some of the interest? Or did a child take one or several to school for show-and-tell?

Perhaps it is time for me to do some research!

	Interest	*PV @ 8.5%*	*PV*
Year 7	$ 100.00	0.921659	$ 92.17
Year 8	$ 100.00	0.849455	$ 84.95
Year 9	$ 100.00	0.782908	$ 78.29
Year 10	$ 100.00	0.721574	$ 72.16
Maturity value	$1,000.00	0.721574	$ 721.57
Present value of cash flows			$1,049.13

The present value of both the interest stream and the principal repayment have increased, and the current holder of the bond should expect a premium over the face value.

Bond prices are quoted as a percent of par value. Therefore, the bond above would be priced at 104.913, meaning that it trades at 4.913% over its par value. The bond is being sold at a premium. The percent pricing method allows investors to compare the return of bonds with different denominations.

Try This for Yourself

Some investment professionals suggest that clients build a laddered portfolio—a series of bonds that mature in successive years. The goal is to benefit from the interest rate differences that occur as a result of the expectations of future interest rates. The plan assumes that the investor will be able to live on the income generated by the bond portfolio and reinvest the principal each time it comes due.

The way to begin a portfolio is to buy a bond with a maturity date in each of the following 10 years. In order to see the effect of interest rates over time, you should choose bonds that have the same rating and basic characteristics. Calculate the income that would be derived from a $100,000 portfolio, with a $10,000 bond maturing each year. Choose bonds whose risk characteristics match your risk tolerance. See the difference in income stream that would result from different risk preferences.

YIELD

Interest earned from a bond is often called its yield. There are two different types of yield, current yield and yield to maturity, and both use the market price of the bond in the calculation.

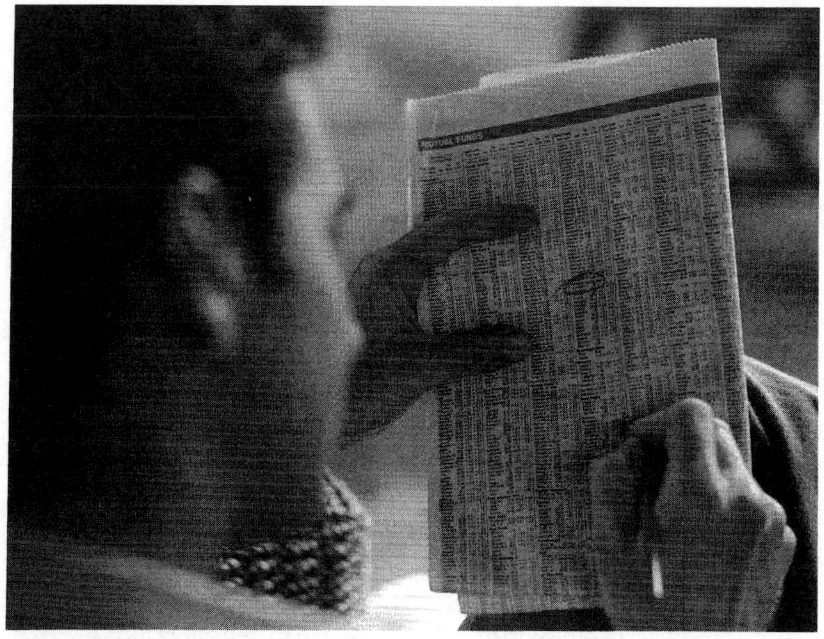

Bond prices are listed in many newspapers. An investor could check to see if his bonds were selling at par, a premium, or at a discount. (Digital Vision Ltd.)

Current yield is the simplest to calculate. It is the percentage that an investor earns annually based on the price paid for the security. If Green Manufacturing's bond is trading for $1,049.13 and earns $100 per year interest, the current yield is

$$\text{Current yield} = \frac{\text{Annual interest payment}}{\text{Price of the bond}}$$

$$= \frac{\$100}{\$1{,}049.13}$$

$$= 9.53\ \%$$

The current yield is less than the 10% face value but more than the 8.5% interest rate that we used to discount the note. One weakness of the current yield is that it ignores the change in principal value that occurs when the bond is purchased for a discount or premium. The current yield is higher than the 8.5% discount, but the principal repayment will not be today's purchase price of $1,049.13. The current interest payments offset the loss of principal that occurs at the end of the bond.

The opposite occurs if the bond is sold at a discount. The current yield for Illusion's bond, which is trading at a 24% discount is

$$\text{Current yield} = \frac{\$100}{\$663.30}$$

$$= 15.08\ \%$$

When the bond matures, the principal repayment will be approximately 50% higher than the price paid for the bond. The current yield does not capture that increase in value of the lump sum payment.

Yield to maturity considers not only the current yield but the value of the increase in capital when it is held to maturity. Because we discounted the Illusion bond, we know that the yield is 24%. However, there is no simple way to calculate the yield to maturity by hand because we are dealing with a current income stream and an increase (or decrease) in lump sum value. One way to set up the equation is to set the left side equal to the market price and using guess and check, find a discount rate for the interest and principal that sets the right side equal. Some financial analysis software programs contain preprogrammed formulas that allow you to calculate yield to maturity. Financial calculators can also compute the value.

TERMS TO KNOW

Bonds
Principal value
Face value
Par value
Coupon rate
Covenants
Inflation risk
Call risk
Secured bonds
Debentures
Convertible bonds
Municipal bonds
General obligation bonds
Revenue bonds
Maturity value
Bonds sold at a discount
Bonds sold at a premium

TERM PAPERS AND PROJECTS

1. Compare bonds of investment grade quality with junk bonds. What company strengths and risks led to each valuation? What is the interest premium for junk bonds?
2. The Treasury Department announced in November 2001 that it would no longer sell a 30-year treasury bill. Who bought the bills? Why was the T-bill discontinued? What other investments will be used to replace the T-bill in investment portfolios?
3. Municipal bonds and school bonds are issued locally. What are the mechanics of issuing bonds? Who is in charge of paying the interest and retiring the debt?
4. Construct a 10-year laddered bond portfolio and describe the differences in yield over time. State the assumptions you have made. Did you invest in the same risk class of security? If not, how much of the difference in interest was due to the quality of the bonds and how much was due to the time horizon?
5. Investigate the value of bonds issued by the Confederate States of America. Did the coupon rate offered at the time match the rate offered by U.S. bonds? Were any of the bonds redeemed after the South surrendered? How many of the bonds were sold abroad? What happened to whatever money was left in the CSA's Treasury? Note: The same project could be completed with any government bonds from a nonexistent government entity.
6. Investigate the types of bonds and bills offered by the United States. Include savings bonds and treasury securities. Explain the difference in face value and coupon rate and describe what type of investor might be interested in each type of security.
7. Compare interest rates on different types of mortgage loans. Assess the difference in rates based on the length of the loan and who accepts the risk of interest rate fluctuations.

REVIEW QUESTIONS

1. What is a bond? How does it differ from stock?
2. Give three examples of covenants that bondholders may request regarding future behavior of the bond issuer.
3. What are bond ratings and how do they affect bond rates?
4. Should a bond that has a call risk carry a higher or lower interest rate? Explain.
5. What are secured bonds?
6. What are debentures?
7. Why would it be advantageous for a firm to issue debentures rather than secured bonds?
8. What is a convertible bond? What is an advantage to the buyer of this type of bond issue? How does the seller benefit?
9. What are municipal bonds?
10. What are junk bonds? Why do they pay a higher interest rate?
11. Would a present value analysis be valuable in determining bond prices? Why?

12. What is meant by a bond premium or bond discount?
13. How is current yield computed for a bond?

REVIEW PROBLEMS

1. A 10-year bond issued 3 years ago had a face value of $10,000 and a coupon rate of 7%. Interest rates on comparably risky bonds have decreased to 5%. What should the investor be willing to pay for the bond?
2. The Amalgamated Andiron Company has declared bankruptcy and its bonds have been downgraded to junk status. You bought a 10-year $5,000 bond yielding 8% interest 5 years ago. The current discount rate on the bond is 25%. What will you get if you try to sell the bond today?
3. A $1,000 Zorro Bond has a coupon rate of 8.25% and a current price of 87½. What is the current yield?

CHAPTER

14 EQUITY

LEARNING OBJECTIVES

1. Describe the distinction between securities and stock.
2. Describe the process for issuing stock.
3. Explain the features of preferred stock.
4. Discuss how common stock differs from preferred stock.
5. Describe the rights that common stockholders have.
6. Calculate earnings per share.
7. Describe different types of stock such as blue chip and defensive stocks.
8. Discuss why companies buy shares of their own stock and what they do with it.
9. Calculate the value of stock using several tools.
10. Describe how stock is bought and sold on exchanges.
11. Explain the value of market indices.
12. Describe how mutual funds work and what benefit they bring to investors.
13. Explain net asset value and how it is calculated.

Throughout this book we have referred to stock and equity when discussing the ownership structure of firms. In this chapter we will look at the mechanics of issuing stock, how it is traded on the public exchanges, and methods for analyzing stock prices. We start by more fully explaining the vocabulary that stock buyers and sellers use.

WHAT DO ALL THESE TERMS MEAN?

More individuals are investing in stock, either as part of a personal investment plan or through a company-sponsored pension fund. As in other industries, there is an entire vocabulary that can seem like a foreign language until you untangle it.

Securities is the word used to describe a wide variety of investments: bonds, stock, options, commodities, and others. Many securities can be traded on primary or secondary markets, but there is no "security" that they will retain their value.

Stock represents an ownership stake in a company and is listed at the bottom of the balance sheet as owner's equity. Like creditors, shareholders have a claim on the company's assets, however all of the creditors have prior claim, even holders of unsecured, subordinated debentures. In the case of liquidation, shareholders have a residual claim and may receive nothing.

Stockholders in a corporation are owners of that firm, however unlike sole proprietorships or partnerships, the stockholders do not have personal liability for the debts of the firm. Because the corporation itself is a legal entity, stockholders have limited liability in case of bankruptcy. The most they can lose is the value of their investment in the firm.

The number of shares of stock that a company issues depends on the amount of money it needs and the price it will receive for each share it issues. The firm's managers meet with the Board of Directors to determine the financing needs of the company and how much stock to sell. Once the Board of Directors has agreed with management's plans, the firm will seek an investment bank to help draw up the prospectus. Stock issues do not require the firm to write an indenture because that is specific to bonds, however, the firm must

A Fairy Tale

As I wrote in an earlier chapter, shares of stock used to be traded using prices expressed in eighths. This is the story that I was told to explain the anomaly:

Once upon a time, a long, long time ago, there lived a navigator, Christopher Columbus by name, who believed that the Earth was round. He didn't really care if he proved that fact; what he wanted to do was find a shortcut to the Spice Islands and he believed that his route would be shorter. Unfortunately, he was poor and couldn't afford to hire a boat for the voyage.

Believing that the Queen was wealthy, he petitioned her to fund his venture. The Queen he appealed to was Isabella of Spain who had just finished fighting a war that had lasted for over 700 years (she didn't fight for the whole time!). She was probably not as rich as he thought, but she agreed to fund the voyage. In return for investing in his expedition, she would receive a *share* of the profits. (See, one of the words has shown up.) Since much of what was traded were goods available for sale, what she was getting was a *share* of the *stock* (inventory) that would be coming in on the boat. (Aha!) At that point in time, Spanish coins were pieces of eight and it would have made sense to value the shares of stock in some denomination that included eighths!

Although the United States has never used eighths, there is an old song about "Shave and a haircut, two bits!" Two bits is another word for a quarter. Therefore, "one bit," if there were such a thing, would be an eighth!

disclose its plans for the money and the anticipated risks that a shareholder will incur. In addition, the **prospectus** describes dividend policies, biographies of the founders and directors, voting rights, how the proposed stock issue will affect the existing ownership structure, and who the transfer agent is. A **transfer agent** is the coordinator for paying dividends and registering changes of ownership in the corporation. A transfer agent is often a major bank. The preliminary prospectus must be submitted to the **Securities and Exchange Commission** (SEC) for their approval. The SEC reviews the prospectus to ensure that it complies with the disclosure requirements. If the issue is approved, the SEC authorizes the firm to sell up to a certain number of shares of stock. Stock that has never been issued before is considered a primary market transaction and the firm receives the proceeds of the sale, minus investment banking fees.

If the firm has never sold stock before, the transaction is called an **initial public offering (IPO).** IPOs are often quite exciting because it is difficult to tell how much people will be willing to pay for stock in a newly public company. Investment bankers try to price the stock at what they believe is a reasonable estimate of its value, but often the stock issue is more desirable than the underwriter had anticipated and the price is bid up. Other times the price that the company would like to obtain is higher than investors are willing to pay. In that case, the company may choose to delay the offering until it feels that market conditions have improved.

A stock issue by a company that already has stock traded in the market is called a seasoned new issue. The specific shares have not been traded before and the proceeds go to the issuer, but the issue price is less volatile since there are existing shares to provide a benchmark.

Stock can carry a par value. However, it is not equivalent to a bond's par value, which is the sum that will be paid to the bondholder at the maturity date. When par value is assigned to a stock, it is for bookkeeping purposes or, for certain kinds of stock, used to calculate dividends. It is not an indication of market value, even the value that the firm expects to receive on its issue date.

The firm does not have to sell all of the **authorized shares** at one time. The shares that are authorized and sold are called **issued stock**; the shares that have been authorized but not yet sold are called unissued stock. In the future, the firm could sell the unissued stock without having it reauthorized by the SEC. Only the issued shares are listed on the firm's balance sheet because they are the only ones that have a claim on the assets. Treasury stock is the name given to issued shares that have been repurchased by the firm. They are listed on the balance sheet after retained earnings.

Unlike bonds, which come in many different types, there are only two forms of stock: preferred stock and common stock.

PREFERRED STOCK

Preferred stock is a form of equity that also has some of the characteristics of bonds. Compared with common stock, it has a "preferred" claim on the assets and earnings of the firm. Although it is not secured, it is less risky than common stock. Unlike common stockholders, preferred stockholders do not have voting rights.

Preferred stock usually carries a par value per share with a fixed dividend rate. The dividend is paid from the firm's earnings and, if the preferred stock has a par value, is calculated as the dividend rate times the par value, not the current market value. Some preferred stock issues carry a specifically stated dividend rather than par value and dividend rate. In either case, the dividend is predictable.

The **dividend** is promised by the issuer, as is the coupon rate on a bond, however there is no maturity date on which the firm will redeem the stock. In addition, if the firm does not have earnings, it can choose not to declare dividends that year. If the firm does not pay dividends, it is said to be in arrears. If the preferred stock is cumulative preferred stock, the arrears must be made up before any dividends can be paid to common stockholders. Most preferred stock is cumulative, however, there are some issues that are non-cumulative preferred stock, in which case arrears do not have to be made up. For a company in financial distress, the type of preferred stock may be irrelevant. The firm could choose to pay dividends even if it shows no profit, but that would drain cash from an already struggling firm, which would not be in its best interests. Although preferred stock is higher in a liquidation payment hierarchy than common stock, it still represents an ownership stake in the firm, and the goal of the "owners" should be to ensure that the firm continues as a going concern. There is no guarantee, however, that any arrears will be made good.

One benefit to issuing preferred stock rather than bonds is the perpetual nature of equity. The firm is under no obligation to retire stock. The firm maintains use of the money in exchange for a set payment, in the form of dividends. That, however, can also be the drawback—the use of the money is perpetual as is the fee for using it. A firm that issues preferred stock can include a call feature that would allow the firm to call in the preferred stock. The call feature is included in the prospectus when the stock is originally sold. The basic structure of the call allows the firm to redeem the stock at its discretion. The redemption price is specified in the prospectus and usually includes a bonus to the shareholder in the form of an extra year of dividends or a lump sum payment. At the end of a specified period of time, shares that have not been surrendered by the shareholder will cease to earn dividends, which is an incentive for the holder to submit the shares.

Preferred shares are designated by a *pf* in stock listing pages. Many firms have more than one issue of preferred stock and each will be listed separately and identified alphabetically, for example, pfA for the first issue. Each issue carries its own dividend rate and place in the order of payment.

COMMON STOCK

Common stock has none of the hybrid qualities of preferred stock. For the investor, it is the riskiest form of investment in a firm. For the firm, it is perhaps the most flexible since it carries no promised dividend or repayment obligation. Common stockholders have a final claim on the earnings of the firm. If the firm is bankrupt, there may be no final value. However, if a firm is successful, the common stockholders receive the rewards. The rewards are often demonstrated by the increase in the firm's stock price.

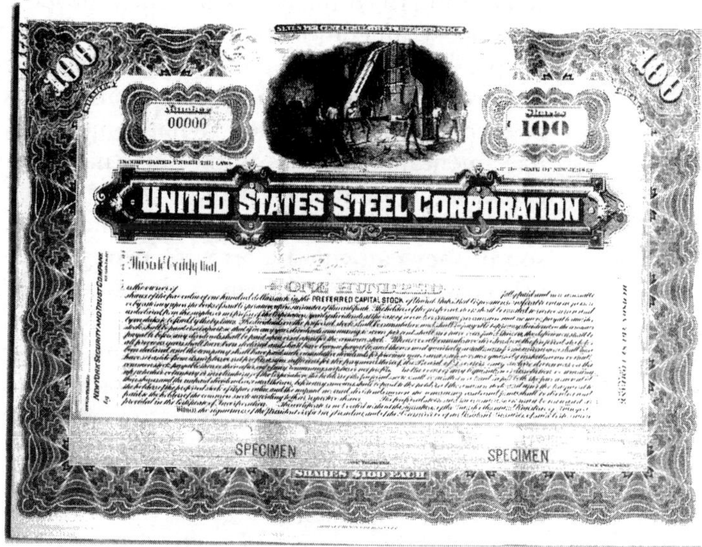

Many of the old stock certificates are ornately decorated with scenes depicting the type of work done by the issuing company. Today most stockholders have an electronic account and do not take possession of a paper certificate. (New York Stock Exchange, Inc.)

If a firm were small, and all of the owners lived or worked near the business, important decisions could be handled at a weekly meeting with the owners sitting around a conference table. However, major corporations have far too many "owners" to allow this type of decision making. For example, at the end of 2000, General Electric Corporation had 9,932,006,000 shares of stock outstanding! Even allowing for the fact that many investors own blocks of stock, there is no practical way for investors-owners to participate in the day-to-day management of the firm. As a result, common stockholders have **voting rights.** Typically, each share of common stock is allowed one vote, however, there are some cases where a company has different classes of stock that carry different voting rights.

RIGHTS OF COMMON STOCKHOLDERS

The common stockholders hire the members of the **Board of Directors** who are charged with the responsibility for acting on behalf of the shareholders and supervising the management of the firm. The firm usually submits a slate of directors, although shareholders can nominate candidates. If stockholders are comfortable with the direction that the company has taken, the company's suggested directors tend to be elected. However, when the company has experienced difficulty, election to the Board of Directors becomes more contentious. In some cases, groups of dissatisfied shareholders have worked together to change the composition of a board.

Common stockholders not only have the right to vote for the board but they also must approve any changes in the rules that govern the corporation.

In addition to voting on management proposals, shareholders are also entitled to propose amendments to the corporate charter. Shareholder activists have proposed rules that would restrict investment in certain foreign countries, require human rights monitoring in overseas factories, and limit the amount of executive compensation. What is more important than whether an individual amendment passes is the fact that shareholders do have an avenue for expressing their concerns about the company they own.

Shareholders may attend the annual meeting and vote their shares in person or they can vote by proxy. A **proxy** is a legal agreement that designates a third party, usually the firm's independent auditor, to vote the shares according to the shareholder's instructions. Shares not voted in person or by proxy can be voted by management. This is an important point to remember: Members of the Board of Directors are representatives of the owners (shareholders), while the Chief Executive Officer and other senior managers are the employees of the firm. By not actively voting, the shareholder has not expressed his or her opinion and given the Board of Directors the collective weight of opinion in order to guide management.

If the firm's business is stable, a shareholder may receive only one proxy package a year, just prior to the firm's annual meeting. However, if the firm is being pursued by an acquirer or if management takeovers or restructurings are threatened, proxy fights may occur. A proxy fight is a battle for the proxy votes of shareholders. For example, in the case of a hostile takeover, the firm's management would send out documents stating why they believe the firm should remain independent and solicit the shareholders' votes in support of the existing structure. The potential acquirer would send information detailing its purchase offer for shares of stock or its desire for a merger. During a prolonged and active proxy battle, shareholders might receive numerous proxies, each of which could be voted. The last proxy signed by the shareholder is the final vote counted.

Some stockholders have preemptive rights. **Preemptive rights** allow the existing stockholders to maintain their proportionate share in the firm if it chooses to issue more stock in the future. If the company issues new stock, it must first offer it to the existing shareholders. This stock sale is called a rights offering. If the shareholder wishes to maintain the same proportion, she or he will buy the shares. If not, the shareholder must release them so that others can buy them. Rights offerings are more expensive for a corporation because it has to go through two steps in marketing new shares. Even without a specific rights offering, existing shareholders can purchase shares in any new issue to maintain their investment or increase it. Many corporations have asked their shareholders to change the bylaws requiring rights offerings, arguing that the costs of a rights offering outweigh the benefits to the shareholders.

Common stockholders are entitled to the profits of the organization. Some companies choose to pay dividends to common stockholders. If dividends are paid, they are issued quarterly and must be approved by the Board of Directors. On the declaration date, the amount of dividends per share is announced along with the date on which they will be paid. Imagine the time it would take to determine who owned all of General Electric's more than 9 billion shares! Because companies need to have time to determine who owns the shares and then process the dividends, there is also an ex-dividend date. Shareholders of record before the ex-dividend date will receive the just declared dividend. Shares that trade after the ex-dividend date will trade without the dividend. Checks are mailed on the payment date.

> **In the News**
>
> Shareholders are not just individuals who have a few hundred shares of their employer's stock. Shareholders can also be large institutional investors. One of the largest is CALPERS, the California state pension fund. When a proxy fight is launched, every investor gets a proxy to vote, with the number of votes corresponding to the number of shares they hold. For the large investor, the proxy vote counts for a lot.
>
> Sam Wyly is a Texas financier who wanted to make radical changes to Computer Associates, a software company headed by its founder Charles B. Wang. Wyly originally planned to overthrow the chairman and the entire 10-member Board of Directors.
>
> The key to this story is that Wyly's moves were seen as too radical by "two influential firms that advise shareholders on proxy fights" according to a *Business Week* article. When he changed his list of demands and reduced the number of nominees to the board to four, the advisors threw their weight behind his proposal.
>
> Even a large institutional investor with a whole staff of analysts seeks the advice of a proxy advisor. Imagine how confusing proxy fights can be for the individual investor who has to sift through competing statements from the company and the challengers.
>
> ---
>
> *Source:* "If At First You Don't Succeed . . . ," *Business Week*, September 3, 2001, by Andrew Park.

EARNINGS PER SHARE

Earnings per share (EPS) represents the amount of earnings per share of common stock outstanding. Earnings per share represents the amount of earnings that would be allocated to common stockholders if all profits were disbursed, and it is calculated by taking net income less the dividends paid to preferred stockholders.

$$\text{EPS} = \frac{\text{Net income} - \text{preferred stock dividends}}{\text{Number of shares of common stock outstanding}}$$

Companies use earnings per share to describe their profitability from year to year. EPS is not the same as dividends and does not obligate the firm to pay dividends.

CLASSIFICATIONS OF COMMON STOCK

As noted earlier, there are only two types of equities: preferred stock and common stock. However, stock market analysts often refer to stock by different classifications such as "blue chip" stock or "growth" stock. The description does not differentiate aspects of stock but attempts to categorize the company that has issued the stock.

Blue chip stocks are issued by large nationally known corporations with sound credit history and firm financial footing. Blue chip stock prices tend to be stable even in difficult economic times because they have a history of steady growth and solid dividend payments. An example of a blue chip stock would be General Electric or Procter & Gamble.

Growth stocks are issued by companies that have earnings and sales growth greater than their industry average. They can be small companies that have developed new products or markets, or companies that continually innovate. Most growth companies do not pay dividends but choose to retain earnings to fund future growth opportunities.

Income stocks pay relatively high dividends. They are in mature industries with little increase in earnings above inflation. Utility companies are an example of income stocks because they pay a stable rate of return and have little or no expected revenue growth.

Speculative stocks carry higher risk than the general market. Start-up companies in new industries are speculative. Companies that have fallen into financial disarray could also be considered speculative stocks. The risk for both of these categories is high and stock prices tend to be volatile.

Cyclical stocks are those belonging to companies whose sales are tied to economic fluctuations. When the economy grows, these companies prosper. In more difficult economic environments, sales slump and earnings are pressed. Durable goods manufacturers, automakers, and the housing industry are all examples of cyclical stocks.

Defensive stocks may offset the swings of cyclical stocks. When the economy weakens, homeowners may turn to remodeling or repair projects rather than trade up to a new home. Hardware stores or home improvement stores may not suffer even if contractors buy less, since consumers may pick up the slack.

Large cap, mid cap, and small cap describe the market capitalization of the firm. Capitalization is the number of shares multiplied by the price per share. The largest companies, with the most shares outstanding and a high total value, are called large cap. As the value of their shares increases, small-cap companies can grow into mid-cap companies and mid-cap companies can become large-cap companies.

MANAGING STOCK

Firms are sensitive to the type of liabilities that they carry on the balance sheet. We've looked at the importance of managing current liabilities in order to maximize working capital. Debt, whether secured or debentures, obligates the firm to pay interest, and the covenants in an indenture can limit the firm's future financing actions. Companies are also interested in managing shareholders' equity.

One sign of a healthy, growing company is an increase in the price of its stock and good sales volume. Sometimes the share price becomes high enough that management is concerned that smaller investors will not be able to afford shares. To keep the price within a range that encourages trading, companies split the stock. A **stock split** takes the existing number of shares and increases it by some factor. For example, a company that had 1,000 shares outstanding with a closing price of $250 per share might split 2-for-1. After the end of the business day, each share of stock would split in half—there would be two "new" shares for every one that had existed before. The next morning, there would be 2,000 shares of stock and the opening price would be adjusted to $125 per share. Existing shareholders would have the same percent ownership in the firm and the same total investment value. However, the lower trading price might increase interest in the stock, and newly released demand could push the price slightly higher.

STOCK BUYBACKS AND TREASURY STOCK

On occasion the Board of Directors authorizes management to buy back shares of the company from the public. This is a called stock buyback. The stock that is purchased is still issued stock; it does not become unissued stock simply because the firm owns it. It is carried on the balance sheet as **treasury stock.** Although the shares are still issued, they are not counted as outstanding shares.

There are several reasons that a company would buy its own shares. If the firm believes that the current market price does not reflect the underlying value, it might use the purchase to signal that opinion. If the price does rise in the future, the company can sell its shares and reap the profit. Buying shares also reduces the number of shares outstanding and is a way for the company to improve earnings per share, even if the earnings themselves are not significantly higher. If earnings are spread over fewer outstanding shares, the profits to the individual shareholders will appear higher. Treasury stock can also be used as a cash management tool. Shares that are owned by the company can be given to employees as performance incentives without reducing the working capital of the firm.

There has been a lot of discussion over the past several years about whether companies should substantially increase the dividends paid to common stockholders. Start-up companies are expected to retain what earnings they have to grow their business into the growth or maturity phase. Organizations with net losses do not have earnings to distribute. The debate focuses around profitable companies with a stable revenue stream and few exponential growth opportunities. Profitable companies that don't pay dividends argue that they increase shareholder value by reinvesting the profits in the company, thus expanding their business and generating further profits. They argue that the stock market rewards this decision by pushing up the price of the company's stock. As long as the company can sustain earnings growth in excess of the corresponding discount rate, the decision is theoretically valid. In a rational market, a shareholder who wishes to capture the added value can sell shares of stock at a higher price than he or she paid for them. The shareholder would also punish an inefficient company by driving down the price of its shares.

Of course, there are many aspects to this issue. If the company retained earnings sufficient to fund the business but issued the remaining profits in the form of dividends, shareholders could decide how to allocate those earnings. If they believed that the firm had growth potential that exceeded their alternate uses of the money, shareholders would reinvest in the same organization. If, however, the firm had not demonstrated that the earnings it achieved were superior to the other investments available, given a corresponding risk factor, investors would reward more profitable firms by investing in their shares. Theoretically, capital would be directed to the most efficient uses. Some contend that by automatically reinvesting profits in their own firm, companies will accept investments with a lower rate of return than an efficient market would require.

VALUING STOCK

After the volatility of the last several years, it might be easiest to state that stock is simply worth whatever anyone is willing to pay for it. However, that statement disregards the fact that stock represents collective ownership of a specific set of assets that should be expected to produce a stream of income now and into the future. We will return to the emotional aspects of stock valuation, but for now we will examine three mathematical approaches.

Book Value

If the company's balance sheet were continually updated to reflect market value of all assets and liabilities, valuation would be simple. The liabilities could be subtracted from the assets and the remaining value divided by the number of shares outstanding.

$$\text{Assets (at true market value)} - \text{liabilities} = \text{equity}$$

$$\text{Price per share} = \frac{\text{Equity}}{\text{Number of shares outstanding}}$$

In fact, balance sheets often reflect historic costs for long-term assets. If the replacement cost is higher than the balance sheet, the stock should trade above **book value.** However, if the value of assets has declined, book value will overstate the price that investors should pay.

Book value also addresses only the assets owned by the firm, not the use to which they are being put. Using book value as a way to establish share price could result in a higher stock valuation for a firm with newly acquired assets and lower income than a firm in the same industry with older equipment and higher earnings per share.

Price-Earnings Ratio

The **price-earnings (PE) ratio** is a measure of a stock's value relative to the market as a whole and competitors in its industry. It is simple to calculate.

$$\text{PE ratio} = \frac{\text{Price per share}}{\text{Earnings per share}}$$

The price an investor is willing to pay per share of stock should increase as earnings per share increase. For example, a firm that has steady earnings that are growing at just about the country's growth rate would not have the same increase in share price as a company whose earnings were growing twice the rate of the economy.

The price-earnings ratio has been used to compare companies within a specific industry. Companies have been said to be "good buys" if their PE ratio is lower than the prevailing rate in the industry. But who sets that base level? PE ratios for the stock market as a whole climbed during the 1990s, reflecting investor confidence in the economy. In general, industries that are experiencing growth will have a higher PE ratio than low-growth industries because investors are basing their decision on not just one year but the expectation that growth will continue into the future. In that sense, the price-earnings ratio is very much like the discounted cash flow method of evaluating the cost of acquiring a business. Like the capitalization rate, PE ratios should take into account not only the current growth rate but also reasonable expectations for growth in perpetuity. The PE ratio should also consider whether the firm is susceptible to economic fluctuations. If so, earnings will be less stable, risk will increase, and the PE ratio should be adjusted accordingly.

Remember that this calculation looks at earnings, not revenue. If the company has no earnings, either because it is in its infancy or because it has sustained a net loss for the year, there is no earnings per share ratio.

Discounted Dividend Valuation Method

The **discounted dividend valuation method** calculates a share price based on the expectation of future dividends. This method uses the same theory as the capitalization rate, which states that the capitalized value of the income stream is what we will pay for the stock. In this case, the income stream is dividends. The investment risk is reduced by the rate of growth in dividends, which is assumed to be steady.

$$\text{Stock price} = \frac{\text{Current yearly dividend}}{\text{Required rate of return} - \text{assumed growth rate}}$$

Let's assume that Terra, Inc., pays \$1.60 per year in dividends. They are a stable company that will grow 2% per year. Our required rate of return on this company is 12%.

$$\text{Stock price} = \frac{\$1.60}{12\% - 2\%} = \frac{\$1.60}{10\%} = \$16.00$$

This method works only if the firm pays dividends, so its application is limited.

Mathematical Models

Institutional investors such as pension funds, insurance companies, and educational and charitable endowments have sophisticated computer programs that attempt to predict changes in the price of stock in order to buy stock when it is undervalued and sell it for a good return. The models they have created are proprietary, belonging to them, and reflect their risk tolerance and any restrictions imposed by the nature of their business such as the payments they must fund from investments (insurance claims, retirement benefits, etc.). Even with access to reams of historic data and trend analysis, these large investors can be surprised by the actual prices paid for stock.

OTHER FACTORS THAT AFFECT STOCK VALUE

Interest rates have an inverse relationship with stock prices. As interest rates rise, the firm's cost of borrowing increases, thus reducing the amount of revenue that is available for shareholders. Earnings per share fall as a result of higher debt costs, which pushes down the price of stock. Added to this is the fact that as interest rates rise, investors can obtain higher earnings at lower risk by investing in bonds or insured accounts.

The health of the individual company can affect its share price, even in an expanding market. A company that has sustained losses or not met its revenue projections will see its share price fall, sometimes precipitously. Investors perceive that the company's risk has increased, and the lower share price reflects the risk-related adjustment.

Although it would be nice to quantify stock prices and create predictable, sustainable valuation models, investors are human and emotions affect stock prices. Optimism, greed, and fear can cause a market rally or slump. If consumer confidence is high, spending follows. New homes sell, which means more washing machines, refrigerators, and other durable goods move off the production line. Retailers sell carpet, lumber for new decks, paint for bedrooms, and new sheets and curtains. The economy as a whole is expanding and with it come higher prices for stocks. Optimism (faith that the economy will continue to expand) pushes stock prices upward in reaction to the economic growth that consumers are fueling.

As long-term investors begin to reap the rewards of increasing stock prices, new investors jump into the market and demand pushes stock prices still higher. Sometimes optimism causes investors to forget fundamental valuation theories.

In the 1990s, investors became caught up in the excitement of the Internet revolution. Computer ownership increased and more households had Internet access. In addition to information, the Internet provided opportunities for shopping, which many companies attempted to capture. Investors rushed to buy "dotcom" companies (companies that had a commercial Internet address, such as anycompany.com) because they believed that the new medium was a gold mine. Demand caused stock prices to increase dramatically, even though the companies were start-ups with high expenses and no revenue. In addition, the firms were attempting to gain sales in an undeveloped marketplace. However, the allure was undeniable. Early investors were able to realize profits by buying dotcom stock when it was first issued, holding it until it reached their personal threshold, and selling it for sizeable profits. Stories about the gains made from trading Internet stocks caused optimism to slip into greed. Greed (the desire for profit) pushes stock prices up when they are already rising, but fear can cause all of the gains to evaporate.

Long-term investors know that there are economic cycles; stock prices will not always increase. If the economy slows or international events cause concern in domestic markets, stock prices will fall on expectations of lower future growth and income. As securities prices fall, some investors become nervous and want to sell their holdings, which adds to the downturn. When the supply of securities for sale exceeds demand, prices fall further. Falling prices cause more fear, which exaggerates the economic difficulties.

So what price is valid for stock? In a rational market, the price should reflect the earnings capability of the firm and the risk factors specific to its industry, its financial structure, and the state of the economy. In an irrational market, stock prices are anyone's guess.

PUBLICLY TRADED STOCK

When a company issues stock, it receives the proceeds of the sale minus investment banking fees. Securities that have been previously issued are traded on a secondary market. Secondary markets can either be an organized exchange where buyers and sellers meet face-to-face in a physical location or an over-the-counter market where transactions are handled over the phone or via computer.

The New York Stock Exchange is the largest secondary market in the United States. The NYSE, also called the "Big Board," is the oldest of all of the organized exchanges. In order to be listed on the New York Stock Exchange, firms must meet strict regulations concerning size, profitability, market value, and equity ownership structure. If a company fails to maintain the minimum membership levels, it can be delisted from the exchange.

In order to actually trade shares on the exchange you need to be a member and buy a "seat." There is no physical seat; the term denotes membership in the exchange. The number of seats is limited and when seats become available they are sold at the price agreed upon by buyer and seller. Seats can be purchased by individuals or brokerage firms.

BUYING AND SELLING STOCK AT AN ORGANIZED EXCHANGE

The New York Stock Exchange operates on the **open outcry method** of trading. Only members can trade on the floor, so individuals who want to buy or sell shares need to use an intermediary.

I live in Washington State, on the opposite coast and three time zones away from New York City. If I wanted to purchase shares of an NYSE-listed company, my first step would be to contact a broker whose firm had a seat on the exchange. I could arrange the trade in person, over the telephone, or via Internet. But no matter what communication medium I used, a broker would be executing my trade.

My order to buy shares would be communicated to a floor broker located at the edge of the trading floor. Upon receipt of the order, the broker would proceed to a trading desk on the floor of the exchange where transactions in that stock take place. Buyers and sellers brandish paper that is color-coded to indicate whether they are buying, selling, or merely checking the current bid or ask price for the stock. Each stock has a specialist assigned to it to ensure that trading in the stock is orderly and fair. If there are sufficient bids and offers to keep the stock trading smoothly, the specialist does not intervene. However if there is a mismatch, the specialist steps in and buys or sells from his or her own account to keep the market moving.

The order I just placed was a market order. I authorized the broker to buy shares at the best price he or she could get in the market. If I had wanted to specify the price I was willing to pay for those shares, I would have placed a limit order. As a buyer, I would specify the highest price I was willing to pay for the shares. A seller could place a limit order stating the lowest price the seller would accept. If the limit price cannot be met, the order goes into the specialist's book until a match can be made.

Millions of shares of stock are held in electronic form—ownership is recorded electronically and the shares are held in computerized form in the owner's account at a stockbrokerage. Companies will mail stock certificates upon request, but like many other financial transactions, most of the transfers are done via computer. Just as it is simpler for money to be transmitted using electronic funds transfer than to carry or mail a check from one business to the other, it is easier for the stockholder to authorize the sale of his or her digitally encoded stock than to take the stock certificate to the local broker's office. Electronic buying and selling of stock can take place even when the stockbroker's office is closed, which would not be the case if the transaction were dependent on surrendering a paper stock certificate.

BUYING STOCK ON MARGIN

Stock that is purchased through a stockbroker can either be paid for in full at the time of the transaction or can be bought on margin. If the stock is bought on margin, the customer pays for a certain percentage of the stock and finances the rest through the brokerage. Let's assume that I want to buy 100 shares of a company that is trading at $54 per share. The total cost of my purchase is $5,400. I pay the brokerage firm 20% of the value of the stock ($1,080) and the rest of the stock is in my margin account. I will, of course, pay a fee for the loan and the shares of stock will be the collateral. As long as the value of the stock stays above the amount of the loan I have outstanding, the shares will remain in the stockbroker's account in my name. If the price of the shares falls below the value of my loan, the stockbroker has the right to sell the shares and recoup his or her loan to me.

One of the causes of the 1929 stock market crash was the fact that so many investors had bought on margin and, as stock prices tumbled, more and more stock from margin accounts was added to the system, pushing prices lower yet. In order to stop panic from ensuing again, the New York Stock Exchange instituted breaker points, rules that determined at what level of loss stock trading would halt. If the market falls by more than a certain percent or number of points, trading is suspended in order to calm market fears. If the free fall continues, the market can be closed for the day.

To keep markets calm in the first few days following the reopening of stock trading in September 2001, Federal Reserve officials, brokerage houses, and the New York Stock Exchange agreed that stock would not be sold to cover margins. There was no way of knowing how the markets would react in the first days and weeks, so the decision was made not to add any extra stress to the system. As we now know, the market tumbled the first week but by the end of the year, it had regained stability and stayed at or around the September 10 levels.

THE AMERICAN STOCK EXCHANGE AND REGIONAL STOCK EXCHANGES

Historically, the American Stock Exchange (AMEX) was the second most important exchange. Companies that were not quite large enough to trade on the New York Stock Exchange traded on the American Stock Exchange. In recent years, the American Stock Exchange has been eclipsed by the over-the-counter market known as NASDAQ. There are also active regional stock exchanges such as the Pacific Stock Exchange in Los Angeles and San Francisco and the Philadelphia Exchange (in Philadelphia and Miami). Regional stock exchanges trade in securities of local or regional interest that have strong management and financial strength.

NASDAQ

NASDAQ is the commonly used name for one of the over-the-counter stock trading systems. The over-the-counter (OTC) market does not have a specific physical location like the NYSE, AMEX, or regional stock exchanges. It is the linking of dealers who trade in certain stock issues. There is no need to buy a seat on this exchange.

Depending on the volume of trading activity, pricing information will be communicated in one of several ways. Thinly traded stocks are priced daily and the information mailed to traders. Because there is so little trading volume and there is a time lag between the quote and its receipt, it may be more difficult for shareholders to make quick trades at the most competitive price. For the most actively traded stocks, traders are linked by high-speed computers as part of the NASDAQ system. NASDAQ is not a location, it is the acronym for National Association of Securities Dealers Automated Quotations system. Dealers are allowed to post bid and ask prices in an attempt to match buyers and sellers. The bid price is the price at which a buyer is willing to purchase stock. The ask price is the selling price the owner is willing to accept. Dealers match buyers and sellers and make their profit by taking advantage of the spread between the bid and ask prices. It is not a leisurely pursuit. Bid and ask prices scroll rapidly down screens as traders try to make the best matches. Often a trader will be watching a televised computer screen and be on one of many phones to another dealer, attempting to capture the bid or ask price that is scrolling down the screen and match it to a client's order.

In terms of number of companies, there are more stocks listed on the over-the-counter market than the New York Stock Exchange. However, due to the size of companies listed on the NYSE, it is responsible for a majority of the dollar value of stock trades that occur in the United States. Many of the companies whose stock is traded in the OTC market are smaller and less capitalized than the companies that trade on the New York Stock Exchange, thus they trade at lower prices and volumes. There are obvious exceptions such as Microsoft and Intel. Many high-tech companies that would qualify for listing on the NYSE have chosen to remain part of the over-the-counter market.

INDICES—HOW DID THE MARKET DO?

Stock prices fluctuate based on the performance of the issuer as well as in response to general market conditions. Indices like "The Dow" or the S&P500 give an indication of the direction of the market as a whole. No one index can give the entire picture, nor will it give the performance of an individual stock. Investors rely on indices to give them a snapshot of market activity.

A typical newcast may report: "The Dow closed up 50 points today on active trading with gainers outnumbering losers 5 to 3." There's a fair amount of information in that statement. "The Dow" refers to the Dow Jones Industrial Average (DJIA), an index of stock from 30 large, well-established companies. Because the DJIA focuses on larger companies, it is less susceptible

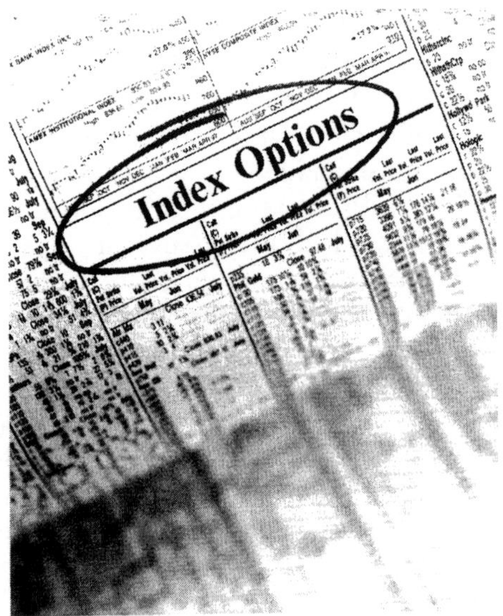

Options based on indices such as the DJIA can also be traded. Investors are betting that the market basket of stocks represented by the index will rise or fall. (Index Stock Imagery, Inc.)

to the volatility that would be experienced by a growth company or nascent industry. The index is widely used to gain a sense of overall market sentiment. "Active trading" indicates that there was enough volume to facilitate fair trading and enable the market to clear buy and sell orders, but the word does not indicate a frenzy. On an especially light trading day, the spread between bid and ask prices could increase and closing prices might not give as much of an indication of the "market's sentiment." A day with heavy trading could indicate uncertainty in the markets and perhaps even panic selling. The ratio of gainers to losers further indicates the direction of the market. In my example, less than 63% of the shares gained value while 37% lost value. A more positive day would have seen gainers outnumbering losers 4 to 1! On that day, 80% of the stocks traded would have gained in value while only 20% declined.

There are other indices in addition to the Dow Jones Industrial Average. The Standard & Poor's 500, also known as the S&P500 is based on the movement of 500 shares of stock, not 30. The companies in the S&P500 trade mostly on the New York Stock Exchange, but it also includes shares from the AMEX and NASDAQ. Because it is broader based, it may be more indicative of the stock market as a whole rather than just large-cap or blue chip stocks. NASDAQ has an index that charts the direction of stock traded over the counter. Because the stocks traded through the NASDAQ system are often issued by smaller firms with less financial wherewithal than NYSE companies, the NASDAQ index tends to be more volatile than the Dow or the S&P500. Not one of the indices predicts future earnings or describes the underlying value of the companies whose shares are tracked. The indices do serve to indicate general trends and the level of investor confidence.

You Should Know

Stock prices are subject to supply and demand, just as any other commodity. If there is terrific news about a company and everyone wants to own a piece of it, the stock price will climb. By the same token, if too many shares are available, the price will fall.

Too many shares may be available because investors are bailing out of a poorly performing company, or it could simply be that a large investor is liquidating its holdings. In late 2001, the price of Disney shares fell after the Bass brothers, wealthy Texas investors, were forced to sell their holdings to cover their margin call.

Another group who can move the market are institutional investors who hold large blocks of stock. If they attempt to sell a large quantity of stock at one time, they will drive the price of the stock downward. In fact, that's allegedly what contributed to the steep drop in prices when the stock market reopened in September 2001. Individual investors sat still and didn't panic. It was reported that institutional investors sold large volumes of shares as soon as the market opened, pushing prices down.

MUTUAL FUNDS

Stock prices rise and fall daily and over the course of months and years. Speculators try to quickly time their purchases to take advantage of temporary price discrepancies. Most institutional and individual investors take a longer-term approach to stock purchases. Although they would be thrilled to stumble across a fast-growing, highly profitable company whose share price does nothing but appreciate, they realize that the best way to choose companies in which to invest is to do a thorough analysis of the company, its market, the competitors, and its financial stability. Unfortunately, there is a limit to the amount of time the firm or individual has to devote to analyzing companies.

Mutual funds allow small investors to pool their resources and buy a mix of securities, either stocks, bonds, or a combination. There are mutual funds with a wide variety of investment parameters and risk levels. Some funds invest in the strongest firms in a specific industry such as mining, biotech, or retail. There are funds that mimic the movement of the market as a whole by investing in the stocks that comprise the S&P500. Risk-tolerant investors can invest in distressed stock or junk bonds.

Investment companies that offer mutual funds hire analysts who are trained to do the type of financial and market research that we have described. They choose the companies they believe will perform best and continue to monitor the company's financial condition after the stock or bond is purchased. Analysts can be generalists or specialize in a certain industry or type of security. Actively managed mutual funds regularly adjust their holdings based on the quality of the securities they hold, selling the stock or bonds that are not performing according to the fund's standards and replacing them with higher-quality issues.

Buying a share of a mutual fund rather than individual stocks and bonds allows smaller investors to diversify their holdings. A $1,000 investment in a single company's stock may be far riskier than a $1,000 investment in a mutual fund that holds a wider variety of shares. The larger number of companies held by a mutual fund smooths the effect of a single company's poor performance.

In the News

First Eagle Fund of America is a mutual fund with holdings of $400 million. Harold Levy, the fund manager, likes to invest in companies that are "in a state of flux." He wants to invest in companies that are about to change because he believes that change of the right sort creates value for the investor. One type of change that Levy looks for includes the hiring of a new chief executive. New management tends to shake up the status quo and creates value for the fund.

First Eagle does not limit itself to one industry. It looks for change and growth opportunities across a wide range of companies.

Source: "First Eagle Looks for Companies 'in Flux,'" *Wall Street Journal*, November 28, 2001, by Adam L. Freeman.

Some funds consciously attempt to adjust for economic risk by holding both cyclical stocks and defensive stocks. If the economy is growing, cyclical stocks will increase in value. If the economy slows and the price of cyclical stock softens, the lower price should be offset or mitigated by the increase in value of defensive stocks. It would be difficult for a small investor to get that type of diversity by purchasing shares of individual companies.

Buying a mutual fund can reduce transaction costs. Because mutual funds buy and sell such large quantities of securities, their commissions are lower per share. If the mutual fund is an index fund and if it mirrors the S&P500, NASDAQ, or another index, there should be no trading costs to speak of since there will be very little change in the holdings.

Buying a mutual fund also provides investment management services such as systems that invest an automatic payroll deduction, transfer money from one fund to another, or allow checks to be drawn against the investment.

Although transaction costs can be lower for a fund than for individual shares, there are significant costs involved in managing a mutual fund. Those costs are passed on to the investor. A load fund is one that charges a sales commission either when you buy or sell the fund. Load funds are often sold by a third party such as a bank or financial planner who does not manage the fund but sells investments in funds managed by others. A mutual fund that does not charge a sales fee is called a no-load fund; most no-load funds are purchased directly from the investment company. In addition to sales commissions, management fees are subtracted from the fund's earnings. High fees can reduce a fund's attractiveness by reducing the amount of earnings that the investor receives. Management fees are usually expressed as an expense ratio, that is, the ratio of expenses to total assets. Investment management firms are required to report the expense ratio to fund holders.

NET ASSET VALUE

A mutual fund is not a share of stock and does not trade in the same way that individual shares do. The price you pay for one unit of a mutual fund is based on the net asset value of the fund. **Net asset value** is calculated by adding the current value of the holdings in that fund, subtracting the liabilities, and dividing by the number of shares outstanding.

$$\text{Net asset value} = \frac{\text{Total market value of all securities} - \text{liabilities}}{\text{Number of shares outstanding}}$$

If you sell your shares in a mutual fund, the fund will pay you the net asset value based on the prices at the close of business on the day you sold the shares. The fund will usually not give you an exact price for your shares until the securities markets have closed because that determines the market value.

Most mutual funds are open-end investment companies. There is no limit to the number of shares they can issue. If there is a balance between fund buyers and sellers, the mutual fund will buy back shares and resell them. If more buyers want to own shares, the investment firm will use the cash inflow to buy securities that meet the investment goals of the fund, increasing the number of shares accordingly. However, if the fund experiences a net loss in investor capital, it may be forced to liquidate its holdings to satisfy the requirements of its shareholders.

There is no security in securities!

TERMS TO KNOW

Securities
Stock
Prospectus
Transfer agent
Securities and Exchange Commission (SEC)
Initial public offering (IPO)
Authorized shares
Issued shares
Preferred stock
Dividend
Common stock
Voting rights
Board of Directors
Proxy
Preemptive rights
Earnings per share (EPS)
Blue chip stock
Growth stock
Income stock
Speculative stock
Cyclical stock
Defensive stock
Stock split
Stock buyback
Treasury stock
Book value
Price-earnings (PE) ratio
Discounted dividend valuation ratio
Open outcry market
NASDAQ
Mutual funds
Net asset value

TERM PAPERS AND PROJECTS

1. Dotcoms were the latest get rich quick scheme. Not all of the share prices could be justified using standard valuation techniques. How were they able to sell at such high prices so quickly? What did investors think they saw that would justify the high prices they paid?
2. Follow an initial public offering during the course of the term. What price was charged on the first day of trading and how did the price change during the weeks that you observed it? What are the prices of companies in the same industry? Does the EPS reflect industry price-earnings ratios or is there a premium or discount? If so, what do you believe caused the difference?
3. How do small companies issue shares? How do they trade? Interview a small company that has issued shares of stock. Why did they choose equity financing rather than debt?

REVIEW QUESTIONS

1. From an investment and profit point of view, why would it be better to be a stockholder rather than an owner or partner in a failing firm?
2. What are the two basic factors in determining the number of shares of stock a company can issue?
3. What is preferred stock? Why might it be a better investment than bonds?
4. What rights are associated with common stock? How does it differ from preferred stock?

5. What does EPS mean and how is it calculated?
6. What is a blue chip stock? A growth stock? An income stock? Give examples of each.
7. What is a cyclical industry? What major companies are members of cyclical industries?
8. What are defensive stocks and why would you hold them?
9. Why might a firm split its stock?
10. What is treasury stock? How might a company use stock that it holds as treasury stock?
11. What is a price-earnings ratio? How would it be used in evaluating stock?
12. Describe three factors that would affect stock value.
13. How is stock purchased?
14. Why are mutual funds advantageous to small investors?

INDEX